STRATEGIC
MINERAL SUPPLIES

STRATEGIC MINERAL SUPPLIES

BY

G. A. ROUSH

Editor of The Mineral Industry
Major, Staff Specialist Reserve, U. S. Army

The series of articles that appeared in
THE MILITARY ENGINEER,
on which the body of this book is based,
was awarded
THE TOULMIN MEDAL FOR 1938
by the Society of American Military Engineers

FIRST EDITION

McGRAW-HILL BOOK COMPANY, Inc.

NEW YORK AND LONDON

1939

Dedicated to
the Interests of
the National Defense

PREFACE

The author has had an active interest in the whole field of mineral production and supply since 1914, when he accepted the appointment as Editor of *The Mineral Industry*, an annual statistical and technical review, and work on this publication has brought constant contact with production and consumption data from all over the world. A more specialized interest in strategic minerals, as distinguished from other members of the group, began to crystallize in 1925, with a request to accept a commission in the Staff Specialist Reserve of the United States Army, and to consent to receive periodic assignments to active duty, to serve as special lecturer on strategic minerals before the then newly organized Army Industrial College. These assignments were followed later by specialized assignments in the Commodity Division of the Office of the Assistant Secretary of War, where the subject was studied more intimately.

In the course of these assignments a large amount of data was collected, most of which was not of a confidential nature, and in 1934 an opportunity was presented to classify and organize the data into a series of articles on the various strategic minerals and metals, for publication in serial form in *The Military Engineer*, the organ of the Society of American Military Engineers. Since the magazine is a bimonthly and most of the commodities treated needed two installments to cover the ground, it required about four and a half years to complete the series. Since completion of the serial publication, all the sections have been thoroughly revised and brought up to date for publication in book form. During the course of the revision, most of the chapters have been submitted to specialists in the various industries for comment and criticism in order that the final publication might be as free as possible from technical errors. To all those who assisted in this way, the author desires to acknowledge his indebtedness and to extend his thanks, as well as to the Society of American Military

Engineers for permission to republish the material in book form.

Although the material was collected primarily from a military standpoint and prepared for presentation in a military publication, the subject matter is not at all confined to the strictly military phases of the problem but is equally applicable to consideration of the situation from a general commercial viewpoint, since the fundamental treatment of each commodity is a broad picture of production, consumption, and trade relations within the industry, and purely military aspects of the problem are only a specialized phase of the general commercial setup.

During the past few years a large portion of the world has been in a state of turmoil, with two wars in progress, another lately finished, and threats of others constantly cropping up. This being the case, it is not surprising that there has been in progress active rearmament programs in various countries, with corresponding emphasis placed on the whole problem of strategic materials, and especially on the strategic mineral supplies. The totalitarian states have been particularly concerned over their low degree of self-sufficiency and have been making strenuous efforts to remedy their shortcomings, which are much more pronounced than those of the democratic states. In fact, their marked lack of self-sufficiency has been one of the leading factors in bringing these states to a totalitarian form of government, whereas the higher degree of self-sufficiency in the others has permitted them to retain the greater degree of freedom as democracies. But despite all efforts, no dictator, however powerful he may be in other respects, can by proclamation engender needed ore reserves in barren rocks; the only ways by which they may be obtained are to take them forcibly from some other country which has fared more fortunately at the hands of nature or to buy them in the open market. Just now the former method seems to be taking precedence over the latter.

With lack of strategic materials leading to war, and with war making the lack more pronounced, we become enmeshed in a vicious cycle that has furnished ample reason for the increased interest in the subject of strategic mineral supplies in the United States as well as in other countries. For, while the United States has a shorter list of strategic minerals than any other country, every member of the group is so closely knit into our modern industrial structure that the whole trend of modern life would be disorganized without them.

On the whole, the total United States imports of mineral origin in 1937 constituted about one-sixth of the total value of all imports; but of this one-sixth more than 40 per cent was in the strategic group, and more than 20 per cent in the one metal tin. This illustrates rather pointedly the exaggerated importance of this small group of a dozen materials, and explains to some extent their indispensable character in our present-day industrial life.

It is a peculiar characteristic of most of these materials that they are to be found only in remote regions of the earth. The general European conflict that has loomed on the horizon so insistently for the past two or three years would be of very little consequence so far as direct involvement of sources of supply is concerned. The only strategic minerals that reach us in any material amounts from a European source of supply are manganese ore from Russia and mercury from Italy and Spain. Our difficulty in the event of a European war would not be from restriction of European sources, but from the effects that would radiate from the involved European nations to their remote colonial possessions, which form the chief sources of supply, as well as from the general disorganization of world commerce and the necessity of buying in world markets at inflated war prices.

There are three stages of involvement to consider in connection with the relationship of the United States to a European War as affecting our strategic mineral supplies:

First, the remote chance that the conflict could be confined to Europe; this is so unlikely that it requires little comment, but if it could be accomplished, the problems involved would be immeasurably simplified.

Second, the much more likely, and in fact almost certain, event that more or less the entire eastern hemisphere would be involved, because of European colonial interests and the joint interests between Japan in the East and Germany, Italy, Spain, and Hungary in Europe.

The third and final stage would be the drawing of the United States into the conflict. This is not at all a remote possibility; it happened during the World War, and the operation of the same natural laws that brought it about once can do it again, in spite of our neutrality laws and pronounced isolationist policy, both of which, incidentally, have already shown signs of giving way in the purely preliminary stages.

It behooves the United States to take effective measures, looking forward to the maintenance of its strategic mineral supplies, to a degree adequate to meet any of the above possibilities that may eventuate.

G. A. ROUSH.

BETHLEHEM, PA.,
    July, 1939.

CONTENTS

                                                                        PAGE
PREFACE.   vii

LIST OF TABLES.   xv

LIST OF ILLUSTRATIONS   xvii

CHAPTER   PAGE   CHAPTER

I. STRATEGIC AND CRITICAL   IV. NICKEL.   70
        MINERALS   1   Requirements   71
        The Strategic List . .   2   Uses   71
        The Critical List. . .   6   Substitutes   75
        The Essential List . .   6   Ores   76
        The Official Lists. . .   7   Ore Reserves   79
        Unofficial Lists. . . .   7   World Output and
        Conclusion   10   Supply   80
        Bibliography.   11   United States Output
                                                   and Supply   87
II. GENERAL SURVEY . . .   15   Prices.   89
        Some of the Shortages 16   Utilization.   90
        Development and   Tariff.   93
            Maintenance of a   Political and Commer-
            Supply   19   cial Control. . . .   93
        Classification of   General Review of Do-
            Strategic Minerals 29   mestic Situation . . 95
                                                Conclusion   96
III. MANGANESE.   31
        Requirements   32   V. CHROMIUM.   97
        Uses   32   Requirements   98
        Substitutes   34   Uses   98
        Ores   34   Substitutes   104
        Ore Reserves   38   Ores   104
        World Output and   Ore Reserves   108
            Supply   41   World Output and
        United States Output   Supply 109
            and Supply   48   United States Output
        Utilization.   53   and Supply 118
        Prices.   58   Prices.   122
        Tariff.   60   Tariff.   124
        Political and Commer-   Political and Commer-
            cial Control 63   cial Control. . . . 125
        General Review of Do-   General Review of Do-
            mestic Situation . . 64   mestic Situation . . 126
        Conclusion.   68   Conclusion   128

CONTENTS

CHAPTER | PAGE

VI. TUNGSTEN 130
    Requirements 130
    Uses 131
    Substitutes 134
    Ores 134
    Ore Reserves 138
    World Output and
      Supply 139
    United States Output
      and Supply 147
    Prices 151
    Tariff 155
    Political and Commer-
      cial Control 157
    General Review of Do-
      mestic Situation . . 159
    Conclusion 161

VII. TIN 162
    Requirements 163
    Uses 164
    Substitutes 165
    Ores 166
    Ore Reserves 170
    World Output and
      Supply 171
    Smelting 180
    United States Output
      and Supply 183
    Utilization 191
    Prices 192
    Tariff 194
    Political and Commer-
      cial Control . . . 195
    General Review of Do-
      mestic Situation . . 198
    Conclusion 198

VIII. ALUMINUM 200
    Requirements 200
    Uses 201
    Substitutes 204
    Ores 205
    Ore Reserves 208
    World Output and
      Supply 210

CHAPTER | PAGE

    United States Output
      and Supply 221
    Smelting 225
    Utilization 226
    Prices 227
    Tariff 231
    Political and Commer-
      cial Control 231
    General Review of Do-
      mestic Situation . . 235
    Conclusion 236

IX. ANTIMONY 238
    Requirements 239
    Uses 239
    Substitutes 241
    Ores 242
    Ore Reserves 246
    World Output and
      Supply 247
    United States Output
      and Supply 256
    Smelting 261
    Utilization 262
    Prices 264
    Tariff 268
    Political and Commer-
      cial Control 269
    General Review of Do-
      mestic Situation . . 270
    Conclusion 272

X. MERCURY 274
    Requirements 275
    Uses 276
    Substitutes 279
    Ores 280
    Ore Reserves 283
    World Output and
      Supply 284
    United States Output
      and Supply 289
    Utilization 293
    Prices 294
    Tariff 298
    Political and Commer-
      cial Control 298

CONTENTS

CHAPTER	PAGE
General Review of Domestic Situation	299
Conclusion	304

XI. PLATINUM ... 305
Requirements	306
Uses	306
Substitutes	310
Ores	312
Ore Reserves	316
World Output and Supply	316
United States Output and Supply	324
Utilization	329
Prices	331
Tariff	334
Political and Commercial Control	335
General Review of Domestic Situation	335
Conclusion	338

XII. MICA ... 339
Requirements	341
Uses	342
Substitutes	343
Ores	344
Ore Reserves	347
World Output and Supply	348
United States Output and Supply	357
Utilization	362
Prices	363
Tariff	367
Political and Commercial Control	367
General Review of Domestic Situation	368
Conclusion	376

XIII. IODINE ... 377
Requirements	377
Uses	378
Substitutes	379
Ores	380

CHAPTER	PAGE
Ore Reserves	382
World Output and Supply	384
United States Output and Supply	385
Utilization	388
Prices	390
Tariff	392
Political and Commercial Control	392
General Review of Domestic Situation	393
Conclusion	394

XIV. NITROGEN ... 396
Requirements	398
Uses	398
Substitutes	400
Ores	400
Ore Reserves	404
World Output and Supply	405
United States Output and Supply	413
Utilization	416
Prices	418
Tariff	420
Political and Commercial Control	421
General Review of Domestic Situation	424
Conclusion	427

XV. DOMESTIC SELF-SUFFICIENCY ... 428
Aluminum and Bauxite	431
Antimony	434
Chromite	436
Iodine	438
Manganese	440
Mercury	442
Mica	444
Nickel and Tin	446
Nitrogen	448
Platinum	450
Tungsten	452

CHAPTER   PAGE

XVI. STRATEGIC MINERAL
     SUPPLIES IN FOR-
     EIGN COUNTRIES . . 454

Comparative Status of
     Minerals 454
Comparative Status of
     Countries. 456
Self-sufficiency Factors 458
Consumption Factors. 461
Relative   Production
     Ability 462

CHAPTER   PAGE

Political and Commer-
     cial Control 464
Significance of Com-
     mercial Data . . . 465
Stock Accumulations . 467
Conclusion 469

XVII. COMMERCIAL INTERESTS
     VERSUS POLITICAL IN-
     TERESTS. 470

INDEX 475

LIST OF TABLES

In numbering the tables, a system has been adopted that will enable the reader to locate readily the corresponding data for the various commodities; in order to accomplish this, tables have been numbered by chapters, rather than consecutively throughout the book, and the same number has been given in each chapter to the same type of data; e.g., Table I in each chapter deals with some phase of world production data, and where further differentiation has been required, this has been obtained by the designations Ia and Ib; in like manner, Table II throughout refers to the available supply in the United States, Table III to imports, and so on.   This has been adopted in spite of the fact that in the higher numbers there are some gaps in the list, with no table presented in certain chapters, for it was felt that the added convenience of uniformity would more than offset the minor disadvantage of not having full consecutive numbering throughout the chapter.

TABLE NUMBER   PAGE

I. WORLD PRODUCTION

Manganese 43, 45
Nickel 81, 83
Chromium . . . 110, 111
Tungsten. . . . 140, 141
Tin Ore. 174
Tin. 175
Bauxite. 212
Aluminum. 213
Antimony. 251
Mercury. 286
Platinum 320
Mica 349
Iodine. 385
Nitrogen 408, 410

II. AVAILABLE SUPPLY IN THE UNITED STATES

Manganese 48
Nickel. 87
Chromium. 119
Tungsten 149
Tin. 184
Bauxite 222
Aluminum. 223
Antimony 258
Mercury. 291

TABLE NUMBER   PAGE

Platinum 326
Mica 358
Iodine. 386
Nitrogen 415

III. IMPORTS

Manganese 50
Chromium. 121
Tin. 186
Antimony 259
Mercury. 291
Platinum 327
Mica 359
Iodine. 387

IV. DISTRIBUTION OF IMPORTS

Manganese 51
Chromium. 122
Tungsten 150
Tin. 188
Antimony 260
Mercury. 292

V. STOCKS

Manganese 54
Tin. 190
Mica 362

TABLE NUMBER | PAGE

VI. UTILIZATION

Manganese 57
Nickel. 92
Tin. 191
Bauxite 227
Antimony 263
Mercury. 293
Platinum 330
Mica 362
Nitrogen. 417

VII. PRICES

Manganese 59
Chromium. 124
Tungsten 154
Tin. 193
Aluminum. 230
Bauxite 230
Antimony 266
Mercury. 297
Platinum 333

TABLE NUMBER | PAGE

VIII. TARIFF

Manganese 63
Nickel. 93
Chromium. 125
Tungsten 156
Tin. 195
Aluminum. 231
Antimony 269
Mercury. 298
Mica 367
Nitrogen. 420

IX. POLITICAL AND COMMERCIAL CONTROL

Manganese 64
Chromium. 126
Tungsten 157
Tin. 197
Aluminum. 243

In addition to these general tables, which cover the same phase of a number or all the different commodities, there are numerous specific tables that refer only to a single commodity, and are not listed here.

LIST OF ILLUSTRATIONS

PAGE

1. World Production of Manganese and Steel 42
2. Utilization of Manganese in Steel 56
3. Annual Prices for Ferromanganese and Spiegeleisen 58
4. World Production of Nickel and Steel 82
5. Published Prices for Nickel, 1840–1937. . . . . 90, 91
6. World Production of Chromite and Steel. 112
7. World Production of Tungsten and Steel. 142
8. Annual Prices for Tungsten Ore. 152
9. World Production of Tin and Steel 172
10. Annual Prices for Tin 193
11. World Production of Bauxite and Aluminum 211
12. Annual Prices for Bauxite 228
13. Annual Prices for Aluminum 229
14. World Production of Antimony. 248
15. Influence of Price on Antimony Production. 250
16. Annual Prices for Antimony 265
17. Silver Equivalents of New York Antimony Prices. 267
18. World Production of Mercury and Steel 285
19. Annual Prices for Mercury. 295
20. New York and London Monthly Average Prices for Mercury. . . 296
21. Salient Factors in the Mercury Industry. 300
22. World Production of Platinum 318
23. Annual Prices for Platinum. 331
24. World Production of Mica 350
25. Annual Prices for Mica 365
26. World Production of Nitrogen 407
27. Annual Prices for Nitrogen. 418
28. Self-sufficiency of Bauxite and Aluminum 431
29. Self-sufficiency of Antimony 434
30. Self-sufficiency of Chromium 436
31. Self-sufficiency of Iodine. 438
32. Self-sufficiency of Manganese. 440
33. Self-sufficiency of Mercury. 442
34. Self-sufficiency of Mica. 444
35. Self-sufficiency of Nickel and Tin 446
36. Self-sufficiency of Nitrogen. 448
37. Self-sufficiency of Platinum. 450
38. Self-sufficiency of Tungsten. 452
39. Self-sufficiency Ratings for Strategic Minerals. 455
40. Indicated Production Ability for Strategic Minerals 463

STRATEGIC MINERAL SUPPLIES

CHAPTER I

STRATEGIC AND CRITICAL MINERALS

Early in the period of the World War there was a great deal of agitation about "mineral independence," and the necessity for the leading industrial nations to make themselves self-sufficient with regard to all of the essential mineral supplies. This agitation was not confined to the nations then involved in the war, but invaded the United States as well, as soon as the disturbed conditions of world commerce began to interfere with the normal flow of imported minerals through the ordinary channels of transportation, and shortages of supply began to develop in those minerals of which there was an insufficient domestic supply. Strenuous efforts were made in various countries to expand the outputs of minerals in the deficiency group, but it did not take long to demonstrate quite conclusively that no nation on the face of the earth, not even the United States or the entire British Empire, had within its own borders sufficient sources of supply to make possible complete mineral independence, as visualized by its advocates.

When Mother Nature laid down the foundations of the earth, it seems that she did not feel impelled to take into consideration the unbalanced ideas of those over-nationalized individuals who were destinated to come along a few million years later, but placed the origins of the future ore deposits wherever her fancy dictated, and we today must make the best of the situation; and since *every* nation lacks *some* of the minerals necessary in modern industry, each is dependent on others for certain essential raw materials. In spite of all of the strenuous efforts that have been made during the past twenty years toward nationalistic independence along raw material lines, this can never be made complete, and it is ridiculous to attempt to force the issue too far, as has been done in a few cases. A certain degree of nationalistic interdependence is not to be avoided so long as we hold to our current standards of civilization, the gradual development of which has made everyday necessities of products that a few years ago were without use or value, and no country can afford, in a misdirected sense of seeming patriotism, to ignore this fact. Many of the excessive tariff rates and the export and import restrictions that are now in existence will in the long run do more harm than good.

THE STRATEGIC LIST

Following the agitation over mineral independence, and the gradual recognition of its impossibility, came an almost equally strident hue and cry over "strategic raw materials," and particularly the mineral raw materials. With war actually in progress, or immediately in the background, it was only natural that this term should be used extensively in its strictly dictionary meaning, that is, a material essential in the promotion of a program of modern warfare. In this sense, the term could be made to cover almost anything and everything, for modern warfare is waged by the nation, and not simply by the army and navy, and everything that enters into the scheme of everyday national life is a contributing factor in the progress of the war, whether it be tooth-paste or T. N. T.; but as usually applied, the word "strategic" was limited to the more important requirements in the munitions program or the industrial requirements directly related to the promotion of war, such as iron and steel, manganese, copper, lead, zinc, tin, antimony, tungsten, and a number of others, some of major importance, and others less so; some of these were of direct, primary importance in the war program, while others were contributory factors, that is materials that themselves are not actually munitions materials, but like fuel and power, are required in the manufacture of the primary items. If we add to the direct munitions requirements the other basic needs along correlative lines, we find included such items as iodine for medical purposes, phosphate rock and potash to help maintain a proper food supply, and tin for cans in which to preserve the food.

It is only natural that out of a comprehensive list of this kind, the particular interest of any nation should center around those particular items of which the domestic supply was inadequate. As a result, at least in the United States, the original meaning of the term "strategic" was soon lost, and it gradually came to be applied and accepted as descriptive of those materials required in a war effort, the domestic supply of which was insufficient, and for which the country had to depend on outside sources for part or all of its requirements. As time passed, and the World War receded farther into the background, more attention gradually came to be paid to the general industrial applications of such materials than to their possible war uses, thus leading to another transition, and at the present time the term "strategic" is used in the United States to designate those materials the domestic supply of which is inadequate, and is just as likely to be applied in a purely industrial sense, with reference to current industrial needs, as it is to refer to prospective future needs in a military program.

Whether the industrial or the military aspects of the term take precedence may usually be judged without difficulty by the context in which it is used and the position of the person using it. When used by an industrialist the term is probably used with its purely industrial aspect in the foreground; while the military man, in his use of the term, will likely have in mind the military aspect, he does not disregard the industrial connection, because he realizes that future military needs for any metal or mineral are largely dependent on current developments in industrial applications, for it is from industrial development that the new uses arise which are the basis of possible future needs along military lines.

Lack of recognition of this gradual change in the accepted meaning of the term "strategic" as it is used in the United States sometimes leads to misunderstanding and misinterpretation among foreign commentators on recent trends along this line in the United States.

In this discussion of the various strategic minerals, the term "strategic" is used in its current accepted meaning in the United States, as outlined above; that is, to designate a mineral or metal the domestic supply of which is insufficient to meet the demands, regardless of whether that demand be industrial or military, but since the material was originally prepared for appearance in a military publication, it is only natural that the military aspects of the problem are discussed in some detail, and in some cases take precedence over the purely industrial aspects; nevertheless, the general discussion presented applies equally well to every-day industrial needs.

On the basis of this definition of the term, each nation has its own particular list of strategic minerals, the items in the list being determined by two factors—the extent to which the industrial development of the country requires the various minerals or metals, and the extent to which the domestic sources of supply are able to meet this demand; or, reduced to the simplest terms, current domestic consumption and production. Although most of the materials concerned have certain primary military uses which, with a metal like steel or lead are outstanding, with one like tin or tungsten practically all of the military uses are secondary, rather than primary. A small amount of tungsten is used in cores of armor-piercing rifle and machine-gun bullets, but this is insignificant in amount as compared with that used in tool steels for machining purposes.

Then to take the next stage, the object to be machined by this steel may be an armor plate, a gun forging, or a projectile, but is more likely to be a crank shaft for an engine, or some other equally prosaic piece of metal; but even so, we have not yet reached the end of the possibilities, for the crank shaft might be for either a tank or a touring car; and a touring car that was designed to carry flappers to a country club may serve to carry a commanding officer from point to point behind the lines, or to carry workmen to a munitions plant. Hence, the increased demand for strategic materials in time of war is not at all confined to strictly military or munitions uses, but may be due in even greater proportion merely to the increased tempo of the general industrial program, which again emphasizes the necessity for considering not only possible future war demands, but also current industrial trends in production and consumption of those materials of which the United States has only a partial domestic supply.

In fact, the more one considers the various phases of the problem, the more one becomes convinced that military needs can not be considered alone, but only as a development or modification of current industrial needs. This again is justification for the use of the term "strategic" in the sense described above, rather than in its broader original meaning. Such use may be classed as loose by sticklers for purity in the use of the English tongue, but nevertheless it is a development of the term demanded by current development of the conditions in which it is used, and if we had no such trends in the development of the use of words, we would have no need for modern lexicographers, and could be satisfied with the dictionaries of the day of Noah Webster or Samuel Johnson.

There is one rather important difference between a strategic mineral from a purely industrial standpoint and from a military standpoint. Under normal conditions, although the domestic industry may be capable of supplying all that is needed so far as tonnage is concerned, a considerable amount of imported material may be absorbed by the domestic industry, due to price competition, low ocean freights on imported material as against high rail freights on domestic goods, availability of special grades for particular uses, and other similar reasons. On the other hand, in the event of war, prices increase, foreign materials are less accessible, shipments may be interrupted, ocean freights soar, and as a result there is a general speeding up of domestic production to fill the gap, so that, under war conditions, it is possible that the supply of some materials that were normally imported to a considerable degree may be expanded to cover the domestic demand, even though normal production was insufficient. This rule also works in the other direction in other cases; a production that was able to supply demand in normal times may not be capable of being expanded to meet war demands, and a material that normally was not strategic, becomes so under war demand.

In the United States the status of the various products has been carefully studied for a number of years by the War Department, and an official list has been compiled including all of those raw materials which are deemed to be strategic from a military standpoint. This list includes those mineral products which, in the opinion of the War Department experts, past experience has shown are likely to be deficient in supply under the conditions of war demand. This official list excludes a number of products the supply of which is deficient for current industrial needs, but which, due to lack of uses of a military character, or, as explained above, to the possibility of stimulating the domestic supply under war demand, need not be considered as strategic from a military standpoint, even though they are now in that class industrially.

Turning from the purely military side of the subject to the purely industrial, there is some difference of opinion as to the exact content of a purely industrial strategic list. A number of these have been compiled by different authorities at different times, but no two of them are identical throughout; some of these differences may be traced to changes in production or consumption during the period of time between the preparation of the lists, and others are due to differences of opinion as to the essentiality of a border-line material. However, the factors that have been responsible for most of the differences in these unofficial lists are the differences in viewpoint of those compiling the lists, and the lack of specific information concerning certain items.

THE CRITICAL LIST

The study of strategic materials had not progressed very far before it was realized that to cover the situation properly two classes or groups would be required, one to cover definite shortages, and the other to include those materials which might be expected to develop a shortage with increased demand, but which, with careful control of consumption and proper stimulation of production, might be maintained on a self-supporting basis. This second group was designated as "critical" materials. To differentiate clearly and definitely between these two groups, there is given herewith the present official definitions of strategic and critical materials as established by the War Department:

Strategic Materials are those materials essential to the national defense for the supply of which in war dependence must be placed in whole, or in large part, on sources outside the continental limits of the United States, and for which strict conservation and distribution control measures will be necessary.

Critical Materials are those materials essential in the national defense, the procurement problems of which in war, while difficult, are less serious than those of strategic materials, because they can be either domestically produced or obtained in more adequate quantities or have a lesser degree of essentiality, and for which some degree of conservation and distribution control will be necessary.

THE ESSENTIAL LIST

In January 1939 the War Department issued a new official list, different from its predecessors, in that it contained three headings: the former strategic and critical listings, and in addition a new one for essential materials neither strategic nor critical. The official definition of this heading is:

Essential Materials Neither Strategic Nor Critical.—In this classification are included those materials, essential to the national defense, for which no procurement problems in war are anticipated, but whose status is such as to require constant surveillance because future developments may necessitate reclassification as strategic or critical.

As will be noted in the accompanying classification table, this new group includes some materials formerly on the strategic and critical lists, and most of those in the various unofficial lists, thus making the list as a whole much more comprehensive than any of its predecessors.

THE OFFICIAL LISTS

The accompanying tabulation shows the development of the official strategic and critical lists so far as data are available. During the earlier years the critical list was not given a great deal of attention, and the records now accessible fail to show its complete history; hence, the record has been filled in only so far back as it could be definitely confirmed, leaving the remainder blank. In the record of the official strategic and critical lists here presented, Number 1 is the so-called Harbord list, prepared shortly after the close of the war by a committee of which General Harbord was chairman. This was the fore-runner of the official lists, but differs from them in that it merely names the various materials with which the army was concerned, dividing them into two classes, depending on whether a given material was required by only one service branch of the army, or by two or more branches. In the official lists that follow, Numbers 2 to 8, the record does not include each individual list compiled by the War Department, but only those lists in which changes had been made in the status of the mineral or metal commodities, disregarding those lists in which the minerals and metals remained the same, but changes were made in other types of material.

UNOFFICIAL LISTS

In this table will also be found the different unofficial lists that have been compiled by various authorities from time to time,

LISTS OF STRATEGIC AND CRITICAL MINERALS

	Official lists									Unofficial lists					
	1	2	3	4	5	6	7	8	9	1	2	3	4	5	6
	1921	1922	1923	1927	1928	1932	1936	1938	1939	1917	1924	1925	1929	1933	1935
1. Abrasives						C	C	C	E	D¹	d				
2. Aluminum	2,1	S	S	S	S	C	C	C	E	D	D	o	D	o	o
3. Antimony						S	S	S	S		d		d		
4. Arsenic						C	C	C	E	D	D		D		o
5. Asbestos						C	C	C	C						
6. Asphalt	1										d		d		
7. Barium															o
8. Bromine															
9. Cadmium															
10. Chalk									C	D					
11. China Clay	1	S	S	S	S	S	S	S	E	D		o		o	o
12. Chlorine						C	C	C	S		d		d	o	
13. Chromium									E	d			A		
14. Cobalt											d				o
15. Copper						C	C	C	C	D		o			
16. Cryolite						C	C	C	C		D		d		
17. Fluorspar						C	C	C	C	D	d	o	d		o
18. Graphite	1	S	S	S	S	S	S	S	E³	A	d				
19. Helium								C³	S		d		A		o
20. Iodine	1								S						
21. Iron and Steel						C	C	C	E		d		d	o	o
22. Lead	2,1	S	S	S	S	C	C	C	E³	d	d	o	d	o	o
23. Magnesia–Magnesite	1	S	S	S	S	C	C	C	S		d	o	A		
24. Manganese		S	S	S	S	S	S	S	S	d	d		d		o
25. Mercury		S	S	S	S	S	S	S	S		d		d		
26. Mica	1	S	S	S	S	S	S	S	E	A	d		d	o	
27. Molybdenum						C	C	C	S	D	d		A		o
28. Monazite															
29. Nickel	2,1	S	S	S	S	S	S	S	E⁴	D	D		A	o	o
30. Nitrates–Nitrogen						S	C	C		d	D		D	o	o

LISTS OF STRATEGIC AND CRITICAL MINERALS (Continued)

	Official lists									Unofficial lists					
	1	2	3	4	5	6	7	8	9	1	2	3	4	5	6
	1921	1922	1923	1927	1928	1932	1936	1938	1939	1917	1924	1925	1929	1933	1935
31. Petroleum	1					C	C	C	E	—	—	O	d	O	—
32. Phosphates	2	S	S	S	S	C	C	C	E	—	—	—	—	—	—
33. Platinum	1	S				S	C	C	C	D	D	O	—	—	O
34. Potash						C	C	C	E	d	D	—	D	O	O
35. Refractories						C	C	C	E	—	—	—	—	—	—
36. Sulfur and Pyrite	1²	S	S	S	S	C	C	C	E	—	—	—	d⁵	O	O
37. Tin	2	S	S	S	S	S	S	S	S	D	D	O	D	O²	O²
38. Titanium		S				C	C	C	C	—	—	—	—	—	—
39. Tungsten	2	S	S	S	S	S	S	S	S	—	d	O	—	O	O
40. Uranium	1					C	C	C	E	—	—	—	—	—	—
41. Vanadium	1	S	S	S		C	C	C	C	D	d	O	—	O	O
42. Zinc						C	C	C	E	—	—	—	—	O	—
43. Zirconium						C	C	C	E	D	—	—	—	—	O

SYMBOLS

1 Used by one service branch.
2 Used by two or more service branches.
S Strategic; War Department official list.
C Critical; War Department official list.
E Essential; War Department official list.
D Deficient in a major degree.
d Deficient to a lesser degree.
O Indicates that the material in question is on a list in which there is no classification as to degree of deficiency.
— Indicates that the material in question is not mentioned in the list.
A blank indicates that the status of the material at the time of the list has not been definitely determined.
2 Emery and grinding pebbles only.
3 Sulfur only.
3 Transferred to magnesium metal.
4 No longer carried as Nitrates or Nitrogen, but as Ammonia and Nitric Acid.
5 Pyrite only.

some of which were made by individuals, and some by committees. The sources of these lists are briefly as follows:

Number 1 was compiled in 1917 by C. K. Leith while serving as mineral adviser to the War Industries Board; this is the first list of the kind on record, and while the time gives it a strong military background, the list is truly industrial in character, rather than military.

Number 2 was compiled by W. S. Culbertson in 1924, and deals primarily with commercial and industrial factors.

Number 3 is the list of materials covered in the report of the Joint Committee on Foreign and Domestic Mining Policy of the American Institute of Mining and Metallurgical Engineers and the Mining and Metallurgical Society of America; it is predominantly industrial in character, but with a military background.

Number 4 was compiled by J. W. Furness in 1929 on a purely commercial and industrial basis.

Number 5 is the list of materials included in the 1933 report of the Mineral Inquiry on The Nationality of Control of World Minerals, no other phases of the problem being included in the report.

Number 6 was compiled by R. S. McBride in 1935, as a purely industrial list.

Further details concerning the various lists may be secured from the original publications in which they appeared, all of which may be located by reference to the bibliography at the end of this chapter.

The selection of the various materials for discussion has been based primarily on the official strategic list, but a comparison of the entries in the table of official and unofficial lists shows that these are also the main items in the purely industrial list, although a number of less important materials are also included in the unofficial lists, most of which will be found included in the official critical lists.   In general then, the official strategic list covers the more important items in the industrial strategic list, and the official critical list covers the remainder.   The present discussion is limited to the first group.

CONCLUSION

Publication of this series of studies on strategic mineral supplies was begun in the May-June issue of *The Military Engineer* for 1934, and continued to appear in regular installments from that time until September 1938. It includes discussions of the twelve commodities of mineral origin that have been on the official strategic list during that time. In the course of the time that elapsed during the preparation and publication of the series, some changes have been made in the official list; at the beginning, the list included eleven items of mineral origin, while at the present time it includes but ten; platinum and nitrogen have been transferred from the strategic to the critical list, and aluminum has been transferred from the critical to the strategic list, but in order to make the series complete, all twelve items have been included in the discussions.

Limitations of space have made necessary the presentation of some phases of the discussion in briefer form than may have been desired, but an attempt has been made to give to the reader as well balanced a picture of the conditions surrounding each of these commodities as the space available and the information at hand would permit. Although the preparation of these reviews has required a considerable expenditure of time and energy, the subject was deemed to be of sufficient importance to justify the effort, and conditions in world politics at the conclusion of the series is such as to make information of this character of much greater importance now than it was at the beginning of the series.

BIBLIOGRAPHY

Since this series of discussions on strategic mineral supplies is intended primarily as a general survey of the field, and not as a critical study, in the treatment of the various subjects no attempt has been made to document the information given, or to cite references of any kind. It is desirable to give a general bibliography of the main sources in which information of this kind may be found, so that the reader who wishes to go deeper into the subject may have some reliable guide to further investigation along these lines. The following list covers the various phases of the subject, historical and current, theoretical and practical, as well as the chief sources of statistical material on production, consumption, exports and imports, but omits detailed mention of references that deal with only a single commodity, many of which can readily be found by those interested in individual members of the list.   The writer is indebted to various of the publications cited here for much of the data included in this volume.

Private Statistical Publications

AMERICAN BUREAU OF METAL STATISTICS.—*Year Book.*   Annual, 1920—.
AMERICAN METAL MARKET.—*Metal Statistics.*   Annual.
METAL INFORMATION BUREAU (London).—Quin's *Metal Handbook and Statistics.*   Annual.
ROUSH, G. A.—*Mineral Industry.*   Annual, 1892—; McGraw-Hill.
INTERNATIONAL TIN RESEARCH AND DEVELOPMENT COUNCIL.—*Statistical Year Book.*   Annual, 1937—.

Government Statistical Publications

IMPERIAL INSTITUTE (London).—*Mineral Industry of the British Empire and Foreign Countries;* Statistical Summary.   Annual.
IMPERIAL INSTITUTE (London).—Numerous monographs on individual commodities.
U. S. BUREAU OF FOREIGN AND DOMESTIC COMMERCE.—*Commerce and Navigation of the United States.*   Annual.
U. S. BUREAU OF FOREIGN AND DOMESTIC COMMERCE.—*Monthly Summary of Foreign Commerce of the United States.*   Monthly.
U. S. BUREAU OF FOREIGN AND DOMESTIC COMMERCE.—*Statistical Abstract of the United States.*   Annual.
U. S. BUREAU OF MINES.—*Mineral Resources of the United States.*   Part I, Metals; Part II, Non-metals.   Annual, 1924–1931.
U. S. BUREAU OF MINES.—*Minerals Yearbook.*   Continuation of *Mineral Resources* (above).   Annual, 1932—.
U. S. GEOLOGICAL SURVEY.—*Mineral Resources of the United States.*   Part I, Metals; Part II, Non-metals.   Annual, to 1923; continued by U. S. Bureau of Mines.
U. S. GEOLOGICAL SURVEY.—World Atlas of Commerical Geology.   Part I, 1918.
U. S. TARIFF COMMISSION.—*Tariff Information Surveys,* covering various commodities and groups of commodities.

Other Government Publications

FURNESS, J. W., JONES, M. L., and BLUMENTHAL, F. H.—Mineral Raw Materials.   U. S. Bureau of Foreign and Domestic Commerce, *Trade Promotion Series* 76, 1929.
LEITH, C. K.—International Control of Minerals.   *Mineral Resources of the United States,* Part I, 1917.
LEITH, K., and LIDDELL, D. M.—The Mineral Reserves of the United States, and Its Capacity for Production.   Planning Committee for Mineral Policy, National Resources Committee, 1936.
NATIONAL RESOURCES BOARD.—Report of Planning Committee for Mineral Policy.   1935.

SMITH, G. O.—The Economic Limits of Domestic Independence in Minerals. *Mineral Resources of the United States*, Part I, 1917.

WAR INDUSTRIES BOARD.—American Industry in the War. 1919.

Committee Reports and Group Surveys

AMERICAN INSTITUTE OF MINING AND METALLURGICAL ENGINEERS.—Industrial Minerals and Rocks. 1937.

AMERICAN INSTITUTE OF MINING AND METALLURGICAL ENGINEERS (with Mining and Metallurgical Society of America).—International Control of Minerals. 1925.

BROOKINGS INSTITUTION.—Mineral Economics. McGraw-Hill. 1932.

CARNEGIE ENDOWMENT FOR INTERNATIONAL PEACE.—Raw Materials and their Effect on Industrial Relations. 1927.

MATHEWSON, C. H., and others.—Modern Uses of Non-ferrous Metals. American Institute of Mining and Metallurgical Engineers. 1935.

MINERAL INQUIRY.—Elements of a National Mineral Policy. American Institute of Mining and Metallurgical Engineers. 1933.

MINERAL INQUIRY.—The Nationality of Commercial Control of World Minerals. American Institute of Mining and Metallurgical Engineers. 1933.

U. S. BUREAU OF MINES, Foreign Minerals Division.—Mineral Raw Materials. McGraw-Hill. 1937.

Magazine Articles

CULBERTSON, W. S.—Raw Materials and Foodstuffs in the Commercial Policies of Nations. *Annals of the American Academy of Political and Social Sciences*, March, 1924.

HOBLEY, A. H.—Strategic Minerals. *Mining Congress Journal*, October, 1928.

LEITH, C. K.—Political Control of Mineral Resources. *Foreign Affairs*, 3, 541–555 (1925).

McBRIDE, R. S.—Strategic Minerals and Metals. *Engineering and Mining Journal*, January, 1935.

Books

ELLIOT, W. Y., and others.—International Control in the Nonferrous Metals. Macmillan. 1937.

EMENY, B.—The Strategy of Raw Materials. Macmillan. 1934.

HOLLAND, T. H.—The Mineral Sanction as an Aid to International Security. Van Nostrand. 1935.

LEITH, C. K.—Economic Aspects of Geology. Holt. 1921.

LEITH, C. K.—World Minerals and World Politics. McGraw-Hill. 1931.

REQUA, M. L.—The Relation of Government to Industry. Macmillan. 1925.

SMITH, G. O.—The Strategy of Minerals. Appleton. 1919.

STALEY, E.—Raw Materials in Peace and War. Council on Foreign Relations. 1937.

SPURR, J. E.—Political and Commercial Geology.   McGraw-Hill.   1920.
SPURR, J. E., and WORMSER, F. E.—The Marketing of Metals and Minerals.
     McGraw-Hill.   1925.
VOSKUIL, W. H.—Minerals in Modern Industry.   Wiley.   1930.
WALLACE, B. B., and EDMINSTER, L. R.—International Control of Minerals.
     Brookings Institution.   1930.
WALLACE, D. H.—Market Control in the Aluminum Industry.   Harvard
     University Press.   1938.

CHAPTER II

GENERAL SURVEY

It is a logical development in the natural course of human life and its needs that certain industries are fundamental, and others secondary; or in other words, that certain basic industries are concerned in supplying the prime necessities of life in their crudest forms, while others are concerned with the modification of these crude products through various stages of higher refinement or with alterations of form, location, et cetera. Of these basic industries, the mineral industry is outranked in importance only by agriculture in the breadth of its distribution over practically the entire face of the earth, and in its close relationship to the general welfare and progress of the various countries concerned. In no other industry has the influence of single localities been so widely felt as in the mineral industry. As soon as civilization reached the stage where the importance of minerals and metals was realized as a factor in development, their centers of production began to be felt as influences in history. From the time, 2,000 years ago, when the tin mines of what is now Cornwall led to the Roman conquest of ancient Britain, the acquisition of sources of mineral supplies has been an active factor in the development of conflicts between nations. We are, however, in this discussion, not concerned with the possession of mineral supplies as a *casus belli*, or even with their use as a weapon of offense, but rather as an item in any program of defense and in the regular course of industrial utilization.

The concentration of the major proportion of the world's supply of a given mineral in a restricted area has in many cases made the leading nations of the world dependent on that area for a much-needed raw material. When civilization was young, and known sources of supply of all minerals were limited, this was not surprising, but in many cases it continued to persist, and, even within the present century, the world went to Ceylon for its graphite, to Silicy for its sulfur, to the Ural Mountains for its

15

platinum, to Chile for its nitrates, and to Germany for its potash. Other examples might readily be cited.

The farther civilization has progressed and the more it has demanded in the way of raw materials, the more the various countries have been bound together by a chain of economic dependence on each other for the various raw materials that each lacks within its own borders. A given locality can no longer produce within its own confines everything that is needed in the course of its life. The luxuries of yesterday are the necessities of tomorrow, and such of its needs as a country can not produce for itself, it will secure elsewhere. During recent years many nationalistic efforts have been made to control this tendency, through tariffs, embargoes, export quotas, and similar expedients, but without any great measure of success.

Previous to and during the early months of the World War, much attention was directed to the fact that the United States produced the bulk of the world's supply of the more important mineral products, and frequent reference was made to the so-called "mineral independence" of the country. As a result, the belief gradually developed in many minds that this catch phrase really meant what it said, but it did not take long after the outbreak of the war to demonstrate the fact that no nation with an industrial civilization can be minerally independent, and that the United States are no exception to this rule. No nation, not even the British Empire, with its wide geographical distribution, has within its borders *all* of the various minerals required by its industries. Hence all are bound together in a net of interdependence from the meshes of which none can completely break away.

SOME OF THE SHORTAGES

If the United States were forced to operate on a strictly independent basis, our ability to produce as much steel as all the rest of the world put together would be of little real value so long as we lacked the manganese which is a necessary ingredient in the finishing operation, and without which the product is almost worthless. Practically every ton of steel made in the United States previous to 1916 was deoxidized with foreign manganese, and all of the manganese produced in the United States since that date, including two years of intensive war production, would not be sufficient for more than about 2 years' average supply, or less than 10 per cent of the total requirement.

During recent years the United States has been consuming from 20 to 25 per cent of the world's supply of manganese, but has been producing only 0.5 per cent. We have consumed about half of the world's nickel output in the production of special steels and other indispensable alloys, but our only production has been a few hundred tons a year as a byproduct in the refining of copper. We have been consuming more than one-fifth of the world's tungsten output, while producing about 7 per cent, and even this small output could continue only under a tariff protection so heavy that at periods of low prices the duty has amounted to more than 500 per cent. We have used more than half of the world's chromium, in making steels and other alloys, and have been importing a thousand tons for every ton of domestic output.

Due to incomplete statistics, the world's output of platinum is not definitely known, but apparently we have for some time been absorbing over half of the output, although we have produced only about 2 per cent of the total. Our total production of tin during the past 10 years has been about 500 tons, but we have been using regularly from 40 to 60 per cent of the world's supply. We have used nearly half of the world's output of antimony, while producing less than 1 per cent. We have been using one quarter of the total supply of quicksilver, only one-half of which we have produced at home.

For many years we consumed nearly one-half of the world's supply of mineral nitrogen, the only source of which is in Chile, and this was a necessary raw material in the manufacture of explosives. Fortunately, during recent years, by the development of the various processes for the production of synthetic nitrates, as well as those, such as the coking of coal, yielding nitrogen compounds as byproducts, the country has been made practically independent of sources of mineral nitrogen in case of emergency, although Chilean nitrates still continue to be imported.

In the case of mica, we are again faced with a difficult problem. Of ordinary grades our supplies are fairly adequate, but we have a large deficiency of high-grade sheet mica, such as is required for insulation in radio and certain other types of electrical equipment. As yet no satisfactory substitute has been devised, and we are dependent on foreign sources for a large proportion of the sheet mica required for such equipment.

These materials, then, of which we do not have a sufficient domestic supply to satisfy our needs are classed as "strategic" materials, when, as in the cases listed above, there is little if any chance that even the pressure of emergency production could make us independent of outside sources of supply.

Try to picture in your minds a war program of munition production without manganese to deoxidize steel; without nickel and chromium for alloy steels; without tungsten for tool steels; without antimony for shrapnel and primers; without quicksilver for detonators; without natural nitrates for powder, and without the platinum necessary to make nitrates synthetically, as well as for the manufacture of the sulfuric acid needed in the various processes in the manufacture of explosives. Tin, mica, and iodine are badly needed for other purposes, but these eight materials are absolute necessities in the development of any modern program of munition manufacture, and deprived of them, properly defending ourselves in any way against a nation not equally handicapped would be an impossibility, for we would be reduced almost to the level of the savage from the standpoint of weapons. Our great supplies of coal and petroleum, iron and copper, lead and zinc, would be next to worthless, for without these comparatively minor products, we would be hopelessly handicapped in our efforts to make proper use of the more important products.

Fortunately such an extreme condition as this is very improbable, for we have partial supplies of some of the strategic minerals, as well as partial substitutes for many of them. The various foreign sources of nearly all of them are sufficiently widely scattered over the earth to require an upheaval of enormous proportions to deprive us of all outside supplies of a majority of the list. Probably the worst condition, involving only one nation, would come in the event of a war with Great Britain, which has direct political control over 90 per cent of the world's nickel, 70 per cent of the chromium, 50 per cent of the tin, 40 per cent of the manganese, 20 per cent of the platinum, 10 per cent of the tungsten, and nearly all of the high-grade mica.

Of other metals and minerals of which we have only limited supplies, we have a fair chance under war conditions of building up a domestic supply that will meet most, if not all, of our needs, but with those specifically cited, with the possible exception of nitrogen, there is little hope, even under the most extreme conditions, of producing more than a fraction of our requirements; and of course, with metals like tin and nickel, the possible production is entirely negligible. The entire production of tin in the United States since the country came into existence would not supply our present needs for more than two or three days.

However, one must not get the impression that it is only under war conditions that the supplies of these materials are in such demand that they are deficient in quantity, and that in times of peace industry can get along without them. Few of these metals have outstanding uses that are specifically of a military character; most of their uses are in everyday industrial lines, and the same properties that make them of importance in a munitions program make them key metals in industry—materials of such a character and importance that, in spite of the comparatively small magnitude of their outputs, their utilization largely controls the advance of industrial developments; hence, these several products are just as strategic in times of peace as in times of war. In peace, the necessary supplies are usually available without difficulty, but war in any quarter of the globe is liable to restrict outputs, or to block the ordinary lines of transportation, and so hinder the importation of the requisite amounts to maintain a normal supply; it is not at all necessary for this country to be itself involved in war for shortages to develop.

DEVELOPMENT AND MAINTENANCE OF A SUPPLY

We must then face, during any period of war disturbance, the necessity of supplying our needs for these indispensable raw materials in the best way possible. While the lack of domestic sources is a handicap, there is, as has already been pointed out, little likelihood that we should be completely and indefinitely cut off from outside sources. This leaves two possibilities for difficulty: first, a partial, but insufficient, supply, the use of which will have to be carefully directed into channels where the most may be accomplished with what is available; or second, a serious delay in establishing a sufficient supply from new sources. Of these the latter is more to be feared than the former. While a sufficiently pressing demand will make it possible to secure the necessary quantities of most of the strategic minerals, considerable time will be necessary to get new deposits and operations into production, and the delay involved may be critical. The means to be adopted to avoid these difficulties vary in each individual case, depending on the surrounding conditions. Following is a brief outline of the "Fourteen Points" involved in the development and maintenance of a supply of a strategic raw material; in most cases a combination of several of these methods will probably be required to solve the problem, and the particular ones to be used will vary more or less in each individual case.

1. Build Up an Increased Peace-time Production, Where This Is Possible and Feasible.—With most of the strategic minerals this is not possible, since we do not have within our borders the necessary mineral deposits to draw on. Our production of copper can be greatly increased simply by increasing the price paid for the metal, for there are extensive known deposits of low-grade copper ore which can not be worked profitably at ordinary prices, and every cent added to the price offered will increase the potential output. Where the necessary ores are lacking, as in the case of tin and nickel, increases in price can affect the supply only to the extent that it increases the incentive to get material into the market from any available source, and makes it possible to recover greater amounts of secondary metal for re-use. With most of the other strategic minerals the building up of an extensive peace-time output is not feasible, even though it were possible, since the known deposits carry such limited quantities that they would quickly become exhausted by extensive operation, leaving nothing as a reserve to fall back upon in time of emergency.

Only in the case of nitrogen is this method adaptable without restrictions other than the current commercial problems involved, since the raw material used in the synthetic nitrate processes is the nitrogen of the air, available to all in unlimited quantities.

2. Where Necessary, Conserve the Existing Reserves by Restricting Current Production.—This method applies to several of the minerals in the strategic group, and particularly to manganese, tungsten, and quicksilver. If it seemed advisable to do so, in order to preserve a sufficient reserve supply for future emergency, production of all three of these metals could be practically completely suspended by rescinding the present tariff schedules pertaining to them, or could be reduced below its present level to any desired degree by lowering the tariff rates. Where the reserves can stand the drain, however, it is preferable to maintain at least a small production, as a small output can be expanded with much less loss of time than would be required to start new operations on properties long idle.

3. Build Up Increased Reserves of Metal in Current Uses, from Which It Can Be Diverted in Time of Emergency, if Necessary.—There has been much criticism of the extensive use of platinum in jewelry, on the ground that the metal was needed more for other purposes. While this is true to a certain extent, there is being accumulated in the country an enormous amount of platinum that could, if necessity demanded, be requisitioned for technical use; the chief difficulty is that much of the metal is in such an elaborate form that the labor involved in making the jewelry may amount to more than the value of the platinum, which would correspondingly increase the cost; another difficulty is the fact that there would be a sentimental value attached to many of the pieces, which would make their owners reluctant to part with them, however much the metal might be needed. For these reasons it is preferable to have metals of this kind in a form that could be changed with less difficulty. For example the recent tendency toward the use of heavy nickel cooking utensils is a move to be encouraged, since metal in this form is readily convertible to other forms, if necessary.

4. Encourage as Extensive a Recovery of Secondary Metals as Is Commercially Feasible.—While secondary recovery of all metals is desirable from a conservation standpoint and particularly so of metals of which the supply is limited, it is doubly important in time of war, when supplies are restricted and unusually difficult to obtain; as the prices of the metals rise under the stimulus of war demand, it becomes possible to recover profitably much metal that would not pay for recovery at ordinary prices.

5. Encourage the Accumulation and Filing, by the Proper Agencies, of All Available Information on Deposits of Strategic Minerals in the Country.—Such agencies as the Geological Survey and the Bureau of Mines are in a position to accumulate a large amount of extremely valuable information on the various mineral deposits, which, if kept available, can be of great use in planning for emergency operation. This should include not only data on all deposits now in operation, but also those that have been operated in the past, and all known deposits that have never been exploited. Ownership, location, and accessibility to transportation and markets; character and grade of the ores; estimates of cost of production of the active properties; cost of development and operation of inactive or undeveloped deposits; and all other items of information that have any bearing on the possibility of operation should be recorded.

6. Encourage the Accumulation and Filing, by the Proper Agencies, of All Available Information on Foreign Sources of Supply, and the Channels through Which the Products Are Obtainable.—This type of information will in many cases not be as detailed or as complete as that suggested in the preceding section, but if properly handled, can be made exceedingly useful in establishing and maintaining the necessary sources of supply in foreign countries. In this connection, due consideration should be given to the relationship between the location of the possible sources of supply and of the enemy country. For example, in the event of a war with Great Britain, we would not only lose access to Indian and Gold Coast manganese, through British political control of the country, but the Russian supply as well, since this must be shipped out through the Mediterranean Sea, which is under British naval control. A war with Japan would not necessarily jeopardize either of these sources of supply, but would probably interfere with the shipment of Malayan and East Indian tin and of Chinese antimony and tungsten to this country.

7. Stock an Emergency Supply, Sufficient to Cover the Needs of One or Two Years.—Theoretically this is the simplest possible method of solving the problems connected with the supply of strategic minerals, for all of the materials are permanent, and can be stored indefinitely without appreciable shrinkage or deterioration. In practical application of the plan, however, there are many difficulties to be overcome, the chief of which are a capital outlay of nearly half a billion dollars, and a heavy annual interest and storage charge. Still, the plan has such evident possibilities, particularly in that it provides the only complete protection against the possibility of shortage of supply, that it has gained much headway since it was first proposed about 15 years ago, and now seems to be on the verge of acceptance by Congress, at least to a partial degree. When this plan was first advocated, no Congress would have dared to venture an appropriation of such an enormous sum as half a billion dollars for anything outside of a routine appropriation bill for the maintenance of current departmental operations, but a mere bagatelle of half a billion could have been slipped into any one of several bills in the past few years and hardly been noticed. The mere fact that half a billion dollars is involved will no longer deter either Congress or the general public, if and when they are convinced of the value of the results. Unfortunately another factor has crept into the problem, that may result in serious handicap, and possibly even complete failure of the stockpile program, and this is the conflict of interests between the domestic and foreign producer.

If we had a potential domestic production of these materials on which any reasonable degree of reliability could be placed for maintenance of an increased supply, there would be no need of stock-piling; the very fact that this seems necessary is in itself sufficient evidence to cause unbiased observers to agree that stocks should be built up from foreign sources of supply, retaining such limited reserves as we may have as an anchor to windward in case of necessity to meet an emergency demand in excess of that planned for, or in case the emergency demand developed before the necessary stocks had been accumulated. If stocks are to be accumulated from domestic output, as is advocated in some quarters, it might well be that in many cases the limited domestic reserves would be pretty thoroughly worked out without providing the necessary bulk of stocks, leaving us in the uncomfortable position of having neither sufficient stocks nor further potential producing capacity to meet current demands even in the incomplete degree to which we have been accustomed in the past.

Another possibility for trouble that is linked with the problem is that domestic reserves of some of these materials are so low in grade that in order to get them in under the wire at all, the standard specifications for stockpile materials would need to be lowered, and if a movement of this kind is once started it is likely to be carried to such a point that the product has a materially lessened degree of usefulness, and may even be next to worthless for the purpose for which it was intended.

If stockpiling is to be done as a measure of national defense, it should be done entirely from foreign production. If there is to be grafted onto the defense program an offshoot of relief to domestic producers, this should be tolerated only to such an extent as can be maintained without exhausting the domestic reserves, and without any sacrifice in the quality of the product turned out. In the long run there could be nothing more disastrous than a policy of restricting foreign purchases in favor of the domestic output, combined with a lowering of standards to permit the acceptance of a larger amount of domestic production.

8. Conserve the Existing Supply by Restricting Use in Non-essential Lines.—Measures taken in this direction immediately after the outbreak of war can do a great deal toward maintaining the supplies necessary for essential uses.   These are of course only to be put into effect at a time of emergency, and are not suitable for peace-time procedure.   Only in a totalitarian state can control of this kind be established and maintained except as a war measure.

9. Develop Substitutes Where Possible and Practicable.—The problem of substitution is a rather complicated one.   In the first place, there are many different types of substitutes, depending on the object in view, and the problem is not only a different one for each individual metal, but for each separate use of the metal.

A *general* substitute is one which can be used entirely interchangeably with the original, for any and all purposes; this is such a broad requirement that the conditions can seldom be met, and most of the substitutes are *limited* ones, that is, restricted to a single use or property, or to a small group of related uses, rather than to the whole field.   For example, platinum has a peculiar combination of properties which have led to its use in a wide variety of ways; no material has ever been found which can take the place of platinum in all of these different uses, but a large number of metals and alloys have been used as substitutes in a limited field of use.   The extent to which this substitution has been carried is largely due to the high cost of the metal, and the fact that cheaper materials could be made to do certain of the things that had formerly been demanded of platinum.   Fused silica has replaced it in some types of chemical equipment, and various alloys in others; a nickel-iron alloy replaced it as a lead-in wire in electric light globes; tungsten and silver replaced it as a contact point in electrical apparatus; and vanadium oxide is being used in its place as a catalyst in the manufacture of sulfuric acid. Numerous other cases might be cited.

A *perfect* substitute is one which can be used in place of another material for any particular use with equal or better results in every way, and at equal or less cost; like all other examples of perfection, they are seldom found. An *imperfect* substitute is one which fulfills the main requirements, but may be lacking in some minor features which are not of sufficient importance to rule it out of consideration. An *incomplete* substitute is one which gives the properties desired, but to a lesser degree than the original material. A *partial* substitute is one which can be used only to a limited degree, taking the place of a certain proportion of the original, but not all of it.

In addition to these purely technical subdivisions, there is the economic factor to be considered. The two usual reasons for the commercial use of a substitute are to replace a high priced material with one of lower price, or to replace a material difficult to obtain with one more readily obtainable. This being the case, only a practical substitute can be used, that is, one which involves equal or less cost in proportion to the work done. In time of war, however, the cost element may be dropped out of consideration in many cases, as it may be advantageous to conserve a strategic material for more important uses by replacing it in some of its less important uses with a substitute which costs more. During the World War cadmium was used as a substitute for tin in solder, in order to save tin for other uses, although the cost of the cadmium was greater than the cost of the tin; the cadmium was a domestic product, obtainable in reasonable amounts, while the tin was imported, and more difficult to obtain. This makes the study of these possible substitutes of almost as much importance as the other types.

The continued and satisfactory use of a substitute may eventually develop into a complete replacement of the original product by the substitute; for example, as has been cited above, a nickel alloy was substituted for platinum in lead-in wires in electric light globes, and although this was in turn later replaced by other combinations, it led to a complete abandonment of platinum for this particular use. A too extensive development of substitutes in time of peace may lead to difficulty when war demands arise, for if wholesale substitutions have been made along ordinary commercial lines, and the demand for the material has been appreciably decreased, the lessened supply will increase the difficulties in expanding the supply to meet a war-time demand, particularly if the military uses of the material in question are much different from the civilian uses, so that the same degree of substitution is not possible. This led to some difficulty in the late war in connection with platinum. The high price of platinum and the lessened Russian supply from 1914 to 1916 had encouraged extensive substitution, not only as cited above, but in many other lines as well, and lessened the floating stocks of metal in use to a point where there was a distinct shortage for war use.

10. Increase the Normal Output as Rapidly as Possible after the Origin of the Emergency.—The output of all of the strategic minerals can be expanded to some degree. In the case of tin and nickel any possible expansion is negligible in amount. Antimony and platinum are in almost as bad a position; there is possibility for some expansion, but the probable output would not be more than a small fraction of the needs. During the World War the outputs of the other strategic metals showed approximately the following percentages, as compared with consumption: manganese and tungsten, 35 per cent; chromium, 45 per cent; quicksilver, 80 per cent. If the reserves have not been too much depleted in the meantime, equal or better records might be expected if necessity demanded it.

The time element in pushing these industries to their maximum output is highly important, and if the precautions recommended in previous sections have been observed, the delay can be cut to a minimum.

11. Foster Production in and Importation from Available Foreign Sources, and Restrict Exportation of the Domestic Product.—Since strategic materials are by definition those of which we have insufficient domestic supplies, it will be necessary to encourage production in those countries whose output is most readily accessible to us, but always bearing in mind the old warning against too many eggs in one basket. For example, do not depend on Brazil alone for manganese, even though the supply should seem adequate, since any difficulty would jeopardize the sole source; draw at the same time from all sources available, with particular attention to those like Cuba and Costa Rica, that are located nearer to us.

If the commerce of any country supplying us with strategic material has been sufficiently disorganized that they have been unable to import products that they need, it may become necessary, in order to secure from them the materials that we require, for us to agree to supply them with certain products in exchange; this will naturally tend to shift our demands to those countries lacking the things that we can best spare from our own needs.

Exportation of the domestic product and re-exportation of imported product will naturally be closely controlled during an emergency, and in some cases it might prove advantageous to limit the exportation of domestic production of a highly strategic material even in time of peace, as a measure of conservation of the reserves for possible future emergency need.

12. Establish Control of Production, Distribution and Prices.—Plans should be made far in advance for the organization of agencies to take over control of production, importation, exportation, distribution, uses and prices of all strategic materials. The sooner this is accomplished after the start of the war, the less will be the delay and confusion in getting things into systematic operation.

13. Plan against the Possibility of Loss of Domestic Supply through Invasion, Sabotage, et Cetera.—The sources of considerable proportions of our supplies of iron, copper, lead, zinc, sulfur, and petroleum, as well as much of our most important manufacturing areas, lie sufficiently near our borders that they may be considered to be in danger of interruption by invasion. Of the strategic minerals, the quicksilver and tungsten outputs of California lie outside the limit of safety set by the War College, and the Montana manganese deposits are on its border. Most of the war output of chromium also came from portions of this zone in Oregon and California. In case of an attack from the west, these industries would be in danger, with quicksilver in the worst position, as about half of our output originates within 100 miles of San Francisco. On the whole, though, the chances for interruption of supply through enemy invasion probably needs less consideration than protection against sabotage. Invasion requires the transport of an army of thousands of men, with all of their necessary supplies and equipment, but one man with the requisite incentive and a stick of dynamite can put a mine out of commission for an indefinite period.

14. Employ Military and Diplomatic Strategy to Make Available Sources of Supply Not Otherwise Open.—This is a field in which little can be done in advance of the emergency, outside of the usual assortment of treaties—which may or may not function at the critical period; but after a war is under way, and the various countries are more or less definitely aligned as ally, enemy or neutral, there is room for a great deal of work in this direction.   One example will suffice to show the possibilities.

At the beginning of the World War about one-third of the nitrate production of Chile was under German ownership. England's control of the seas made it impossible for this German-owned material to be used to their own advantage, and of course they refused to sell to the Allies, who were in a position to transport it and use it.   This meant that by the time the United States entered the war, there was a very considerable stock of German-owned nitrate accumulated in Chile, and at the same time Chilean currency was constantly depreciating for lack of gold to support it, since the main Chilean gold reserve was deposited in German banks and they refused to release it.   When this condition became known to the United States military authorities, arrangements were made with Chile for governmental seizure of the German nitrates in reprisal for the refusal to release Chilean gold; these nitrates were then sold to the United States in return for the gold necessary to support their declining currency.

An integral part of military strategy is the exercise of political and commercial control.   These two factors enter largely into the production and distribution of mineral raw materials.   The United States has political control not only over the industries in this country owned by domestic capital, but also over those owned by foreign capital, and in case of necessity can, as it did in the late war, confiscate enemy property and use it for its own purposes; but in the same way, industries under the commercial control and ownership of United States capital, located in foreign countries, are subject to the political control of the countries in which they lie, and these countries may exercise such control as they see fit to impose.   This control is of course more drastic in an enemy country than in a neutral country.   Conditions are often such, or can be so manipulated, that this control may be operated in our favor, as in the case of the Chilean nitrates, cited above; on the other hand, care must be taken to prevent, so far as possible, the manipulation of these same conditions by the enemy in their own favor, and to our detriment.

Since the demonstration in the World War of the importance of political and commercial control, many countries have established a much stricter political control over foreign-owned resources, to avoid future complications in time of war.

At the beginning of the World War the bulk of the Canadian nickel production was owned and controlled by United States capital, and only the crude smelting operations were carried on in Canadian territory. The intermediate products were then shipped to the United States, and all of the finished metal was produced in a plant in New Jersey. Some time before we entered the war, the German commercial submarine "Deutschland" succeeded in making two trans-Atlantic trips carrying back to Germany as part of her cargo 50 tons of nickel. As soon as this became known, it created a great uproar in Canada because a material originating in Canada was reaching the enemy, to be used directly against Canadian and Allied soldiers. This eventually resulted in the requirement on the part of the Canadian government that the nickel mined in Canada must also be smelted within their territory, in order that they might maintain proper control over the exportation of the products. As a result, the smelting company had to abandon their New Jersey plant, and built a new one on Canadian soil.

Later the leading producer of aluminum in the United States sought a mining concession covering a large area in British Guiana containing enormous supplies of aluminum ores. This concession was finally granted, but only on the condition that the ore produced should be smelted into metal in British territory. This resulted in the building of the largest single aluminum plant in the world, on the Saguenay River in the Province of Quebec, Canada, although this location is not one that otherwise would have been selected, due to its remoteness from the centers of consumption of the finished metal. These are only two examples of the manner and extent to which political control may be exercised in favor of the controlling country.

CLASSIFICATION OF STRATEGIC MINERALS

The various strategic minerals fall logically into three groups: (1) the ferro-alloy group, made up of those metals used extensively or predominantly in the iron and steel industry; (2) the non-ferrous group, metals not associated with the steel industry; and

(3) the non-metallic group.   The members of these three groups are as follows:

FERRO-ALLOY	NON-FERROUS	NON-METALLIC
Manganese	Tin	Mica
Nickel	Aluminum	Iodine
Chromium	Antimony	Nitrogen
Tungsten	Quicksilver	
	Platinum	

The above summary outlines the general phases of the situation with respect to strategic minerals.   Conditions differ widely with the different minerals, and in later chapters, these different materials will be taken up in turn, and discussed in some detail, giving the particular features of each individual problem which is considered.

CHAPTER III

MANGANESE

Of all of the strategic minerals, manganese is the most important, being both the one of which the greatest tonnages are required, and the one concerning which there is the most difference of opinion as to the domestic possibilities. Previous to the World War the manganese output of the United States was entirely negligible, amounting to only 3,000 to 7,000 tons of ore a year out of a consumption ranging from 300,000 to 600,000 tons, or about 1 per cent. In 1917 we managed to produce about 14 per cent, and in 1918 about 35 per cent of our requirements. Since then production has been much greater than before the war, but has averaged less than 8 per cent of the consumption. All of the remainder of the supply has been imported, either as manganese ore, or as ferromanganese or other alloys. Manganese is an absolute necessity in the steel industry, and the stability and accessibility of the supply of raw material is a controlling factor in the maintenance of this industry on a proper basis.

One of the outstanding characteristics of the utilization of manganese is that in process of use, most of the metal is dissipated in a form not susceptible to subsequent recovery as a secondary metal; in fact, the amounts that do return to use in this way are so small as to be practically negligible, and almost the full requirements for each year must be met from new production. No other metal in the strategic list has such a low secondary return as manganese. Another prominent feature in connection with manganese is that little of it is produced in the form of the pure metal, most of it being converted from the ore into the ferro-alloys, ferromanganese or spiegeleisen; furthermore, what small proportion is converted into more or less pure metal does not go into use in the pure form, but is used in making various non-ferrous alloys; there is at present no commercial use for metallic manganese, except in the form of an alloy with some other metal or metals.

31

REQUIREMENTS

The figures on world production presented in Table I*a* do not at all represent the true requirements for manganese ore, since there has been more or less stocking of ore for emergency supplies for the past 15 years; the outputs reported therefore include not only current consumption, but also fairly large amounts for stocks. While there are no means of determining the extent of these stocks with any great degree of accuracy, such rough indications as are available point to a total which approximates 25–30 per cent of production during the period covered by the stocking, leaving about 70 per cent of the reported output to cover current consumption. These are average figures for the 15 year period, and the recent years show a still higher rate of stocking, as is evidenced by the fact that the world steel output of 1937 was approximately double that of 1922, but the manganese ore output had increased by five times, and the estimated 1937 total was split between consumption and stocks in the proportions of 55 per cent and 45 per cent respectively.

With a steel industry in the United States that reached a maximum output of 45,000,000 tons during the World War, averaged 43,000,000 tons from 1920 to 1930, made a high point of 56,000,000 tons in 1929, and might easily reach 60,000,000–70,000,000 tons in another war, an annual manganese supply of at least 400,000–450,000 tons, or 800,000–900,000 tons of ferro-grade ore, needs to be anticipated. In addition to this there will be required some 35,000 tons of chemical ore, 525,000 tons of spiegel ore, and 2,500,000 tons of manganiferous iron ore. There is no particular need for concern over these latter ores, as the supplies are fairly adequate, but with the ferro-grade ores the situation is radically different.

USES

The consumption of manganese falls under two general heads, *metallurgical* and *chemical*, in the proportion of about 95 per cent and 5 per cent respectively of the total. In general, metallurgical uses require the conversion of the ore to a metal or alloy, while for chemical uses it is converted into some chemical compound other than that in the ore, but with manganese the largest chemical use requires an especially pure grade of ore, high in MnO_2, which is used as such, while minor uses require the usual variety of chemical compounds.

Metallurgical Uses.—The great majority of the manganese required in metallurgical work goes into the manufacture of ordinary steels; a small percentage is used in the production of special high-manganese alloy steels, in foundry work, and in other types of alloys.

The chief duty of manganese in steel manufacture is as a deoxidizer and desulfurizer. It is usually added to the bath in the form of ferromanganese while the metal is being tapped from the furnace, and by combination with the residual oxygen and sulfur of the bath, helps to produce a sound, clean metal. Small amounts of manganese also improve the physical properties of the steel, and enough manganese is added to the bath to leave a fraction of a per cent in the finished metal. The amount of manganese required varies with the kind of steel being made and with the process being used but, over a long period of years, the total has averaged about 14 pounds of manganese per ton of steel made.

The most important form in which manganese appears on the market is ferromanganese, an alloy averaging 80 per cent manganese, the rest being chiefly iron and carbon. Smaller amounts of spiegeleisen are made, containing about 20 per cent manganese, with the remainder iron and carbon. The so-called metallic manganese is usually a high-grade ferro-manganese, running 90 per cent or better in manganese. Two other alloys of minor importance are silicomanganese, with 55–70 per cent manganese and 18–25 per cent silicon, and silicospiegel, which has the usual manganese content of spiegeleisen, and in addition carries 4–12 per cent of silicon, replacing part of the iron.

The excessive demand for ferromanganese in preference to the other alloys is due to the better and more economical utilization, resulting from its higher concentration of manganese, which commercial practice has set at 78–82 per cent as about the highest that can be maintained. During the World War the standard for ferromanganese was lowered to 70 per cent, and that for spiegeleisen to 16 per cent, and some alloys were made with even lower percentages. This made it possible to use lower grades of ore during the emergency, but later the usual standards were resumed.

Chemical Uses.—The chemical uses of manganese are comparatively small, but are of an importance far beyond their bulk. The chief demand is for a high-grade manganese dioxide ore, with a minimum of iron and other harmful impurities, for use as a depolarizer in the manufacture of dry batteries. Other chemical uses are found in the manufacture of glass, enamel, paint and varnish dryers, pigments, dyes, and fertilizers, but since the total amount of manganese required for chemical uses is not over 5 per cent of the total consumption, the metallurgical uses take precedence.

Military Uses.—There are no strictly military uses for manganese; they are merely the ordinary commercial uses, increased in magnitude and importance by the stress of the emergency.

SUBSTITUTES

Many efforts have been made to secure a satisfactory substitute for ferromanganese as a deoxidizer for steel, but with no material degree of success, so that, at the present time, there is no adequate substitute and no immediate prospect of one. Silicomanganese and silicospiegel are applicable to certain limited uses and, while they contain little less manganese than the standard alloys, the silicon content helps in the work of deoxidization. Ferrosilicon may be used to replace some of the ferromanganese in deoxidization, but it can not be used as a complete substitute.

The main relief in time of emergency will not be from the use of substitutes but from a lowering of the manganese content of the alloys used, so as to permit their production from ores of a lower grade than is now required. There is also hope of some relief from beneficiation processes to raise the grade of the ore, or from special production processes for turning out a high-grade alloy from a low-grade ore, although thus far none that have been proposed have been developed to a commercial success.

ORES

There are four grades of manganese ores, based on the character of the ore, and its manganese content. The commercial ores are all oxides, or the carbonate.

Chemical Ores.—Dry battery manufacture consumes the bulk of the so-called chemical ores, and for this purpose the ore must be the dioxide, with 72 to 87 per cent of manganese dioxide and with a low content of iron, copper, and other harmful impurities. The domestic supplies of ore of the necessary high quality are limited, and are practically restricted to the Phillipsburg district of Montana and small amounts in Virginia.

Metallurgical Ores (Ferro Grade).—Ores from which standard grade ferromanganese can be made should have a minimum of 40 per cent manganese, and preferably more. Although the manganese-iron ratio in ferromanganese usually approximates 5:1, the losses of manganese incurred in the smelting operation require a ratio of about 8:1 in the ore. During the World War the reduction of the standard for ferromanganese to 70 per cent made possible the use of ores with 35 per cent manganese and a manganese-iron ratio of 5:1, but under normal conditions an ore with less than 42 per cent manganese can hardly be classed as ferro-grade material.

The chief impurities to be considered in these ores are silica and phosphorus; amounts of these over 8 per cent and 0.25 per cent, respectively, are considered undesirable and are liable to incur a penalty for the excess.

The manganese content of these ores is mostly in the oxide form but, in the Butte district of Montana, the leading domestic source, the ores are largely carbonates, which are calcined to the oxide before use.

Ferruginous Manganese Ores (Spiegel Ores).—Ores with less than 35 per cent and more than 10 per cent manganese are classed as ferruginous manganese ores, and are available for the production of the standard 20 per cent grade of spiegeleisen, if the iron content is not over 2.7 times the manganese content. Formerly the minimum content for these ores was 15 per cent manganese, or about what is necessary in order to produce a 20 per cent spiegel; since many of the ores are above this figure, this permits the inclusion of some ores of lower grade in the classification, while still maintaining the average.

Manganiferous Iron Ores.—Officially, ores with 5 to 10 per cent manganese are classed as manganiferous iron ores, for the production of high-manganese pig iron, but in practice many producers segregate ores with as little as 2 per cent manganese and sell them separately.

Beneficiation.—Efforts at beneficiation of low-grade ores have been under way for a number of years, and in some cases have made marked progress.   In 1931 a mill was operated on the Cuyuna range in Minnesota, using a combination of tabling and flotation, and turned out several thousand tons of a concentrate carrying 17 per cent manganese, suitable for spiegeleisen, but little has been accomplished on a commercial basis toward the conversion of low-grade ores to ferro-grade.   The best that has been done along this line is the sintering of rhodochrosite (carbonate) ores at Butte, Montana, by which a 35–40 per cent ore is converted into a sinter carrying nearly 60 per cent manganese.   Due to the depression of the market, this plant has been shut down since 1931.

Flotation of carbonate ores has also been proven on a practical basis, but flotation of oxide ores is still in the experimental stage in this country.   A project is under way in Cuba, however, for the flotation and sintering of oxide ores, and, due to the fact that Cuban ores enter the United States duty free, it is claimed that the product can be landed at United States ports at a price that can compete with the lowest Russian price plus duty.

Various attempts at magnetic concentration and volatilization have thus far not gotten beyond the experimental stage, nor have any of the solution and precipitation processes except the Bradley process, which has reached the pilot-plant stage.   The Bradley process was designed for a certain type of Cuyuna ore, and has not yet been adapted to any other ore.   The process consists of a roasting operation to convert MnO_2 to MnO and Fe_2O_3 to Fe_3O_4, after which the manganese can be dissolved out as sulfate by a solution of ammonium sulfate, from which it is later precipitated; the insoluble residue may also be treated by magnetic concentration for the recovery of the magnetic iron oxide.

The United States Bureau of Mines has been working on a smelting process for the production of ferromanganese from the low-grade Cuyuna ores, but this has not yet gone beyond the experimental stage.   The process involves three steps:

1. Smelting the manganiferous iron ore to high-manganese pig iron in the blast furnace.

2. Converting this pig iron to steel in the basic open hearth furnace, making a high-manganese slag.

3. Using the open-hearth slag as a raw material for the production of ferromanganese, in either the blast furnace or electric furnace.

During the World War the writer suggested the use of a somewhat similar process, smelting the ore to a high-manganese pig iron, or a low-grade spiegel, followed by:

1. Blow the pig iron in the bessemer converter, slagging off the manganese and enough of the iron to make the slag of the proper manganese-iron ratio.

2. Smelt the slag in either the blast furnace or electric furnace, to make ferromanganese.

3. After the removal of the desired amount of carbon from the pig iron in the bessemer, transfer the metal to the basic open hearth furnace, and finish it to steel.

This method would keep the phosphorus out of both the ferromanganese and the steel, while in the Bureau of Mines process the phosphorus goes into the open-hearth slag, and thence into the ferromanganese.

The great difficulty with all of the beneficiation processes is that none of them have yet been developed to a point where they can be operated successfully at current prices, although some have demonstrated their ability to operate at somewhat higher prices. This leaves the question open as to just what or how much these processes might be able to accomplish under emergency conditions, and at what prices they will be able to accomplish their work effectively. This combination of large supplies of low-grade ore and of beneficiation processes, most of which have yet to prove their practical possibilities, forms an immense *potential* reserve, but one from which no very definite results can be expected in the near future.

Another of the very interesting features of the problem of utilizing low-grade ores is in connection with the enormous deposit near Chamberlain, South Dakota, which has been estimated to contain more than 100,000,000 tons of manganese in nodular material running about 16 per cent manganese and 11 per cent iron. Extensive work has been done with low grade ores by the U. S. Bureau of Mines, in an attempt to develop an electrolytic process for the recovery of the manganese; results are as yet unsatisfactory, as costs are too high, but should the process prove commercially successful at a reasonable price, our manganese problem would be solved for some time to come.

Metallurgy.—Ferromanganese may be produced from the appropriate ores in either the blast furnace or the electric furnace, but spiegeleisen is made only in the blast furnace. The general procedure is very much the same as the operation of the iron blast furnace, using coke as a reducing agent, and limestone as a flux to combine with the silica and other gangue of the charge. Silicomanganese may also be produced in the same way. The chief difficulty encountered is the extent to which the manganese tends to volatilize from the charge, resulting in considerable losses.

The so-called manganese metal is reduced from a pure ore, low in iron, using silicon or aluminum as a reducing agent, to avoid contaminating the product with carbon.

Secondary Recovery.—There is no secondary recovery of manganese, since in use most of the metal is dissipated in unrecoverable form. The only recovery is in the scrap of high manganese alloys, which is returned for reworking.

Forms in Which Manganese Appears on the Market.—The chief form in which manganese appears on the market is as ferromanganese, with 78–82 per cent Mn, and second in importance is spiegeleisen, with 18–22 per cent Mn, most of the remainder of both being iron and carbon. Regular quotations are also available on the so-called manganese metal and silicomanganese, as well as on the ores from the various sources, and the leading chemicals.

ORE RESERVES

Without going into statistical details on the ore reserves of the various countries, it is sufficient to say that there is a plentiful supply of ore to cover all possible demands for many years to come. The difficulty in the manganese situation lies not in the amounts of ore available, but in their location. Ore supplies are plentiful, but unfortunately their location does not coincide with the centers of consumption in the steel industry. Of the 1937 total steel output, 78 per cent was produced in six regions, United States, Germany, Great Britain, France, Japan, and Belgium-Luxemburg, while these same areas produced less than 2 per cent of the total manganese output; and even in the maximum year of war demand this was raised only to 21 per cent, four-fifths of which was in the United States. Of the major steel making countries of the world, only Russia has an adequate manganese supply.

The only other major steel-producing country that has even a reasonable amount of manganese reserves to fall back on in case of emergency is the United States. During the World War the maximum outputs of manganese ores in the leading steel-producing countries were 311,000 tons in the United States, 1,000 tons in Germany, 18,000 tons in Great Britain, 10,000 tons in France and 57,000 tons in Japan. But while the fact that the United States is better off in regard to possible emergency supply than the other countries mentioned is some small comfort, the unpleasant fact still remains that for all of our strenuous efforts expended on the support and expansion of our manganese industry during the World War, we were able, in 1918, to produce only one-third of our requirements, and subsequent peace-time efforts have been still less successful.

The difficulty in the United States is not so much in the amounts of manganese available as in the grade of the ore. Enormous amounts of low-grade ores are known, but the quantity of high-grade ores is comparatively small, and the problem is still further complicated by the small size of most of the deposits and their wide distribution geographically, involving some 60 districts in 19 states.

Such reserves of manganese as we have in the United States are to be measured not in terms of tonnage, but in terms of the price which the product will bring in the market. That we have no real tonnage reserves that can meet the open competition of the world markets is evidenced by the complete absence of any pre-war output, and by the very moderate later outputs, made under a tariff protection amounting to about 100 per cent. The only thing that made possible our increased outputs in 1917 and 1918 was the high price prevailing at the time. It is only at prices well above the normal that we can expect domestic production on any appreciable scale, and the higher the price, the greater the possible output. The production in 1918 was largely brought on the market under the official price schedule issued by the War Industries Board setting a sliding scale of prices varying from 86 cents per unit for 35 per cent ore to $1.30 per unit for 54 per cent ore, plus an additional 15 cents per unit for ore produced east of Chicago.

With the technical advances that have been made since 1918 in the beneficiation of the lower grades of ore, higher outputs would undoubtedly be obtained now for a given price than was the case in 1918, and while just what can be expected in the way of output at any given price is difficult to determine, it is not impossible to estimate the prospective production that any particular price should develop, if one has access to the necessary data.   In the report of the Subcommittee on Manganese of the American Institute of Mining and Metallurgical Engineers, "International Control of Minerals," published in 1925, and a later report on "Manganese for National Defense," published in 1933, estimates of this kind were presented.

In applying the findings of this committee, one must bear in mind that the 400,000 tons of manganese metal ready for use, the minimum requirements laid down in a preceding section, becomes about 535,000 tons in the ground, after allowing for losses in mining, ore dressing and smelting, so that for a two years' supply we should need reserves of 1,070,000 tons.   The committee estimated that reserves of this size would be established at an *index price* of 85 cents per unit[1] for manganese ore, and that at an index price of $1 per unit, the potential reserves would be 1,650,000 tons of metal in ore averaging 38 per cent.   At first glance, it might appear that the prospective needs were adequately covered by this reserve, but two points must be made clear before these figures can be evaluated in their proper perspective.

1. By *index price* is meant a price which is scaled to a purchasing power equivalent to the 1913 level.[2]   The 1918 scale of ore prices was 98 cents for 38 per cent ore, but the commodity index at that time was about 200, so that the index price was only 49 cents; hence, the price required to establish the needed reserves is not 13 per cent less than the 1918 scale, but 73 per cent greater.

2. An even more important point is the difference between ore in reserves and current production.   Although the price set may establish a potential reserve that is equal in size to the requirements to be filled, nothing has yet been said about the time element in converting reserves into production.   The rate of production that can be developed is an entirely different matter, for

---

[1] A "unit" is 1 per cent of a long ton of ore, or 22.4 pounds of manganese metal.

[2] The index price for any given period may be obtained by dividing the dollar price for the period by the commodity index for the period.   Further discussion of the index price will be found in the section on *Prices*.

in the normal course of events it usually takes from 10 to 20 years to work out a reserve, and the more this time is shortened, the greater the difficulties involved, and the greater the expense. The importance of this point may be better appreciated when it is learned that the committee estimated that even a $1 index price, assured for three years in advance, would probably not bring into the market more than 3.5 per cent, 7 per cent, and 9 per cent of the total reserves in the three successive years.

WORLD OUTPUT AND SUPPLY

During the past 25 years the world output of manganese ores has about trebled in amount, reaching a maximum of about 6,100,-000 metric tons in 1937. The countries that have contributed to the output during the period have numbered more than 40, but 80 per cent of the total has come from four major producers, and another 10 per cent from five intermediate producers, leaving less than 10 per cent to be distributed among more than 30 minor producers. Table I*a* shows the annual outputs of the major and intermediate producers, the period totals for each, and the percentage distribution of the total. While four countries have been classed as major producers, possibly these four should be divided into two groups, since Russia has provided 36 per cent of the total and India 27 per cent, while Brazil has contributed only 9 per cent and Gold Coast 8 per cent. The low figure for Gold Coast is due however to its late start as a producer, for since 1924 it has outranked Brazil for third place in the list.

Figure 1 shows in graphical form the world production of manganese ore and of steel, and it is particularly significant to note the closer approach of the two curves since 1929. This does not indicate a greater consumption of manganese ore per ton of steel made, but rather a marked tendency to accumulate emergency stocks of ore, some of which had been done even before 1929.

Table I*b* is derived from the data in Table I*a* for the purpose of tracing the comparative development of the various producers through the successive periods of increasing and decreasing output since 1913: the pre-war year, 1913; the war period, 1914–1918; the maximum year of war output, 1918; the post-war readjustment period, 1919–1921; the low year, 1921; the inflation period,

1922–1929; the maximum year of inflation, 1929; the depression period, 1930–1932; the depression low point, 1932; the recovery period, 1933–1937; and the top year of recovery, 1937.   This table tells its own story of the various transitions so thoroughly that there is little need to elaborate on it in the text; it suffices to call attention to the heavy fluctuations in Russia; the war period

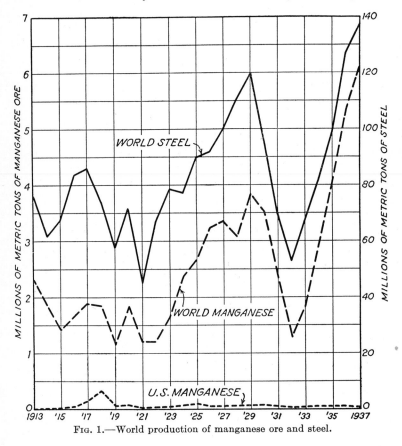

Fig. 1.—World production of manganese ore and steel.

decrease in India, and its later decline in competition with the reviving outputs from Russia and other sources; the extent to which Brazil bore the brunt of the heavy war demand, and the subsequent decline; the position gained by the Gold Coast; the even more rapid and spectacular rise of South Africa, to rank ahead of Gold Coast and Brazil; recent improvements in Cuba which have brought output back well toward the war peak; the gradual growth of intermediate producers as a whole; and finally, the extent to which intermediate and minor producers take on

TABLE Ia.—WORLD PRODUCTION OF MANGANESE ORE
(Thousands of metric tons)

	Russia	India	Brazil	Gold Coast	Egypt	South Africa	United States	Czecho-Slovakia	Cuba	Others	Total
1913	1,245	824	122	....	[1]	....	4	[1]	12	114	2,321
1914	906	694	184	....	[1]	....	3	[1]	10	74	1,871
1915	537	458	289	....	[1]	....	10	[1]	9	113	1,416
1916	251	656	503	4	[1]	....	32	[1]	34	168	1,648
1917	205	601	534	32	[1]	....	131	[1]	45	346	1,894
1918	152	526	393	31	[1]	[2]	311	[1]	183	259	1,855
1919	54	547	206	36	49	[2]	56	[1]	35	184	1,167
1920	179	748	454	44	78	[2]	96	50	8	170	1,827
1921	29	690	276	7	55	[2]	14	44	3	84	1,202
1922	91	482	341	67	104	[2]	14	24	4	77	1,204
1923	271	706	236	142	132	[2]	32	42	20	90	1,671
1924	494	816	159	259	150	[2]	57	79	25	279	2,318
1925	718	853	332	344	81	[2]	100	54	52	136	2,670
1926	803	1,031	261	350	122	1	47	78	28	526	3,247
1927	831	1,147	273	375	153	1	45	95	1	632	3,553
1928	766	994	360	330	137	....	48	108	2	342	3,087
1929	1,415	1,010	316	415	191	9	61	97	1	325	3,840
1930	1,328	843	207	424	121	147	68	85	1	289	3,513
1931	884	546	147	251	102	102	40	84	7	151	2,314
1932	832	216	20	52	[2]	....	18	33	10	108	1,289
1933	1,021	222	25	269	[2]	21	19	17	91	141	1,826
1934	1,821	413	8	345	1	66	27	59	65	160	2,965
1935	2,384	652	42	405	87	95	27	71	45	292	4,100
1936	3,002	826	156	418	135	258	33	93	38	351	5,310
1937	2,700[3]	994	228	536	188	631	40	106	135	555[3]	6,100[3]
Totals	22,919	17,495	6,072	5,136	1,885	1,329	1,333	1,219	864	5,966	64,208
Per cent	35.7	27.2	9.4	8.1	2.9	2.1	2.1	1.9	1.3	9.3	100.0

[1] Data not available.   [2] Less than 500 tons.   [3] Estimated.

increased loads in periods of heavy demand, but drop back when demand slackens, leaving a greater share of the load for the major producers.

The leading producing countries, having annual outputs of more than 100,000 tons at any time, have been, in the order of magnitude:

BEFORE 1914	DURING WORLD WAR	SINCE 1930
India	India	Russia
Russia	Russia	India
Brazil	Brazil	Gold Coast
	United States	Brazil
	Cuba	South Africa
		Egypt

Any country having an output of this magnitude during either of these three periods may be considered as a potential producer of sufficient importance to justify a brief outline of the history of the industry in the country.

Brazil.—A pre-war output averaging less than 200,000 tons a year increased to more than 500,000 tons during the war, due to demand from the United States, which had formerly been supplied from India and Russia; production has since fluctuated widely, with a low of 159,000 tons in 1924 and a high of 360,000 tons in 1928. Production dropped to only 8,000 tons in 1934, but recovered to 228,000 tons in 1937. The local consumption is small, and practically the entire output is exported, mostly to the United States. The foremost Brazilian deposits are in the State of Minas Geraes, about 300 miles north of Rio Janeiro. A small output has been made in the vicinity of Nazarath, near Bahia, and extensive but largely undeveloped deposits are known near Corumba, in south-western Matto Grosso, and near the mouth of the Piracaua River, in Para. Other deposits of lesser importance are also known, but have been left undeveloped.

Cuba.—Although its pre-war outputs of manganese ore were insignificant in amount, in 1918 Cuba supplied 183,000 tons and 135,000 tons in 1937. While this is not a large figure, it is sufficient to justify including Cuba among our future potential sources of supply, not only for emergency, but also for current demand, particularly when one considers its accessibility with respect to other possible sources. The known deposits are all comparatively small, but are of such a character that they respond to beneficiation, and facilities have recently been completed for increasing the output. Most of the deposits are in Oriente Province, but others are known in Matanzas, Santa Clara, and Pinar del Rio.

TABLE Ib.—WORLD PRODUCTION OF MANGANESE ORE BY PERIODS
(Thousands of metric tons)

Period	Average World Output	Percentage Distribution of World Total											
		Major Producers				Intermediate Producers					Total Major	Total Inter- mediate	Other Coun- tries
		Russia	India	Brazil	Gold Coast	Egypt	South Africa	United States	Czecho- Slovakia	Cuba			
1913	2,321	53.6	35.5	5.3	—	....	—	0.2	....	0.5	94.4	0.7	4.9
1914–18	1,737	23.6	33.8	21.9	0.8	....	—	5.6	....	3.2	80.1	8.8	11.1
1918	1,855	8.2	28.3	21.2	1.7	....	—	16.8	....	9.9	59.4	26.7	14.0
1919–21	1,399	6.2	47.3	22.3	2.1	4.3	0.0	4.0	2.2	1.1	77.9	11.6	10.4
1921	1,202	2.4	57.4	22.9	0.6	4.6	0.1	1.2	3.7	0.2	83.3	9.7	7.0
1922–29	2,699	25.0	32.6	10.5	10.6	5.0	0.2	1.8	2.7	0.6	78.7	10.3	11.1
1929	3,840	36.9	26.3	8.2	10.8	3.1	3.5	1.6	2.5	0.0	82.2	9.3	8.5
1930–32	2,372	42.8	22.6	5.3	10.2	3.1	....	1.8	2.8	0.3	80.9	11.5	7.7
1932	1,289	64.6	16.7	1.6	4.0	0.0	....	1.4	2.6	0.8	86.9	4.8	8.4
1933–37	4,060	53.9	15.3	2.3	9.7	2.0	5.3	0.7	1.7	1.8	81.2	11.5	7.4
1937	6,100	44.3	16.3	3.7	8.8	3.1	10.3	0.4	1.7	2.2	73.1	17.7	9.1

Note.—Zeros only indicate an amount less than 0.1 per cent; a dash indicates no production; leaders indicate no data available.

Czecho-Slovakia.—The manganese output of Czecho-Slovakia is not large enough to be of importance, except for the fact that it is the only output of even intermediate size in Central Europe. The two leading mines are at Kisovce, in Slovakia, and Chvaletice, East Bohemia; the ores are of low grade, the former averaging 20 per cent Mn, and the latter 12–14 per cent.

Egypt.—Egypt has maintained a manganese ore output of 100,000 to 150,000 tons since 1922 and reached a maximum of 191,000 tons in 1929. During the early depression years production exceeded demand and operations ceased early in 1932 until accumulated stocks had been reduced, but since 1935 the output has returned to its former high level. This source, like South Africa, is too remote from the United States for emergency use but is an important possible source of supply for European countries.

Gold Coast.—This new producer entered the list in 1916, passed the 100,000-ton mark in 1923, and reached 424,000 tons in 1930 and 526,000 tons in 1937. This rapid growth, combined with the simultaneous decline in Brazil, brought Gold Coast into third place as a manganese producer. Although imports to the United States from this source were more than 93,000 tons in 1930, and 254,500 tons in 1937, it is too remote to be useful as an emergency supply, unless nearer sources are insufficient. It is the nearest large source after Brazil.

India.—During the past two decades the manganese ore output of India has nearly doubled from its former level of 500,000 to 600,000 tons. Deposits have been worked in at least nineteen different states, but Balaghat, Bhandara and Nagpur, in the Central Provinces, and Sandpur, in Madras Presidency, furnish more than three-quarters of the output. The local steel industry consumes 10 per cent or less of the total, and the remainder is exported through the ports of Bombay and Calcutta, and Mormugao in Portuguese India, with France and England as the chief buyers. New railroad construction and harbor improvements at the port of Vizagapatam are being made to shorten the haul on much of the output.

Russia (U. S. S. R.).—A pre-war output of about 1,000,000 tons a year dropped to almost nothing during the post-war period of internal disturbances in Russia, but later developed to 1,400,000 tons, in 1929, which in turn has been doubled.

There are two main manganese producing districts in Russia: Tchiaturi, in Georgia, to the east of the Black Sea; and Nikopol, in southern Ukrania, northwest of Crimea. The former furnishes the bulk of the exports, while the latter supplies most of the domestic consumption. During 1932 mining operations were begun on the Mozul River in Siberia, to supply the Stalinsk steel plant at Kuznetsk. The chief importers of Russian ore during recent years have been United States, Netherlands, France, Germany, and Belgium; most of the shipments to the Netherlands were evidently intended for some of the adjacent countries, as the local demand is small. Exports have been taking up to three-quarters of the total output, but during the recent industrial development in Russia the domestic consumption has been increasing. Production has grown more rapidly in other countries than in Russia, whose pre-war share of half or more of the world total has shrunk to about a third.

South Africa.—The manganese ore output of South Africa first became of importance in 1930, when a production of 147,000 tons was made in the Postmasburg district; due to generally depressed industrial conditions, operations ceased after a production of 102,000 tons in 1931, and were not renewed until April, 1933, since when recovery has been rapid, the 1937 output of 631,000 tons being exceeded only by that of Russia and India. While this district is capable of supplying increasing amounts of ore, it is too far removed from the United States to be important as a possible source of emergency supply, although small amounts have been imported in several years.

United States.—While the pre-war manganese output of the United States was so small as to be negligible, it reached a maximum of 311,000 tons in 1918, under the pressure of war demand. Since that time continuous efforts have been made to maintain the industry at an important level, but without ever passing the 100,000-ton mark. The domestic situation will be discussed in more detail in a later section.

Other Countries.—Among the intermediate producers, that is, those with outputs ranging from 10,000 to 100,000 tons annually, are China, Hungary, Italy, Japan, Malay, French Morocco, Netherlands East Indies, Philippines, Rumania, Spain, and Sweden. In addition to these, smaller amounts, usually less than 10,000 tons annually, are produced in Algeria, Australia, Bulgaria,

Chile, France, Germany, Greece, Portuguese India, Indo-China, Mexico, Rhodesia, Puerto Rico, Tunis, Turkey, and Yugoslavia.

UNITED STATES OUTPUT AND SUPPLY

The manganese supply of the United States reaches the consumer through several different channels: (1) ore mined in the United States, and reduced to ferromanganese or spiegeleisen in domestic furnaces, or sold directly to the consumer in the case of chemical ores; (2) ferromanganese and spiegeleisen imported from other countries, chiefly Canada, England, and Norway, which countries in turn are dependent on still others for their ore supplies; (3) ferromanganese and spiegeleisen smelted in domestic furnaces from ore imported from other countries.

TABLE II.—AVAILABLE SUPPLY OF MANGANESE ORE IN THE UNITED STATES
(Thousands of long tons)

	Ore Imported	Equivalent Ore Imported[1]	Total Ore Imported	Domestic Ore Output	Equivalent Ore Supply	Actual Ore Supply[2]	Per Cent from Domestic Sources		Per Cent of Equivalent in Actual Supply
							Equivalent Supply	Actual Supply	
1913.......	345	332	677	4	681	349	1	1	51
1914.......	283	208	491	3	494	286	1	1	57
1915.......	321	169	490	10	500	331	2	3	66
1916.......	576	246	822	31	853	607	4	5	71
1917.......	630	132	762	129	891	759	14	17	85
1918.......	491	77	568	306	874	797	35	38	91
1919.......	333	87	420	55	475	388	12	14	82
1920.......	600	167	767	94	863	694	11	14	80
1921.......	393	20	413	14	427	407	3	3	95
1922.......	421	229	650	13	663	434	2	3	65
1923.......	403	255	658	32	690	435	5	7	63
1924.......	486	134	620	57	677	543	8	10	80
1925.......	586	189	775	98	873	684	11	14	78
1926.......	709	114	823	46	869	755	5	6	87
1927.......	622	86	708	45	753	667	6	7	89
1928.......	428	116	544	47	591	475	8	10	80
1929.......	664	151	815	60	875	724	7	8	83
1930.......	586	86	672	67	739	653	9	10	88
1931.......	503	41	544	39	583	542	7	7	93
1932.......	111	35	146	18	164	129	11	14	79
1933.......	157	84	241	19	260	176	7	11	68
1934.......	281[3]	54	335	27	362	308	7	9	85
1935.......	371[3]	67	438	26	464	397	6	7	85
1936.......	762[3]	99	861	32	893	794	4	4	89
1937.......	1226[3]	64	1290	40	1320	1266	3	3	88

[1] Ore equivalent of the Mn content of imported ferro and spiegel; the latter is included because it replaces an equivalent amount of ferro. [2] Total of ore imports and domestic production. [3] General imports, estimated to correspond with previous years; from Table V.

During the past few years the domestic share of the supply has varied from 5 to 10 per cent of the total, but reached 33 per cent in 1918. Ferro and spiegel imports have recently ranged from 10 to 30 per cent of the total, and foreign ore imports from 66 to 90 per cent. During the past 25 years the domestic supply has averaged 7 per cent, foreign alloy imports 15 per cent, and foreign ore imports 78 per cent of the total consumption. For the past 15 years, during which a special effort has been maintained to establish the domestic industry on a permanent basis, the corresponding percentages have been 6 per cent for domestic supply, 13 per cent for alloy imports and 81 per cent for ore imports.

The quantities of the various high-grade manganese materials making up the United States supply during the period 1913–1937 are shown in Table II. In order to bring everything to a comparative basis, alloys have been converted to their ore equivalent. The import figures on alloys are reported in terms of manganese content, but include spiegel as well as ferro; however, the amount of manganese in imported spiegel is unimportant, averaging less than 500 tons a year.

Imports.—Since 94 per cent of the manganese consumed in the United States is imported, either as ore or alloy, it is necessary to give some consideration to the sources from which these come. As most of the imported alloy comes from countries which in turn do not have adequate ore supplies and must secure their ore from the same sources that supply our own needs, the alloy does not require separate discussion, but can be lumped in with the general discussion of ore supply. It is not even necessary to trace down the sources of ore supply for the countries exporting alloys to this country, for, if we should be deprived of the alloy imports, we should import the additional ore to offset the deficiency from the sources to which we have most ready access, rather than from the same sources used by the alloy-exporting countries.

The countries furnishing important amounts of manganese ore to the United States during the period 1913–1937 are shown in Table III. In 1913 India supplied 43 per cent of the imports, Russia 36 per cent, Brazil 20 per cent, and other countries less than 1 per cent. During the World War Russia stopped shipments, and India dropped to a small amount, the main supply coming from Brazil, with smaller quantities from Cuba and a

TABLE III.—IMPORTS OF MANGANESE ORE INTO THE UNITED STATES
(Thousands of long tons)

	Brazil	Russia	India	Gold Coast	Cuba	Others	Total
1913................	70	124	148	....	....	3	345
1914................	114	53	103	....	....	13	283
1915................	276	....	36	....	5	4	321
1916................	472	....	52	....	31	21	576
1917................	513	....	49	....	45	23	630
1918................	346	....	29	....	83	33	491
1919................	247	7	9	....	35	35	333
1920................	422	19	71	....	8	80	600
1921................	262	....	114	1	....	17	393
1922................	275	....	25	23	13	85	421
1923................	176	23	51	56	9	88	403
1924................	110	82	109	46	23	116	486
1925................	219	229	47	63	13	15	586
1926................	262	245	61	96	14	31	709
1927................	174	253	93	87	9	6	622
1928................	142	160	84	24	3	15	428
1929................	217	329	73	34	3	8	664
1930................	185	226	58	93	2	22	586
1931................	134	196	48	87	3	34	502
1932................	22	55	2	25	7	1	111
1933................	....	84	....	44	28	1	157
1934[2]...............	56	125	21	74	64	3	341
1935[2]...............	30	153	57	95	44	5	384
1936[2]...............	110	290	127	242	38	7	813
1937[2]...............	78	384	70	255	123	2	912
Totals..............	4,912	3,037	1,537	1,344	603	671	12,097
Per cent............	40.6	25.1	12.7	11.1	5.0	5.5	100.0

[1] Not reported separately previous to 1922.   [2] Imports for consumption; preceding years, general imports.

number of other minor sources. Since the war Indian ore has never regained its former level and the Cuban output was insignificant until 1933. The post-war expansion of the consuming industries was shared by Russia and Brazil and by Gold Coast, a new producer in the field. Of the total imports of the past 5 years, Russia has supplied 40 per cent, Gold Coast 27, Cuba 11, India 11, Brazil 11, and other countries 1 per cent.

Of the four leading sources of ore supply, Gold Coast ore will grade 50 per cent or better of manganese content, India 47 to 52 per cent, Russia 41 to 48 per cent, Brazil 38 to 50 per cent and Cuba 36 to 50 per cent. From the standpoint of accessibility, India is the farthest, Russia second, and Brazil and Gold Coast are about on a par as third while Cuba is nearest; in round numbers the distances are in the ratio of 7, 5, 4, and 1.

The distribution of the manganese ore imports received in the United States in 1937 at all of the more important ports of entry and from all important export sources is shown in Table IV; in addition to the imports listed in the table, about 4,000 tons was received from various minor producers, or from the listed producers, but at other ports of entry. This table emphasizes most strongly the importance of the port of Baltimore, at which was entered 48 per cent of the 1937 imports. The next largest port of entry was Pittsburgh, with 37 per cent of the total; Pittsburgh is of course a "port" only in the statistical sense, and the ore destined for the Pittsburgh area was probably also received through Baltimore, since this location would have the lowest freight rate to Pittsburgh. Combining these two figures, we then have 85 per cent of the 1937 imports handled through the port of Baltimore, against 3 per cent in Philadelphia, 6 per cent in Newport News, 5 per cent in Mobile, and 1 per cent through other ports.

TABLE IV.—DISTRIBUTION OF MANGANESE ORE IMPORTS IN 1937
(Thousands of long tons)

	Phila-delphia	Balti-more	Pitts-burgh	Norfolk	Mobile	Buffalo	Total
Russia.............	4	301	72	....	2	5	384
Gold Coast..........	18	50	162	22	....	1	253
Cuba...............	10	53	....	16	44	....	123
Brazil...............	....	24	54	....	....	....	78
India...............	....	....	53	17	....	....	70
Total............	32	428	341	55	46	6	908

Exports.—There is no record of exports of manganese ore. There is a small export of alloys, chiefly ferromanganese, but since the amount is small, and separate figures are not reported for ferro and spiegel, no attempt has been made to incorporate exports in the table of available supply.

Consumption.—Due to lack of information on stocks, it is impossible to arrive at any data on consumption other than the table of available supply.

Stocks.—Specific information is lacking on the amounts of stocks of manganese ore available in the United States, but it is possible to arrive at an approximation which seems to be reasonably accurate, through a study of the published data on general imports, imports for consumption, ore consumed in the production of ferromanganese, and stocks in bonded warehouses. Bonded stocks did not come into the picture until 1922, when a tariff was placed on manganese ore, but since then consumers carry a large proportion of their stocks in bond, as in this way they may defer payment of duty until the ore is withdrawn from the warehouse.

Up to September 1922 all stocks were at the plants of the consumers, chiefly the producers of ferromanganese, and the only gage of their amount is the annual changes in stocks, which can be approximated by a comparison of imports for consumption with ore consumed during the year, attributing any difference between these two items as a change in consumers' stocks. From September 1922 ore was accumulated in bond in increasing amounts, and stocks at the consumers' plants was permitted to decline to an amount just sufficient to cover current demands. Theoretically, any difference between general imports and imports for consumption should correspond with the annual change in stocks in bond, but for some reason not yet explained, these figures seldom agree, and sometimes differ quite widely, introducing a factor of uncertainty into the resulting data.

In the determination of consumers' stocks, in order to convert the annual changes into actual stocks, the amount of stocks held at some one time is required. No figures of this kind are known to have been reported, but conditions make it possible to estimate the amount with a fair degree of accuracy. In 1923, when the shift was made from stocks at the plant to stocks in bond, imports for consumption were only 153,000 tons, causing a decrease of 385,000 tons in plant stocks to provide the 538,000 tons used during the year in the production of ferro, and indicating that at that time stocks must have been in excess of this amount, but by how much can only be estimated. As an absolute minimum, a supply for at least two or three weeks must have been left in the plant stocks, as that time would be required to replenish the stocks from the warehouse. On the other hand, if we assume stocks much greater in size at this time, the figures work back to excessive amounts during the war period, when we know that large amounts of ore were not available. Comparison of the conditions in the various years seems to indicate that at the end of 1912 plant stocks must have been at least 200,000 tons, and possibly were more. Accepting this amount as a probable minimum, the successive annual changes were applied, giving the approximate year-end stocks for each year.

In order to take into account the differences in the stocks in bond, as between the amounts officially reported and those

TABLE V.—STOCKS OF MANGANESE ORE IN THE UNITED STATES
(Thousands of long tons)

Year	General Imports (1)	Imports for Consumption (2)	Change in Bonded Stocks (3) (1 − 2)	Cumulative Change (4)	Stocks in Bond (5)	Consumed in Ferro-manganese (6)	Change in Consumers' Stocks (7) (2 − 6)	Cumulative Change (8)	Apparent Total Stocks (9) (4 + 8)	Apparent Total Stocks (10) (5 + 8)
1913	345	[1]				302[2]	+43	243[3]	243[3]	
1914	283	[1]				246[2]	+37	280	280	
1915	321	321				428[2]	−107	173	173	
1916	576	570				541[2]	+29	202	202	
1917	630	630				606[2]	+24	226	226	
1918	491	491				569[2]	−78	148	148	
1919	333	334				272[2]	+62	210	210	
1920	607	607				620[2]	−13	197	197	
1921	401	401				208	+193	390	390	
1922	421	363	+58	58		235	+28	418	476	
1923	403	153	+250	308		538	−385	33	341	
1924	486	449	+37	345	318	443	+6	39	384	357
1925	586	555	+31	376	346	519	+36	75	451	421
1926	709	595	+114	490	367	620	−25	50	540	417
1927	622	620	+2	492	370	565	+55	105	597	475
1928	428	566	−138	354	236	567	−1	104	458	340
1929	664	661	+3	357	234	615	+46	150	507	384
1930	586	455	+131	488	413	459	−4	146	634	559
1931	503	294	+209	697	614	288	+6	152	849	766
1932	111	91	+20	717	622	91		152	869	774
1933	157	288	−131	586	491	234	+54	206	792	697
1934	281[4]	341	−60	526	431	257	+84	290	816	721
1935	371[4]	384	−13	513	418	402	−18	272	785	700
1936	762[4]	813	−51	462	367	595	+218	490	952	857
1937	1,226[4]	912	+314	776	681	698	+214	704	1,480	1,385

[1] Not available; presumably the same as General Imports. [2] Estimated. [3] Assuming stocks of 200,000 in hands of consumers at end of 1912; for discussion, see text. [4] Not reported; estimated from change in bonded stocks.

derived from general imports and imports for consumption, total stocks have been calculated from both, so that the differences can be seen at a glance. Although these differences, cumulative to the end of 1937, amount to 95,000 tons, this is not a very material factor, in view of the other assumptions that have been necessitated in developing the data; as a matter of fact, actual stocks may be somewhat under 1,385,000 tons, or somewhat over 1,480,000 tons. The main point is that manganese ore consumers have seen the necessity of protecting their future supplies of ore, and have been gradually increasing the magnitude of the stocks, to a point where they now approximate a two years' normal supply. So long as this condition prevails, any emergency stocking of ore as a national defense measure need not be carried to the extent that might formerly have been thought advisable. The idea should not be abandoned entirely, however, since no one can foresee what conditions might arise in the future which might cause the consumers to permit their stocks to decline below the danger line.

Besides these stocks of ore, there are in bond a few thousand tons of imported ferromanganese, and of course an unknown amount of stocks of ferro in the hands of producers and consumers.

UTILIZATION OF MANGANESE

It is estimated that 95 per cent of the high grade manganese supply of the United States is consumed in the production of steel, mostly in the form of ferromanganese. Outside of the war period the bulk of the ore requirements for ferromanganese production has been supplied by imported ore; during 1923–1930 domestic ore used in the production of ferromanganese averaged about 5 per cent of the total, but has since dropped to 2 per cent. When the ore used is higher in manganese than is required to maintain the standard Mn:Fe ratio in the alloy, low grade ores may be mixed in the charge; this reached a maximum of 10 per cent in 1930, but previously and since has been only 2–3 per cent.

In Table VI an attempt has been made to present the salient features of the utilization of manganese in the steel industry. In making up this table, the disturbing effects of variations in holdovers and stocks, and heavy fluctuations from one year to the next, have been minimized by using for all of the basic data (Columns 1, 2, 3, and 4), not the usual annual outputs, but running three-year averages; that is, the figure attributed to any given year is the average of the value for that year, the preceding year, and the following year.

Ferromanganese is not the only form in which manganese is used; spiegeleisen is used to a limited extent, and since the former requires high grade ore, while the latter is made from low grade ore, the extent to which spiegel may replace ferro is an important feature in manganese utilization. In 1913, we find (Column 5) that 90 per cent of the manganese used by the steel industry was in ferro, and 10 per cent in spiegel; as we progress into the war period the ferro figure gradually decreases to a minimum of 84 per cent as the shortage of high grade ores became more acute. This was followed by a recovery which did not stop at the 1913 level, but continued to a high of 94 per cent, after which there was a gradual decline to about the 1913 level. The high values from 1921 to 1931 just about balance the low values during the war period, so that the average for 1913–1937 is practically identical with the average for 1932–1937.

The total consumption of manganese per ton of steel made (Column 6) has varied between a low of 12.5 pounds and a high of 15.1 pounds, with an average of 14.3 pounds, while the amount used as ferro (Column 7) has varied from 11.1 pounds to 13.8 pounds, with an average of 13.0 pounds. In this connection it is interesting to note that unfavorable business conditions during the depression period resulted in practically the same sort of a reduction in manganese requirements as did the ore shortage during the war period, so that in 1933 the manganese used as ferro was practically the same as in 1918, that is, 11.6 pounds, as against 11.1 pounds. One must bear in mind, however, a difference in the means of arriving at this low value; in 1918 it was obtained by a greater degree of substitution of spiegel for ferro, while in 1933 the spiegel ratio was at its normal level, and the low consumption was due to improved technology in the smelting and use of manganese.

The next item of interest is the amount of high grade ore required per ton of steel (Column 9). This is found to vary between wider limits, since technological improvements in ore smelting have resulted in increased recovery. In general, the trend of the curve for ore used, as shown in Fig. 2, was downward from 1913 to 1933, with some rise since then. The marked

irregularities in the curve during the war period are probably due
as much to uncertainties in the statistics as to actual variations
in ore requirements.   Smelting recoveries during the war period
seem to have been of the order of 60 per cent, increasing to 70 per
cent about 1920, 80 per cent by 1925, and 85 per cent a few years
later.   This marked increase in recovery has been the chief factor
in the decline in the amount of ore required per ton of steel, but of
course there has also been some improvement in the utilization of
ferro, resulting in smaller consumption per ton of steel.

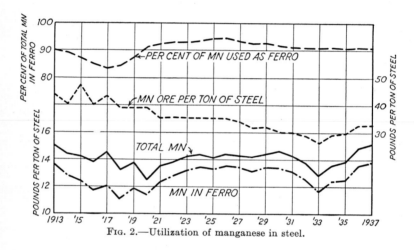

Fig. 2.—Utilization of manganese in steel.

Having the pounds of ore per ton of steel (Column 9) and the
tonnage of steel, we may easily determine the total ore requirement for the current steel tonnage (Column 10), and for ferro
production (Column 11).   For comparison with this, the Equivalent Ore Supply (Column 12) and the Actual Ore Supply (Column
13) are repeated from Table II.   These last four columns (9, 10,
11, and 12) are all calculated on actual annual figures, rather than
on the three-year average basis.   The differences between Total
Ore Required (Column 10) and Equivalent Ore Supply (Column
11) are due to holdovers and changes in stocks some place along
the line.   The differences between Equivalent Ore Supply (Column 12) and Actual Ore Supply (Column 13) are a measure of the
imports of manganese in alloy form, rather than in ore.   Both of
these last two items have already been discussed in connection
with Table II.

TABLE VI.—UTILIZATION OF MANGANESE IN THE STEEL INDUSTRY
(Thousands of long tons)

| | Manganese Content of Alloys Used | | | | Pounds of Mn Used per Ton of Steel Made | | | | Total Ore Required | | | |
| Steel Output | In Ferro-manganese[1] | In Spiegel-eisen[1] | Total Mn[1] | Per Cent in Ferro | Total | In Ferro | Ore/Mn Ratio[2] | Pounds of Ore Used per Ton of Steel | For Steel[3] | For Ferro[4] | Equivalent Ore Supply[5] | Actual Ore Supply[6] |
1	2	3	4	5	6	7	8	9	10	11	12	13
1913.... 28,699	173.4	19.0	192.4	90.1	15.0	13.6	3.22[7]	43.8	613	644	681	349
1914.... 28,988	166.2	20.3	186.4	89.2	14.4	12.8	3.15[7]	40.3	423	460	494	286
1915.... 32,812	181.7	26.7	208.4	87.2	14.2	12.4	3.83[7]	47.5	682	596	500	331
1916.... 39,995	208.7	36.3	245.0	84.9	13.8	11.7	3.42[7]	40.0	764	834	853	607
1917.... 44,099	237.7	46.7	284.3	83.6	14.5	12.1	3.57[7]	43.2	869	809	891	759
1918.... 41,398	205.3	38.6	243.9	84.2	13.2	11.1	3.48[7]	38.6	766	844	874	797
1919.... 40,422	215.3	30.9	246.2	87.4	13.7	11.9	3.24[7]	38.6	598	475	475	388
1920.... 32,196	163.4	15.8	179.2	91.2	12.5	11.4	3.41[7]	38.9	732	876	863	694
1921.... 32,507	180.6	15.0	195.6	92.3	13.5	12.4	2.85	35.3	312	110	427	407
1922.... 33,444	191.0	14.7	205.7	92.9	13.8	12.8	2.86	36.6	582	568	663	434
1923.... 39,493	232.4	17.9	250.3	92.9	14.2	13.2	2.87	37.8	759	826	690	435
1924.... 42,757	255.6	17.7	273.3	93.5	14.4	13.4	2.79	37.4	634	588	677	543
1925.... 43,873	259.6	16.1	275.7	94.2	14.1	13.3	2.74	36.4	738	736	873	684
1926.... 46,208	279.0	17.0	296.0	94.3	14.4	13.5	2.60	35.1	757	780	869	755
1927.... 48,591	289.8	19.6	309.4	93.6	14.3	13.1	2.54	34.0	682	684	753	667
1928.... 50,971	298.5	24.1	322.6	92.5	14.2	13.1	2.41	31.6	727	724	591	475
1929.... 49,559	295.7	23.5	319.2	92.6	14.4	13.4	2.39	32.0	807	779	875	724
1930.... 41,026	246.0	21.9	267.9	91.9	14.6	13.4	2.27	30.4	553	592	739	653
1931.... 26,775	156.8	14.9	171.7	91.3	14.3	13.1	2.29	30.0	347	346	583	542
1932.... 20,953	116.4	11.7	128.1	90.9	13.7	12.5	2.32	29.0	177	136	164	129
1933.... 20,989	108.8	11.1	119.9	90.7	12.8	11.6	2.26	26.2	272	316	260	176
1934.... 27,793	153.3	15.3	168.6	90.9	13.6	12.4	2.36	29.3	341	313	418	364
1935.... 35,972	200.2	20.8	221.0	90.6	13.8	12.5	2.39	29.2	455	459	477	410
1936.... 44,143	265.3	26.4	291.7	91.0	13.8	13.5	2.41	32.5	693	676	944	845
1937[8].. 49,169	301.9	30.2	332.1	90.9	15.1	13.8	2.36	32.5	736	763	1,016	952
Totals... 933,832	5,382.6	552.2	5,934.6	90.8	14.3	13.0	2.77	36.0	15,019	14,934	16,650	13,406

1 Domestic production plus imports. 2 Tons of manganese ore used per ton of manganese content of ferromanganese produced. 3 Amount of ore required for the actual annual steel output. 4 Amount of ore required for the actual annual output of ferromanganese used during the year. 5 Total of domestic and imported ore, plus the ore equivalent of the manganese content of imported ferro and spiegel. 6 Domestic ore output, plus imports. 7 Data on the actual ore consumption for ferromanganese are not available previous to 1921; lacking these, the ore supply available for ferro production was used instead, eliminating annual fluctuations and changes in stocks as much as possible by using a three-year running average, instead of the actual annual figures. The results are probably somewhat high, but not by any great amount, as the figures for 1922 and 1923 check reasonably closely by both methods. 8 Two year average instead of three, as 1938 data are not yet available.

PRICES

The price of manganese ore is determined by the price that can be obtained for ferromanganese or spiegeleisen, the maximum, minimum, and average annual prices for which are shown graphically in Fig. 3.

The standard price quotation on ore is in cents per unit, a unit being 1 per cent of a long ton, or 22.4 pounds of metal. The price varies somewhat with the source of the ore, depending on the average metal content of the ore and the amounts of impurities

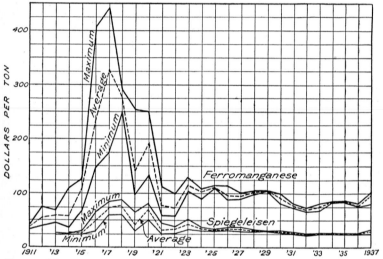

FIG. 3.—Maximum, minimum and average annual prices of ferromanganese and spiegeleisen.

usually found in it. Imported ores are sold on a c. i. f. basis (cost, insurance and freight) at the Atlantic seaboard, but the price quoted does not include the duty.

Chemical ore is quoted in dollars per long ton for ore of a specified grade, three of the common listings being 80 per cent minimum, 85 per cent minimum, and 70–72 per cent of contained manganese dioxide.

There are so many different grades and sources of ore that it is impossible to give detailed data on prices, but as a general guide to the trend of prices there is presented in Table VII the annual average prices for standard 50 per cent ore, duty paid, based on data compiled by the U. S. Bureau of Mines.

TABLE VII.—MANGANESE ORE PRICES IN THE UNITED STATES
(Cents per unit)

	Average Quoted Price	Duty	Total	Commodity Index	Manganese Index Price
1913......................	25.00	....	25.00	100.0	250.0
1914......................	26.00	....	26.00	97.6	266.4
1915......................	31.66	....	31.66	99.6	317.8
1916......................	50.00	....	50.00	122.5	408.2
1917......................	97.06	....	97.06	168.3	574.4
1918......................	127.26	....	127.26	188.1	676.6
1919......................	66.12	....	66.12	198.6	333.0
1920......................	67.26	....	67.26	221.2	304.0
1921......................	28.08	....	28.08	139.8	200.8
1922......................	29.57	22.40[1]	31.80	138.5	229.6
1923......................	41.30	22.40	63.70	144.1	442.0
1924......................	39.00	22.40	61.40	140.5	437.0
1925......................	42.16	22.40	64.56	148.3	435.4
1926......................	39.00	22.40	61.40	143.3	428.4
1927......................	39.00	22.40	61.40	136.7	449.2
1928......................	37.66	22.40	60.06	138.5	433.6
1929......................	31.50	22.40	53.90	136.5	394.8
1930......................	27.48	22.40	49.88	123.8	403.0
1931......................	24.66	22.40	47.06	104.6	450.0
1932......................	21.26	22.40	43.66	92.8	470.4
1933......................	17.00	22.40	41.40	94.4	438.6
1934......................	23.42	22.40	45.82	107.3	427.0
1935......................	25.00	22.40	47.40	114.6	413.6
1936......................	26.50	11.20	37.70	115.6	325.6
1937......................	44.28	11.20	55.48	123.6	448.8

[1] In effect from Sept. 22.

On the face of these figures, there has been a wide variation in prices, from a low of 25 cents in 1913 to a high of $1.27 in 1918, declining again to 28 cents in 1921; after 1922 prices show much less variation, with a low of 37.70 cents in 1936, and a high of 64.56 cents in 1925. It must be remembered, though, that the dollars in which these prices are measured have themselves a varying value, and in order to compensate for this, the quoted price is divided by the current commodity index, giving a manganese index price, from which dollar fluctuation has been eliminated. There still remains a considerable degree of fluctuation during the period of inflated war prices and deflated post-war prices, but from 1923 on, the index price takes on a surprising degree of stability, with a high of 47.07 cents in 1932, a low of 32.56 cents in 1936, and an average of 42.06 cents; aside from the two extreme years, in 1932 and 1936, the spread from high to low for the other 13 years was only 5.52 cents.

In spite of the wide variations up to 1922, the average during this time was approximately the same as for the later years; the weighted average for the index price from 1913 to 1937 was 41.22 cents, against 42.06 cents for 1923–1937.

It is only on an index price basis that comparisons can be made over a long period with any degree of accuracy; and this is particularly true when speaking of the future. Some of the most important features of the index price are met in connection with the consideration of ore reserves and possible future emergency production from these reserves.

TARIFF

The Underwood tariff schedule admitted manganese imports free of duty, but when the Fordney-McCumber tariff legislation was under construction in 1922, advocates of the American manganese industry claimed that a tariff of 1 cent per pound on metallurgical ore, and proportional rates on other products, would serve to establish an adequate manganese industry in this country, and this schedule was written into the law. During the succeeding three years manganese production did increase, reaching about 10 per cent of the total requirements in 1925, after which it again declined to about half the 1925 level for another three years. In 1929 an additional protection of ½ cent per pound was asked for, but a sufficient case could not be presented, and the request was not granted. In spite of this, however, the output increased somewhat in 1929 and 1930, even in the face of declining prices, but the American producers had evidently underestimated the ability of foreign competition to reduce prices, and in the face of the general decline in manganese prices that had been under way since 1927, the domestic industry was forced to give way, as import prices dropped below the cost of production of the various producers, and the restricting action of the general business depression became more marked.

We are not here particularly concerned with the question of chemical ores, as that situation is largely independent, but for metallurgical ores, the experience of the past 10 years has pretty definitely shown that a tariff of approximately 100 per cent has not and can not promote the development of the domestic industry to anything like the extent that its advocates predicted. This led directly to the question as to whether the tariff should be increased to a point where it *would* develop the domestic industry. If the American tungsten industry can have a tariff protection of

400–600 per cent, why not do as much for the manganese industry, if necessary, in order to support the industry properly?
Disregarding the fact that even this excessive amount of protection has thus far failed in its purpose of supporting the domestic
tungsten industry, and assuming that it would be possible to
give to the manganese industry a sufficient degree of protection
to make it really an important factor in the supply, if not to a
point of complete independence of foreign sources, would this
move be a desirable one to make?   Naturally it would be desirable from the standpoint of owners of manganese mines who wish
to realize a profit on their investment, but would it be desirable
from a standpoint of national welfare?

The duty of 1 cent per pound made a current delivered price
of about 50–55 cents per unit in 1934; an additional cent of duty
would bring the price level up to about that at which the estimated
total reserves would be 800,000 tons of manganese—providing
foreign competition did not still further reduce its prices.   If this
material were placed on the market at a rate to supply half of our
demand, it would cover possibly 5 to 6 years of normal demand,
and then we should be in the same position as now, except that we
should have left only the poorer half of our reserves, and the
remainder would require another cent of duty to bring them out of
the ground.   If this were granted, another 5 to 6 years would see
us with our entire manganese reserves exhausted, except for such
new ones as had been developed in the meantime, and we should
be again entirely dependent on foreign sources for future supplies.
And in the meantime the consumer would have footed a bill for
about $180,000,000 in increased cost of manganese.

Possibly this might not be too high a price to pay for keeping
an essential industry in operation, if it could be expected to continue indefinitely, but it is entirely too much to pay for the privi-
lege of watching the steady exhaustion of a limited reserve of a
highly important strategic mineral, with nothing in sight beyond
a brief period of 10–12 years.   Should such a policy have been
inaugurated in 1922, when the first tariff was imposed, and maintained ever since, we should now in all probability be faced with
very much the same sort of a situation as we are today—that is
practically entire dependence on foreign sources for our manganese
supply—but with two important points of difference: we should
have little if any reserve to fall back on in case of emergency

demand, and we should have paid $180,000,000, for the privilege
of having ourselves placed in such a position.

To go to the opposite extreme, suppose the same sum, or such of
it as is needed, were used to purchase all the known manganese
deposits of importance from their private owners, and the industry nationalized; the mines could then be closed down, and the
reserves kept intact as an insurance against emergency demand
that could not be supplied from other sources. In either case
the public would have to pay the price, but with the difference
that in the latter it would still have possession of its cake, instead
of finding that it had been nibbled down to a few crumbs by the
delivery boy while *en route*.

However, only a brief analysis is necessary to show that neither
of these plans is satisfactory. The former leads to the disappear-
ance of the cake before it has served its intended purpose, and the
second places it on the shelf where it dries up until it becomes so
hard that it can be broken off only in small bits. In other words,
the former leads to the exhaustion of the reserves, while the latter
would result in a long period of inactivity during which data
on the various operations would be shelved and more or less
forgotten; the men familiar with the operating conditions of the
various deposits would be scattered and lost; machinery and
equipment would deteriorate; mines would fill up with water,
or collapse as timbering decayed; open pits would fill up with
water and debris; and all semblance of organization in the industry would be dissipated, so that when the necessity arrived for
restarting production, work could proceed only slowly and ineffi-
ciently, and at abnormal expense, probably even worse than the
conditions that prevailed in 1917, and possibly with not even as
good results.

Probably the best solution of the problem lies at some point in
between these two extremes, scaled so that a minimum amount of
the reserves are sacrificed, but the industry is still kept alive.
Since it is much easier to speed up a producing industry than
it is to start up an idle one, particularly after a long period of
idleness, apparently what is needed is to find the happy medium
at which there will be enough demand for domestic manganese to
keep a nucleus of the industry in production, but to keep the
scale of operations down to a point where they will eat up the
reserves as slowly as possible. At just what level of production
this intermediate point lies will probably be a matter involving

considerable difference of opinion, but it seems feasible to establish a control of this kind, using the tariff as the agency.

We are not here interested in the tariff as an instrument in either national or international politics, nor as a source of revenue, but solely as an agency for promoting the national defense, and since there seems no reasonable hope that an increased tariff could develop the necessary emergency supply of manganese, it seems justifiable to use the tariff level to insure the best protection that we can against a shortage in the event of an emergency demand.

The manganese tariff was given further consideration in 1935, and in view of existing conditions, when a trade agreement was made with Brazil late in the year, a concession was granted, lowering the tariff on manganese to ½ cent per pound. This went into effect on Jan. 1, 1936, and in due course was extended to other producers through the action of the "most favored nation" policy. This rate was in effect during 1936 and 1937, and in spite of the lowering of the tariff, the domestic production of metallurgical ores continued to increase from the low of the depression period, though possibly not to as great an extent as it would have under the higher rate.

The rates that have been applied to the various forms of manganese under the different tariff acts are as follows:

TABLE VIII.—TARIFF RATES ON MANGANESE
(In cents per pound of contained manganese or per cent ad valorem)

	1913–22	1922–30	1930–35	1936
Manganese ores				
Over 30 per cent Mn..........	Free	1c.	....	....
10–35 per cent Mn...........	....	....	1c.	½c.
Over 35 per cent Mn..........	....	....	1c.	½c.
From Cuba...................	....	Free	Free	Free
Manganese alloys				
Ferromanganese..............	Free	....	....	....
Less than 1 per cent C......	....	1⅞c. + 15 %	1⅞c. + 15 %	1⅞c. + 15 %
1–4 per cent C........... }	....	1⅞c.	1⅞c.	{ 1⅞c.
Over 4 per cent C......... }				{ 1c.
Spiegeleisen (less than 1 per cent C), manganese silicon, manganese boron and manganese metal.....................	Free	1⅞c. + 15 %	1⅞c. + 15 %	1⅞c. + 15 %
Spiegeleisen, over 1 per cent C..	Free	75c./ton	75c./ton	75c./ton
Manganese copper, silico-spiegel.	15 %[1]	25 %[1]	25 %[1]	25 %

[1] Under heading Ferro-alloys not specially provided for.

POLITICAL AND COMMERCIAL CONTROL

Table IX presents data showing the distribution of production and control of manganese ores in 1929, adapted from the report of the Mineral Inquiry of the American Institute of Mining and Metallurgical Engineers, supplemented by a comparative table of world output in 1937, to show the radical changes in distribution of the output in the interval, although no additional data are available on the shifts in commercial control that may have taken place. It is significant to note that in 1929 more than 70 per cent on the manganese output covered by the table was produced under the control of domestic capital. In addition to the major producers listed in the table, another 5 per cent was made by domestic capital in the minor producing countries, and while the 13.5 per cent credit to the Gold Coast is listed under foreign capital, the actual ownership of the deposits is vested in British capital, but the operation is carried on by an American company, under lease. All told, then, 89 per cent of the output came from properties owned by domestic capital.

Aside from a small participation by local capital in the Brazilian operations, and the nationalized Russian operations, control was divided between British and American capital, which together accounted for 56 per cent of the 1929 output. Since then there has been a marked shift in production, with several new countries producing, and a heavy increase in Russian output, so that production by both British and American capital has been considerably reduced.

TABLE IX.—POLITICAL AND COMMERCIAL CONTROL OF MANGANESE ORE PRODUCTION
(In percentage of 1929 world output)

	Output		Control					
	1929	1937	Domestic	Foreign	British	Brazilian	Russian	American
Brazil................	9.2	3.7	4.2	5.0	....	4.2	....	5.0
Cuba.................	0.03	2.2	....	0.03	....	....	....	0.03
Egypt...............	5.6	3.1	....	5.6	5.6	....	....	....
Gold Coast..........	13.5	8.8	....	13.5	....	....	....	13.5¹
India...............	29.4	16.3	29.4	....	29.4	....	....	....
Russia..............	34.4	44.0	34.4	....	....	....	34.4	....
South Africa.........	0.3	10.3	0.3	....	0.3	....	....	....
United States........	1.8	0.4	1.8	....	....	....	....	1.8
Totals.............	94.2	88.8	70.1	24.1	35.3	4.2	34.4	20.3

¹ American interests hold a lease from British fee owners.

GENERAL REVIEW OF THE DOMESTIC SITUATION

In closing the discussion, let us review the controversy on the domestic manganese situation in the light of actual developments during recent years as compared with the claims made for the industry by those actively promoting it. This comparison is made not with the idea of criticizing the supporters of the industry, or of finding fault with their ideas and attitude in regard to its future possibilities, but solely as steps in the analysis of the existing conditions. The *Manufacturers Record* of November 10, 1927, contained an article under the heading "The Truth About Manganese," in which the producers' side of the question was presented at some length. In this article it was stated that "during the past few years, under the encouragement of the tariff, developments of manganese in America have proceeded as never before in history, and recent increases in reserves in both high and low grade ores, and the inauguration of new and successful processes in the beneficiation of low grade ores, give assurance of a domestic production sufficient to guard the security of the nation in an emergency and promise eventually to make it independent of foreign sources of supply"; and further on—"one need not be an optimist to foresee the time, in the near future, when the major portion of American needs of this essential mineral will be supplied from American mines, if the present tariff is not removed." In support of these statements, the status of operations in various important producing districts is briefly stated, as abstracted or quoted below. Following each of these abstracts is a summary of the facts as established by subsequent history and statistics, as developed up to 1934. In comparing these statements one must of course not lose sight of the fact that the depression period caused heavy reductions in output, but even after making generous allowance for this, the discrepancies are still far too large to be ignored.

1. *In the Butte district of Montana, contracts have been made covering the delivery during the next 5 years of 875,000 tons of calcined ore, with 50 to 66 per cent of manganese. The mining companies have large deposits of ore determined, and opened up ready for mining.*

The earlier estimates of the reserves in the Butte district, 500,000 tons, were later raised to 700,000 tons. If contracts were made covering 875,000 tons of calcined ore, the mining companies were apparently counting on being able to increase their reserves by further operation; they were justified in this, as the admitted reserves were later increased by about 75 per cent, largely through the application of the flotation process to the carbonate ores, which enabled them to use lower grades of ore. But the shipments specified failed to materialize, as total shipments during 1928–1932 were in the neighborhood of 100,000 tons, part of which was not calcined.   The maximum output was 30,000 tons, in 1929.

2. *In the Philipsburg (Montana) district, 20,000 tons annually of high-grade chemical ore is produced, and large reserves have been developed.*

The Philipsburg district produced 23,500 tons of chemical ore in 1924, decreasing annually since to 16,400 tons in 1927 and 7,000 tons in 1932.   The reserves in this district are large enough, if restricted for chemical use, to supply the demand for many years to come.   There is no real need for the importation of foreign chemical ore, except for uses requiring a higher manganese dioxide content than the 72–74 per cent secured in the Philipsburg ore.

3. *"Minnesota reports sufficient ore with a manganese content, which, when recovered, would alone supply the needs of the United States for more than half a century.   A conservative estimate of this ore, which it is claimed may be recovered, is put in excess of 100,000,000 tons.   Present production of higher grade manganiferous ores in Minnesota is approximately 2,000,000 tons a year."*

The latest estimates of the Minnesota reserves puts the middle-grade ore at 18,000,000 tons, averaging 14 per cent manganese, and the low-grade at 45,000,000 tons, averaging 7 per cent, or a total of 5,670,000 tons of manganese in 63,000,000 tons of ore.   The Minnesota production of low-grade ore (5–10 per cent) was slightly over 1,000,000 tons in 1928 and 1929, but declined rapidly in the subsequent years, and in 1932 was zero.   The output of 10–35 per cent ore ranged from 3,500 to 5,400 tons up to 1930, and in 1931 increased to 27,000 tons, due largely to the installation of a concentration process at one of the plants.   In 1932 the production dropped to 1,400 tons.   These ores are useful only for high-manganese pig iron and spiegeleisen, and at the present time, more than 6 years after the above statement was written, it is still very doubtful if any of the proposed recovery processes will be able to operate commercially to produce ferro-grade ore.

4. *New Mexico has a production of 40,000 tons annually of manganiferous ore and a substantial production of high-grade ore.*

The New Mexico output of high-grade ore dropped from 3,000 tons in 1929 to 1,100 tons in 1931, with nothing since.   The output of 10–35 per cent ore was 36,250 tons in 1928, with nothing since, while 5–10 per cent ore increased to 67,600 tons in 1929, but dropped off in 1930, and ceased in 1931 and 1932.

5. *Arkansas reports a production of approximately 15,000 tons of high and low grade ores, and is steadily increasing; this district claims in excess of 30,000,000 tons of manganiferous ores, from which the manganese may be profitably recovered.*

During the period 1928–1932 the Arkansas output of manganese ore varied between 4,300 tons and 1,300 tons, and of 10–35 per cent ore, between 13,800 tons and 200 tons.

6. *Georgia is prepared to ship 20,000 tons of ferro-grade ore.*

Shipments of high-grade ore from Georgia were 2,500 tons in 1929, increased to 18,900 tons in 1930, and decreased to 200 tons in 1932.

7. *In Virginia one company is making ready to market 30,000 tons of high-grade ore, yearly, and two others are developing deposits.*

Virginia shipments of high-grade ore, including chemical ore, reached a maximum of about 3,900 tons in 1930, and had dropped to 525 tons in 1932.

8. *Considerable development is in progress in Washington, in both high and low grade ores.*

Washington has produced about 16,000 tons of ore during 1924–1926. No output has been reported since.

9. *Research in beneficiation of low-grade ores is under way in a number of states; methods of beneficiation have passed the experimental stage and plants are in process of erection for commercial treatment, notably in the Bradley Process.*

Beneficiation has made considerable progress since 1927, but to date there has been little actual commercial output from any of these processes, most of them never having gone beyond the laboratory or pilot-plant stages of development, and until they have demonstrated their commercial ability to make ferro-grade material they can not be counted on with any degree of assurance.

After giving due consideration to all of the phases of the manganese problem, it is difficult to see how one could come to any other conclusion than that it is unsafe to depend on domestic sources for more than a minor proportion of any future emergency supply. About the only factor that at present gives any promise of altering the situation is the possibility of developing the electrolytic recovery of manganese from low grade ores on a commercial scale at a cost low enough to compete with current standard metallurgical practice.

Turning now to another phase of the problem, let us again examine Table VI, with a view of obtaining some idea as to possible future emergency requirements. During the World War steel production increased about 40 per cent; assuming, as a basis for estimation, a similar increase in a future emergency, over the 50,000,000 tons in 1937, we should need to be prepared for an output of some 70,000,000 tons of steel. What would a steel output of this magnitude mean when translated into terms of manganese requirements? At 36 pounds of ore per ton of steel, the average during 1913–1937, this would call for a supply of 1,125,000 tons of high grade manganese ore. This figure, however, is quite properly subject to reduction on two separate counts. In the first place, the average of 36 pounds of ore per ton of steel includes the war period with its low recoveries, which are now a thing of the past. In 1933, the ore figure was cut to 26.2 pounds, but this was in a period of restricted production, when only the most efficient methods and equipment were in use; that this low figure could not be maintained for high-capacity emergency operation is evidenced by the increase that has taken place since 1933 as production increased from the depression low. With production capacity pushed to the utmost, maximum recovery would be sacrificed to some extent in favor of increased output, so that it would probably not be safe to count on recoveries any better than the 32.5 pounds per ton of steel that was maintained during 1936 and 1937. At this level, the manganese ore requirement would drop to 1,015,000 tons. This million odd tons is, however, based on an average ferro:spiegel ratio of 91:9; dropping this to the 84:16 ratio maintained during 1916–1918 would further reduce the ore requirement to about 936,000 tons. Actual conditions may be expected to cause some variation above or below this estimate, but it seems evident that it will be necessary to anticipate a high grade manganese ore supply of the order of 800,000 to 900,000 tons.

CONCLUSION

Taking all things into consideration, there seems no simple, direct solution of the manganese problem. It is pretty well established that increased production under the protection of increased tariff will merely serve to fritter away such limited reserves as we have of high-grade ore, with no definite assurance that they can be replaced in the meantime by new discoveries or by beneficiation of lower grades of ore. Assuming that reserves remain in sufficient amounts to produce a material proportion of our needs at the time of some future emergency, a considerable amount of time, effort, and money will have to be expended in building up production to the necessary scale, and we should insure ourselves against the possibility of an interval during which neither foreign nor domestic ores are available in sufficient amounts. The only reasonable answer to this seems to be a stock pile.

France and Germany both apparently stocked manganese previous to 1914, but did not lay in sufficient supplies to see them through, and before the end of the war Germany especially was in serious difficulty over her manganese supply. About 1922 France embarked on a program of stocking manganese; whether this was a definite governmental program, or whether it was a measure of self-protection on the part of the steel industry, is not known, but the fact is evidenced by the magnitude of her imports, which increased so far beyond the demands of the current steel output that in 1929 France imported more manganese for an output of less than 10,000,000 tons of steel than did the United States for an output of over 56,000,000 tons. During the period 1922–1932 France imported about 5,770,000 tons of manganese ore, against a steel output of less than 81,000,000 tons, with practically no deductions for exports. Similar accumulations of reserve stocks have been made by Russia, Germany and Belgium. Under the circumstances it is the only logical thing to do, and that the United States so long postponed taking such an elementary precaution left her open to the charge of culpable negligence in a vital item of national defense. It now appears that unofficial steps have been taken to remedy the shortage, but it still remains to take official action on stockpiling. The only point that is open for debate is the amount of ore that should be stocked. The Manganese Sub-committee of the American Institute of Mining and Metallurgical Engineers put the amount at the estimated shortage of supply for the first year of emergency demand, which they estimated at 700,000 tons of ore. In view of all the circumstances, this amount is certainly modest enough, and possibly should be considered only as an irreducible minimum, to which additions should be made from time to time if changing conditions seem to demand it, such as increasing domestic consumption and gradual depletion of the domestic reserves, with a consequent reduction in possible future recoveries or a marked reduction in the bonded stocks or those held by consumers. If, following the example set by France, two or three hundred thousand tons of surplus ore were imported each year, the necessary amount could be accumulated in a reasonable time, without excessive drain in any one year.

But finally, regardless of the method that is chosen on which to proceed, efforts should be made to get a start made on the accumulation of a reserve stock of manganese ore with the least possible delay, for this is the only *certain* way in which we can assure ourselves of the necessary emergency supply.

CHAPTER IV

NICKEL

Next to manganese, nickel is probably the most important metal in the development of a modern munitions program, and it is one of the few for which the country is practically entirely dependent on outside sources for its supply; there is no direct production of nickel in the United States, such small output as does exist (a few hundred tons a year) being a byproduct of the electrolytic refining of copper.

Like manganese, nickel is used extensively in the steel industry, but there is also a multitude of other applications, both in the form of metal and alloy. Again, like manganese, the commercial deposits of nickel ores are all in countries in which the steel industry, as well as other consuming industries, is developed only to a limited extent, if at all, so that the bulk of the output is exported to other countries for use. A still further similarity is found in the fact that there are known ore reserves in sufficient quantities to supply the demand for many years to come, but here the similarity ends. Manganese is used in the production of all kinds of steel, but nickel is used only in certain special types, so that the amount needed is small as compared with the manganese requirements, but the qualities imparted to steel by the presence of nickel are such that the metal acquires an importance out of all proportion to the amount used.

Another marked difference is that manganese is found in appreciable quantities in a score or more of countries, and in important amounts in at least half a dozen, while really important amounts of nickel are found only in one country, with minor outputs in three or four more. Fortunately for us, this major occurrence is in the neighboring country, Canada, only a short distance from our own borders, so that the required material is more readily available than in the case of manganese. And the final points of dissimilarity are the most uncomfortable of all. Of manganese we have a moderate domestic supply, which can be expanded to help take care of an emergency demand, while the possibilities of a domestic supply of nickel are practically *nil.* Also, with a number of widely scattered sources of manganese, if accessibility to one is cut off, another may be drawn on to supply the deficit, but in the case of nickel, if Canada were to be eliminated as a source of supply, the output of all the rest of the world would not be sufficient to supply our needs, even though it were available—and most of it would not be, due to the isolation of the sources, and the competition of other consumers.

From the outset, then, it is evident that access to Canadian nickel is necessary for our industrial development along the lines in which this metal is needed. From a commercial standpoint the situation is favored by the fact that the bulk of the Canadian output is controlled by United States capital, and from a political and military standpoint it is fortunate that the two countries are closely allied, and it is difficult to imagine conditions which would lead to a rupture of the friendly relations that have existed for more than a century.

REQUIREMENTS

The amount of nickel required to supply the world demand has varied widely at different periods. With most metals there is a more or less steady increase in demand as industry develops and uses increase, and abrupt changes in output are usually the result of changed industrial conditions in periods of activity and depression, but in the case of nickel this has been complicated by extensive alterations in the uses to which the metal is put, which will be discussed in more detail in a later section. In 1913 the world output was 32,700 metric tons, increasing with war demands to 47,900 tons in 1918. The post-war depression and the absorption of excess war stocks cut this to 10,300 tons, followed by an increase to 57,000 tons in 1929. Industrial depression lowered this to 20,000 tons in 1932, but recovery was rapid; the 1934 total considerably exceeded that of 1929, and heavy annual increases brought the 1937 total up to 113,000 tons.

USES

For a metal produced in such moderate amounts as has been the case with nickel, the uses that have been developed are remarkably varied and extensive, for it has an exceptionally wide range of applications as metal and alloy, besides the usual type of uses in chemical compounds.

Metallurgical Uses.—The following list presents the leading metallurgical uses of nickel, giving both the form in which the metal is used and the type of use or equipment:

Low Nickel Steels (0.5 to 7 Per Cent Nickel).—These furnish a metal of high strength, ductility, and toughness, that finds a place in numerous industries.

Automotive and Aircraft Construction: Axles, gears, crank and cam shafts, frames, roller bearings, connecting rods, steering knuckles, bolts and nuts.

Railway Equipment: Locomotive frames, forged main and side rods, valve gear, axles, roller bearings, boiler plate and tubes, staybolts, engine bolts, crossings, frogs and switch points.

Power Equipment: Turbine rotor forgings, turbine blades, reduction gears, marine crank and turbine shafts, pump shafts, roller bearings, chain drives, high pressure steam valves.

Architectural and Bridge Construction: Bars, plates, eye-bars, angles, beams, channels, and other shapes.

Mining and Excavating Machinery: Racks and pinions, crusher jaws, forged and rolled shafts, cast and forged gears, oil-well drilling bits.

Heavy Mill Machinery: Hydraulic press columns, cross heads, hammer piston rods, cast and forged rolls, die blocks, shear blades.

Shop Machinery: Shafts, spindles, gears, chains.

Agricultural Machinery: Tractor shoes, sprockets, gears, shafts.

Miscellaneous Machinery: Heat-treated forgings, gears, axles, shafts, chains, roller and ball bearings.

Machine Tools: Die blocks, punches, track chisels, band and disc saws, cutters, shovels.

High Nickel Steels (7 to 35 Per Cent Nickel, Usually Accompanied by Chromium).—This group includes the heat-resistant and corrosion-resistant (stainless) steels, of which a few of the leading uses are: Building trim, cooking utensils, marine fittings, automobile hardware and trim, power equipment, oil-well equipment, furnace parts, submarine periscope tubes, turbine blades, stranded cable, chemical apparatus, pump rods, bolts, nuts, nails, wire.

Cast Nickel Steels (1 to 4 Per Cent Nickel).—These uses coincide in many cases with those of the wrought nickel steels, for applications where lower stresses will permit the use of castings: Mining and excavating machinery, locomotive and ship construction, steel mill machinery, road-building machinery, electrical machinery, rolling mill machinery, oil-refining and power-plant equipment, large gears, crusher frames, tube mill balls, tractor and power shovel frames, oil-well tools, sheaves and sprockets, gears and cams, tractor shoes, bucket teeth, conveyor link chains.

Low Nickel Cast Irons (0.5 to 3 Per Cent Nickel, with Sometimes the Addition of Chromium or Manganese).—This group gives castings of improved hardness, strength, and machining properties, used in: Cylinders; cylinder sleeves and liners; cylinder heads; pistons and piston rings for gas, oil, gasoline, and steam engines, pumps and compressors; valve lifters, bushings and seat rings; cut gears and cams; machine tools; glass molds; forming and stamping dies, pipe mill plugs, automobile manifolds, clutch plates, couplers, differential spiders, and brake drums; machine tool tables and beds; grate bars and stoker parts; crusher frames; pots for lead, zinc, aluminum, and caustic.

Medium Nickel Cast Irons (3 to 5 Per Cent Nickel).—Resistance grids for current control and for heating; heavy stamping dies.

High Nickel Cast Irons (10 to 15 Per Cent Nickel).—These are nonmagnetic, and have high electrical resistance. They are used mainly in electrical machine castings.

White Nickel Cast Iron (4 to 5 Per Cent Nickel).—Where extreme hardness and resistance to abrasion is required, this is used in crusher liners, rolls, and pumps handling abrasive material.

Corrosion-resistant Cast Iron (12 to 30 Per Cent Nickel).—The ability to withstand atmospheric and chemical corrosion at elevated temperatures makes these irons well suited for oil refinery equipment, automobile and Diesel engine parts, resistance grids, sheaves for glass lehrs, mine equipment, and chemical apparatus of various types.

Ferro-nickel Alloys.—These alloys may be made with wide variations of magnetic, electrical and thermal properties, depending on the percentage of nickel used.

Nonmagnetic Alloys (10 to 25 Per Cent Nickel).—Transformer, motor and generator parts, and other varied uses in the electrical industry.

Highly Magnetic Alloys (45 to 80 Per Cent Nickel).—Electrical sheathing of submarine cable, radio and other special types of electrical transformers, telephone and telegraph relay parts.

Low Expansion Alloys (35 to 45 Per Cent Nickel).—Length standards, measuring tapes, precision instruments, watch making, bimetallic thermostats, wire for wire glass, control devices for temperature and electricity, struts in aluminum automobile engine pistons.

Nickel Silver (10 to 30 Per Cent Nickel, with Varying Percentages of Copper and Zinc, and Sometimes Small Amounts of Aluminum, Lead, Tin, or Iron).—Used as a base metal in silver-plated ware and jewelry, for flat keys, plumbing fixtures, architectural trim, building and marine hardware, lighting fixtures.

Nickel Bronzes (0.5 to 7.5 Per Cent Nickel, with Varying Percentages of Copper, Zinc, Tin and Lead).—Used in valve castings, steam packing, pressure castings, worm gears, bearings, rolling mill housing nuts, and ship propellers.

Nickel Brasses (1.5 to 6.5 Per Cent Nickel, with Varying Percentages of Copper and Zinc, and Frequently Small Amounts of Manganese, Aluminum, Iron, or Lead).—The nickel serves as a decolorizer, giving a lighter color to the brass or making even a white brass, and improves the mechanical properties and resistance to corrosion for any of the ordinary uses for brass.

Copper-nickel Alloys (2.5 to 45 Per Cent Nickel).—Used in condenser tubes, corrosion resistant castings, valves and valve trim, electrical resistance wire, coinage, and numerous minor applications.

Monel Metal (67 Per Cent Nickel, 28 Per Cent Copper, and Small Percentages of Iron, Manganese, Silicon, Carbon, and Sulfur, and Sometimes Aluminum). This is a special type of the copper-nickel alloys, developed originally by the International Nickel Company as a natural alloy, by reduction of the nickel matte without separation of the metals; other companies now produce similar compositions.   The manifold uses to which monel has been put are too detailed to give in full; the following items give only a few of the more important applications in the different fields.

Aeronautics: Gasoline tanks, propeller sheathing, pontoons, landing gear, and instrument parts.

Architecture and Building: Roofs, flashing and trim.

Automotive: Instrument panels, molding, and windshield frames.

Chemical: As a corrosion resistant element in a wide variety of chemical equipment.

Dry Cleaning: Solvent handling systems and cleaning machinery.

Electrical: Pole line hardware.

Food Preparation and Service: Processing and handling equipment for packing and canning; service and steam tables, counters, dish washers, et cetera, in hotels, restaurants and hospitals; soda fountain tops, sinks and bars; ice cream freezing, packing, and serving equipment.

Hospital: Utensils, sterilizers and operating room equipment.

Laundry: Washers, extractors, starching machinery.

Marine: Fittings, hardware, shafting, propellers.

Metal Pickling: Baskets, tanks, tie rods, racks.

Petroleum: Pump rods and valves, filters, condenser tubes, and strainers.

Power: Pumps and pump parts; valves and valve parts, shafts, impellers, turbine blades, expansion joints, gaskets, and instruments.

Pulp and Paper: Cylinder molds, beater bars, and evaporator tubes.

Textiles: Dyeing, finishing and bleaching equipment, tanks, vats, pails, and dippers.

Heat and Electrical Resistance Alloys (35 to 85 Per Cent Nickel, Along with Chromium, and Sometimes Iron).—These alloys have a high electrical resistance, and a marked resistance to atmospheric corrosion at high temperatures, making them applicable for carburizing boxes, rabble arms and shoes, shafts and discs in annealing and heating furnaces, the interior construction of enameling furnaces, heat exchangers, and electrical resistors for ovens, furnaces, stoves, grills, toasters, percolators, and other industrial and domestic heating appliances.

Light Alloys.—Several of the aluminum base alloys contain up to 5 per cent nickel, with small percentages of other metals, such as copper, iron, silicon, manganese, and titanium.

Other Alloys.—Some of the minor alloys in which nickel plays an important rôle are gold-nickel (white gold), aluminum and zinc base die castings, a nickel-molybdenum-iron alloy highly resistant to corrosion by hydrochloric acid, and a nickel-cobalt-titanium alloy used in rectifier tubes.

Malleable Nickel.—Pure nickel metal is produced in various forms, rods, bars, plates, strips, sheets, tubes, wire, angles, channels, and other special shapes, as well as in forgings and castings, and in these forms finds uses in the chemical, electrical, dairy, food, and petroleum industries, as well as in coinage. Where the equipment is too massive to permit the use of a solid nickel construction, a nickel-clad steel plate may be used.

Catalyst.—Finely divided nickel may be used as a catalyst in a number of chemical reactions, the most important of which is the hydrogenation of oils, such as cocoanut or cottonseed, to form a solid fat.

Plating.—Pure nickel is extensively used in electroplating on such metals as steel, brass, copper, zinc alloy die castings, and a number of others, either as a primary coat, or as an undercoat for a subsequent chromium plate. Although the thickness of the plate applied is usually only 0.0001 to 0.001 inch, the process is used so widely that the aggregate tonnage of nickel consumed in plating anodes is considerable.

Storage Batteries.—Nickel is used in storage batteries of the Edison type, not only in electroplating on the steel making of the body and container of the cell, but also in the form of oxide as the active material of one electrode.

Chemical Uses.—Industrial uses for nickel compounds are largely confined to the oxide and sulfate, although a wide variety of nickel chemicals are produced for laboratory purposes, as well as for minor industrial uses. The oxide is used in the positive electrode of alkaline storage batteries, in the ceramic industry in ground coat enamels for steel, and as a raw material for the production of nickel chemicals. The sulfate, either in simple form or combined with ammonium as the double salt, in extensively used in electroplating baths.

Military Uses.—Many of the military uses are identical with the ordinary industrial uses of the metal, the only difference being the emphasis which the emergency demand establishes, but, in addition to these, there are many strictly military uses, among which are armor plate for both naval and military use, many items of naval construction, gun forgings, recoil springs, and bullet jackets.

SUBSTITUTES

In general, the possible field for substitutes for nickel is limited, for a number of reasons. First, in ordinary times the price of the metal is low enough that the need for substitution from a cost standpoint is small; second, many of the commercial uses are of such recent development that there has been neither time, necessity, nor opportunity for much consideration of substitutes; and third, many of the uses of nickel are themselves substitutions for some other metal or alloy.

The chief need for substitutes for nickel will come at a time of emergency, when the supplies available are insufficient, and military uses must be given precedence over ordinary industrial uses.   Under such conditions those uses of nickel that have been developed as substitutes for other metals may have to be abandoned, with reversion to the former practice; for example, the use of brass or bronze instead of monel metal or some other nickel alloy.   In the plating field, galvanizing, cadmium plating, or possibly even enamel, may be substituted for nickel.   In the specific military uses, some work has already been done on the use of gilding metal (a special type of brass) instead of cupronickel for bullet jackets, and it is possible that other alloy steel combinations may be developed to take the place of nickel steel in many places where it is now used.

ORES

The commercial ores of nickel fall into two general classes: silicate ores and sulfide ores.   The silicate ores of New Caledonia are the best example of this type, and for many years they furnished the bulk of the world's nickel output.   They are mostly mixed silicates of nickel and magnesium, carrying considerable amounts of combined water, and 4 to 6 per cent of nickel, although in earlier years the grade was about double this amount.   Ores of a similar character have been worked to some extent in Greece, and are known in Madagascar and in the United States, where they occur in North Carolina and Oregon.

The outstanding sulfide ore is that of the Sudbury district of Ontario, 40 to 50 miles north of the Georgian Bay of Lake Huron, and 200 miles northwest of Toronto.   These ores consist of a mixed sulfide of iron and nickel, associated with sulfides of iron and copper.   In 1913 this ore carried about 3 per cent nickel and about half as much copper, but as the mines worked into the lower levels the character of the ore changed, the nickel content decreasing somewhat, and the copper ratio increasing, sometimes to as much or more than the nickel.   Ores of this type have been mined in Norway, and are known in Tasmania, Sweden, Italy, South Africa, and Pennsylvania.

A second type of sulfide ore is that in which the nickel is associated with arsenic, cobalt, and other metals.   Small amounts of nickel are recovered from silver ores of this type from the

Cobalt district of Ontario, and other small outputs have been made in India, Germany (Saxony), Czecho-Slovakia (Bohemia) and in France.

Limited amounts of nickel are recovered as a byproduct in the refining of copper, many ores of which contain small amounts of nickel, and certain iron ores, particularly in Cuba, contain nickel, which forms a valuable constituent of the iron or steel produced from the ore, although the nickel is never produced separately.

Metallurgy.—Due to their widely different character the silicate and sulfide ores require radically different metallurgical treatment. The New Caledonian ore is smelted in blast furnaces to form a matte (a fused mixture of the sulfides of iron and nickel) containing 30 to 45 per cent of nickel; since the ore carries no sulfur, this is added to the charge as gypsum. The furnace matte is then blown in a bessemer converter to remove the iron and part of the sulfur, leaving a rich matte carrying 75–80 per cent nickel. A number of years ago some smelting was done without the addition of sulfur to the charge, producing a ferro-nickel alloy, but this was soon discontinued on account of the difficulty in handling the alloy. In 1927, ferro-nickel smelting was again put into operation on a small scale, using an electric furnace instead of the blast furnace; this ferro-nickel is refined by sulfurizing it to form a matte, and then treating it in the same way as the ordinary matte. The bessemerized matte is shipped to Europe (Belgium and France) for the production of nickel, by crushing, roasting to oxide, and reduction to metal.

The Canadian sulfide ores are partially roasted to remove the excess sulfur, and smelted in blast furnaces to a matte carrying about 45 per cent iron and about half that amount of copper plus nickel, which is then bessemerized, giving a matte of about the same composition as in New Caledonian practice, except that the metal content, instead of being only nickel, is copper and nickel, in the proportions present in the ore used. The bessemerized matte is subjected to a special smelting process which serves to separate the copper and nickel sulfides, after which the latter are roasted, smelted to a crude metal and electrolytically refined to a pure metal.

Monel metal, a natural alloy of nickel and copper in approximately the proportions of 2:1, is made from matte adjusted to these proportions, by reduction without separation of the copper and nickel.

The Norwegian ores are handled in a manner similar to the Canadian, except for some differences in the method used for the separation of the nickel and copper, and in the details of the electrolytic refining.

Secondary Recovery.—There has been gradually built up a moderate recovery of secondary nickel, the maximum being 4,500 short tons in 1928, or 13 per cent of the supply for the year. The secondary recovery of nickel is far below what it should be for a metal of its permanence; unfortunately many of its uses are of such a character that secondary recovery of the metal at the end of its useful life is either impossible, impracticable, or uneconomic; in other cases recoveries are low, due to carelessness on the part of the owner, or to lack of proper training and organization on the part of the secondary metal buyers. Much of the nickel that goes into electroplating is never recovered. If it is plated on copper that is recoverable, the nickel is saved in the course of the refining operation, but if plated on iron it is the same as lost, for even if the iron is recovered as scrap, the nickel is alloyed with the steel in the melting furnace and loses its identity, unless sufficient amounts of the material are available to make it worth while to use them in making up a charge of nickel steel.

One of the biggest items of loss of nickel is in old automobiles. Comparison of the records of car production and registration shows that some 30,000,000 automobiles have been discarded, most of which had more or less nickel steel in their construction, in crank shafts, gears, et cetera, in addition to that used in plated parts. Some of these parts have been salvaged, and used in repair work, and some have been included in ordinary scrap, where the nickel content was lost, but comparatively few have been recovered under conditions where the nickel steel was saved separately, for the reason that the work of dismantling the car to the point where the alloy steel parts can be recovered separately is usually more than is justified by the value of the metal saved. As a result, there are probably 50,000 tons or more of nickel lying scattered about the country in abandoned automobiles, or lost in scrap that has been sold and used without regard to its nickel content.

Another item of some importance is the nickel content of the armor plate of abandoned naval vessels. When the 1920 Disarmament Conference led to the scrapping of the warship

Washington before it was completed, it was dismantled so far as was practicable to salvage the material, but the hulk was sunk at sea, although it contained thousands of tons of nickel steel armor plate, since the cost of breaking up such a mass into usable scrap would have exceeded the value of the scrap obtained.

Forms in Which Nickel Appears on the Market.—Nickel appears on the market in a number of different forms, to make it more readily applied to the various uses.

1. Finely divided nickel powder, made by the reduction of the oxide without fusion.

2. Electrolytic cathodes, sold entire (100 pounds or more each), or cut into smaller pieces for convenience in compounding and melting.

3. Ingots or pigs, 25 to 50 pounds, made by casting metal reduced from the oxide at temperatures above the melting point of the metal; melted cathodes may also be similarly cast if the higher purity is desired, but this is usually not necessary.

4. Shot of various sizes and grades, made as in (3), by granulating the melted metal in water.

5. Malleable nickel, in shot or ingot, made as in (3) and (4), except that the metal is treated with a deoxidizer before pouring.

6. Anodes for plating, made as in (3).

7. Nickel oxide, made by roasting the pure nickel sulfide, after separating from the copper.

8. Nickel salts, made from fine nickel powder or nickel oxide by solution in acid, or, in the case of the sulfate, recovered directly in the electrolytic refining of copper.

In addition to the above, nickel is also marketed in various alloys, particularly as monel, as nickel-aluminum (50 per cent Ni), as copper-nickel shot (50 per cent Ni), as nickel-silver pigs (20 per cent Ni), as a nickel-copper-iron alloy (30 per cent Ni), and as a nickel-copper-chromium alloy (56 per cent Ni). While these are the usual forms found in the domestic market, foreign production may be found in one of the following forms:

a. Grains, cubes ($\frac{1}{4}$ inch), or rondelles (discs $1\frac{1}{2}$ inches in diameter by $\frac{3}{4}$ inch thick), made as in (1), above.

b. Shot or balls of various sizes (up to $\frac{3}{8}$ inch) made by the Mond process, by depositing concentric layers of metal from a gaseous form (nickel carbonyl).

ORE RESERVES

As with manganese, the ore reserves of nickel are sufficient to last for a much longer time than we can foresee future developments, the only cause for dissatisfaction on this score being the scarcity of reserves in the United States. None of the known deposits in this country is of any significant value, and we must resign ourselves to the necessity of practically complete dependence on foreign sources, and be satisfied with the knowledge that plentiful supplies are only a short distance from our borders.

Concerning the New Caledonian and Norwegian ore reserves, little is known, except that they are so small in comparison with the Canadian as to be almost insignificant, in spite of the fact that an estimate made during the war attributed to the New Caledonian reserves a nickel content of 160,000 tons.

The proven ore reserves of the Canadian mines at the end of 1937 were about 213,000,000 tons, and development work is being continued. Although this amount of ore is sufficient to last for more than a century at the maximum rate attained up to 1929, and is nearly seven times the total amount of ore that has been mined in Canada since mining began in 1887, it is not an inexhaustible supply, and when one considers the rate at which the demand for nickel has been expanding during the past 50 years, the wisdom of continuing development work is confirmed, since the present rate of mining is more than three times that of 1929. There has been a total nickel output in Canada of about 1,160,000 short tons, and its production in this period of time has required an average increment of between 5 and 6 per cent each year. If the 1937 reserves are used up at the 1937 rate of mining, they would last about 34 years.

Actually, of course, it is impossible to set a date for the exhaustion of the reserve. In the first place, no one knows the rate at which consumption of nickel will continue to develop; it may be at a rate similar to that of the past, it may be less, or it may be more; or it may increase for a time, and then slowly approach a saturation point, beyond which it does not go. And, in the second place, development work will constantly add new limits to the reserves, until the deposits are completely worked out; and when this point will come, no one can say. For example, during the recent years new ore has been developed faster than mining has proceeded, and the reserves are greater now than they were 10 years ago.

WORLD OUTPUT AND SUPPLY

During the past 25 years the world output of nickel has more than trebled, reaching a maximum of 56,300 metric tons in 1929; the total production during this period, 1913–1937, was 1,103,900 metric tons or 1,216,600 short tons, of which 85 per cent was supplied by Canada, 10 per cent by New Caledonia, 1 per cent each by Norway, Greece, India, and the United States, and 1 per cent by other countries. This makes the industry one of the most highly centralized ones on the entire group of strategic minerals.

TABLE I*a*.—WORLD PRODUCTION OF NICKEL
(Metric tons)

	Canada[1]	New Caledonia[2]	Norway[5]	Greece[3]	India[4]	United States[6]	Others	Total
1913........	22,500	8,100	700	900	....	200	300	32,700
1914........	20,600	7,800	800	700	....	400	300	30,600
1915........	31,000	5,300	900	1,100	....	700	400	39,400
1916........	37,600	4,000	800	600	....	800	1,700	45,500
1917........	38,200	4,700	400	100	....	400	2,100	45,900
1918........	41,900	2,700	400	700	....	400	1,900	48,000
1919........	20,200	1,800	200	100	....	500	600	23,400
1920........	27,800	2,200	400	....	....	300	300	31,000
1921........	8,700	1,500	....	....	....	100	....	10,300
1922........	8,000	3,500	....	....	....	200	....	11,700
1923........	28,300	2,700	100	....	....	100	....	31,200
1924........	31,500	3,700	....	....	....	200	....	35,400
1925........	33,400	3,400	....	....	....	200	....	37,000
1926........	29,900	3,800	....	....	....	300	....	34,000
1927........	33,000	3,400	....	100	200	800	....	37,500
1928........	43,900	4,100	700	700	700	500	400	51,000
1929........	50,000	4,400	600	300	800	300	600	57,000
1930........	47,100	5,100	700	....	1,000	300	1,100	53,300
1931........	29,800	4,100	500	600	800	400	300	36,500
1932........	13,800	3,000	900	1,000	900	200	200	20,000
1933........	37,800	4,500	900	1,400	1,000	100	100	45,800
1934........	58,400	5,000	1,100	1,100	1,200	100	1,100	68,000
1935........	62,800	5,400	1,100	1,100	1,500	100	2,400	74,400
1936........	77,100	4,800	1,200	1,200	1,300	100	3,600	89,300
1937........	102,000	5,800	900	?	1,200	200	?	113,000
Totals......	935,300	104,800	13,300	11,700	10,600	7,900	17,400	1,103,900
Per cent....	84.8	9.5	1.3	1.1	1.0	0.7	1.6	100.0

[1] Metal produced from ore of Canadian origin.   [2] Metal content of ore and matte exported.
[3] Metal content of ore.   [4] Nickel content of speiss produced.   [5] Domestic production only.
[6] Mostly byproduct in copper refining.

Nickel production began in Canada in 1887, as against 1875 in New Caledonia, and for a number of years after the beginning of operations in Canada, New Caledonia kept in the lead, but the Canadian deposits proved so much more extensive that, in spite of their lower grade of ore, Canada definitely took the position of leading producer in 1905, and her proportion of the total continued to increase until it reached a maximum of 90 per cent in 1920, 1923, 1925 and 1937. During the past few years, and particularly during the period of the depression, New Caledonia has maintained its output somewhat better than Canada; in fact the New Caledonian output during 1930–1933 was about equal to that in 1926–1929, while in Canada the output declined 18 per cent; and in 1932 Canada's percentage of the total dropped to 69 per cent, while that of New Caledonia increased to 15 per cent.

The world production of nickel during the period 1913–1933 is shown in Table I*a* for all of the more important producers;

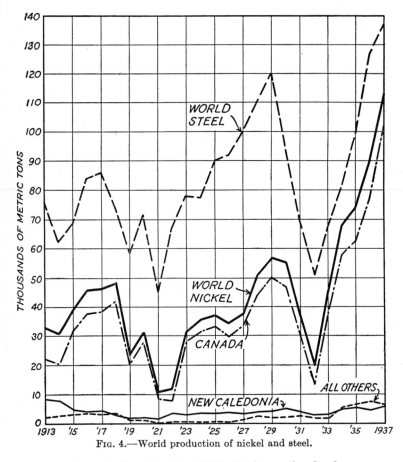

Fig. 4.—World production of nickel and steel.

the same data in Fig. 4 and in Table I*b* shows clearly the successive periods that have prevailed in the development of the industry: (1) the pre-war period, with an output of 30,000–33,000 tons, largely consumed in armament material; (2) the war period, when munition demands brought production up to 47,900 tons; (3) the post-war decline to 25,000–30,000 tons; (4) a still further drop

to 10,000–12,000 tons as a result of disarmament; (5) the recovery
to 30,000–37,000 tons as a result of the preliminary efforts to
establish new uses; (6) the marked advance to 56,300 tons as the
new uses accumulated; (7) the decline to 20,000 tons during the
world-wide industrial depression; and (8) the recovery from
the depression, which carried the 1934 output to a new high record,
which was in turn broken by each succeeding year, culminating
in a world total of 113,000 tons in 1937.

TABLE I*b*.—WORLD PRODUCTION OF NICKEL BY PERIODS
(Thousands of metric tons)

Period	Average World Output	Percentage Distribution of World Total						
		Canada	New Caledonia	Norway	Greece	India	United States	Others
1913...............	32.7	68.8	24.7	2.1	2.8	....	0.6	0.9
1914–18...........	41.9	80.9	11.7	1.6	1.5	....	1.3	3.0
1918...............	48.0	87.3	5.6	0.8	1.5	....	0.8	4.0
1919–21...........	21.6	87.6	8.5	0.9	0.2	....	1.4	1.4
1921...............	10.3	84.4	14.6	....	....	....	1.0	....
1922–29...........	36.8	87.5	9.8	0.5	0.4	0.6	0.9	0.3
1929...............	57.0	87.7	7.7	1.1	0.5	1.4	0.5	1.0
1930–32...........	37.3	81.1	10.9	1.9	1.4	2.4	0.8	1.4
1932...............	20.0	69.0	15.0	4.5	5.0	4.5	1.0	1.0
1933–37...........	78.1	86.6	6.5	1.3	1.5	1.6	0.2	2.5
1937...............	113.0	90.3	5.1	0.8	?	1.1	0.1	?

Canada.—A few miles to the west and north of the town of
Sudbury, Ontario, lies a roughly oval formation, about 40 miles
long and 15 miles wide, oriented southwest-northeast, around the
borders of which, particularly on the southern side, lie a collection
of more than forty nickel mines, the most important of which at
the present time are the Creighton, 9 miles southwest of Sudbury,
and the Frood, 3 miles north of Sudbury, owned and operated by
the International Nickel Company. The Frood mine is one of the
outstanding mines of the world, capable in itself of producing the
entire nickel requirements of the world for the next generation or
more.

For a number of years there have been only two companies
producing nickel in Canada. In 1913 about 85 per cent of the
output was by the International Nickel Company, and the
remainder by the Mond Nickel Company. In 1914 the British-
American Nickel Corporation was organized, but in 1924 it was
liquidated and its mining property was acquired by International
Nickel. In 1928 the International and Mond companies con-

solidated, and in 1929 the Falconbridge Nickel Mines started operations at a small mine 13 miles northeast of Sudbury. The Falconbridge matte is shipped to Norway for reduction and refining, and is sold mostly in Europe. The International matte is now mostly smelted and refined in Canada, but some is exported to England, and smaller amounts to the United States for the production of monel metal. Efforts are now being made to establish mining in British Columbia, where minor deposits have been known for many years.

Germany.—There was a minor production of nickel in Germany before the war, amounting to 200–300 tons a year, which increased during the war to 2,000 tons, but this practically ceased in 1920. In addition to the local production, ores and matte have been imported, giving a metal output of some 5,000 tons just before the war, and 2,000–4,000 tons since.

Burma (India).—Minor occurrences of nickel have been long known in India, but it was not until recently that there has been any production. Since 1927 there has been a small but increasing recovery of byproduct nickel from a lead smelting plant in Burma.

New Caledonia.—Starting in 1875, the nickel industry in New Caledonia slowly developed and expanded until, after 25 years, it reached a level of 7,000 tons annually, almost the entire output being exported in the form of ore, although in the years 1879–1885 and 1889–1891 small amounts were smelted locally, and the matte exported to other countries.

At the time New Caledonia started production, the world output of nickel was only about 400 tons a year and, since the local output after the first year was equal to this amount, it was inevitable that surplus stocks should accumulate. However, a native rebellion interrupted the operation of the mines in 1878–1879, and difficulties were postponed somewhat; but the inauguration of local smelting speeded up production to such an extent that, by 1885, much surplus stock had accumulated. As a result prices had so declined that, in 1886, smelting stopped and production was restricted for two years more.

It was at this inauspicious time that Canada entered the field as a producer and, for the next 10 years, there was active competition for the market, with Canada forging to the front and New Caledonia declining until, in 1896, the New Caledonian output was little more than half that of 1891. At this point the two contenders for the market arrived at an agreement, and for the next few years production increased in New Caledonia, but, in spite of this, the plentiful supplies of ore in Canada put that country in the position of leading producer and New Caledonia again declined.

In 1910 smelting was reëstablished on the island, and since then matte shipments have averaged about 5,000 metric tons a year, but with ore exports declining from the maximum of 142,000 tons in 1911.

TABLE A.—NICKEL PRODUCTION IN CANADA AND NEW CALEDONIA
(Metric tons)

	Canada		New Caledonia	
	Ore Mined	Nickel Produced	Ore Mined	Nickel Produced
1875–1878			8,300	1,000
1879–1883			22,500	2,100
1884–1888			32,000	2,600
1889–1893	340,000	5,800	181,000	13,700
1894–1898	466,000	9,900	249,000	15,500
1899–1903	1,060,000	20,500	543,000	30,000
1904–1908	1,440,000	41,400	570,000	30,700
1909–1913	2,938,000	87,200	656,000	33,200
1914–1918	6,608,000	169,400	603,000	24,500
1919–1923	3,097,000	93,100	292,000	11,700
1924–1928	6,136,000	169,000	498,000	18,400
1929–1933	7,495,000	178,500	690,000	19,000
1934–1937	16,036,000	300,300	788,000	21,000

Since only average figures are known as to the nickel content of the ore and matte shipped, no accurate figures can be given for the output, but 1911 seems to have been the peak of New Caledonian production, with about 10,000 tons of metal. As the Canadian output grew, New Caledonian ore exports dwindled, and finally disappeared in 1920; since then only occasional small amounts have been shipped, up to 1936, when regular shipments were again started, mostly to Japan. Another big factor in the loss of precedence by New Caledonia was the gradual decrease in the grade of the ore, which, from 11–12 per cent in the beginning, had declined to 5–6 per cent in 1900, and to 4–5 per cent in 1930.

The trend of the struggle for supremacy in the nickel field between Canada and New Caledonia is shown in Table A, which includes, so far as data are available, the ore and nickel produced in the two countries from the beginning. Due to the lower nickel content, the ore production in Canada was greater throughout, but it was not until 1903 that Canada actually produced more metal, only to lose out again to New Caledonia in 1904; but in 1905 Canada definitely took the lead in production.

In 1931 the Société Calédonia and the Société Le Nickel, the only companies left active on the island, consolidated as the Société Caledonickel.

Norway.—Previous to the discovery of the New Caledonian deposits, Norway was the chief source of nickel, but the richer ores of New Caledonia enabled the new producer to replace Norway in the market, just as, in turn, New Caledonia was later replaced by Canada with her more plentiful if leaner ore supplies. A small production began again in Norway about 1900, and by 1915 had grown to about 900 metric tons, only to decrease and disappear in 1920. The industry was again reëstablished in 1928, and in addition, the matte production of the Falconbridge company in Canada is brought to Norway for reduction and refining; including this, the metal output of Norway has now grown to more than 6,000 tons a year, about 1,000 tons of which is of domestic origin.

United States.—There are several minor deposits of nickel in the United States, and before the discovery of the New Caledonian ores, some of these were worked on a small scale in Connecticut, Pennsylvania, and California. In 1909 and again during the war period there was a small production in Missouri, but almost the whole of such small output as is made in this country is a byproduct recovery in the refining of copper.

Although never a producer of more than insignificant amounts of nickel ore, the United States has had an important place in nickel smelting from the beginning of the development of the Canadian deposits by the Canadian Copper Company, this company, and its successor, the International Nickel Company being United States corporations. For many years the bulk of the Canadian matte output was shipped to New Jersey for reduction. The factors that led to the discontinuance of this will be discussed later.

Other Countries.—Nickel ores are rather widely scattered over the earth, and many other countries have small deposits, some of which have been worked intermittently, but mostly on a very small scale. Among the countries that may thus be mentioned are: Australia, Borneo, Brazil, Celebes, Cuba, Finland, Great

Britain, Greece, Italy, Mexico, Philippines, Rhodesia, Russia, Sebokoe, South Africa, and Spain.

UNITED STATES SUPPLY

Practically the entire United States supply of nickel is obtained from imports, chiefly from Canada. Only in two or three out of the past 25 years has there been any direct production from nickel

TABLE II.—AVAILABLE SUPPLY OF NICKEL IN THE UNITED STATES
(Short tons)

	Production		Approximate Imports				Ex-ports	Avail-able Sup-ply
	Pri-mary	Sec-ondary	In Ore and Matte	Metal and Alloys	In Oxide	Total Im-ports		
1913..............	200	......	23,600	200	......	23,800	14,600	9,400
1914..............	400	......	17,500	100	......	17,600	13,800	4,200
1915..............	800	......	28,200	......	......	28,300	13,200	15,900
1916..............	900	800	36,300	......	......	36,300	16,700	21,300
1917..............	400	900	37,800	......	......	37,800	11,000	28,100
1918..............	400	1,400	36,600	......	......	36,600	8,700	29,700
1919..............	500	2,500	14,700	3,600	......	18,300	1,900	19,400
1920..............	400	2,200	20,800	3,500	......	24,300	600	26,300
1921..............	100	900	1,000	1,200	......	2,200	200	3,000
1922..............	200	1,500	1,500	5,700	200	7,400	4,700	4,400
1923..............	100	1,600	7,300	11,900	800	20,000	900	20,800
1924..............	200	2,200	5,700	12,300	300	18,300	1,300	19,400
1925..............	300	2,300	3,600	16,000	400	20,000	1,800	19,800
1926..............	300	3,100	5,100	14,700	500	20,300	1,600	22,100
1927..............	900	3,400	3,100	14,600	400	18,200	1,800	20,600
1928..............	500	4,500	5,200	24,500	600	30,300	1,900	33,400
1929..............	300	4,400	7,700	32,300	1,100	50,100	2,000	52,800
1930..............	300	2,900	5,500	19,200	500	28,300	2,400	29,100
1931..............	400	2,100	3,100	11,800	100	15,000	1,200	16,300
1932..............	200	1,500	1,600	7,500	200	9,300	1,300	9,700
1933..............	100	1,700	5,000	15,800	800	21,600	1,000	22,400
1934..............	200	1,900	3,100	22,900	400	26,400	2,700	25,800
1935..............	200	2,000	4,200	29,400	400	34,000	2,200	34,400
1936..............	100	2,000	6,200	40,300	1,000	47,500	4,100	45,500
1937..............	200	2,400	6,700	40,800	800	48,300	4,500	46,400

ores, and this, combined with the byproduct recovery from copper refining, has averaged only 300 short tons a year, with annual figures varying from 100 to 900 tons.

The sources of the available supply are shown in Table II. This table would be more valuable if it included information on excess stocks, which, particularly during the post-war period and the recent depression period, had considerable influence on production, but unfortunately no data on these are published. Figures on imports and exports are also only approximate, as they include the gross weight in the case of nickel alloys, and in addition to the imports listed there were small amounts of nickel imported in manufactures, which were listed by value only. The original figures on imports in ore and matte since 1925 give only the gross weight; the nickel contents as given in the table are estimated from various items of supplementary information, particularly the Canadian export statistics, which list the nickel content of the ore and matte exported. On the whole, though, while the figures shown in the column for available supply are not strictly accurate, it is felt that they are close enough to the facts to be representative of the conditions in the industry.

Imports.—Nickel is imported into the United States in a number of different forms:

1. In crude form, in ore or matte.
2. In metal and alloy form, in pigs and ingots.
3. In nickel oxide.
4. In semi-fabricated metal and alloys, in bars, plates, sheets, et cetera.
5. In finished manufactures of all kinds.

Most of the crude metal imported is in the form of matte; although some ore has been imported, the amounts of nickel involved are smaller. In 1919 about 36 per cent of the crude metal imported was in ore, in 1920 only 4 per cent, while in 1921 it increased again to 32; for other years separate figures for ore and matte have not been recorded; apparently there has been little if any ore imported during the past few years.

Most of the matte imported, as would be expected, comes from Canada, but, until within the past few years, fairly large amounts were brought from New Caledonia. In 1928 over 1,300 tons of matte was entered from New Caledonia and Australia, and since Australia is not a nickel producer, it is assumed that the imports attributed to that country were of New Caledonian origin, transshipped at an Australian port. Since then imports from countries other than Canada have been insignificant in amount. Previous to 1919–1920, as is shown in Table II, the imports were almost exclusively in ore and matte, which were smelted in this country, and a large proportion of the product was then reëxported. At that time, smelting was shifted to Canada, and subsequent imports of ore and matte have been largely confined to such amounts as are required for monel metal and similar alloys, the production of which is still carried on in the United States.

Since 1919 an increasing amount of metal and alloy in pigs and ingots has been imported. Although the greater part of this came directly from Canada, fairly large amounts came from England, and some from France. The French shipments have practically ceased, and those from England have been reduced since the consolidation of the International and Mond companies, and increasing amounts have been received from Norway, amounting to nearly 1,000 tons in 1932. Both the English and the Norwegian shipments were produced largely from matte of Canadian origin, while the French material was of New Caledonian origin.

The nickel oxide comes almost entirely from Canada, and nickel in semi-finished and finished manufactures is imported from a number of different countries, with Germany in the lead.

Exports.—As has been indicated in the discussion of imports, the United States was formerly the smelting center for most of the Canadian matte, and consequently exports were large. During the five years 1913–1917 the exports amounted to nearly half of the imports. Since the shift of the main smelting operations to Canada, United States exports have been confined mostly to monel metal and similar alloys, the manufacture of which is centered in this country.

PRICES

With the establishment of nickel mining in New Caledonia, the first production in quantity, prices dropped rapidly from the high level that had been reached just previous to this, and shortly after the entry of Canada as a producer prices declined still further; but since that time there has been comparatively little variation in the price, due probably to the close concentration of the output in the hands of only a few producers. The trend of nickel prices over nearly 100 years is shown in graphic form in Fig. 5. As can readily be seen, the price level for nickel has shown very little fluctuation since 1902, even during the war period. Prices for recent years are those quoted by the International Nickel Company and those for earlier years are taken from a paper presented by the president of that company in 1926. Prices for small quantities and for remelted material are somewhat higher than those indicated, and on large contracts, are lower.

UTILIZATION OF NICKEL

During the past 25 years the United States has consumed about 47 per cent of the world's total new nickel output, of which 1 per cent was domestic production, and an additional 4 per cent was recovered secondary metal, leaving 42 per cent to be supplied from foreign sources. In the years immediately preceding the World War, with a world output of about 30,000 metric tons a year, the chief item of consumption was in the production of various types of nickel steel; this took probably half or more of the nickel output, and a large proportion of this went into armor plate,

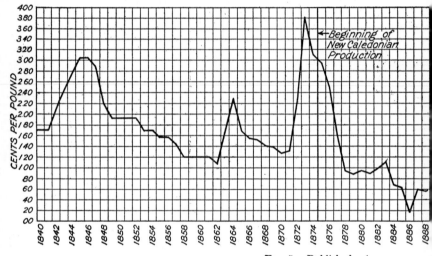

FIG. 5.—Published prices

and other types of armament and munition material. Included in the ferrous alloy group were also a number of high-nickel alloys, with 20–40 per cent nickel, but the output of these was comparatively small.

Next in importance after the nickel steels was the nonferrous alloy group, including monel metal, nickel silver (nickel-copper-zinc alloys), the nickel-chromium series of electrical resistance alloys, the cupronickel series (nickel brasses and bronzes), and a large number of less important combinations.

The uses of the pure metal were largely confined to anodes for nickel plating, to finely divided nickel as a catalyst in the hydrogenation of oils, and to a limited amount used in cooking and table utensils. Nickel oxide was used in the construction of the Edison storage battery, and as a coloring agent in glasses and ceramic glazes. Certain salts, chiefly the sulfate, were used in electro-plating baths. These items cover the more important uses of nickel at that time, but there is not sufficient data available to make any reliable estimate of the amounts consumed by the various uses.

By 1918, under the pressure of war demand, world output had increased to about 48,000 metric tons; of this amount various estimates allocate 60–75 per cent to steel production, the greater

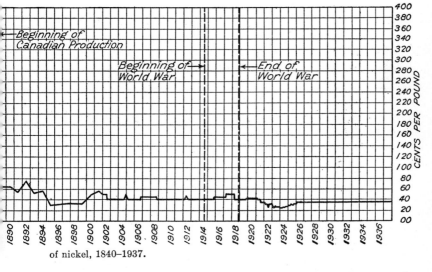

of nickel, 1840–1937.

part of which was for armor plate and munitions. Consumption in other lines was proportionately reduced. After the close of the war, munition manufacture practically ceased, and in 1920 the Washington Disarmament Conference effectively ended the production of armor plate for the time being. The large amount of nickel that had been going into these products was no longer required. This faced the world nickel producers with the necessity of either contracting their output to the level of the reduced demand, or of developing new uses for the metal sufficient to offset the drop.

The use of nickel in armament has undergone a marked change since the war period. It is impossible to trace the exact amounts,

TABLE VI.—PERCENTAGE DISTRIBUTION OF NICKEL BY USES

	1919	1926	1929	1933	1937
Ferrous alloys	60	41	37	39	61
Alloy steels		38		35	55
Cast irons		1		4	5
Iron alloys		2			1
Nonferrous alloys	30	47	51	47	27
Brass and bronze¹		2			2
Resistance alloys²		5		3	3
Copper alloys³		15		18	10
Monel⁴		25		26	12
Electrodeposition	5	5	10	10	10
Unclassified	5	7	2	4	2

A blank indicates inclusion in "Unclassified" or with some closely allied use.
¹ Includes alloys with aluminum.   ² Heat resistant and electrical resistance alloys.
³ Copper-nickel alloys and nickel silver.   ⁴ Included malleable nickel.

but of the 60–75 per cent of consumption used in ferrous alloys during the war period, presumably the greater part was for munitions, as was also a good percentage of the nonferrous uses. Nickel still plays the same important part in a munitions program, but the extensive development of other uses since the Disarmament Conference of 1920 has so overshadowed the armament uses that they no longer bulk so large in the picture. According to estimates of the International Nickel Co., only about 5,000 tons of nickel went into armament in the United States and Great Britain in 1938, and these two countries normally consume about half of the total supply. Armament consumption in Continental Europe was probably considerably greater, but there is no basis on which to estimate the amount. It is important to note, however, that while nickel consumption was formerly increased by armament demand, during 1938, in a period of active rearmament, it decreased, because the increase from armament demand was more than offset by the accompanying decrease in industrial uses.

During the next few years production was restricted in accordance with the smaller demand, but active efforts were made to develop new uses, with such marked success that in 1928 production exceeded the war-time peak, although consumption in steels had dropped heavily, since there was little used for armament purposes. All told, these changes have resulted in a remarkably extensive revision of the consumption list from that of 25 years ago. Table VI gives the percentage distribution to the various types of uses for several years since 1919, as estimated by the International Nickel Company from annual sales.

While figures are available for only a few years, and these do not always cover the same grouping of uses, they are sufficiently comparable to show several marked trends, the more important of which are: the diversion of nickel from munition steels to industrial steels; the recent growth of the use of nickel cast irons; and a decline in monel and malleable nickel. There has also been a big increase in the use of nickel steels in automotive work, also of corrosion-resistant steels, of high-nickel alloys for resistance to heat and chemical corrosion, and of pure nickel in coinage, but separate figures are not available for the exact amounts of each.

TARIFF

The tariff rates on the various forms of nickel imported into the United States during the past 20 years have been as follows:

TABLE VIII.—TARIFF RATES ON NICKEL

	1913–22	1922–30	1930—
Ore and matte.................................	Free	Free	Free
Oxide......................................	10 %	1c./lb.	Free
Nickel and alloys, in ingots, pigs, cathodes, shot, cubes, et cetera.................................	10 %	3c./lb.	3c./lb.[1]
Bars, rods, plates, sheets, et cetera	20 %	25 %	25 %
Cold rolled or cold-drawn		35 %	35 %
Manufactures		40 %	45 %

[1] Reduced to 2½ cents per pound in the new trade agreement with Canada, signed Nov. 17, 1938.

POLITICAL AND COMMERCIAL CONTROL

The history of the nickel industry in Canada and the United States presents an interesting example of the effect of political and commercial control on the development of an industry. Although the leading deposits are under the political control of Canada primarily, and secondarily of the British Empire, the commercial control has from the beginning been largely in the hands of United States capital.

The Canadian Copper Company, the original producer, started, as its name indicates, as a copper company in 1886, but in 1887 the nickel content of the ore was discovered, and this soon overshadowed the copper. In the application for a charter, the organizers of the company asked power to establish treating or smelting plants in Canada or elsewhere, as the interests of the company might dictate, but in recommending the charter the Parliamentary committee struck out the words "or elsewhere," with a view of forcing the smelting and refining of the ores in Canada. However, considerable difficulty was encountered in securing a method of treatment which would satisfactorily and economically accomplish the separation of the nickel and copper in the ore, and when it was found that the best process was that of the Orford Copper Company of New Jersey, the practice was established of smelting the ore to matte in Canada, and then shipping the matte to New Jersey for reduction and refining.

Various efforts were made by the Provincial Government of Ontario to enforce the charter clause concerning treatment in Canada (including a license fee on ore produced, a royalty charge on nickel not refined in the Province, and later a bounty to be paid on nickel that was so refined), but these were eventually dropped without having accomplished the desired end, and in the meantime the Mond Nickel Company received the approval of the Ontario Government for the refining of their matte in Wales.

It soon became evident that the consolidation of the producing and refining agencies was desirable, and in 1902 a holding company, International Nickel Company, capitalized at $24,000,000, was formed to take over the Canadian Copper Company and the Orford Copper Company, along with some smaller companies associated with each. The holding company was reorganized in 1912 under the name of The International Nickel Company, with a capital of $62,000,000, and in 1928, with the absorption of the Mond Company, the capital structure of the company was again expanded, and the corporate name changed to The International Nickel Company of Canada.

At the time of the outbreak of the World War practically the entire Canadian nickel output was being exported in the form of matte, 90 per cent of it going to the United States, of which about two-thirds was later reëxported as finished metal, and in 1915 the Royal Ontario Nickel Commission was appointed to study and report on the question of enforcing refining in Ontario. Previously, agitation along this line had centered around the industrial and economic features of the problem, but now there was added to this the question of safeguarding the supply of an important war material, and keeping it out of the hands of the enemy.

Agitation on this latter score was much increased in 1916, when it was learned that the German submarine *Deutschland* had

taken back from New York, as a part of her cargo in July, 376
tons of nickel, and in December an additional 208 tons.   There
was a furor of publicity over a fundamentally Canadian product
getting directly into the hands of the enemy, and although it was
later shown pretty conclusively that the nickel in question was
not supplied by the refiners of Canadian matte, but was secondary
metal, picked up in the open market, still the effect was much the
same, and the forced establishment of the refining operation on
Canadian soil was given greater emphasis than ever before.

The Commission reported early in 1917, advocating the home
refining of nickel, and after an interval for the erection of the
necessary plants, the exportation of refined metal was begun in
1919.   Since 1920 crude metal imported into the United States
has been confined to that used in the production of monel metal,
but some matte still goes to Wales, presumably in continuation
of the agreement with the Mond Nickel Company and, since the
beginning of operations by the Falconbridge Nickel Mines, their
matte goes to Norway for refining.

Thus we see the effect of political control of an industry taking
precedence over commercial control, and diverting the operations
along the lines dictated by nationalistic policies.

GENERAL REVIEW OF THE DOMESTIC SITUATION

Since there is no prospect of domestic production in appreciable quantities, the entire domestic supply, both present and future,
rests on imports from foreign countries.   Due to its close proximity, and its plentiful supply, Canada has been furnishing most
of our demand for many years, and will probably continue to do
so, although some of this has reached our shores by way of English
and Norwegian refineries.   With almost unlimited reserves available so close at hand, the only situation that would be likely
to interfere with a satisfactory supply would be a war in which we
find ourselves opposed to Great Britain, which, while not impossible, is at least improbable.   The situation is also simplified
by the ownership of the chief producer by United States capital,
but as has been pointed out in the preceding section, political
control takes precedence over commercial.   An even greater
measure of protection is provided by the large stocks of metal
that are maintained in the United States by the producers.
While no figures are available on the actual size of these stocks,

they are apparently of such magnitude as to cover a material proportion of any deficiency in supply that might eventuate.

CONCLUSION

It is clearly shown by the facts here presented that nickel is a metal highly important in a modern munition program, and with a well-established and rapidly expanding list of uses in industry, but with no appreciable domestic supply, either present or prospective.   The only safeguard in a situation of this kind is a reserve stock on which to draw in the event of an emergency demand that can not be supplied directly from the mines.   As compared with manganese, the problem is simpler in that the main source of supply is close at hand, with lessened likelihood of interference with access to this supply, but is complicated by the fact that there is no domestic reserve on which one can depend for at least part of the supply.   This necessitates that the entire dependence be placed on reserve stocks.

In addition to the reserve stock pile, there will be some metal available by diversion from other uses; the increased application of nickel along many different lines during the past few years has been storing up in the country in one form and another an increasing amount of metal, some of which can be drawn on in the event of an emergency of sufficient importance to justify it; examples of this are the increasing amounts of malleable nickel going into cooking utensils and decorative material.   This same trend is also increasing the amounts of nickel to be obtained by secondary recovery.

CHAPTER V

CHROMIUM

The strategic situation with regard to chromium is in many ways similar to that of manganese: domestic output previous to the World War was negligible, but expanded to cover a material proportion of the demand during 1916–1918, and then dropped back to the pre-war level; both have moderate domestic ore reserves, but of too low a grade to be economically operated at normal prices; both are consumed largely by the steel industry, but while manganese is used almost entirely in the metallic form, chromium is used extensively in the form of chromite, as a refractory material in furnace construction.

In this connection, the consumption of chromium has undergone a considerable transformation since the pre-war period. At that time the use as a refractory predominated, and only a comparatively small proportion was reduced to the metallic condition, mostly as ferrochromium, for use in the production of chromium and nickel-chromium steels, and of nickel-chromium-iron alloys for heat-resistant and electrical alloys. But since the development of the so-called stainless steels, carrying up to 30 per cent chromium, as against 1–2 per cent in the former steels, the use of chromium in alloy steels has been much increased. The development of electrical heating equipment in both household and industrial uses has multiplied the demand for chromium in this direction, and many new applications have similarly expanded the consumption in heat resistant alloys. As a result, the consumption of chromium in metallic form is several times what it was twenty years ago, and absorbs the greater percentage of the supply of raw material. Previous to these developments, chromite was regarded primarily as furnace construction material, but now more attention is given to it as a metallurgical ore, and the growing list of new uses for chromium alloys has caused a marked development in the metallurgy of the metal.

Another point of similarity with manganese is found in the fact that all of the commercially important deposits of chromium ores are found in countries having little or no local demand for the material, since the steel industry is either nonexistent in the country, or is developed only to a minor degree.   This means that the chromium supplies for the important steel-producing countries must be imported from comparatively remote sources.   Also, as with manganese, these sources are fairly numerous and widely distributed, there being a score or more of countries that have contributed to the supply.

REQUIREMENTS

Being dependent so largely on the steel industry for consumption, the chromite production fluctuates with the demands of this industry, although the correlation is not as close as in the case of manganese.   Inspection of the accompanying graph of chromite production, or of the world production figures in Table I, shows that in the years preceding 1915, and again in 1919 and 1921–1922, the world output averaged about 150,000 metric tons, while in 1916–1918 and in 1920 it rose to an average figure of about 260,-000 tons.   With the recovery from the post-war depression, production increased rapidly and steadily up to 1929, closely paralleling the growing steel output, and reaching a maximum of 635,000 tons.   Beginning in 1930 there was a uniform annual decline, to 305,000 tons in 1932, with a recovery to about 1,350,-000 tons in 1937.

USES

The industrial uses of chromium may be classed under three headings: metallurgical uses, refractory uses, and chemical uses. The chemical uses are small as compared with either of the others. No definite data are available on which a distribution by uses can be made, but estimates of the distribution to consuming industries in the United States have been made at various times.   These estimates are as follows:

PERCENTAGE DISTRIBUTION OF CHROMITE BY INDUSTRIES

	1918	1922	1925	1927	1937
Metallurgical industries.................	52	40	32	46	45
Refractories industries..................	17	35	41	41	40
Chemical industries....................	31	25	27	13	15

With the increasing development of new chromium steels, as well as other alloys, the metallurgical uses have taken a decided upward trend during recent years, mostly at the expense of the chemical industries. Previous to the increase in metallurgical demand incident to the World War, refractories consumed the greater proportion. The increased consumption of chromium in alloy steels has been promoted not only by expanding uses for the alloys, but also by the development of alloys using higher and higher percentages of chromium. A ton of stainless steel with 18 per cent of chromium requires as much chromium as 10 to 20 tons of the ordinary chrome steels with 1–2 per cent, and many of the newer alloys call for chromium contents of two and even three times this amount.

Metallurgical Uses.—The leading metallurgical uses of chromium are in alloys in which the other major constituent is either iron, nickel, or cobalt, but in many cases other metals are also incorporated in the composition. Depending on the percentage of chromium used, and on the other alloying agents present, quite a wide variation of properties may be obtained, centering largely around strength, toughness, hardness, resistance to abrasion and wear, resistance to chemical and atmospheric corrosion, resistance to oxidation and mechanical weakness at high temperatures, and high electrical resistance. In some cases only one of these properties is desired, but in others a combination of two or more is needed. For example, in a stainless steel for hospital use, corrosion resistance is the chief requirement, but for architectural use strength also becomes a factor, and in both cases a pleasing appearance is important. In electrical resistance wire, not only the high electrical resistance is essential, but also resistance to oxidation at high temperature. In oil refinery stills strength at high temperature must be accompanied by resistance to oxidation and chemical corrosion at the same temperatures. As a result, there is a multitude of varying compositions on the market, with chromium contents ranging from a fraction of a per cent, up to 50–60 per cent.

Some are fundamentally binary alloys, with only minor percentages of other elements, but many have three or four, or even more constituents in their make-up. Some are fundamentally steels—that is, they depend on carbon in amounts up to 3 per cent for some of their basic properties—while in others carbon, if present at all, is merely an impurity that can not be readily eliminated below a certain point, just as is the case with sulfur or phosphorus, and the same may be said of silicon and manganese, after making due allowance for metals added as deoxidizers. Among the other elements added to these alloys, for the sake of some special improvement, are aluminum, copper, molybdenum, nitrogen, titanium, tungsten, vanadium and zirconium.

Since we are here primarily concerned with the alloys as consumers of chromium, we shall classify them mainly on the basis of their chromium content, with only secondary consideration for the other constituents, or for the specific use for which the alloy may have been designed.

Low Chromium Steels (0.5 to 5 Per Cent Chromium).—The older chromium steels and most of the newer compositions for automotive work, in which high strength and ductility are required, fall within the range 0.5–2 per cent chromium, but certain of the special steels for connecting rods and gears use up to 4–5 per cent. In many cases 1–4 per cent nickel, or small percentages of molybdenum, tungsten, or copper are used in addition to the chromium. The steels used for armor plate and armor-piercing projectiles also come in the lower range of this group.

Cast Chromium Steels (0.6 to 1.1 Per Cent Chromium).—There are several low chromium steels carrying 1–3 per cent of nickel that are used in the cast condition, for work requiring a higher resistance to stress and shock than what can be obtained with ordinary steel castings.

Chromium Cast Irons (0.2 to 4 Per Cent Chromium).—Alloy cast irons carrying 0.75–3 per cent nickel in addition to the chromium are now used for many types of high grade castings. A special corrosion-resistant cast iron containing 1.5 per cent chromium, 12–15 per cent nickel and 5–7 per cent copper is used in oil refinery and power plant equipment, and in many of the chemical industries. A high-strength nickel-bearing cast iron for gears, turbine castings and rotors, sheaves, bushings, heavy machinery frames, and similar uses, is sometimes modified by the addition of 0.35–0.8 per cent chromium. An extra hard and tough type of chilled cast iron carries 1.4–1.6 per cent chromium and 4.25–4.75 per cent nickel.

Intermediate Chromium Steels (3 to 12 Per Cent Chromium).—This group includes the high-speed tool steels, which in addition to tungsten carry 3.5–5 per cent chromium, and steels for valves for automotive engines; American steels of the latter type contain 7–9 per cent chromium and 2.5–4 per cent silicon; British steels use up to 12 per cent chromium and 9 per cent nickel, with sometimes the addition of molybdenum. A number of the compositions for steels with mild corrosion or oxidation resistance fall within the range 4–12 per cent chromium, although in most cases the protective action of the chromium is supplemented by 15–35 per cent nickel, or sometimes by small percentages of molybdenum or tungsten.

Stainless Irons (12 *to* 15 *Per Cent Chromium*).—These alloys are very low in carbon (usually 0.05–0.12 per cent) and were among the first to be developed in the stainless group. Their marked characteristics are resistance to corrosion and oxidation at ordinary and moderately elevated temperatures; these properties are sometimes modified by the addition of small percentages of nickel, molybdenum or zirconium. In some cases the chromium content is increased beyond the usual range, to 18 per cent, and occasionally even as high as 21 per cent.

Stainless Steels (12 *to* 18 *Per Cent Chromium*).—These steels usually carry 0.25–0.4 per cent carbon, but in some cases go considerably higher, even up to 1.15 per cent. The chromium content is also often carried beyond the normal range, up to 30 per cent being used where oxidation resistance is desired at high temperatures. The normal percentage range gives resistance to atmospheric and chemical corrosion, with greater strength and hardness than the stainless irons.

Super Stainless Steels (12 *to* 30 *Per Cent Chromium*).—The super stainless steels are modifications of the regular stainless type by the addition of varying amounts of nickel, with sometimes small percentages of aluminum, copper, molybdenum, tungsten, or vanadium. The normal composition of this type of steel, and the one most used, is 18 per cent chromium and 8 per cent nickel, hence the common technical designation of 18–8 steels. In the various commercial brands the chromium varies from 16 to 20 per cent, and the nickel from 7 to 10 per cent. This, however, is not by any means the only composition range used, the details of the compositions varying widely with the variations in the work required of the steel, the degree of corrosion resistance, the particular acids, chemicals, or other agents to which it is to be rendered inert, the degree of oxidation resistance required at high temperature, and the plant practice of the manufacturer. In many cases, chromium contents as low as 12 per cent are supplemented by abnormally high percentages of nickel, particularly for oxidation resistance, the nickel content in this case usually being from 25 to 40 per cent. For high temperature equipment, requiring the maximum of oxidation resistance the chromium usually ranges from 20 to 30 per cent; for the lower chromium percentages the nickel is usually about equal to the chromium content; in the intermediate ranges the nickel is about one-half the chromium; and in the upper ranges the nickel is about one-third the chromium content, although there are numerous variations from this generalization.

Chromium-nickel Ferrous Alloys (14 *to* 30 *Per Cent Chromium*).—As the chromium and nickel contents of the super stainless steels increase, they gradually merge into alloys that can hardly be considered as steels; while there is no specific point at which a division can be made, it is convenient to consider the upper limit of the steels as 50 per cent chromium plus nickel, and to designate those compositions in which iron is definitely in the minority as ferrous alloys of nickel and chromium. These alloys are mostly used for high temperature work, and contain 14–20 per cent chromium and 60–80 per cent nickel, although some have nickel contents as low as 35–45 per cent.

Electrical Resistance Alloys (8 *to* 20 *Per Cent Chromium*).—A section of the chromium-nickel-iron alloys group, with 8–20 per cent chromium,

54–80 per cent nickel, and the remainder iron, have been extensively used as resistance elements in all types of electrical heating equipment, due to their combination of high electrical resistance and freedom from oxidation at elevated temperatures.   While the percentage range is such as would include these alloys in the preceding group, their special properties and applications justify this separate designation for them.

Chromium-cobalt Alloys (20 *to* 35 *Per Cent Chromium*).—After having undergone a certain amount of variation in composition in the course of their development, these alloys have largely settled down to a content of 30 per cent chromium, 50–65 per cent cobalt, with tungsten (and sometimes molybdenum) for the remainder.   This makes an exceedingly hard alloy, which is used as a substitute for tool steel for very heavy work, and, when spread in place by electrical or oxy-acetylene welding, as a surfacing material for all types of equipment subject to heavy wear by abrasion.   The alloys also have a considerable resistance to chemical corrosion by many acids and chemicals, making them useful where corrosion resistance is needed along with abrasion resistance.

Chromium Metal (97 *to* 100 *Per Cent Chromium*).—The so-called chromium metal of commerce is usually 96–98 per cent pure.   It has no use as such, but is used in the compounding of non-ferrous chromium alloys in which very little iron is permissible.

The only commercial use of 100 per cent pure chromium metal is in the form of an electroplate on other metals.   This, however, does not call for anode material of corresponding purity, as is the case in electroplating with other metals, such as nickel and copper.   Because of its characteristic high resistance to corrosion, which makes chromium so useful in the production of permanent alloys, which owe their immunity to corrosion largely to their chromium content, chromium anodes can not be dissolved in the plating bath, and the metal as it is deposited from the bath must be replenished by addition to the bath in the form of a chromium salt, usually chromic acid, CrO_3.   The results in the rather contradictory condition that the only commercial use of the pure metal appears as a part of the chemical side of the industry, rather than of the metallurgical.   Although chromium plating has become an operation of wide application and great industrial importance, the layer of metal deposited is so thin (0.000002–0.0005 inch) that the amount of metal consumed is insignificant.

Refractory Uses.—The second largest use of chromium is in its crude form, as chromite, in refractory materials for furnace construction.   In some cases the entire furnace hearth has been built of chromite, but the commoner application is as an insulating layer between a basic hearth and an acid roof, since the chromite is neutral in composition, and will not react with either hearth or roof.   Most of the chromite used as a refractory is in the form of bricks, but crushed chromite and chromite cements are also used to some extent.

In the past, consumption of chromite refractories has been considerably restricted by high prices. Twenty years ago chromite brick cost four to five times as much as magnesite, limiting the use to places where magnesite would not serve the purpose. Since about 1922, prices have been more nearly on a par, and this has resulted in an increased use of chromite, particularly since 1927. For some time the price of chromite bricks has been less than that of magnesite, and this has led to still greater use, even to a point of substitution of chromite for magnesite in uses that formerly were considered as belonging to magnesite alone. In 1918 the price of chromite brick rose to a point where they cost in excess of $1 each, and naturally their use was restricted as much as possible, as is indicated in the table of distribution by uses. Since then, declining prices have permitted increased use, and the proportion absorbed by refractory uses has grown at the same time that total uses were expanding rapidly, so that the amounts used in refractories in 1927 were about three times the amount used in 1922.

Chemical Uses.—Chromium goes into a number of chemicals for industrial use, of which the following are the more important:

Chromates and bichromates are used extensively in dyeing and tanning, bleaching oils, treating boiler feed water, as an oxidizing agent (bichromates), as paint pigments, and in the production of other chromium chemicals.

The oxide Cr_2O_3 is used in the production of pure chromium metal, and also as a pigment; the oxide CrO_3 and the sulfate are used in making up chromium plating baths, and the basic sulfate is used in tanning.

The acetate, chloride and double sulfate (chrome alum) are used in dyeing and tanning.

Military Uses.—The military uses of chromium are all directly connected with the corresponding industrial uses. Chrome steel, on account of its hardness and toughness, is used in the production of armor plate and armor-piercing projectiles, and during recent years there has been considerable use of stainless steels in naval construction. As a chemical, chromium is important in the tanning of leather for shoes and other items of military equipment. Also important from a military standpoint is its use as a dye for olive drab cloth.

SUBSTITUTES

There has been little direct work done in the development of substitutes for chromium. In case of necessity, certain of the other alloy steels might be made to serve in place of the low chrome steels, but for armor plate and the stainless steels there is no adequate substitute. For some types of equipment requiring resistance to chemical corrosion certain other alloys may be used, particularly high silicon cast irons, but the physical properties of these are such that their applications are much restricted. As an electrical resistance material there is nothing as good as the nickel-chromium alloys for the higher temperatures. Other alloys are available for lower temperatures, but their resistivity is materially lower, and in addition, most of them contain appreciable amounts of nickel, so that their use would depend on the supply of that metal, as well as of the chromium. In the refractory field, magnesite may be substituted for many uses where the physical properties, cost, and availability are the deciding factors, but where the chemical neutrality of chromite is required, there is nothing that can replace it.

ORES

The only commercial ore of chromium is chromite, $FeO.Cr_2O_3$, which when pure carries 68 per cent Cr_2O_3 and 32 per cent FeO. As it occurs in nature these constituents have always been partly replaced by others, chiefly alumina (Al_2O_3), ferric oxide (Fe_2O_3), magnesia (MgO), lime (CaO), and silica (SiO_2), bringing the Cr_2O_3 content down to 45–55 per cent, or even lower. For purposes of rough comparison the general average of chromite production may be considered about 45 per cent Cr_2O_3, or 30 per cent metallic chromium. Deposits of chromite are found in numerous countries, although only a few of them are rich enough or large enough to be worked consistently; the more important of these deposits will be discussed briefly in a later section.

At the present time Indian ores are quoted on a basis of 45–47 per cent Cr_2O_3 or 50–51 per cent; Russian ores, 45 per cent and 48 per cent; Rhodesian ores 48 per cent; and New Caledonian 55–57 per cent. Silica is usually limited to 5 per cent, as a high silicon content would be undesirable in ferrochromium when used for the making of many alloys. Other impurities, such as magnesia, alumina and lime, are objectionable chiefly because they increase the slag volume in smelting, and thus complicate and increase the cost of the smelting operation. For the manufacture of ferrochromium, as will be pointed out later, a certain amount of magnesia is desirable.

Domestic ores are low in chromium and high in iron, and, hence, are little in demand except when there is a decided shortage in the supply from other countries.

As is the case with manganese, there are enormous supplies of iron ore carrying small percentages of chromium, particularly in Cuba and Celebes. While these deposits are of no present value as a direct source of chromium, they yield a pig iron to which the chromium content imparts exceptional qualities, and the uses for which are gradually growing. They also provide a large reserve of low grade chromium which future developments may make available as metal.

Beneficiation.—The replacement of the normal constituents of chromite by impurities falls into two definite classes, depending on whether it is the FeO or the Cr_2O_3 that is replaced. The FeO may be replaced by magnesia, or to a lesser extent by lime, while the Cr_2O_3 may be replaced by alumina or ferric oxide, and in addition to these there may be varying amounts of silica present. The combined action of these impurities frequently reduces the normal 68 per cent of Cr_2O_3 to such a point that the ore is useless unless it can be improved by ore-dressing methods.

The response of a chrome ore to beneficiation depends greatly on the character and extent of the impurities present. Purely mechanical impurities, like silica, are fairly readily removed, but as a rule silica is a minor impurity, although cases are known where it runs as high as 10–20 per cent. The impurities received by chemical replacement are more difficult to handle, and if the replacement is uniformly disseminated throughout the body of the ore, little can be done; but if the replacement is not uniform, and has been carried to an extreme in certain portions of the ore and not in others, some separation of the poorer parts may be effected. For example, a complete replacement of the Cr_2O_3 by Fe_2O_3 would give magnetite, which can be removed by magnetic separation; and a complete replacement by Al_2O_3 would give a product responding to gravity concentration.

A moderate replacement of FeO by MgO is an advantage, rather than a disadvantage, in a metallurgical ore, since it improves the Cr:Fe ratio of the ore, and makes it possible to produce a higher grade of ferrochromium.   Since the Cr:Fe ratio desired in the ferrochromium is 2:1 or better, and since there is some loss of chromium in the smelting operation, the ore for metallurgical use should have a Cr:Fe ratio of about 2.5:1.   As the Cr:Fe ratio in pure chromite is about 1.9:1, an ore with some FeO replaced is required for the best grades of metallurgical ore, and the more Cr_2O_3 replacement there has been in the ore, the more FeO replacement is required to offset it, in order to maintain the desired Cr:Fe ratio, particularly if the Cr_2O_3 replacement has been by Fe_2O_3 rather than by Al_2O_3.

Too much iron in the ore not only spoils it for metallurgical use, but also may reduce the normal infusibility to a point where the ore is of no value as a refractory.   The Cr:Fe ratio in refractory ores varies within wide limits, depending on the temperature to be withstood and the particular combination of impurities in the ore, but roughly 2:1 may be set as the upper limit and 1:1 as the lower limit, although the latter is greatly influenced by the fusibility of the impurities present.

While beneficiation may be satisfactorily applied to many low grade ores to bring them within the limits set for the various requirements, no general rules can be laid down, for the response of each ore to concentration methods is determined by the character, extent, and distribution of the impurities, as well as by the methods applied.   Beneficiation was used quite extensively on low grade ores during the war period, especially in the United States and Canada, the treatment usually being confined to crushing and gravity separation.   Due to the intimacy of the mixture of the impurities in most cases of chemical replacement, mechanical separations are limited in their application, and economic considerations have prevented the use of chemical methods of beneficiation such as have been tried out with manganese, but as yet without any very great degree of success.

Another point of considerable importance in the beneficiation problem is the fact that while mechanical methods may improve the Cr_2O_3 content of the ore, they usually increase the iron content in about the same proportion, so that the Cr:Fe ratio is not improved. The chief exception to this rule is found where magnetite can be removed from the ore.

Metallurgy.—The so-called chromium metal of commerce may be produced by the reduction of Cr_2O_3 with carbon in the electric furnace or, if a very low carbon content is desired, by reduction with aluminum in the thermic process. Various chemical methods are possible, but are little used, as they involve the separation of the reduced metal from other products of the reaction, and the fusion of the chromium. Pure chromium is produced only by electrodeposition of the metal from a solution of a chromium salt, and is not available except as a plating on other metals; it has not yet been commercially produced in thicknesses great enough to be stripped from the cathode and marketed, although some work has been done along this line, which may later be developed more fully.

Most of the chromium is placed on the market in the form of ferrochromium, of which the standard grades carry 66–72 per cent chromium, varying percentages of carbon, up to 0.5 per cent manganese, and 2.5 per cent silicon, and the remainder iron, except for small amounts of impurities such as sulfur and phosphorus. Most of this alloy is produced by smelting chromite in the electric furnace with appropriate fluxes, and with carbon as a reducing agent. Since chromium has a high affinity for carbon the product normally carries 4–6 per cent C; if lower percentages are required, as is necessary in the compounding of many alloys, particularly the low-carbon stainless irons and steels, the ferro-alloy is resmelted with an oxidizing slag to remove carbon to the desired extent, or the alloy is produced by the use of aluminum or silicon as a reducing agent in place of carbon. Since the latter is more expensive, the former is the method most used.

Secondary Recovery.—There is no wide-spread public junk-pile recovery of chromium alloys of any kind, such as exists for many of the more important metals, like nickel, lead, copper, and iron, but there is a considerable recovery of used material among the heavier industrial consumers of the metal. The comparatively high value of the metal assures a fairly complete recovery of scrap among manufacturers and fabricators of the alloys, and consumers of any great amount of the alloys, particularly in units of appreciable weight, such as carburizing boxes, cyanide and lead pots, retorts, heavy electrical heating units, furnace equipment, et cetera.   These make a regular practice of returning worn out parts to the makers for credit on the scrap value, which amounts to 10–20 cents per pound, or in some cases more, depending on the composition of the alloy.   There is no information available as to the amounts of metal that are recovered for reuse in this way.

It is quite probable that as the expanding demands for the high chromium steels put more and more metal into everyday use, a more extensive secondary recovery program will be built up, particularly as so many of the chromium alloys also carry large percentages of nickel, which materially increases the value of the scrap.   There is also a possibility of developing a secondary recovery of chromium salts from the solutions used in dyeing and tanning.

In addition to the regular secondary supply, the newer uses of chromium alloys, particularly the more decorative ones, and the more specialized applications, as in cooking utensils, are gradually building up a potential reserve of metal in use that can be drawn on in case some future emergency should demand a shift from non-essential to essential uses.

Forms in Which Chromium Appears on the Market.—The chromium metal regularly quoted in the market carries 96–98 per cent chromium.   It is cast into a slab when produced, and broken into lumps.

Ferrochromium is listed in three grades: 66–70 per cent chromium and 4–6 per cent carbon; 67–72 per cent chromium and 2 per cent carbon; and a maximum of 0.1 per cent carbon.

As already stated above, the ore is listed in various grades, according to the sources from which they are derived.

For refractory use, a special grade of Grecian ore is listed, as are also chromite brick and chromite cement.

Although a wide variety of chromium chemicals are listed by laboratory supply houses, only a few of these are of industrial importance, as mentioned above under chemical uses.   The various chromium pigments are also listed in publications in the paint trade.

ORE RESERVES

Few of the large occurrences of chromite have been examined sufficiently carefully or extensively to form any very definite idea as to the real extent of the reserves, but enough is known to assure plentiful supplies for many years to come. The most extensive reserves are found in Rhodesia, South Africa, and Turkey. A survey of the available data indicates fairly well established reserves amounting to 20,000,000 to 25,000,000 tons of ore, with good indications that deposits as yet only partially developed will eventually add several times this amount. In fact, the South African deposits alone, which are as yet very little developed, and are not included in the above estimate of reserves, as stated to have potential reserves running into hundreds of millions of tons, and the Rhodesian deposits also are very incompletely developed.

It is not the foreign reserves, however, in which we are most concerned, but in the domestic reserves, on which we might have to depend for an emergency supply, as was the case in 1916–1918. These reserves were estimated in 1925 at about 1,250,000 tons; later data have reduced this estimate somewhat, to about a million tons, chiefly in California, Montana, and Alaska, a moderate amount in Oregon, and comparatively small amounts in Washington, Wyoming, Maryland, Pennsylvania, North Carolina, and Georgia. These deposits, mainly those in California, produced 84,000 tons in 1918, and 176,000 tons in 1916–1918, and it is from them that possible future emergency demand must be satisfied, so far as they are able to supply it.

WORLD OUTPUT AND SUPPLY

As nearly as can be ascertained from the data available, the total output of chromite by all producers, from the beginning of the mining records, amounts to approximately 12,525,000 metric tons, of which about 2,400,000 tons or 19 per cent was produced before 1913, and 10,125,000 tons or 81 per cent from 1913 to 1937. It would be difficult to find a more striking means of emphasizing the rate at which chromite output has been expanding than by pointing out that the 2,400,000 tons produced previous to 1913 was surpassed in the 12 years 1913–1924, and was almost equaled in the *two* years 1936–1937. Data on production are presented in Tables I*a* and I*b*, the former covering annual outputs for all producers of more than 1 per cent of the gross total, period totals for each country, and the percentage distribution, while the latter covers the transitions of production through the various subperiods and the critical high and low years. Following the different producing countries through these various stages gives an

TABLE Ia.—WORLD PRODUCTION OF CHROMITE
(Thousands of metric tons)

	Southern Rhodesia	New Caledonia	Russia	Turkey	India	South Africa	Cuba	Yugoslavia	Greece	Japan	United States	Canada	World[2] Total
1913	63	63	15[3]	14[3]	6	....	....	1	7	1	1	....	171
1914	49	42	15[3]	14[3]	6	....	....	1	7	2	1	1	167
1915	62	67[4]	15[3]	14[3]	4	....	....	1	10	3	3	11	181
1916	81	74[4]	15[3]	14[3]	20	....	1	1	10	8	48	25	279
1917	66	42[4]	5	5	27	....	1	2	10	9	44	33	250
1918	28	26[4]	14	14	59	....	9	1	3	6	84	20	287
1919	32	24[4]	4	4	37	....	15	....	4	6	5	8	145
1920	55	92[4]	3	25	27	....	1	1	12	4	3	10	239
1921	46	29[4]	4	10	35	1	1	1	8	3	1	3	141
1922	85	11[4]	1	3	23	1	....	1	9	4	1	1	146
1923	88	23[4]	3	....	55	....	11	1	15	5	1	3	205
1924	157	23	12	3	46	5	20	12	15	5	1	....	291
1925	123	25	30	8	38	14	30	16	8	6	1	....	308
1926	164	34	30	7	34	12	37	9	20	7	1	....	364
1927	198	38	19	18	58	17	17	17	17	10	1	....	410
1928	199	57	22	12	46	32	34	17	21	10	1	....	457
1929	266	53	53	16	50	64	54	43	24	9	1	1	635
1930	206	62	82	28	51	14	42	52	23	11	1	....	574
1931	82	74	87	25	20	23	15	58	6	10	1	....	394
1932	16	69	62	55	18	19	1	44	2	12	....	1	299
1933	35	50	112	75	16	34	24	23	15	20	1	1	409
1934	72	55	131	120	22	45	50	47	31	27	1	1	605
1935	106	55	184	151	40	97	49	52	30	36	1	1	805
1936	183	48	220	164	50	97	71	54	48[4]	38	1	1	992
1937	276	48	?	193	63	169	95	60	54[3]	?	2	4	1,350
Totals	2,738	1,184	1,133	987	851	643	576	491	409	252	192	120	10,104
Per cent	27.1	11.7	11.2	9.8	8.4	6.4	5.7	4.9	4.1	2.5	1.9	1.2	100.0

[1] Less than 500 tons.   [2] Including output of minor producers, averaging 5 per cent of the total.   [3] Estimated.   [4] Exports.   [5] Data not available.

TABLE Ib.—WORLD PRODUCTION OF CHROMITE BY PERIODS

	Average World Output[1]	Percentage Distribution of World Total										
		Southern Rhodesia	New Caledonia	Russia	Turkey	India	South Africa	Cuba	Yugoslavia	Greece	Japan	United States
1913	171	36.8	36.8	8.8	8.2	3.5	—	—	0.0	4.1	0.6	0.0
1914–18	233	25.0	21.6	6.4	6.0	10.0	—	—	0.0	3.4	2.4	15.5
1918	287	9.8	9.1	4.9	4.9	20.5	—	0.1	0.3	1.0	2.1	29.2
1919–21	175	25.3	27.6	2.1	1.9	18.8	0.2	3.1	0.2	4.6	2.5	1.5
1921	141	32.6	20.6	2.8	7.1	24.8	0.7	3.2	0.0	5.7	2.1	0.0
1922–29	365	43.9	9.1	5.8	2.3	12.0	4.9	0.7	3.3	4.4	1.9	0.1
1929	635	41.9	8.4	8.4	2.5	7.9	10.1	7.0	6.8	3.8	1.4	0.0
1930–32	422	24.0	16.2	18.2	8.5	7.0	4.4	4.6	12.1	2.4	2.6	0.1
1932	299	5.3	23.1	20.7	18.4	7.0	6.4	0.3	14.7	0.7	4.0	0.0
1933–37	832	16.1	6.2	21	16.9	4.6	10.6	6.9	5.7	1.9	3.4	0.1
1937	1,350	20.4	3.6	?	14.3	4.7	12.5	7.0	4.4	4.0	?	0.1
Mining dates from	—	1906	1875	?	1860	1903	1921	1916	1925	1881	?	1827
Total to 1912	2,400	8	25	17	27	2	—	—	—	5	?	12

Note.—A dash indicates no production; zeros only, an amount less than 0.1 per cent.   [1] Thousands of metric tons.

interesting picture of the response of the producing facilities to current demand. Figure 6 presents graphically the growth of chromite production, and its relationship to steel production. Recent expansion in the demand for chromite has raised the output to a level of one tone for each 100 tons of steel output, while in 1913 this ratio was one ton for each 445 tons of steel output.

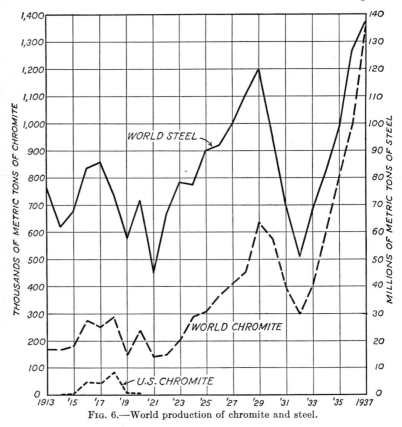

FIG. 6.—World production of chromite and steel.

Canada.—Chromite deposits are known in Quebec, Ontario and British Columbia, most of the production having come from those in Quebec. Only during the war period was the Canadian output of importance, amounting then to 10 per cent of the world total, with a maximum of 33,000 metric tons in 1917; a minor production was maintained from 1886 to 1911, and later, from 1914 to 1923 the war period output was built up and then died

away.   A deposit in Ontario is now being worked on a small scale
and a still smaller one in Quebec.

Cuba.—A small output of chromite was developed in Cuba during the war period, and was then discontinued, but in 1923 active
operations were begun again, with a gradual increase in output to
54,000 metric tons or 8 per cent of the world total in 1929.   Later,
during the depression, production declined, and almost ceased in
1932, but reached 95,000 tons in 1937 or 7 per cent of the world
total.   Production to date has been 576,000 tons.

The chief Cuban deposits are in Camaguey Province, with less
important ones in Oriente and Matanzas.   The ore is of low grade,
33–43 per cent Cr_2O_3.   In addition to the chromite output there
are extensive deposits of iron ore carrying small percentages of
chromium and nickel, which, while not recoverable separately,
appear in the pig iron reduced from the ore, with corresponding
improvement in the quality of the ore.

Greece.—Although one of the older producers, Greece has
never had a large output, its proportion of the world total usually
ranging from 3 to 6 per cent, but in 1932 it dropped to less than
1 per cent.   The output was 24,000 metric tons in 1929 increasing
to 54,000 tons in 1937.   The deposits lie mostly along the eastern
coast, approximately in a line with the Serbian deposits to the
north.   Although there are numerous small and scattered deposits, the main output is from two mines in Thessaly.   The ore is
only of moderate grade, much of it running 38–42 per cent Cr_2O_3,
and is used mostly for refractories.   Production to date is about
533,000 metric tons.

India.—Chromite production in India was only a few thousand
tons a year until the war period, increasing to 59,000 metric tons,
or over 20 per cent of the world total, in 1918, and averaging 13
per cent of the total during 1917–1918.   This increased to 27 per
cent in 1921, when India was the second largest producer, but
dropped to 8 per cent in 1929 and 6 per cent in 1932, and 5 per
cent in 1937, as other producers increased their outputs.

The principal deposits are in Mysore, most of the ore averaging
52–53 per cent Cr_2O_3.   Smaller deposits in Baluchistan yield ore
of 50 per cent grade or better, and still smaller ones are worked
in Bihar and Orissa.   There is little local consumption, and practically the entire output is exported to Europe and the United
States, mostly through Indian ports, with smaller amounts

through Mormugao, in Portuguese India.   Total production to date has been about 810,000 metric tons.

Japan.—Chromite production began in Japan in 1907, gradually increasing to 38,000 metric tons in 1936.   The output has never been large enough to be of importance in the world market, and is of interest chiefly because it is sufficient to make local consumption practically independent of foreign supplies.

New Caledonia.—Chromite production began in New Caledonia about 1875, and, with that of Turkey, and to a lesser extent Russia, furnished the greater part of the world supply until development was started in Rhodesia.   New Caledonia supplied 25 per cent of the total output recorded up to 1912, and 12 per cent during 1913–1937.   In 1913 the New Caledonian percentage reached 37 per cent, and in 1914 was 43 per cent, but due largely to the remoteness of the source and the consequent transportation difficulties, production declined during the war period.   Even after the post-war depression it did not show much recovery until 1925, except for a brief boom to 40 per cent in 1920.   In the meantime, the expansion of the demand had increased outputs in other countries, particularly Rhodesia, to such an extent that even though the New Caledonian figures materially improved, the 1929 output was only 8 per cent of the world total, against 20 per cent in 1921, 19 per cent during the war, and 37 per cent in 1913. New Caledonia was almost the only producer to show a marked improvement in output after 1929, and this continued increase and the simultaneous decreases in other countries brought the 1932 proportion up to 23 per cent, but this was followed by a decline to 12 per cent in 1933 and 4 per cent in 1937, when most of the other producers were showing increases.

The ores range from 42 to 57 per cent Cr_2O_3, and the higher grades furnish most of the world's supply of ore for chemical uses. Total production to date is about 1,826,000 metric tons.

South Africa.—Beginning in 1924 South Africa built up an output of 64,000 metric tons by 1929, or 10 per cent of the world total, but declined to 14,000 tons in 1930, surpassing the former figure in 1934 and increasing to 169,000 tons in 1937.   Since 1934 South Africa has ranked as the fourth largest producer.   Practically the entire output is from Transvaal, and averages about 43 per cent Cr_2O_3.   A small tonnage of 56 per cent ore is produced in Natal.   Extensive reserves indicate that in the future South

Africa will likely be a strong competitor of its neighbor Rhodesia in the world markets. Production to date has been 641,000 metric tons.

Southern Rhodesia.—Chromite production in Rhodesia began in 1906, and by 1909 had reached second place in the list, with 23,000 metric tons against 39,000 tons in New Caledonia; in 1910 the two were about on a par, and in 1911 Rhodesia took the position of leading producer, with an output that increased rapidly, reaching 63,000 tons in 1913, or 37 per cent of the world total. Since then Rhodesia has held first place in most years, but it was not until the recovery following the post-war depression that the gap between the two became so large, due to rapid expansion on the part of Rhodesia, while recovery in New Caledonia was slow, not reaching the war-period level until 1928, by which time Rhodesia had risen to 48 per cent of the world total. During the war period the Rhodesian output decreased materially, and with a generally increasing output elsewhere, Rhodesia's share for this period dropped to 21 per cent, with a minimum of 10 per cent in 1918. The reaction to the 1930 depression was also very pronounced; although the output dropped from 266,000 tons in 1929 to 82,000 tons in 1931, this was still the leading figure, but in 1932 Rhodesia dropped to seventh place, with only 16,000 tons, or 5 per cent of the total. Reaction to the recovery was evident in 1933, the output being 35,000 tons, or 10 per cent of the total. Subsequent recovery resulted in a new high record of 276,000 tons in 1937.

The chromite deposits of Southern Rhodesia lie on or near the Great Dyke, an outcrop of basic rock about 4 miles wide and stretching across the central part of the country for a distance of 330 miles in a southwest-northeast direction. The bulk of the output is from the vicinity of Gwelo and Victoria, near the southern end of the dyke, with a comparatively small amount from the region of Lomagundi and Hartley, in the northern section. There is no local consumption, and the entire output is exported, mostly by rail to the port of Biera, in Portuguese East Africa, and thence by boat. Published analyses of Rhodesian ores show a composition ranging from 45 to 55 per cent Cr_2O_3. Total production to the end of 1937 was about 2,937,000 metric tons.

Turkey.—With production dating back to 1860, Turkey was for many years the leading producer, and furnished 27 per cent of the world supply up to the year 1912, although during the later years New Caledonia and Rhodesia were gradually forging ahead; the results of this transition are shown in the 10 per cent of the total output furnished by Turkey during 1913–1937, and it was not until within the last few years that operations again became active. Turkey's proportion of the total output increased from 3 per cent in 1929 to 18 per cent in 1932 and 1933, and 20 per cent in 1934; subsequent years showed a decline to 14 per cent in 1937, in spite of heavy increases in output, since other producers were expanding at an even greater rate.

The ore deposits are rather widely scattered over Asia Minor, especially in the north, near the Sea of Marmora, and in the south, along the Mediterranean coast, with a few scattered deposits in outlying districts. Most of the current development is in the first named group. Several mines furnish ore with 50–52 per cent Cr_2O_3, while others range from 43 to 50 per cent. Production to date is estimated at 1,668,000 metric tons.

Russia (U. S. S. R.).—Although the leading producer of chromite in 1907, Russia was superseded by New Caledonia and Rhodesia, and after the collapse of the Czarist government the output was only nominal for a number of years. The first year to show an important tonnage was 1925, and while there was a decline in 1927 and 1928, the output has since increased to 220,000 tons in 1936. Consistent with the current Soviet policy of expanded mineral production, which ignored declining outputs in other countries, Russia increased her share of the world total from 8 per cent in 1929 to 22 per cent in 1932 and 1937, declining to 19 per cent in 1933, not from any decrease on her own part, but only because of the partial recovery in other countries, with consequent increases in their outputs.

The leading deposits are in the Urals, but smaller occurrences are known, and have been worked to a limited extent, in other regions, particularly Orenburg, Bashkirian, and Kazaksky. The concentrates produced range from 42 to 48 per cent Cr_2O_3. Russia probably has the largest domestic consumption of any important chromite producer; about half of the output is used in the production of ferrochromium at Cheliabinsk and in chromium chemicals at Shaitansky, and the remainder is exported. Production to 1936 has totaled about 1,537 metric tons.

United States.—Chromite was discovered in Maryland in 1810 and mining was begun near Jarrotsville in 1827, for use in the manufacture of yellow and green paint pigments. Later, other deposits were discovered, and although the production was small as compared with present-day standards, the United States became the world's leading producer, and continued to hold the lead until the Turkish deposits were developed. The output then gradually declined, and ceased entirely in 1897; in 1900 production was renewed, but remained on a small scale until the war period. In 1918, the year of maximum output, mine production was 127,000 metric tons, of which only 84,000 tons was shipped, the excess remaining in stock at the mines.

Up to 1912 it is estimated that the United States had produced 12 per cent of the total recorded output, but since then the proportion has been only 2 per cent, nearly all of which was during 1916–1918, when the United States output was 20 per cent of the total. Total production to date has been 290,000 metric tons.

The bulk of the later production has been from California. The deposits are small and widely scattered, and most of them can be worked only when the product commands an exceptionally high price, which accounts for the small output in normal times. The small size of the individual deposits and their scattered character can be judged from the fact that the 1918 shipments were contributed by 450 shippers, distributed as follows: California 374, Oregon 60, North Carolina 5, Montana 3, Pennsylvania-Maryland 3, Alaska 3, Georgia 1, Wyoming 1, and Washington 1. The ore varied widely in grade, from as low as 20 per cent to as high as 55 per cent; of the total mine output about one-quarter was better than 45 per cent, one-half ranked between 35 and 45 per cent, and one-quarter contained less than 35 per cent. The average of the 1918 shipments was 42 per cent.

Yugoslavia.—While there was a minor pre-war output of 200 to 500 tons of chromite in Bosnia, production from the territory now included in Yugoslavia did not become important until 1925, increasing by 1929 to 43,000 metric tons, or 7 per cent of the world total, and to a maximum of 60,000 tons in 1937.

In addition to the deposits formerly worked in Bosnia, mostly in the Dubostica Valley about 25 miles north of Sarajevo, there are a series of deposits extending from Uzice and Čačak southward

along the Kapaonik Mountains through central and southern
Serbia, and across the Macedonian border into Greece.

Other Countries.—The occurrence of chromite has been
reported in numerous other countries, widely scattered over the
world, and a small amount of production has been made at various
times from a number of these, some with a fair degree of regularity.
Among the localities in this list are Algeria, Argentina, *Australia*,
Borneo, *Brazil*, Celebes, Ceylon, Chosen, Colombia, *Cyprus*,
Czechoslovakia, Dominican Republic, Egypt, France, Germany, Greenland, *Guatemala*, Indo-China, Italy, Mexico, New-
foundland, New Zealand, *Norway*, Palestine, Persia, *Philippines*,
Portugal, Rumania, *Scotland*, Sierra Leone, Spain, Sweden, Syria,
and Togoland.   The length of this list is quite impressive, but the
outputs that have been made are insignificant in most cases.   The
names given in italics indicate the localities that made the more
important contributions to the supply during the World War
period, and those that have since seemed worthy of consideration
in the event of a future emergency demand.

UNITED STATES OUTPUT AND SUPPLY

Except during the war period domestic production of chromite
has been of negligible proportions, and almost the entire supply
has been imported, mostly in the crude form; imports of chromium
metal, alloys and chemicals are comparatively small, having
reached 1,000 tons of chromium content in only two years.   The
approximate chromite supply of the United States during the
period 1913–1937 is shown in Table II.   A total supply of
65,400 long tons in 1913 increased to 163,200 tons in 1916,
and declined again to the pre-war level in 1919.   With increasing
new uses during the next decade, consumption increased rapidly,
reaching a maximum of 327,200 tons in 1930.   The industrial
depression wiped out most of this increase, the 1932 figures being
practically on a par with those for 1922, but 1937 brought a new
record high of 556,900 tons.

The approximate consumption of chromite in the United
States, as compared with the world output, indicates that the
proportion absorbed has varied during the past twenty years
from one-third to two-thirds of the total output, and for the entire
period 1913–1937 was 45 per cent.   This table also shows that
while this country was able under the pressure of war demand to

develop a production equal to 44 per cent of consumption in 1918, under normal conditions the amount produced was insignificant, for during two-thirds of the period the total production was only about 0.1 per cent of the total consumption.

TABLE II.—AVAILABLE SUPPLY OF CHROMITE IN THE UNITED STATES
(Thousands of long tons)

	Imports		Produc-tion	Avail-able Supply	Percentage of Supply	
	Ore	Alloys[1]			To World Produc-tion	Produced in U. S.
1913	65.2	....	0.2	65.4	39	[2]
1914	74.7	....	0.6	75.3	46	1
1915	76.5	1.2	3.3	81.0	45	4
1916	115.9	0.3	47.0	163.2	60	28
1917	72.1		43.7	115.8	47	37
1918	100.1	....	82.4	182.5	65	44
1919	61.4	1.2	5.1	67.7	47	5
1920	150.3	3.0	2.5	155.8	66	2
1921	81.8	0.9	0.3	83.0	60	[2]
1922	90.1	0.9	0.4	91.4	64	[2]
1923	128.8	3.7	0.2	132.7	66	[2]
1924	118.3	1.0	0.3	119.6	42	[2]
1925	149.7	1.5	0.1	151.3	50	[2]
1926	215.5	1.1	0.1	216.7	60	[2]
1927	222.4	0.4	0.2	223.0	55	[2]
1928	216.6	1.6	0.7	218.9	49	[2]
1929	317.6	1.9	0.3	319.8	51	[2]
1930	326.6	0.5	0.1	327.2	60	[2]
1931	212.5	0.3	0.3	213.1	55	[2]
1932	89.1	0.4	0.2	89.7	30	[2]
1933	116.5	0.5	0.8	117.8	29	[2]
1934	192.3	0.3	0.4	193.0	32	[2]
1935	259.1	0.2	0.5	259.8	33	[2]
1936	324.3	0.4	0.3	325.0	33	[2]
1937	553.9	0.7	2.3	556.9	42	[2]

[1] Approximate ore equivalent of imports in metal and alloys.   [2] Less than 0.5 per cent.

About 96 per cent of the consumption for the entire period, and practically the entire consumption outside of the war period, has been imported, and the sources which have supplied important amounts are shown in Table III, so far as they can be obtained from the various sources. The official statistics on imports show the port of shipment from which imports are received, and not the country of origin, so that strictly accurate distribution of imports by sources can not be made. Most of the Rhodesian shipments are made through Portuguese East Africa, and in the table all shipments received from this source are attributed to Rhodesia. This does not take into consideration Rhodesian ore exported through some other country, or the possibility that some small portion of the exports may actually have originated in Portuguese territory. Likewise, all shipments received from Australia have been attributed to New Caledonia, although a small amount may have been of true Australian origin. Most of the Yugoslavian exports are shipped from Grecian ports, so that the imports from Greece include those from Yugoslavia. Since production in South Africa did not reach significant proportions until 1924, and did not equal the imports received from South African ports until 1928, it is evident that most of the imports from this country in the earlier years must have originated elsewhere, presumably in Rhodesia.

The fluctuations in the supply from the various sources may be traced readily in Table III. The outstanding features are the predominant position of Rhodesia, and its gradually increasing proportion of the supply up to the past three years; the marked decline on the part of New Caledonia to a minimum in 1925, followed by a partial recovery; and the increasing number of sources of supply. In 1913 Rhodesia and New Caledonia furnished 80 per cent of the United States supply, and only two other countries appeared on the list with appreciable amounts; in 1930, the year of maximum imports, Rhodesia and New Caledonia furnished 55 per cent, and six other countries supplied amounts in excess of 1,000 tons; in 1933 Rhodesia and New Caledonia supplied only 23 per cent, while Turkey reached 24 per cent, Cuba 20 per cent, Greece and Yugoslavia 13 per cent, Russia 11 per cent, and four others appeared on the list with smaller amounts. In 1922 Rhodesia dropped from first place in the list, and in 1933 was exceeded by four other countries, although this is presumably a temporary position that will be remedied as industrial recovery proceeds. However, to regain the former position of supplying half to two-thirds of the United States supply will not be so easy with a dozen producers competing for the market as it was when only three or four had to be taken into consideration.

Imports.—The distribution of chromite imports by producing countries since 1913 is shown in Table III. From time to time there has been considerable shifting from one source to another, but in the main Rhodesia has held the lead, followed by New Caledonia, Cuba, and South Africa.

Table IV gives the distribution of the imports received in 1937 according to the ports of entry at which the material was received.

TABLE III.—IMPORTS OF CHROMITE INTO THE UNITED STATES
(Thousands of long tons)

Year	Rhodesia[1]	New Caledonia	Cuba	South Africa[1]	Greece	India	Turkey	Canada	Russia	Philippines	Brazil	Guatemala	Total[3]
1913	30	22			5		9						65
1914	23	31			8		12	1					75
1915	11	28	[2]	23	4			10					76
1916	39	34	[2]	23	8			12					116
1917	38	10	9	25				19				[2]	72
1918	8	42	14	1				21			18	1	100
1919	4	20	1	[2]	5	5	4	9			5	2	61
1920	11	57	1	39	8	1	13	8			4	1	150
1921		35		23	9	13	6	8					82
1922	11	12	10	41	11	29	3	1					90
1923		7	8	52	13	7		3					129
1924	63	4	30	22	13	8						[2]	118
1925	78	2	36	18	21	4							150
1926	113	11	17	18	23	14					2		215
1927	150	12	34	7	17	14					1		222
1928	116	15	53	16	27	18	[2]						217
1929	167	27	41	18	46	21	2		14		[2]		318
1930	148	31	14	24	29	15	3		18		2		327
1931	70	40		5	16	9	2		5			[2]	213
1932	15	12	24		11	8	18		13			[2]	89
1933	12	15	49	1	23	4	28		20			2	117
1934[4]	48	20	48	1	21	[2]	29	[2]	3	1	2	1	192
1935[4]	73	56	70	19	27	15	16	[2]	2	5			259
1936[4]	78	65	93	42	25	15	19	[2]		44			324
1937[4]	207	52		70		24	39	[2]					554
Totals	1,513	660	552	468	370	220	203	92	75	50	30	7	4,331
Per cent	35.0	15.2	12.7	10.8	8.5	5.1	4.7	2.1	1.7	1.2	0.7	0.2	100.0

[1] Exact division of imports from Rhodesia and South Africa somewhat uncertain. [2] Less than 500 tons. [3] Includes minor sources not listed.
[4] Imports for consumption; preceding years, general imports.

While omitting some of the minor sources and ports of entry, the table covers 99 per cent of the imports for the year, 43 per cent being received at Philadelphia, 32 per cent at Baltimore, and 20 per cent at New York.

TABLE IV.—DISTRIBUTION OF CHROMITE IMPORTS IN 1937
(Thousands of long tons)

	New York	Phila- delphia	Balti- more	Norfolk	Mobile	Total
Rhodesia	81	54	51	17	....	203
Cuba	....	72	21	....	....	93
South Africa	18	5	48	....	1	72
New Caledonia	....	41	8	....	....	49
Philippines	1	35	6	....	....	42
Turkey	3	9	28	....	....	40
Greece	....	11	15	....	....	26
India	7	14	3	....	....	24
Total	110	241	180	17	1	549

PRICES

The market for chromite is not sufficiently important to justify the compilation of monthly and annual average prices, and the only means of following the market is through the running trend of the current quotations, and the average values of the total annual output. In 1913 and 1914 the price of 50 per cent imported ore was $14–$16 per long ton, cost including freight Atlantic ports. By the end of 1914 transportation difficulties were making themselves felt, and during 1915 the price reached $25–$35. Shortage of supply, increased prices, and difficulties in importation stimulated domestic production to 3,300 tons, and in 1916 and 1917 to more than 40,000 tons. Due to wide variations in the grade of the domestic ore (from 25 to 55 per cent), and the ability of the seller to command a good price, domestic prices fluctuated rather widely—from $11 to $18 for 40 per cent ore, with a premium of 50 cents for each 1 per cent above 40, equivalent to a top price of $23 for 50 per cent ore. In 1916 prices continued to climb, to $25 for 50 per cent domestic ore, and to $35–$45 for imported ore. Since the trans-continental freight on California ore amounted to nearly $15, the two sources were about on a par at the eastern seaboard.

About this time, due to the variations in grade in the domestic ore, prices began to shift over from a flat price per ton, first to a premium or penalty for variations above or below an average grade of 40 per cent, and then to the "unit" system of quotation, the unit being 1 per cent of the long ton, or 22.4 pounds of Cr_2O_3. This system is highly suitable for the pricing of any material with wide variations in grade, by establishing a sliding scale of prices, increasing with the increasing grade of the ore; for example, 50 cents per unit for 40 per cent ore is $20 per ton, and 60 cents per unit for 50 per cent ore is $30 per ton.

During 1917 the price situation became highly disorganized. The generally increasing trend in prices, resulting from shortage of supply and growing demand, was complicated by the great distances between producer and consumer, lack of coördination between a large number of domestic producers, unrestrained competition between buyers, shortage of shipping facilities, speculative activities on the part of irresponsibility brokers, and the willingness of the consumer needing a small amount in a hurry to pay a high price in order to get it. As a result, prices ranged from 50 cents to $1 per unit for 40 per cent domestic ore. This top price was equivalent to about $60–$65 per ton for imported 50 per cent ore.

In order further to increase the domestic output, early in 1918 a price of $1.25 per unit was offered for 40 per cent ore, and at mid-year a sliding scale of prices was established, ranging from 85 cents per unit for 30 per cent ore to $1.50 per unit for 48 per cent ore, or $25.50 to $72 per ton. This was equivalent to $90–$95 per ton for imported ore. With the close of the war, late in 1918, prices dropped, but not as much as might be expected under the circumstances, and there was still a great deal of uncertainty in the market, so that as late as 1920 prices varied over as wide a range as 60 cents to $1.25 per unit for imported ore. In 1921 domestic production practically ceased, and accumulated stocks having been cleared up fairly well, prices settled down, to 55–65 cents per unit. With the low-grade domestic ores no longer a factor in the market, the unit system was dropped, and 1922 quotations ranged from $20 to $28 per ton for imported ore, and from then on until 1930 did not vary greatly from $19.50–$22.50 for 46–48 per cent ores, and $24–$28 for the higher grades. Since 1930 there has been a rather steady decline, and recent prices range from $16 to $22 for the different grades, in 1936, rising to $20–$26 in 1937.

Of the chromium products, ferrochromium is by far the most important. The earliest published quotations available are for 1921, when the price for alloy carrying 65–70 per cent chromium and 4–6 per cent carbon was 17–18 cents per pound of contained chromium; this shortly dropped to 12 cents, then to 11 cents, and in 1933 stood at $9\frac{1}{2}$ cents rising to $10\frac{1}{2}$ cents in 1937. Alloy with 67–72 per cent chromium and not over 2 per cent carbon dropped from 30 cents to $16\frac{1}{2}$ cents per pound of contained chromium, and alloy with not over 0.1 per cent carbon had a similar decline to $19\frac{1}{2}$ cents per pound of contained chromium. Chromium metal, 97 per cent grade, was quoted in 1933 at 88 cents per pound, against 85–90 cents in 1930, when it was first quoted separately, dropping to 80–85 cents in 1937.

A compilation of average prices on chromite from 1913 to 1937, recently prepared by the U. S. Bureau of Mines is presented in Table VII.

TABLE VII.—CHROMITE PRICES IN THE UNITED STATES
(Dollars per long ton)

	Average Quoted Price	Commodity Index	Chromite Price Index
1913	$11.19	100.0	$11.19
1914	14.75	97.6	15.11
1915	11.20	99.6	11.24
1916	15.44	122.5	12.60
1917	24.00	168.3	14.26
1918	44.99	188.1	23.92
1919	17.25	198.6	8.69
1920	17.93	221.2	8.11
1921	10.28	139.8	7.35
1922	22.53	138.5	16.27
1923	19.00	144.1	13.19
1924	21.35	140.5	15.20
1925	21.92	148.3	14.78
1926	22.46	143.3	15.67
1927	22.88	136.7	16.74
1928	23.00	138.5	16.61
1929	22.00	136.5	16.12
1930	21.50	123.8	17.37
1931	22.10	104.8	21.13
1932	19.25	92.8	20.74
1933	18.55	94.4	19.65
1934	20.95	107.3	19.52
1935	19.30	114.6	16.84
1936	19.00	115.8	16.41
1937	24.00	123.6	19.42

TARIFF

Chromite was subject to a duty of 15 per cent from 1833 to 1894, and since then has remained on the free list. New legislation was introduced late in 1919, in order to protect the domestic industry, proposing a duty of 60 cents per unit of Cr_2O_3 on imported ore, 65 cents per unit on chrome brick, 90 cents per unit on chromium chemicals, and $11\frac{1}{2}$ cents per pound on ferrochromium, but in view of the patent unfeasibility of maintaining an appreciable domestic output, this never became a law. The tariff rates covering various chromium products, as specified in the three different tariff laws that have been in force since 1913, are shown in Table VIII.

TABLE VIII.—TARIFF RATES ON CHROMIUM

	1913–1922	1922–1930	1930—
Chrome brick..........................	10 %	25 %	25 %
Ferrochromium, over 3 % C..............	15 %	3½c./lb. Cr	2½c./lb. Cr
Ferrochromium, less than 3 % C..........	15 %	30 %	30 %
Iron and steel, Cr content in excess of 0.2 %..	Free	Free	3c./lb. Cr + 8 %
Chromium metal.......................	15 %	30 %	30 %
Chromium alloys and carbides............	15 %	25 %	25 %
Chromic acid..........................	Free	Free	25 %
Chromium pigments.....................	20 %	25 %	25 %
Potassium chromates and dichromates......	1c./lb.	2¼c./lb.	2¼c./lb.
Sodium chromates and dichromates........	¾c./lb.	1¾c./lb.	1¾c./lb.
Chromium chloride and sulfate............	25 %	25 %	25 %

POLITICAL AND COMMERCIAL CONTROL

The sometimes conflicting interests of political and commercial control have not played any outstanding part in the history of the chromite industry, as it did in the case of nickel. According to the distribution of the output as reported by the Mineral Inquiry of the American Institute of Mining and Metallurgical Engineers, about two-thirds of the peak output of 1929 was produced by British companies, and one-sixth by United States companies. The participation of United States capital as thus shown, however, is considerably less than it should be, owing to the fact that there are extensive holdings by United States capital in British-controlled companies in Rhodesia. The Russian output, amounting to 8 per cent of the total, was entirely state controlled. French capital controlled 4 per cent, in Greece, New Caledonia, Turkey, and Yugoslavia; and German capital controlled 3 per cent, in Turkey and Yugoslavia. All of the Japanese and about half of the Grecian output was controlled by local capital, and a small proportion of the Turkish and Yugoslavian was also locally controlled. Of the 66 per cent under British control, 57 per cent was in British territory (Rhodesia, South Africa, India, and Cyprus), while 4 per cent was in New Caledonia and 5 per cent in Yugoslavia. United States capital controlled the small domestic output, all of the Cuban, 4 per cent in New Caledonia, and 3 per cent in Rhodesia, in addition to participation in British-controlled companies in that country.

All told, 69 per cent of the total output was under the control of home capital, and 31 per cent under foreign capital. British capital leads the field in the control of production within its own territory, with control of 57 per cent out of 60 per cent of the total, while United States capital leads in the control of production in outside territory. Table IX gives the approximate distribution of control of the 1929 output, in terms of percentage of the total produced or controlled by domestic and foreign capital, supplemented by a comparative distribution of world production in 1937.

TABLE IX.—POLITICAL AND COMMERCIAL CONTROL OF CHROMITE PRODUCTION

	Percentage of World Output		Control					
	1929	1937	Domestic	Foreign	British	United States	French	German
Cuba...............	9	7	....	9	....	9	....	.....
Greece.............	4	4	2	2	....	....	2	.....
India..............	8	5	8	......	8	....	....	.....
Japan..............	1	3	1	......	....	....	....	.....
New Caledonia.......	9	4	1	8	4	4	1	.....
Rhodesia............	42	20	39[2]	39[2]	3	....	....	.....
Russia..............	8	16	8	......	....	....	....	.....
South Africa..........	10	13	10	......	10	....	....	.....
Turkey..............	2	14	[1]	2	....	....	....	2
Yugoslavia..........	7	4	[1]	7	5	....	1	1

[1] Less than 1 per cent.   [2] Disregarding stock held in British companies by United States capital.

GENERAL REVIEW OF DOMESTIC SITUATION

There is a considerable degree of similarity in the possibilities of domestic production of chromite with the corresponding situation in manganese, but at the same time there are marked differences. In both cases there are limited domestic reserves, those of manganese being greater in actual tonnage, but less in proportion to the rate of consumption. In both cases the domestic output during normal times has been insignificant, due to the low grade of the ore, this being particularly true in the case of chromium. In both cases the domestic output during the World War, under the stimulus of abnormally high prices, rose to a material percentage of the consumption, 33 per cent for manganese and 44 per cent for chromium. In both cases the product is used mostly in the steel industry, but more so with manganese than with chromium, since manganese is required in the production of all steels and has comparatively few other uses, while chromium is used only in the production of special types of steel. Other alloys, as well as refractory and chemical uses, absorb considerable amounts. In both cases, while there are many occurrences widely scattered over the earth, only a few of these are sufficiently large or high enough in grade to make them of outstanding commercial importance at the present time, and as a result not only the United States but every other important steel-making country is dependent on outside sources for its supply. And finally, in both cases most of the deposits on which we must depend for a domestic supply are in the western states, far removed from the centers of consumption.

Among the differences between manganese and chromium, the outstanding one is that of the size of the deposits; these are small in the case of manganese, as compared with those of other countries, but with chromium the deposits are extremely small. In 1918 somewhat more than 300,000 tons of manganese ore was supplied by 247 domestic producers, an average of about 1,250 tons each, but the output of 84,000 tons of chromite came from 450 shippers, an average of less than 200 tons each. The small size of the deposits and the comparatively low grade of the ore were recognized as such a heavy handicap on production that no great effort was made to maintain output after the cessation of war prices. But, with manganese, conditions were somewhat better, and repeated efforts were made to keep the industry alive with the help of tariff protection, but chromite remains on the free list. The more varied uses of chromium, as compared with manganese, are in favor of the former, as the diversity of uses widens the range of ore grades that can be satisfactorily used.

The known domestic reserves are estimated at approximately 1,000,000 tons. A million tons in reserve, even when compared with consumptions of 200,000 to 300,000 tons annually, looks like a fairly reliable anchor to windward, but unfortunately there are two serious flaws in the picture. The first is that the ores are so low in grade: the bulk of them runs less than 40 per cent; the average grade of the 1918 output was only 42 per cent; and the 1925 survey listed only 88,000 tons of readily accessible reserves better than 40 per cent. The second difficulty is that the deposits are so small and widely scattered, the listed reserves being distributed in over two thousand different deposits, an average of only 500 tons each.   This necessarily means small and temporary high-cost operation in order to secure a few hundred tons of moderate or low grade ore, and such operations can be carried on only at excessively high prices for the product.   In addition, the low grade of the ore restricts its applicability for many purposes, particularly the most important ones, and the small scale of the operations and the large number of new developments that must be inaugurated and carried on in order to maintain even a moderate supply, will militate heavily against speed in building up the output, and a considerable time will be required in order to build up the maximum output.

All angles of the situation being taken into consideration, it is exceedingly fortunate that the limited domestic chromite reserves have not been depleted by attempts to maintain production on any great scale since the cessation of war demand, as the known reserves are far too small to supply any appreciable current production and leave a sufficient amount as a safeguard against possible emergency demand.

CONCLUSION

In view of the extent and the character of its uses, chromium ranks with manganese and nickel in importance as a strategic material, and with the rapid development that is now being made in the way of new uses, its importance is constantly increasing. World production in 1929 was more than double the war-time peak, was nearly four times the pre-war level, and more than four times the post-war depression level, while the 1937 output was more than double that of 1929.

Such small and inadequate reserves as we are fortunate enough to possess should be left undisturbed, and the entire current demand should be drawn from foreign sources.   The arguments in favor of this attitude are much the same as have already been outlined in a preceding chapter in the discussion of the similar situation in respect to manganese, and need not be repeated here.

No information is available on stocks of chromium carried in the United States, but presumably they have been only such as are normally carried by the various branches of the industry as a safeguard against temporary irregularities in supply and demand. While these stocks may be sufficient for normal conditions, they are not adequate to tide over any extended interruption in supply, complicated by abnormal increases in demand, such as might be caused by war. Since the domestic reserves can not be counted on for more than partial relief, and since local conditions are such that emergency production can not be built up rapidly, the only other recourse is an emergency stock pile of one or two years' prospective requirements, as has been advocated for manganese and nickel. The amount to be stocked should not be set at a certain fixed tonnage, but should be in terms of current consumption requirements, for a tonnage that might today be deemed sufficient to cover a year's demand might not be sufficient for half that time a few years in the future, if the new applications for the metal continue to increase the demand as it now seems possible that they may.

CHAPTER VI

TUNGSTEN

With tungsten we reach the last of the ferro-alloy group of the strategic minerals, that is, those metals used primarily in the steel industry, usually in the form of an alloy with iron. Here again we have conditions very similar to those dealt with in connection with manganese and chromium, but with the marked difference that the domestic tungsten industry has been much more nearly on a self-supporting basis, not only during the war period, but in the preceding and succeeding years as well, except during the immediate post-war years, when prices were so low, and the United States output was not yet under tariff protection. The United States is the only first-rank steel producing country in the world that has tungsten resources within its borders sufficient to satisfy an appreciable amount of its needs. All the other large steel producers must draw on remote sources of supply, while the United States was able during the period 1913–1937 to furnish about one half of its requirements from domestic production and, outside of the four years of post-war depression, when the industry was almost totally disorganized, it has supplied two thirds of its needs—a record which has been outstanding, for only one other strategic mineral product, mercury, has attained a position comparable with this.

REQUIREMENTS

Although most of the tungsten produced is used in the steel industry, the applications are confined to a few special types of alloy steels, in contrast with manganese, which is used in the production of all steels, and with chromium and nickel, which have found their way into a wide variety of alloys, both ferrous and nonferrous. As a result, although the production curve of tungsten follows in a general way that of steel, there is not the same close correlation between the curves.

During the war period the demand for tungsten increased enormously, the output in 1917 being over three times that of 1913,

although the steel output had increased only about 11 per cent, and in 1918 the increase jumped to four times the 1913 figure, although the steel output dropped to less than that of 1913. The abnormal amount of heavy machine work involved in an extensive program of munition manufacture and the desire for plentiful supplies during the emergency accounted for this. With the cessation of war demand, tungsten production decreased rapidly for several years while surplus stocks were being absorbed and in 1921 was back at approximately its pre-war level with respect to the steel output, with about 0.11 pound of tungsten per ton of steel, as against 0.44 pound per ton of steel in 1918. From 1921 to 1929 was a period of constant expansion, with tungsten growing slightly more rapidly than steel, and ending with 0.14 pound per ton of steel made. Production decline was more marked with steel than with tungsten in 1930 and 1931, and the latter rose to 0.21 pound per ton of steel, but in 1932 dropped back to 0.14 pound, increasing again during the recovery period to 0.27 pound in 1937.

The world production graph reproduced herewith, or the figures in Table I, show an output of less than 4,000 metric tons of tungsten metal in 1913 and 1914, growing rapidly with war demand to 15,200 tons in 1918, and dropping just as abruptly at the close of the war to 2,300 tons in 1921; this was followed by a gradual increase to 8,000 tons in 1930, and a drop during the depression to 3,200 tons in 1932, with consistent recovery to a new high record of 16,600 tons in 1937.

USES

Metallurgical uses predominate with tungsten, while the relatively minor chemical uses are largely for laboratory purposes, there being few purely industrial uses for tungsten compounds.

Metallurgical Uses.—The chief use of tungsten is in the production of high speed tool steels, which have the very useful property of retaining their hardness up to a red heat, and can therefore be used at much higher speeds and for heavier cuts than ordinary tool steels. The usual range of composition is 15–20 per cent of tungsten, with smaller amounts of chromium and vanadium; a common analysis is 18 per cent tungsten, 4 chromium, and 1 vanadium. Sometimes molybdenum is used in these steels as a partial substitute for tungsten.

Another type of steel with 4–12 per cent of tungsten and smaller amounts of chromium and manganese gives a self-hardening steel, which can not be softened by any known methods. This type of steel has an unusual degree of hardness, making it suitable for heavy work, but it will not stand the high cutting speeds of the high-speed steels, which are a later development of the self-hardening steels.

An important supplementary use of high tungsten steel is in the manufacture of valves and valve seats for internal combustion engines, where its ability to retain its hardness at high temperatures adds greatly to the life of the valves.

During recent years tungsten has been incorporated in small amounts in a number of complex alloy steels for special purposes, including the stainless steels, and products using some form of tungsten steel include railroad rails, car springs, sounding plates for pianos, grinding rolls, shear blades for cutting hot metals, cold chisels, razor blades, knife blades, files, hacksaws, stamps, drills, watch springs, armor for submarine cable, telephone conductors, transformer cores, electrical resistance wires, and many others.

Among the nonferrous alloys, the best known is the stellite group; these carry 4–15 per cent tungsten, 30 chromium, and 50–65 cobalt, and are used in cutting tools, machine tools, and hard facing to resist abrasion and wear. The hard facing of materials is rapidly growing, and is absorbing a constantly increasing amount of tungsten. Tungsten-cobalt alloys (75–95 per cent W) and manganese-chromium-tungsten alloys are used in wire-drawing dies. A copper-tungsten alloy that does not soften at a red heat is used as an electrode in electric welding equipment. Several different alloys have been developed in which tungsten has been used to harden aluminum for various uses, and numerous other minor applications of nonferrous alloys containing tungsten have been used or proposed.

The most outstanding recent development in the uses of tungsten is the application of tungsten carbide in various forms as a super-hard cutting tool for machine work. This application verges on the chemical, since it requires a compound, rather than the metal, but the use itself is purely metallurgical. The finely ground carbide, sintered into a solid mass with finely powdered cobalt as a binder, or bound together in a fused alloy, forms the hardest known cutting agent with the exception of the diamond.

This tool not only has the ability to stand up under the same speeds as high-speed tool steel, but lasts from 25 to 100 times as long between sharpenings, and in addition will cut glass, porcelain, and other materials which no ordinary tool can touch. A similar use is made of tantalum carbide cemented together with metallic tungsten, and other carbides are being tried out. Tungsten carbide is still moderately costly, even after nearly 15 years of development work, but in spite of this it is finding many applications in industry.

A use of tungsten which affects the average individual even more, however, is in the filaments of electric lights. The actual cost of all the tungsten filaments in the light bulbs in the average home is less than one cent, but they save the householder several times their cost during each and every hour of their entire life. All told the total lamp production of the United States consumes only about 60,000 pounds of tungsten, equivalent to 57 metric tons of 60-per cent concentrates. Although this amounts to only about 1.5 per cent of the average annual consumption, the savings resulting from it probably are in the neighborhood of one half of all savings made by the use of the other 98.5 per cent.

In addition to lamp filaments, the uses of pure tungsten metal include filaments in radio tubes, contact points in many types of electrical apparatus, electrodes in alternating current rectifiers, and targets or cathodes for X-ray tubes.

Chemical Uses.—Sodium tungstate is used in the production of certain types of lakes and mordants, in the making of white leather, in flame-proofing cloth, and in the weighting of fabrics such as silk. Oxides and several other combinations are used as pigment in paint and ceramic work and cadmium tungstate is used in X-ray screens.

Some very interesting developments have been made recently in electroplating with tungsten, but so far as is known no commercial use has as yet been made of the process.

Military Uses.—The most important military uses are the ordinary commercial applications that are involved in the production of military equipment of all kinds. There are, however, several specific military uses that have been proposed. Tungsten alloy steels have been used as a core in small armor-piercing projectiles, and for large caliber projectiles of high penetrating power; in the manufacture of armor plate; as an erosion-resistant liner in heavy ordnance; and an alloy of tungsten and cobalt has been proposed as a material for gun breeches for naval work.

SUBSTITUTES

For many of the uses of tungsten there are more or less satisfactory substitutes, but unfortunately in most cases the emphasis is on the less, rather than the more.   In the ordinary tungsten alloy steels other alloy combinations can be made to serve many purposes, although not always so satisfactorily.   In the high-speed tool steels tungsten may, in case of necessity, be partly replaced by molybdenum, and other alloy combinations have possibilities in limited fields; these latter usually contain uranium, vanadium, or zirconium.   The tungsten-carbide tools are serving as a partial substitute, since in this form a smaller amount of tungsten does the same work as a larger amount in high-speed tool steels; some of the other metals have hard carbides which show possibilities of competing with tungsten in this field, among which are chromium, molybdenum, tantalum, titanium, uranium, vanadium, and zirconium.   Another substitute for the high-speed steels is found in the stellite alloys but again the substitute is only partial, as these alloys contain tungsten, but in considerably less amounts than in the high-speed steels.

For tungsten in electric lights there is no adequate substitute, but in case of necessity we could go back to the carbon filament, but at a considerable increase in power cost; the metals tantalum and osmium also have some possibilities in this direction, both having been in use to some extent at the time of the development of the tungsten filament.

The use of tungsten in contact points in electrical apparatus is in itself largely as a substitute for platinum, as a matter of economy; this leaves the possibility of reversion to platinum if that metal were available in sufficient quantities, but this would not likely be the case, for our supplies of platinum are even less abundant than those of tungsten; otherwise the chief possibility lies in silver, and in a few cases where a fairly large area of contact surface can be provided, graphite may be used.

ORES

The ore situation with respect to tungsten is similar to that of manganese and chromium in that the sources of supply are rather widely distributed, but differs from these, and from nickel as well, in that instead of there being only a single important type of ore, there are several. The most important ore in wolframite, a tungstate of iron and manganese ($FeO.MnO.WO_3$). These same compounds are also found separately, the iron tungstate being known as ferberite, and the manganese tungstate as huebnerite. A fourth ore of a somewhat different character is scheelite, calcium tungstate ($CaO.WO_3$). Only a dozen tungsten minerals are known, and of these only the four named are recovered in commercial quantities.

All of the ores are found in both lode deposits and placers. Although the grade of the lode ores is usually low, frequently less than 1 per cent, the ore is readily amenable to concentration, giving concentrates containing 50–65 per cent WO_3. The WO_3 content of pure ore of the iron-manganese type is 76.3–76.6 per cent, depending on the relative proportions of iron and manganese present, and that of scheelite is 80.6 per cent. The placer ores, having already been subjected to disintegration and partial concentration, are richer, and even more readily concentrated.

The standard grade of concentrates in the United States is 60 per cent WO_3, and in England is 65 per cent. Some of the United States concentrates fail to reach the standard grade, but much of the foreign material not only exceeds this, but some, especially the Chinese, exceed the 65 per cent English standard. The impurities that may be tolerated in the ores depend on the process of reduction to be utilized. In concentrates to be subjected to chemical treatment for the production of tungstic acid or sodium tungstate the ordinary impurities are not particularly troublesome, as they are eliminated in the chemical process. Concentrates for the production of ferrotungsten in the electric furnace should preferably have at least 65 per cent WO_3, and not more than 0.05 per cent of tin, copper, arsenic, antimony, bismuth, phosphorus or sulfur. For reduction by the electrothermic process the highest quality of concentrates is desired, with a minimum of impurities.

Where harmful impurities are present in excessive amounts, it is sometimes necessary to subject the concentrates to special purification processes, as roasting to reduce the arsenic and sulfur, acid treatment to remove phosphorus, or magnetic separation to remove tin, copper, lead, antimony, bismuth, and iron.

During the war period, when the metallurgy of the different ores was not so fully developed, the prices for the various ores differed considerably, scheelite and ferberite ranking about 20 per cent and 10 per cent respectively above wolframite, and huebnerite about 5 per cent below.   Since then improved metallurgical treatment has eliminated most of these differences, and now there is frequently little if any difference in price for the various ores, if they are of the same grade and are equally free from impurities, although for certain uses scheelite still commands a small premium.

Beneficiation.—The very high specific gravity of the tungsten minerals (5.5 to 7.5) makes their concentration a fairly simple problem, as a rule, and also helps in the elimination of harmful impurities, most of which are of considerably lower gravity. The operations involved include hand picking, crushing and screening, followed by concentration on jigs or tables, or both, and such special treatment as is necessary to remove the impurities.

Among the inherent difficulties in the beneficiation of tungsten ores are the excessive losses in recovery from the very low grade ores, which may be as much as 40 per cent with an ore carrying 0.5 per cent WO_3.   There is some prospect that the use of the flotation process of concentration may eventually provide a way out of some of these difficulties.

Metallurgy.—The metallurgy of tungsten centers largely around the more or less pure metal and the alloy ferrotungsten, as all of the metallurgical uses depend on one of these two products for the source of their raw material.

For the production of the pure metal the concentrates are first converted to pure tungstic oxide by chemical means, and then reduced to a metallic powder by heating in an atmosphere of hydrogen.   The various commercial forms are then prepared from this powder by sintering, welding, swaging, wire drawing, rolling, et cetera.   In the earlier days much of the tungsten used in the making of alloy steels was introduced into the steel as metal powder, reduced from the oxide by heating in a crucible with carbon, but this has now been replaced almost entirely by the use of ferrotungsten.   For use in compounding nonferrous alloys, the highest purity is not often required, and for this the carbon reduction method is still used, since it is much cheaper than the hydrogen reduction.

Ferrotungsten is produced in the electric furnace from high grade concentrates with carbon as a reducing agent. Formerly, in order to maintain a low manganese content in the product, the ores used were given the following preference—ferberite, wolframite, huebnerite—but this prejudice has been swept away with the development of improved methods of slagging off the manganese in the furnace. Scheelite is not used, since it contains no iron for the ferro-alloy, and huebnerite will not be used alone because of the insufficiency of iron, but may be mixed in the charge with ferberite. The standard ferrotungsten contains 75–80 per cent of tungsten, and may carry from 0.5 to 3 per cent carbon; in some cases the product must be given a refining smelting to reduce the carbon and phosphorus content. Previous to the introduction of the electric furnace, ferrotungsten was reduced in crucibles with carbon, using either concentrates or tungstic oxide. It is possible to produce ferrotungsten by the thermic process, using aluminum or silicon as a reducing agent; this gives a product of higher purity, and with no carbon, but is apparently little used, probably due to the higher cost.

In the production of low tungsten steels, the tungsten is frequently introduced into the charge directly in the furnace in the form of concentrates, the tungsten going into the steel, and the accompanying base being slagged off. The calcium base of scheelite is slagged off the most readily, so this ore is usually preferred for this purpose, and it is this application that is largely responsible for the premium in the price of scheelite over the other ores. Some ferberite is also used in the same way, but the manganese content of wolframite and huebnerite is more difficult to slag off, and these ores are not used.

Secondary Recovery.—So far as the general public is concerned there is little opportunity for secondary recovery, for the tungsten that reaches the hands of the individual consumer is too small in aggregate amount for profitable recovery, even if the material were of a size and condition that were favorable to recovery. Secondary recovery goes little beyond such saving of scrap and waste as can be made by manufacturers and the larger users, but since the scrap in some manufacturing operations is large, the aggregate amount returned for re-use is a considerable percentage of the total supply.

Forms in Which Tungsten Appears on the Market.—Tungsten metal may be purchased in the pure form as powder, or consolidated into billets, slugs, wire, rod, sheets, et cetera. The crude 98 per cent powder is sold for the compounding of nonferrous alloys but is now little used for the manufacture of alloy steels.

Ferrotungsten is listed at 75–80 per cent W in the United States, and 80–85 per cent in England, where the standard ore grade is 65 per cent, as against 60 per cent in this country.

Due to the direct use of ores for steel production, particularly scheelite and ferberite, the ores are quoted for the consumer, as well as for the smelter.

The latest addition to the list of tungsten products on the market is tungsten carbide. This is sold as granular powder and in the form of finished tools and as blanks, under a wide variety of trade names, the different brands varying somewhat in the methods used to unite the powder into a coherent mass.

In the chemical field the chief products listed are sodium tungstate and tungstic oxide.

ORE RESERVES

Little is known of the extent of the ore reserves in most of the producing countries. This is particularly true of China, the leading producer, but the continued maintenance of a high percentage of the world output seems to indicate plentiful supplies still available and the discovery of several new deposits has recently been reported. In adjacent sections of the Orient, where the production of tungsten is largely as a byproduct in tin mining, the output is naturally dependent on the demand for tin. In general, available reserves seem sufficient to cover probable demand for many years to come and, while production has declined in many countries, this is, in most cases, due not so much to the exhaustion of the reserves as to the fact that the ores can not be worked profitably at prevailing prices in competition with the cheap Chinese supplies but will remain in the ground for future utilization at any time when the price rises to the proper level.

Little more specific information is available as to reserves in the United States than in foreign countries. More is known about the character and extent of the individual deposits, but the information seldom extends to statements of ore blocked out in reserves. Indications seem to point to sufficient reserves to maintain a fairly extensive domestic industry for a reasonable time, if the price is high enough to meet the cost of production. Estimates of the producing situation at the close of the World War indicated the probability that, had the demand kept up, both the 1918 and 1919 outputs could have been made to exceed that of the preceding year.

The 1936 report of the National Resources Committee places known reserves at 25,000,000 pounds of metal in the Nevada-Massachusetts mines (Nevada), 1,115,000 pounds in the Boriana mine (Arizona), and 540,000 pounds in the Atolia mine (California), a total of 26,655,000 pounds.

WORLD OUTPUT AND SUPPLY

The production of tungsten on anything like a commercial scale did not begin until after the development of high-speed tool steels started an active demand for the metal about 1900, so that the industry had only 14 years of real growth before the opening of the World War, with its resultant heavy increase in demand. From an output of some 500 tons a year in the nineties it grew under the stimulus of the new steel to 3,650 tons in 1905, to 6,900 tons in 1910, and then to 8,100 tons in 1913, when our more detailed survey of the industry begins. During this earlier period Spain, Australia, United States, Portugal and Burma had in turn been important producers. The war demand brought China in as a producer in 1914, and in spite of the extensive developments in the older fields, pushed the newcomer into the front rank in 1918, a position which has been held ever since, except for 1919, and Burma has just as persistently been found in second place.

Table I*a* shows the annual output of all countries that have during the 1913–1937 period contributed as much as 1 per cent of the total output, the annual totals, the period totals for each country, and the percentage of the total output for the period that has been supplied by each country.

Although the general disturbance to all kinds of industry during the early months of the war resulted in a small decrease in output in 1914, this was followed by feverish activity in all tungsten-producing countries during the remainder of the war. Production having been pushed to a point where it exceeded even

TABLE Ia.—WORLD PRODUCTION OF TUNGSTEN CONCENTRATES
(Metric tons, containing 60 per cent WO₃)

	China	Burma (India)	United States	Bolivia	Malaya	Portugal	Japan[2]	Australia	Argentina	Indo-China	Spain	Siam	Great Britain	Total[1]	Tungsten Content
1913	....	1,572	1,394	297	362	1,126	257	848	575	127	169	280	197	8,123	3,860
1914	18	2,166	898	290	460	667	204	724	437	162	135	273	222	7,427	3,530
1915	35	2,464	2,116	859	488	953	456	889	169	333	189	432	360	10,866	5,170
1916	109	3,510	5,373	3,228	841	1,418	1,285	1,052	854	343	425	530	407	21,046	10,210
1917	1,361	4,294	5,574	4,215	1,171	1,580	1,682	1,306	1,085	433	446	726	255	25,819	12,290
1918	10,577	4,182	4,591	3,703	1,547	1,150	1,729	1,367	614	378	534	231	307	31,942	15,190
1919	2,654	3,624	297	2,161	1,288	706	771	1,249	204	284	302	258	177	14,744	7,020
1920	4,712	2,983	196	766	553	237	175	624	182	284	57	137	83	11,494	5,370
1921	2,657	673		174	72	306	....	17	52	452	25	76	81	4,336	2,300
1922	3,873	1,038		9	362	527	14	44	125	112		.....	3	6,221	2,960
1923	4,554	960	219		434	289	....	119	144	129	9	.....	2	6,053	3,310
1924	3,398	814	513		321	304	....	75	137	150	161	.....	2	6,159	2,930
1925	6,708	849	1,080	82	425	207	....	220	4	189	26	.....	20	10,051	4,780
1926	7,989	1,634	1,254	109	333	358	19	99	11	92	123	10	12	12,231	5,820
1927	5,666	1,277	1,056	79	192	174	54	179	10	213	164	8	12	9,282	4,420
1928	8,283	843	1,096	29	144	151	215	238	24	211	158	.....	95	11,648	5,540
1929	9,978	1,484	753	1,630	513	358	76	248	63	198	257	62	27	15,800	7,520
1930	9,454	2,699	637	888	1,232	499	94	241	98	220	254	7	153	16,700	7,940
1931	7,492	2,474	1,274	410	703	274	73	94	20	248	135	12	121	13,400	6,370
1932	2,249	2,226	359	686	553	272	84	50	6	247	43	.....	6	6,800	3,230
1933	6,000	3,056	812	240	1,279	358	175	150	....	250	46	....	12	12,400	5,890
1934	5,099	3,913	1,859	794	2,011	610	469	419	392	300	49	36	223	16,450	7,820
1935	7,998	4,527	2,173	1,423	2,035	1,140	1,045	491	579	417	?	82	256	22,500	10,800
1936	7,638	5,299	2,370	1,741	2,037	1,379	1,910	426	702	503	?	82	221	24,800	11,900
1937	16,257	5,415	3,175	1,802	1,234	1,948	?	763	731	647	?	?	140	34,800	16,600
Totals	134,159	63,976	39,067	25,605	20,590	16,991	12,600	11,932	7,218	6,922	3,900	3,300	3,395	362,600	173,600
Per cent	37.0	17.4	10.8	7.0	5.7	4.7	3.5	3.3	2.0	1.9	1.1	0.9	0.9	100.0	......

[1] Includes minor outputs from countries not listed.　　[2] Includes Chosen.

TABLE I*b*.—WORLD PRODUCTION OF TUNGSTEN BY PERIODS
(Thousands of metric tons, containing 60 per cent WO_3)

	Average World Output	Percentage Distribution of World Total									
		China	Burma (India)	United States	Bolivia	Malaya	Portugal	Japan	Australia	Argen-tina	Indo-China
1913	8.1	—	19.3	17.2	3.7	4.5	13.9	3.2	10.4	7.1	3.3
1914–18	19.5	12.5	17.1	19.1	12.7	4.6	6.0	5.5	5.5	3.3	1.7
1918	31.9	33.1	13.1	14.4	11.6	4.8	3.6	5.4	4.3	1.9	1.2
1919–21	10.4	32.2	23.4	1.6	10.0	6.1	4.0	3.0	6.1	1.4	3.3
1921	4.8	54.9	13.7	—	3.6	1.5	6.3	—	0.4	1.1	9.4
1922–29	9.8	64.4	11.4	7.6	2.5	3.5	3.0	0.5	1.6	0.7	1.7
1929	15.8	63.1	9.4	4.8	10.3	3.2	2.3	0.5	1.6	0.4	1.3
1930–32	12.3	52.0	20.0	6.2	5.4	4.0	2.8	0.7	1.0	0.3	1.9
1932	6.8	33.1	32.7	5.3	10.1	8.1	4.0	1.2	0.7	0.0	3.6
1933–37	22.2	38.8	20.0	9.4	5.4	7.8	4.9	5.0	2.0	2.1	3.9
1937	34.8	46.7	15.5	9.1	5.2	3.5	5.6	?	2.2	2.1	1.9

Note.—A dash indicates no output; zeros only, an amount less than 0.1 per cent.

the inflated war demand, there were extensive surplus stocks and during the post-war years outputs dropped heavily in all countries, particularly in those having the higher costs of operation. Then began a second period of advancing production, paralleling that of 1900–1913, broken by declines in 1924, 1927, and 1931–1932, reaching a new high record in 1937. Table I*b* shows the transitions in output from period to period.

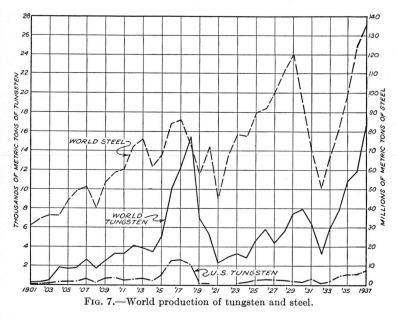

Fig. 7.—World production of tungsten and steel.

Argentina.—Tungsten production in Argentina dates back at least to 1906 and in 1909 the country stood third in the list of producers but in the subsequent years other countries increased production much more rapidly. The war peak of production was only 1,085 metric tons and it is only since 1934 that production again became important.

Australia.—In the early years of the tungsten industry Australia was the leading producer, but had passed its prime before the war period began, and even the war demand failed to bring it up to its former level. The local production was slow in recovering from the post-war depression, but in 1937 reached the highest figure since 1920. Queensland has been the heaviest producing state, with New South Wales second, but both are now comparatively unimportant, Tasmania and Northern Territory now being in the lead.

Bolivia.—Bolivia had been a small producer of tungsten since the beginning of the industry, but not in any great amounts until the war period; production grew rapidly then, reaching 4,200 metric tons in 1917, followed by a decline and complete inactivity during 1922–1924. A revival of the industry during the boom period brought production to 1,630 tons in 1929, followed by another decline, to a minimum of 240 tons in 1933, recovering to 1,802 tons by 1937. Until recently the Bolivian output has been mostly wolframite, accumulated from a large number of small operations. In 1929 the Conde Auque mine, near Oruro, which had been worked intermittently for some 10 years, was first put into active operation and turned out to be a surprise package, in the form of one of the richest deposits ever discovered. The ore (scheelite) is reported to carry 50 per cent or more of WO_3 as taken from the mine. This mine has furnished most of the Bolivian output since 1929.

During the war period much of the exports came to the United States but, in recent years, nearly all have gone to Europe.

China.—Although tungsten production did not begin in China until late in 1914, and did not reach any great proportions until 1917, the increasing demand brought out in 1918 the heaviest output ever turned out by any country in a period of one year; slackened demand resulted in a considerable decline in 1919 but, ever since that year, China has headed the list of producers and has contributed over 37 per cent of the total output during 1913–1935, and more than 31 per cent of the output since 1900, which date really marks the beginning of the tungsten industry. Since attaining the lead in 1918, China has averaged 46 per cent of the total output, with a minimum of 18 per cent in 1919, and a maximum of 71 per cent in 1928, and in twelve of the 20 years has furnished more than half of the supply.

The Chinese deposits are located in the mountainous region to the northeast, north and northwest of Canton. The most important deposits are in the southern part of the Province of Kiangsi, with smaller ones in southern Hunan; a small amount has been produced in northern Kwantung and northeastern Kwangsi, but these sources are comparatively unimportant. Although the Kiangsi deposits, which furnish something like 90 per cent of the output, are less than 200 miles from Canton, they are in the northern watershed of the mountains, and in preference to transportation over the mountains, the concentrates were shipped down the Kan and Yangtze Rivers a distance of about 1,000 miles, to Shanghai. The Hunan ores also went north to Changsha, and thence to Shanghai. In spite of the internal wars that have troubled China for so many years, there was until recently comparatively little disturbance to the tungsten industry, for the very good reason that, whatever party happened to be in power, the industry was fostered as a source of taxation. In 1929 difficulties between the producers, ore buyers, and the provincial government, and repeated heavy taxation over the long northern route to Shanghai, with each district through which the ore passed taking its levy, led to the abandonment of the old established route in favor of the much shorter but more laborious trip south over the mountains with coolies and pack horses, and thence down the Pei River to Canton and Hong Kong. More recently roads have been opened in this section, and it is reported that transportation is now by motor trucks. Some of the Hunan ore still goes north to Shanghai, but the shift of the Kiangsi ore to Canton made this port the leading market for tungsten ore. Late in 1933 the Kiangsi Government took over the local industry as a state monopoly.

The seizure of the industry by the local government and subsequent disagreement between the provincial government and the national government over the control of the mines and the division of the income from their taxation has led to considerable disorganization, and to heavy losses by the former producers and ore buyers, but, in spite of all these difficulties, production has been maintained at a high level.

Very few white men have visited the remote districts where the mines are located, and little is known of the character or extent of the deposits. Apparently both vein and placer deposits exist and that these are considerable in extent is evidenced by the output that has been consistently maintained. The ore is almost entirely wolframite, with small amounts of scheelite; it is hand-picked in China but on arrival in Europe or America requires further treatment for the removal of impurities. As shipped the concentrates average about 67.5 per cent WO_3. In the earlier years more ore was exported to Europe than to America and often the Chinese ore that reached the United States had first been shipped to England or Germany. More recently most of the United States imports have come directly from China.

Great Britain.—The tin mining section of Cornwall has long been a producer of small tonnages of tungsten, which reached a maximum of 421 metric tons in 1909. After a decline of more than half, war demand brought the output back practically to its former level; recoveries practically ceased during the post-war and depression periods, but reached 153 tons in 1930 and 256 tons in 1935, declining to 140 tons in 1937.

Burma (India).—The development of tungsten mining in Burma was even more meteoric in character than that of China. Beginning in 1910, the country stood second in the list of producers in 1911, and first from 1912 to 1915. Then, although the output continued to grow, it was surpassed in 1916 and 1917 by the peak of the war production in the United States, and in 1918 by China; the Chinese slump in 1919 left Burma again in the lead for that year but since 1920 it has consistently held second place, except in 1925 and 1928, when it was surpassed by the United States. The total output during the period 1913–1937 was 64,000 tons, or 17.4 per cent of the world total, but was less than half that of China. While production during the boom period, 1922–1929, was not as well maintained as in China, it increased materially in 1930, showed little decline during the depression and made three successive new high records in 1935, 1936 and 1937.

Almost the entire Indian output has been in Burma. In the earlier years 80 per cent or more came from Tavoy, less than 10 per cent from Mergui, about 5 per cent from the Southern Shan States, and the remainder from scattered locations in other sections of Burma, Rajputana, Bihar and Orissa, and the Central Provinces. Since then the sources have shifted, and now about 60 per cent comes from the Mawchi mine, in the Southern Shan States, 35 per cent from Tavoy, and the remainder from Mergui.

Indo-China.—The French colony of Tonkin, or Indo-China, had little output before the war period, but has been a consistent small producer ever since 1913, largely as a byproduct of tin mining.

Japan.—Japan was a small producer of tungsten early in the history of the industry, and Chosen appeared in the list when production began to increase under war demand. The combined output reached 1,729 metric tons in 1918, but declined rapidly, and has been small and irregular ever since the post-war period, but since 1934 has been expanding rapidly, reaching 1,910 tons in 1936. The bulk of the war production was apparently exported. The ores worked are predominatingly scheelite.

Malaya.—Both the Federated and Unfederated Malay States have been moderate producers of tungsten as a byproduct in tin mining, since early in the industry. During the beginning years, the Federated States led in production and increased gradually under war demand but, in 1918, the Unfederated States forged to the front with 75 per cent of the combined output and continued to hold the lead until 1929, when the order was again reversed. Most of the Unfederated output has been from Trengannu, with small amounts from two or three other states; the early Federated production was largely from Perak and Selangor, and most of the remainder from Negri Sembilan, but for several years past almost the entire yield has been from one mine in Perak, near Ipoh. The product is an exceptionally high grade of scheelite, running up to 74 per cent WO_3. Small amounts of wolframite are also shipped.

Portugal.—Portugal is by far the most important European producer of tungsten and, in 1908, was the second largest producer in the world, with 17 per cent of the total output. Production was already so high that it increased little during the war period, 1,580 metric tons in 1917 as against 1,466 tons in 1912, but rose to 1,948 tons in 1937. The tungsten is found associated with tin in both veins and alluvial ground. The bulk of the output is from the vicinity of Silvares and Viseu, Province of Beira Baixa.

Siam.—Tungsten production was almost entirely a war project. Production is recorded for only two or three years before the war and has since been almost at a standstill, with little improvement even under the present heavy demand.

Spain.—The Portuguese deposits extend somewhat over the border into Spanish territory, so that Spain has been a small but fairly consistent producer since the early days of the industry. In fact, in 1905, the Spanish output was greater than the Portuguese and was almost as large as the maximum attained during the war.

United States.—Active work on tungsten mining was started in the United States immediately after the discovery of the high-speed steels in 1900, and in 1907, 1909, 1910, 1916 and 1917 this country held the position of leading producer. Although production during much of the period was comparatively small and for two years ceased entirely, the consistent maintenance of a moderate output during most of the time, and of a quite heavy one during the war years, brought the United States output for the years 1913–1937 to third in the list, with 39,067 tons, or 10.8 per cent of the total, only a third less than Burma, and a half greater than its nearest competitor, Bolivia.

The bulk of the output has been from three states, Colorado, California, and Nevada, but eleven other states have furnished smaller amounts at various times. The ores are of both vein and placer type, although chiefly the former; they are low in grade, mostly under 1 per cent, with a correspondingly high cost of operation.

This puts the domestic production under a heavy handicap, for, as was proven in 1921–1922, none of the mines can operate in competition with foreign ores at the low price level normal to the bulk of the output, particularly the Chinese, and it is only with the protection of a heavy tariff that the industry can be kept alive.

Other Countries.—Tungsten ores are widely scattered over the earth and many other countries have shown minor outputs at various periods, particularly during the war, but the sum total of all of these during the period 1913–1937 was only 3.8 per cent of the total output. Among these countries, each of which contributed less than 1 per cent of the 1913–1937 total, are the following: Austria, Brazil, Canada, Chile, Czechoslovakia, *France*, *Germany*, Italy, *Mexico*, Netherlands East Indies, *New Zealand*, Nigeria, Norway, *Peru*, Rhodesia, Russia, South Africa, and Sweden. The five countries listed in italics furnished nearly three-quarters of the combined output, leaving only about 1 per cent to be supplied by the other thirteen.

UNITED STATES OUTPUT AND SUPPLY

Among the various strategic minerals tungsten stands in a class almost alone with regard to the scale on which past requirements have been met from domestic sources, for, of the entire list, only mercury can compare with it in this respect. Pre-war import data lack sufficient detail to enable one to determine accurately the amounts of foreign metal being used and, in fact, it was not until a tariff was imposed on tungsten imports in 1922 that anything better than estimates could be obtained on the total amounts imported.   Apparently in 1913, the United States was producing 42 per cent of its tungsten requirements.   This figure gradually increased under war demand, reaching 70 per cent in 1917. Excessive imports in 1918 reduced this to 31 per cent and, during the post-war depression and period of absorption of excess war stocks, the domestic output declined in 1919–1920 to a nominal figure and, in 1921–1922, ceased entirely.   With the placing of a tariff on imports late in 1922 the domestic industry took a new lease on life.   In 1923–1924 the coming boom had not yet gotten sufficiently under way to develop heavy demands and the moderate outputs of those years covered 75–80 per cent of consumption. Although production increased considerably in the succeeding years, demand increased still more and the percentage supplied from domestic output gradually dropped to 11 per cent in 1929. The industrial depression beginning late in 1929 decreased both domestic output and imports and the percentage increased slightly in 1930.   Another factor that contributed largely to the low percentages of 1929 and 1930 was the active agitation for an increase in tariff duties, which led to expanded imports in anticipation of the rise in rates; unfortunately no data are available on stocks, and the figures on available supply include both actual consumption and additions in stocks.

Even before the advent of new tariff rates in 1930, domestic production dropped heavily, since the excess imports cut the demand for domestic ore, as did also the general industrial depression.   During 1931–1933, production was greater than consumption for the first time in the history of the industry and exports exceeded imports by a considerable margin, leaving the domestic industry, at least for the time being, not only on a self-sustaining basis, but with an exportable surplus, although this condition would probably not have been possible except for the restricted demands of domestic consumption and for the excess stocks that had been accumulated during the heavy imports of 1929–1930.

Imports.—Imports grew rapidly under war demand, reaching a maximum in 1918 but still continuing at a high level in 1919, presumably due largely to deliveries on unexpired contracts.

After the imposition of a tariff on tungsten in September, 1922, there was a complete cessation of ore imports until 1925 and only minor amounts of metal and alloys were imported. Then followed another series of increasing imports, reaching a maximum just before the increase of duty in June, 1930, since when imports for consumption have remained at a low level, although there have been considerable amounts of ore imported for reduction and re-export which in no way affect the domestic supply.

TABLE II.—AVAILABLE SUPPLY OF TUNGSTEN IN THE UNITED STATES
(In thousands of pounds of tungsten metal)

	Domestic Production	Imports		Exports	Available Supply	Percentage of Supply Produced in U. S.	Percentage of World Output		Total World Production
		For Consumption	In Bond for Re-export[1]				Produced in U. S.	Consumed in U. S.	
1913	1,463	2,047			3,510	42	17	41	8,515
1914	942	775			1,717	55	12	22	7,785
1915	2,220	1,848			4,067	55	19	36	11,400
1916	5,637	4,304		614	9,326	61	25	41	22,515
1917	5,847	5,054		2,489	8,412	70	22	31	27,100
1918	4,817	12,233		1,319	15,731	31	14	47	33,500
1919	311	10,388		41	10,658	3	2	69	15,475
1920	206	4,205		5	4,403	5	2	37	11,840
1921		2,257			2,257	0	0	44	5,072
1922		2,908		1	2,907	0	0	45	6,526
1923	229	79		4	304	75	3	4	7,300
1924	538	142		3	677	80	8	11	6,361
1925	1,133	1,694		10	2,817	40	11	27	10,540
1926	1,315	2,884		24	4,175	32	10	33	12,830
1927	1,108	2,198		16	3,289	34	11	34	9,640
1928	1,150	2,969		13	4,106	28	9	34	12,215
1929	790	6,446		82	7,154	11	5	43	16,580
1930	668	3,998		24	4,642	14	4	27	17,510
1931	1,336	189		846	679	197	9	5	14,285
1932	377	106		113	371	102	5	5	7,123
1933	852	379	414	683	962	89	7	7	12,985
1934	1,950	954	361	563	2,701	72	11	16	17,240
1935	2,279	892	815	798	3,187	72	10	13	23,810
1936	2,486	3,767	579	104[2]	5,956[2]	42	10	23	26,235
1937	3,331	5,696	442	449[2]	9,031[2]	37	9	25	36,596

[1] Concentrates imported in bond for smelting and re-export do not contribute in any way to the domestic supply, but these amounts must be included in the table, since the materials produced from them, are included in the domestic exports. [2] Beginning with 1936 the figures for exports do not include ferrotungsten, which is reported with other ferro-alloys, and hence Available Supply can no longer be estimated except by assuming exports equal to imports in bond.

Imports are mainly in the form of ore but at times fairly large amounts of metal and alloys, particularly ferrotungsten, have been imported. The metal and alloys come chiefly from England

and Germany, as did also much of the ore in former years.   Until comparatively recently, so much of the ore imported had reached here by way of some other country than the producer that it is impossible to make any estimate of the amounts received from the various producers.   Also, from 1922 to 1930, the tungsten content of the ore, metal, and alloys were all grouped together under a single heading in the import returns.   During recent years ore shipments have been more direct and the bulk of the imports have come to us directly from China.

Table IV shows the distribution of the 1937 imports according to the country of origin and the port of entry into the United States.   The bulk of the imports were received in Pittsburgh and New York, 49 per cent by the former and 41 per cent by the latter.

TABLE IV.—DISTRIBUTION OF TUNGSTEN CONCENTRATE IMPORTS IN 1937
(Thousands of short tons)

	New York	Phila-delphia	Pitts-burgh	Buffalo	Cleve-land	Total
China	1,478	84	2,014	202	157	3,935
Malaya	430	....	324	42	....	796
Australia	182	....	133	58	....	373
Mexico	17	....	73	....	....	90
Bolivia	41	....	40	....	....	81
Japan	28	....	28	....	....	56
Argentina	38	....	1	....	....	39
Peru	21	....	....	....	....	21
Total	2,235	84	2,613	302	157	5,391

Exports.—Up to 1916 exports of tungsten were so small that they were not recorded.   During 1916–1918 there were fairly large exports, chiefly as ferrotungsten, to the Allies but, with the cessation of war demand, exports again dropped to a nominal figure until 1931.   The heavy exports of 1931–1935 were due to sales of ferrotungsten to Soviet Russia, which accounted for 95 per cent of the exports during these years; exports to other countries remained at their former low level.   Beginning with 1936, separate figures were no longer published for exports of ferrotungsten, but were lumped in with other ferro-alloys.   Presumably a large proportion of these exports were from ore imported in bond, for smelting and re-export, but total exports exceed the amounts imported in bond, indicating the exportation of some domestic material.

Consumption.—The consumption of tungsten in the United States, as measured by available supply, has been about 33 per cent of the world output, averaged over the 1913–1935 period, or, in terms of 60 per cent concentrates, about 4,250 metric tons; in this long-period average the high figures of the war years more than offset the low ones of the post-war and the industrial depressions, so that the average for the years in between the two depressions was about 3,950 tons, which also figures out at 33 per cent of the production for these years.   A survey of corresponding figures for the other leading consuming countries indicates a slightly smaller figure for Germany, probably 30 per cent or less, and possibly 20 per cent for England and 10 per cent for France. During the past few years, Russia has been taking about 10 per cent of the currently produced output but before that the amount was small.

Stocks.—No record is kept of tungsten stocks in the United States, but at several different times estimates have been made of the amounts on hand.   After the close of the war, stocks were high, probably 13,500 metric tons.   While the increased imports preceding the imposition of the tariff in 1922 caused a small increase and those anticipating the tariff increase in 1930 made a considerably greater increase in the current stocks, at other times the trend has been downward and, at the end of 1931, there were about 1,800 metric tons in bonded warehouse and possibly an equal amount in the hands of the consuming industry, with no information on stocks of unshipped ore at the mines.   Since then bonded stocks have dropped and, while the present status of industrial and mine stocks is not known, it is probable that they also have been reduced, in view of the comparatively heavy exports and increased domestic demand.

PRICES

As with chromium, there is no compilation of monthly or annual average price quotations on tungsten, so that our only means of following the market are the running trend of the current quotations and the average value of the annual domestic output.   The accompanying chart of United States prices gives the maximum and minimum quotations and the average price paid for all domestic production sold during the year, the figures being in dollars per short ton unit, 20 pounds of WO_3, or 15.86 pounds of pure metal content.

The price previous to 1913 had shown variations from \$1.00 to \$6.50 for the minimum, \$3 to \$14 for the maximum, and \$2.30 to \$9.00 for the average, with a gradually increasing trend from 1901 on. With the advent of the World War the price structure underwent a complete change, marked particularly by high prices and wide fluctuations and a hysteria of buying among those not protected by contracts, that inflated prices beyond all reason, with a maximum of \$93.50 per unit in March, 1916. These

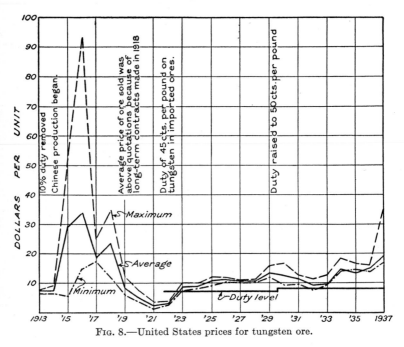

Fig. 8.—United States prices for tungsten ore.

high prices stimulated production to a point where it temporarily outran demand and the price dropped sharply; in 1917 the maximum was \$25 and the minimum \$11.50; another flurry took the maximum up to \$35 in 1918.

After the close of the war, prices dropped steadily to a maximum of \$3.50 and a minimum of \$1.50 in 1921. This abrupt decline very quickly brought prices below the production costs of most of the domestic mines and output dropped to almost nothing, and with the bottom prices of 1921, ceased entirely. Agitation for a tariff sufficient to make domestic operation possible resulted in the establishment on September 22, 1922, of a duty of 45 cents per pound on tungsten contained in ore, equivalent to $7.14 per unit. This brought a small output in 1923, and an increase in price to between $7.50 and $10, with an average price of $8.50 for the year's output. Coinciding, as this did, with the beginning of the inflation period, both production and prices showed a general improvement until 1928. In 1929, difficulties in China caused temporary shortage of shipments and disturbed local prices; then, contrary to all expectations, domestic production dropped nearly one-third; and, finally, a new tariff bill was in preparation, and a 50 per cent increase in the duty on tungsten was being agitated. As a result, domestic prices became rather unsettled and rose sharply from an average of $10.40 in 1928 to $13.13 in 1929, in spite of largely increased imports, for these were being brought in not to compete with the immediate domestic market but for stock, in anticipation of the coming increase in duty.

When 1930 brought the beginnings of the depression, a settlement of the new tariff rate at 50 cents per pound instead of 45 cents was not sufficient to block a decline which, with more or less fluctuation, continued until 1932, when, during part of the year, the minimum price was less than the duty rate. The improved conditions of 1933 brought a considerable increase in domestic output but little advance in prices. Although quotations on foreign ore increased during the year from $9.50 to $15, the average sales value of the year's domestic output was only $9.58, as compared with $9.20 in 1932. This difference on the part of foreign ore, however, was more apparent than real and completely disappears when one considers that the foreign ore must be bought on a foreign exchange basis, and the price of foreign ore quoted in dollars had to increase as the exchange value of the dollar dropped after the United States abandoned the gold standard. As a matter of fact, the London quotations of December 31, 1933, and January 1, 1933, each converted into dollars at the current rate of exchange, are almost identical.

Following the depression low of 1933, prices have increased, except for a drop in 1935, and with the heavy rearmament demand of 1937 reached a record level of $35.00 in September, but declined to $22–$25 by the end of the year. In general the price of domestic ore is determined by the world price of foreign ore plus duty ($7.93 per unit), but at times there is a considerable margin between the two prices, depending on the relative demand and supply at the moment.   With normal conditions the price of domestic ore will be slightly less than that of foreign ore plus duty, since the grade of the ore is lower.   Before the imposition of duty in 1922, the foreign price alone was the determining factor.

While there are no regularly prepared monthly or annual averages of tungsten prices, Table VII presents a series of annual averages recently compiled by the U. S. Bureau of Mines, expressed in dollars per short ton unit of WO_3 in 60 per cent concentrates, including duty, with a corresponding conversion of the annual averages to a tungsten index price.   The index prices show an even wider fluctuations than do the ordinary annual averages.

TABLE VII.—TUNGSTEN ORE PRICES IN THE UNITED STATES

	Average Quoted Price	Commodity Index	Tungsten Index Price
1913	$ 7.24	100.0	$ 7.24
1914	7.32	97.6	7.50
1915	29.30	99.6	29.42
1916	33.98	122.5	27.74
1917	20.85	168.3	12.39
1918	22.27	188.1	11.84
1919	8.69	198.6	4.38
1920	7.26	221.2	3.28
1921	3.15	139.8	2.25
1922	4.02	138.5	2.90
1923	8.33	144.1	5.78
1924	8.51	140.5	6.06
1925	11.07	148.3	7.46
1926	11.23	143.3	7.84
1927	10.70	136.7	7.83
1928	10.81	138.5	7.81
1929	14.76	136.5	10.81
1930	13.40	123.8	10.82
1931	11.45	104.6	10.95
1932	10.51	92.8	11.33
1933	11.36	94.4	12.03
1934	16.70	107.3	15.56
1935	16.00	114.6	13.96
1936	15.46	115.8	13.35
1937	21.79	123.6	17.63

Metal and Alloy.—In 1913, crude tungsten powder for compounding alloy steels sold for 67 cents per pound and ferrotungsten for 73–75 cents per pound of contained tungsten.   Immediately after the outbreak of the war, prices increased and, by the end of 1914, both were selling at $1.35, rising to $8 in 1915 and $8.50 in 1916.   Toward the end of 1916 the price broke to $2.40 with continued decline in succeeding years to a low of 75 cents in 1923, later rising to the neighborhood of $1.   Since 1927 the price has fluctuated in this vicinity for ferrotungsten, but the powder has ranged somewhat higher. In 1933 ferrotungsten sold at $0.94–$1.25 per pound of contained tungsten, and powder at $1.25–$1.75, rising to $2 for ferro and $3 for powder in 1937.

The price of the pure metal varies widely with the amount of work that is required to put it into the desired shape and size. The 1934 price for rods is $7.50–$10 per pound, while heavy wire (0.03 inch) is $16–$20 per pound and sheet is $20–$30. For a very small wire the labor costs increase rapidly, bringing the price of 0.0006 inch wire up to about $600 per pound, but, since wire of this size runs nearly 100 miles to the pound, it figures out at $6.40 per mile, which does not look so large, even though it is the same thing, merely stated in another way. All of these prices have been dropping since the peak of demand in 1929, the total decline since then amounting to about 40 per cent.

In the early days of the development of tungsten carbide tools, these sold at $1 per gram, or $450 per pound; tungsten carbide powder now sells at $10–$15 per pound, to which of course will be added the cost of forming and finishing the tool.

TARIFF

Ever since the post-war depression lowered the price of tungsten concentrates to below the domestic production costs and brought the industry to a halt, the question of tariff on imports has been a live one. The Payne-Aldrich Tariff Act of 1909 provided a 10 per cent *ad valorem* duty on tungsten ores, but this was ended by the Underwood Tariff Act of 1913, which admitted ores free of duty.

How much, if any, of the 25 per cent decrease in domestic tungsten production in 1914 was due to the loss of tariff protection, and how much to the general disturbance incident to the outbreak of the war, is problematical. Before it could be determined whether the loss of protection was particularly detrimental to the domestic demand, consumption for war material began to develop in sufficient amounts to raise the price to a point where tariff was unnecessary. But, with the fall in prices after the war, when Chinese concentrates were selling for $1.50–$1.60 per unit in New York, a high tariff became necessary if the industry were to survive. The Fordney-McCumber Tariff Act of 1922 established a rate of 45 cents per pound of tungsten contained in imported concentrates, equivalent to $7.14 per unit. On the basis of $1.50 per unit, the price at which Chinese ore had recently been sold in New York, this was equivalent to an *ad valorem* duty of 476 per cent, and brought the duty-paid price on foreign ore up to $8.64.

At this price domestic production was begun again and gradually grew almost to the pre-war status, when the 10 per cent duty was in effect. The increased domestic price brought increases in the foreign price also, so that the duty ranged from 140 to 240 per cent in 1926–1928 and, with the increase in price in 1929, dropped to 80–160 per cent, increasing again with decreasing prices during the depression period, and with the passage of the Smoot-Hawley Tariff Act of 1930, which increased the rate to 50 cents per pound, or $7.93 per unit. The $9.50 price for Chinese ore at the beginning of 1933 left only $1.57 for the ore, which brought the new duty rate up to 505 per cent.

It seems well substantiated that, as large as they are, these rates are not excessive if viewed only from the standpoint of maintaining the industry, for the average output that they have brought is less than that resulting from the 10 per cent rate during 1909–1913. Part of the difference is due to the general increase in the cost of operation and part to the fact that the heavy production during the war pretty well cleaned out the ores that could be produced at moderate costs, leaving only high cost operations for future work.

Table VIII shows the changes in tariff rates on various forms of tungsten that have prevailed since 1909.

TABLE VIII.—TARIFF RATES ON TUNGSTEN

	1909–1913	1913–1922
Ore..	10 %	Free
Metal and alloy, valued at $200 per ton or less..............	25 %	15 %
More than $200...	20 %	15 %

In 1922 a reclassification was made and the duties were set at a specific charge per pound of contained tungsten plus a percentage of the value, as follows:

	1922–1930	1930—
Ore...	45c.	50c.
Metal and carbide, lumps, grains and powder............	60c. + 25 %	60c. + 50 %
Chemicals...	60c. + 25 %	60c. + 40 %
Alloys...	60c. + 25 %	60c. + 25 %
Ingot, shot, bars, scrap.................................	60c. + 25 %	50 %
Sheets, wire, etc..	60c. + 25 %	60 %
Iron and steel, scrap, scale, containing W in excess of 0.6 %.	72c. + 8 %	....
in excess of 0.2 %.....................................	....	72c. + 8 %

The rates given for the last item are in addition to any duty on the base material.

POLITICAL AND COMMERCIAL CONTROL

A statistical survey of political and commercial control is difficult to evaluate, because of the rapid and extreme fluctuations in conditions affecting production. A country has direct political control of the production within its boundaries and direct commercial control of production in other countries made from deposits owned by its own nationals. In addition to the direct control, there is the possibility of indirect political control through tariffs, trade agreements, and treaties, as well as various methods of exerting indirect commercial control. But although these established political and commercial rights carry with them a potential control over the disposition of output under their

TABLE IX.—POLITICAL AND COMMERCIAL CONTROL OF TUNGSTEN PRODUCTION

	Percentage of World Output		Percentage of Control				
	1929	1937	Domestic	Foreign	Chinese	British	United States
Australia..............	1	2	1	....	....	1	....
Bolivia................	5	5	2	3	....	....	3
China.................	55	47	55	....	55	....	....
Great Britain..........	1	0.4	1	....	....	1	....
Burma................	21	16	21	....	....	21	....
Indo-China............	1	2	1	....	....	....	....
Malaya................	7	4	7	....	....	7	....
Portugal..............	2	6	....	2	....	2	....
Spain.................	1	3	....	1	....	1	....
United States.........	4	9	4	....	....	....	4
Totals.............	98	94.4	92	6	55	33	7

jurisdiction, they can maintain little actual control over the magnitude of the production; that falls within the province of the economic laws of supply and demand and the resulting price levels as compared with production costs involved in operating the various deposits within the country. Political control can modify this to some extent by restrictive control of imports or exports, by the imposition of import or export duties, or by the payment of subsidies on production, but all of these methods of control have practical limits of operation beyond which they can not be enforced. As a result, outputs in various countries fluctuate over wide ranges from year to year under the conflicting pressure of these various forces.

China built up her tungsten output from nothing to 10,600 tons in four years under the positive action of these forces, and in the fifth year lost three-quarters of it under the negative action of the same forces. Positive action increased the United States output six fold in the same four years, and negative action during the next four years stopped production completely; then the modifying force of tariff was brought into play to revive the industry, but only with partial success. We therefore repeat that, while political and commercial control carries the potential control of the disposition of the output, it has comparatively little to say as to whether there is going to be any output over which to exert its control, except by the methods adopted by the Communist and Fascist states.

The accompanying table of political and commercial control of the world tungsten output as it existed in 1929 is adapted from the Report of the Mineral Inquiry of the American Institute of Mining and Metallurgical Engineers and is supplemented by a comparative distribution of world output in 1937. This shows only direct control and does not take into consideration any factors of indirect control. An important example of this was manifested in 1933, when German and British interests in turn attempted to secure an indirect commercial control of Chinese output through the establishment of operating or sales organizations under license from the national government, after the industry had been taken over as a government monopoly.

One of the most striking features brought out by this table is the preponderance of domestic control, the entire output being under domestic control, except for 1 per cent in Spain, 2 per cent in Portugal, and 3 per cent in Bolivia. A second point of interest is the concentration of control—55 per cent Chinese and 33 per cent British, 30 per cent of the latter being in British territory and 3 per cent in foreign territory. United States control is limited to 4 per cent in domestic output and 3 per cent in Bolivia, the other 2 per cent of Bolivian output being in the hands of local capital. French control is limited to the 1 per cent in Indo-China and Japanese to 0.5 per cent in Japan and Chosen while German control is conspicuous by its absence.   ·

In a somewhat similar survey of the industry in 1917–1918, F. L. Hess not only showed direct control but also gave an estimate of the additional amounts to which indirect control gave access through trade arrangements and political and diplomatic influence.

	Direct		Indirect		Total	
	1917	1918	1917	1918	1917	1918
British...............................	28	24	21	10	49	34
United States........................	22	14	22	45	44	59
French..............................	......	......	......	......	6	4
German.............................	......	......	......	......	1	1

The size of the fluctuations shown here in two consecutive years again emphasizes the instability of control, due to changes in production and to alterations of trade arrangements.

GENERAL REVIEW OF THE DOMESTIC SITUATION

There seem to be sufficient reserves of tungsten ore in the United States to justify the assumption that, at least for a limited time, the industry could operate on a self-sustaining basis if the price could be maintained at a sufficiently high level to cover operating costs. It is evident, however, that this would mean excessive prices and would probably result in practically complete exhaustion of the ore supplies within a comparatively short time, and there are few, if any, even among the most active protagonists of the industry that advocate this extreme stand. The question rather resolves itself into one as to the proper point of compromise between the three different and more or less conflicting angles from which the situation may be viewed.

The purely industrial view calls for the conversion of an idle asset into useful form with adequate financial return to the operators; the conservationist view calls for the utilization of the asset over as long a period of time as possible, consistent with the maximum economy and efficiency. These two views are somewhat at variance with each other and require some compromise, but the chief difficulty lies in reconciling them, not with each other, but with the accepted principles of national defense. Tungsten is recognized as one of the most important raw materials in a modern munitions program for national defense, and it is in the interests of the people as a whole that needs in this direction should take precedence over purely industrial or conservationist arguments. But even if we grant this premise without reservation, we are still not out of our difficulty, for the question still remains as to the extent to which the industry should be kept in operation.

If it is allowed to lie idle, the time interval necessary to get it into production again when needed is too great. On the other hand, if it is operated too extensively in the effort to keep it in shape to be readily and quickly amenable to expansion when the demand should arise, we incur the danger that the reserves may be so depleted in the meantime that when an emergency demand does arise, there will not be sufficient reserves of ore left to supply it.

It is pretty well established that under existing conditions, with low grade ores than can be recovered only at abnormally high prices, the status of the industry is controlled by the tariff rate. Chinese ore can be laid down in New York at a price far below the operating costs of any domestic mine, so that, under the same controlling conditions of supply and demand, domestic production can be increased or decreased, within reasonable limits, by increasing or decreasing the tariff to make the price cover the production costs of the amount required. A $10 price will start work in those mines whose operating cost lies below this level; if this output is not sufficient to cover the need, a $15 price will put more mines to work. The problem then that lies before those interested in the industry from all the different angles is to determine the rate of production that gives due consideration to all phases of the question, and then to determine and set a tariff rate that will maintain the desired production as nearly as the conditions of supply and demand will permit.

It has been pointed out in a preceding section that the present tariff rate has at times resulted in duties that on a value basis were as high as 500 per cent, and one of the factors that must be taken into consideration in setting the tariff rate is the amount which the consuming industry is to be required to pay in order to accomplish the desired output. At the present time, for every pound of tungsten that is consumed in the United States, from 50 to 75 cents is collected by the government as duty, if it is from foreign ore, or approximately the same amount is collected by the producer, if it is from domestic ore; without the tariff the metal would be bought just that much cheaper.

It is a question then, as to how far we are justified in penalizing the consumer for the joint benefit of the government and the producer. Unless a fair percentage of the total consumption is supplied by domestic producers, much more of the increase in cost goes into the public treasury than into the hands of the producers; this is not necessarily an adverse argument, for the general public benefits by this in that the amounts collected in duty would otherwise have to be collected by taxation, but at the same time it must be borne in mind that this is fundamentally a tariff for protection and not for revenue; there never has been any sentiment advocating tariff on materials of this character primarily for revenue. With a tariff as high as the present one on tungsten and with the resulting domestic output no larger than it is, we need to give serious thought to the possibility that matters have been carried too far and that, in the long run, the consumer is being penalized large amounts in increased costs without really accomplishing what was intended.

CONCLUSION

With these facts before us it is inevitable that we should come to the same conclusion with regard to tungsten as with the other metals that have been discussed in this series, namely, that for purposes of national defense there should be maintained in the country sufficient emergency stocks of concentrates to tide us over the necessary period of readjustment while production is speeded up to meet an emergency demand and to fill the possible gap between consumption demand and probable production plus imports. With the past record of tungsten for production at a fairly high proportion of demand, these stocks will probably not need to be quite so extensive as with most of the other strategic metals, nor do present trends of development in consumption indicate the likelihood of a need for material increases in the supply in the near future to cover new uses, as is the case with chromium. But the inadequacy of our knowledge of the extent of our reserves brings in a large factor of uncertainty which should be adequately balanced in the size of the emergency stocks. Also it must be borne in mind that, while our average consumption of tungsten concentrates during the past 10 years has been less than 3,000 metric tons a year and during the inflation period was about one-quarter greater than this, at the close of the World War consumption was at the rate of 18,000 tons a year.

CHAPTER VII

TIN

The fundamental factor in all of the strategic minerals is the inequality of distribution between producing and consuming countries, and in no case is this more marked than with tin. About 74 per cent of the total recorded production comes from a single geographic area extending from southeastern Asia, through the islands of the East Indies, to Australia; South America has contributed 12 per cent, Europe 11 per cent, Africa less than 3 per cent, and North America has furnished the magnificent amount of 0.02 per cent. The amounts of tin that have been produced by the important industrial countries that are the heavy consumers, are insignificantly small; of these only Great Britain has a tin output that is of material proportions—if one can justify placing in that category an output so small that it requires the output of 15–20 years to supply one year's normal consumption. So far as the United States is concerned, although it is the world's largest consumer, it not only has had practically no production at all, but the entire recorded output of the whole continent of North America would satisfy normal domestic consumption for only about a week.

The importance of tin in our industrial life is not generally recognized in its true aspect, probably largely because of the small amounts of tin with which the average person comes in contact in everyday life; it is an inherent result growing out of the types of use in which most of the tin is consumed that it is dissipated in small amounts, and so the aggregate amounts involved are not fully realized. But even in the aggregate, the bulk of our tin consumption is not particularly impressive; our 1937 imports of tin were 88,100 long tons, which is less than one-tenth of the amount of manganese ore imported in the same year, but the unit value of tin is so high (over $1,000 per ton) that the total value represented by the imports was not only greater than that of any other material of mineral origin, but even greater

162

than the total value for any other group of related materials in the mineral field. In 1937 imports of strategic mineral supplies accounted for 44 per cent of the value of total mineral imports, while 52 per cent of the strategic value and 22 per cent of the total value was in tin alone.

REQUIREMENTS

Tin is industrially the most important of the nonferrous group of strategic metals. Although tin is not used directly in the production of steel, as is the case with all of the previous metals discussed, its consumption is almost as closely linked with the steel industry, due to the character of its main uses: tin coated on steel sheets to make tinplate, solder for use on this and other metals, and bearing alloys for use in machines made of steel account for nearly two-thirds of the tin consumption. This has made the trend of tin production follow quite closely that of steel in normal times, but during the World War period the shortage of tin and the conservation of the available supplies kept the tin output from following the war expansion in steel production.

The accompanying graph of world production, and the figures in Table I, covering the period since 1913, show that, in the first decade under consideration, tin production remained fairly constant at 120,000–130,000 long tons, but with a downward trend; the second decade covers the increase during the inflation period up to 1929, ending with a maximum of 192,000 tons, followed by the depression decline to 89,439 tons in 1933 and recovery to a new record high of 208,500 tons in 1937. The graph also shows the uniformity with which the Oriental tin belt mentioned above has maintained the lead in production. The total known production of the world, dating back to 1800, has been about 7,565,000 tons, of which 3,482,000 tons has been produced during the period under review.

The fact that tin is fundamentally an industrial material, and is not required in war to the extent that other members of the strategic group are, is evidenced by the production figures during the war period. While nickel production doubled, chromium did almost as well, and tungsten quadrupled during the war, tin production declined. If forced by necessity, a war could be carried on with only comparatively small amounts of tin available; Germany did this during the World War, but only with great effort and inconvenience. This does not mean that tin is not properly to be classed as a strategic material, but emphasizes its need on the industrial side of the war effort, rather than on the military; also, conditions have developed to such a stage that in these days, when a war is being waged, practically all industries are war industries, indirectly, if not directly.

USES

Industrial uses for tin in compound form are minor as compared with the metallurgical uses, and are confined largely to the oxide and chloride.

Metallurgical Uses.—The metallurgical uses of tin, which account for about 94 per cent of the consumption of new metal, automatically divide themselves into two groups—as pure metal and as alloy, the former accounting for somewhat more than half, and the latter for a little less than half of the consumption.

The outstanding use is in the production of tinplate, that is, mild steel sheets covered with a layer of tin as a protective coating; a small amount is used in a similar manner to put a lead-tin coating on steel in the manufacture of terne plate, and small amounts are also used in coating metals other than steel. The other main uses for the pure metal are in foil, used in wrapping foods, tobacco, et cetera, and in collapsible tubes for salves, ointments, tooth pastes, and other similar products.

Solder and babbit (bearing metal) account for the bulk of the metal used in alloy form, with lesser amounts in bronze, die casting alloys, and similar combinations.

Chemical Uses.—Industrial uses for tin in the form of various compounds account for about 6 per cent of the consumption, about one-quarter in the form of the oxide, and three-quarters in other compounds, of which the chloride is the most important. The oxide is used as an opacifying agent in white glasses and enamels, and the chloride as a weighting agent in fabrics, particularly silk.

Military Uses.—There are no specific military uses, but war demand considerably increases the consumption of tin in many of its ordinary industrial uses, particularly tin cans, solder, and bearing metal. Such uses as we find of tin in military equipment are merely adaptations of the ordinary industrial uses, applied to a product that happens to be of a military character.

SUBSTITUTES

There is no direct substitute for tin in any of its uses, although there are many partial substitutes. In tinplate the only means of conservation is to use as light a coating as possible, consistent with the life required for the product, and to restrict, if necessary, the uses to which the product may be put, eliminating unessential uses. In many cases a light coating of tin may have its effective protective action considerably increased by a supplementary coating of enamel; this practice is now extensively used in food containers.

Although there is no substitute for tin in the manufacture of tinplate, there has been considerable progress during recent years in the development of substitutes for tinplate in several lines of use. Some work has been done on the use of stainless steel instead of tinplate, but cost is a deterrent in most cases. Greater progress has been made in the use of aluminum, particularly in the canning of fish; here again first cost is an important factor, and more extensive application may depend considerably on the possibilities of secondary recovery of the metal thus used. In containers for other than food products, enamel coatings are being used to some extent to replace tin. For many uses glass containers are a satisfactory substitute for tinplate, so far as the container itself is concerned, and if the display of the contents of the package is desired, glass is necessary; but when packing and transportation are taken into consideration, particularly for long distances, the additional cost of packing to prevent breakage is a disadvantage, and the additional space required by this type of packing is also a factor if transportation space is at a premium.

Among the minor uses of tinplate, enameled ware, aluminum, and nickel have largely replaced the tinplate used in cooking utensils in earlier years, and copper, zinc, and various composition materials have extensively supplanted tinplate and terne plate for roofing.

In the form of foil, aluminum, lead, cellophane, and waxed paper have been extensively substituted for tin, and in collapsible tubes, aluminum and lead, except that in both cases its poisonous character bars lead from use in contact with most food products.

In solder, the most extensive use of tin in alloy form, some saving can be made by the substitution of cadmium for part of the tin, but just how far this substitution can be carried, and how much tin can be saved if necessity demanded, has not yet been determined. In bearings on machines of all types, babbit metals are being replaced by other alloys. The introduction and extensive application of ball and roller bearings have already done away with the demand for much bearing alloy, particularly in heavy machines, and in the past year considerable progress has been made in the application on tinless alloys. Copper-lead alloys, and Frary metal, lead hardened by the addition of barium and calcium, have been used for a number of years in gradually increasing quantities; the more recent additions to the list include lead hardened with lithium, and alloys of cadmium-copper-silver, cadmium-copper-lead, and cadmium-silver, with several others in the experimental stage. The cadmium alloys are particularly effective as prospective savers of tin, as they are being adopted extensively in the automobile industry, which is the heaviest user of bearing metals.

In bronze there is no satisfactory substitute for tin, but various brasses, particularly the aluminum brasses, may replace the bronzes for some uses, as may also monel metal, providing the necessary nickel is available.

In the chemical field the chief item of saving is found in the wide replacement of silk by rayon, which does not require the use of tin salts in dyeing and finishing.

Although the position of a strategic metal is usually improved by the development of substitutes, this is seldom a direct factor in the search for substitutes, the controlling factors being improved technical results or a saving in cost. Since cost is so large a factor in determining the extent to which substitutes are sought, it is only natural that research on tin substitutes should have been active during the past year, prices having been the highest since early in 1928.

ORES

There is but a single commercial ore of tin, the oxide, SnO_2, known as cassiterite, which when pure carries 78.8 per cent tin. The ore is widely distributed, but only in a few countries are the deposits extensive enough to supply an output of any appreciable size. Tin ores occur in both lode and placer form, the latter predominating. The principal lode deposits are in Bolivia, with minor occurrences in England, Malaya, China, Australia, and elsewhere. The Asiatic, East Indian and Australian deposits are predominantly placer.

The Bolivian lodes usually carry 4–8 per cent tin, but in some cases have run as high as 40 per cent. The low limit for commercial operation is usually 1–2 per cent tin, and, in many cases, these low grade ores can not be profitably handled unless they carry some associated mineral, such as tungsten, which helps to pay the cost of operation. The eastern deposits, operated mostly by dredging or hydraulic mining, range from 0.5 to 3.0 pounds of ore per cubic yard.

Cassiterite has a high specific gravity (6.8–7.1), which aids greatly in the concentration of the ore. Malayan concentrates run 70–76 per cent, while others are sometimes as low as 55 per cent; the average is about 70 per cent. Bolivian concentrates vary considerably in grade, depending on the character of the ore; the usual range is a variation of 6–8 per cent from the average of 62 per cent. Lode concentrates are of lower grade and consequently produce a lower grade of metal, unless extensive refining operations are used.

Bolivian concentrates, the only ones that have ever reached the United States in any quantity, are usually sold on a 60 per cent basis, with a premium or penalty for purities above or below the standard. Penalties are also provided for iron in excess of 5 per cent, and sulfur in excess of 1 per cent; undesirable impurities such as lead, copper, arsenic, antimony, and bismuth are covered by an increased treatment charge to meet the cost occasioned by their presence.

Beneficiation.—Due to the high gravity of cassiterite, most of the ore dressing processes utilize gravity methods of separation, and, as the major producing centers are far removed from civilization, many of the methods used are crude but reasonably effective. In the case of Bolivian concentrates, with their higher content of impurities, special treatment is frequently required for further purification before smelting; roasting with proper reagents, followed by leaching, will remove many of the undesirable impurities; flotation processes are also sometimes used, where the impurities are present as sulfides.

Metallurgy.—The fact that tin is present in the ore as oxide simplifies the smelting operation, which consists in heating with carbon as a reducing agent, and with the necessary fluxes to combine with the gangue to form a slag. The smelting may be done either in a blast furnace or a reverberatory furnace. The tin oxide is readily reduced to metal, but there are two complicating factors in the operation. The first of these is that the oxide readily combines with the silica of the gangue to form tin silicates, resulting in a considerable slag loss; nor can this be combated by the use of a strongly basic slag, for then the tin switches over to the rôle of an acid, with the formation of stannates. As a result, the slags carry 10–25 per cent tin, and have to be subjected to a second smelting to recover the high tin content. With careful manipulation the second-run slag can be cut to a tin content of 1 per cent, although it sometimes is allowed to run higher.

The second difficulty is the ready reducibility of many of the impurities in the concentrates, giving a metal of too low a grade for many of the commercial uses unless it is given a subsequent refining. Only a few of the highest grade ores give a metal of the best quality without refining, and the metal recovered from slag smelting is so high in impurities (up to 25 per cent), that it requires extensive purification.

Due to the marked effect which small amounts of various impurities have on the properties of tin, making the metal unsatisfactory for many uses, a refining operation is usually required, in order to bring the metal as originally smelted up to the required standard. Difficulties in the satisfactory removal of some of these impurities make the purity of the original metal of primary importance, and, as result of this, the character of the ore from which the metal was reduced has more effect on the final product than is the case with any other metal.

Tin from certain localities has acquired a recognized reputation for high purity, not because of outstanding excellence in the metallurgical treatment of the ores, but because the ores themselves were of such high purity that ordinary metallurgical methods gave a metal of high quality. "Straits tin" smelted from Malayan ore has long been accepted as the standard of high quality, and that from Banka and Billiton is of even higher purity.

Up until the World War, tin refining was entirely a fire process, and this still remains the prevailing procedure. With metal from the purer ores, of alluvial origin, refining is a minor but usually necessary process; but lode ores, particularly those from Bolivia, are so high in impurities that the refining is a most extensive and necessary part of the treatment if high grade metal is desired. If a mild refining is sufficient, the process used is liquation; if more extensive purification is required, this is followed by boiling or tossing.

Liquation is done by slowly heating the cast slabs of crude metal on the sloping floor of a reverberatory furnace, so that the tin melts and runs away, leaving behind those impurities that have a higher melting point than the tin. If, in order to secure the desired degree of purity, it is necessary to remove impurities with a melting point lower than that of tin, the liquated metal is heated to a high temperature in a kettle, and is boiled or poled by immersing a bundle of green wood under the surface of the metal; the gases given off by the wood cause a violent agitation of the bath, and the fresh metal brought to the surface is freed of its dissolved impurities by oxidation from the air, the accumulated drosses being skimmed from the surface of the bath as they accumulate; some of the more modern refineries use a stream of compressed air to agitate the metal. The same effect may be secured by tossing the metal, which consists in repeatedly lifting ladles full of metal from the kettle and pouring them back in a thin stream. Most of the iron and a considerable proportion of the arsenic and antimony are removed by liquation; boiling will almost completely remove the iron remaining after liquation, and will partially remove other impurities, particularly arsenic, and antimony left by liquation.

Electrolytic refining was inaugurated in the United States in 1916, but was abandoned in 1924 for economic reasons, although it permitted the production from impure Bolivian ores of a metal equal in quality to the best Straits tin. It is understood that the electrolytic process is still in use in one plant in Japan, and three in Germany.

Secondary Recovery.—The secondary recovery of tin has developed to a considerable extent in the United States, Germany, and Japan, and other countries are slowly following the lead. It is possible to make recoveries that represent a very appreciable percentage of the total consumption, secondary tin having supplied from one-quarter to one-third of the total United States consumption during recent years. About 10 per cent of the secondary recovery is obtained from the treatment of tinplate scrap from the manufacture of tin cans. The recovery of tin from used cans had been tried to some extent, but has not proved economical, largely due to the problem of collecting and cleaning the used cans; should this eventually be worked out on an economic basis, secondary recovery will increase considerably in importance.

Forms in Which Tin Appears on the Market.—Tin comes on the market in pigs, usually of about 100 pounds, but in some cases more or less; the regulations of the London Metal Exchange, the world's central market for tin, permit a minimum pig of 28 pounds, and a maximum of 120 pounds.

The standard grades of the leading smelters have so firmly established a reputation for quality that practically all buying is based on standard brands, rather than on specifications. Two general classes of tin are recognized by the New York Metal Exchange, Standard, or Straits tin, and Common, or 99 per cent tin. Although Standard tin is based on Straits quality, any other brand or locality will be accepted if it assays better than 99.75 per cent tin. On contracts calling for Common tin, any brand assaying not less than 99 per cent is good delivery.

ORE RESERVES

As one might expect, when one considers that the bulk of the tin output comes from remote and almost uncivilized sections of the world, and that much of it is produced by native miners using primitive methods, information on ore reserves is fragmentary and incomplete. Only the larger and well established operating companies have developed ore reserves to cover any extended future working; the remainder work largely from hand to mouth. Only about one-quarter of the production comes from deposits which have been developed for future work to a sufficient extent that definite reserves are laid out, and, of these, the life of the known reserves is often only one or two years.

The largest single operating company in the world produces about half of the Bolivian output, but records for several years show only about two years' reserves blocked out, and other lode deposits show little better development, although the inference may be drawn from long life in the past, and the trend of the ore bodies, that they are good for many years to come. As has already been mentioned, one mine in China has been worked for 500 years, and others even longer. The character of the placer deposits is such that they can be developed with much less work than the lode deposits, and some have reserves blocked out for 15 to 30 years in advance; but on the other hand, there is little definite information on the majority of them beyond the fact that they have been worked for a great many years and seem to promise plentiful supplies at least for the immediate future.

Since a modern dredge has a useful life of 15 to 20 years, it is not likely to be installed unless the ground has been tested to a sufficient extent to demonstrate the presence of enough ore to last for a reasonable proportion of this life, and the same holds true for the simpler mining methods; but as the cost of installation decreases, the necessity for blocking out large future supplies lessens, until eventually, with the crude hand-washing methods, and others using equipment that is cheap and easy to move, a small deposit may be attacked without any knowledge of its size and, when it is worked out, the equipment is transferred elsewhere.

In many ways the mining of tin bears a striking similarity to the mining of gold. Following out this comparison, we can in the future look forward to the gradual depletion of the extensive alluvial deposits of tin, and an increasing dependence on lode deposits to maintain the supply.

WORLD OUTPUT AND SUPPLY

Tin is one of the oldest of the known metals, and some of the deposits still being mined today were sources of supply in the pre-Christian era. Tin from Cornwall was brought to the Mediterranean peoples by the Phoenician traders, and the control of this supply was one of the reasons for the conquest of Britain by Julius Caesar, while the tin content of the ancient Indian and Chinese bronzes is believed to have come from Malaya. In these early days the uses of tin were limited and production was small. It was not until within the last century that the increasing development of civilization and of industrial effort demanded increasing supplies. Such figures as are available indicate that at 1800 the total world output was less than 9,000 tons, supplied mostly by Malaya, England, and China.

It required 50 years to double this output, but later, in the seventies and eighties, production was doubled in as few as 15 years. Since then the rate of increase slowed down to 20–25 years for doubling the output.

As has already been pointed out, during the war and post-war deflation periods, tin production was on the decline. It was not

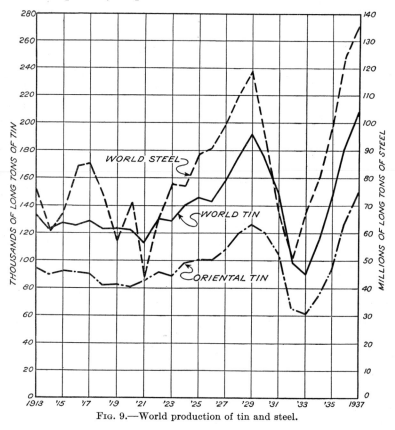

Fig. 9.—World production of tin and steel.

until 1923 that the 1913 output was exceeded. The inflation period maximum was reached in 1929, and the depression period minimum in 1933. Increasing demands during the inflation period and the resulting competition for the expanding market had, by 1928, pushed production well beyond consumption, and efforts were initiated by individual producers to reduce the over-production by restriction of output. During the summer of

1928 a Tin Producers' Association was formed to regulate the output of the mines, but before any effective reduction could be accomplished, the beginnings of the depression period cut consumption to such an extent that conditions remained relatively as bad as before.

In 1930 steps were taken to establish a legally enforcible curtailment program to replace the former more or less voluntary one, and eventually the Governments of the leading producing countries, Malaya, Bolivia, Netherlands East Indies, and Nigeria, agreed on a compulsory restriction program that went into effect March 1, 1931. Under this plan the International Tin Committee assigned export quotas to the participating countries; each Government supported the plan with the necessary legislation, and divided the export quota into production quotas to the various producers, covered by individual permits limiting production to a specified tonnage, proportioned against previous performance. Later, Siam, Indo-China and Belgian Congo joined in the restriction scheme, with certain limitations.

Continued decrease in consumption as the depression advanced resulted in several lowerings of the quota levels, eventually reaching a minimum of one-third of the 1929 basis, in order to permit the absorption of excessive stocks that had accumulated since 1928. As the market improved and the stocks were gradually worked up, the quota was increased, and, at the end of 1934, was 40 per cent of the 1929 output, or about 30 per cent of actual production capacity. The original restriction agreement expired in 1933, and was extended for another three years, to the end of 1936. In spite of considerable opposition from minor producers, as well as from consumers, restriction has become fairly well stabilized, and will presumably play an important part in the recovery of the industry to more normal levels.

Table I*a* shows the annual outputs since 1913 for all countries which have contributed as much as 1 per cent of the total output, the annual totals, the period totals for each country, and the percentage of the period total that has been supplied by each country, while Table I*b* gives the same data for the smelter output. On the whole, production has been more steady, and fluctuations have been less pronounced under the stress of the conditions imposed during the successive periods than has been

TABLE Ia.—WORLD PRODUCTION OF TIN IN ORE
(Thousands of long tons)

	Malaya[1]	Bolivia[2]	Netherlands East Indies	Siam	China[2]	Nigeria	Australia	Great Britain	Burma (India)	Belgian Congo	Total[3]
1913	51.4	26.3	20.5	6.7	8.4	3.9	7.8	5.3	0.3	......	133.4
1914	50.6	22.0	19.6	6.6	7.3	4.3	5.4	5.1	0.3	......	123.9
1915	49.8	21.5	19.2	9.0	8.0	4.8	5.5	5.0	0.4	......	126.8
1916	47.2	21.0	21.3	8.8	7.6	5.5	5.7	4.7	0.4	0.1	125.1
1917	42.9	27.6	20.7	9.2	11.8	5.8	4.9	3.9	0.6	0.1	129.8
1918	40.1	29.1	19.2	8.8	8.7	5.9	4.7	4.0	0.6	0.1	123.2
1919	39.2	28.7	19.9	8.5	8.7	5.7	4.8	3.3	1.2	0.2	123.5
1920	36.9	27.8	21.2	6.2	10.6	5.2	5.2	3.7	1.6	0.4	122.0
1921	36.2	18.8	26.4	6.2	11.2	5.1	3.6	0.7	1.4	0.6	113.5
1922	37.2	31.8	29.3	7.0	14.0	5.1	2.6	0.4	1.5	0.9	132.2
1923	39.4	29.8	29.1	7.7	8.7	5.9	3.1	1.0	1.4	1.0	129.0
1924	46.9	31.6	31.6	7.8	7.0	6.2	3.1	2.0	1.4	1.0	140.8
1925	48.1	32.6	32.7	6.8	8.9	6.5	3.0	2.3	1.3	1.1	145.8
1926	47.7	29.6	33.0	7.5	6.8	7.0	2.9	2.3	2.5	1.1	143.6
1927	54.2	35.8	33.9	7.6	6.2	7.6	3.1	2.6	2.4	0.9	158.4
1928	64.4	40.3	35.0	7.6	7.0	9.0	2.9	2.8	1.9	0.8	176.0
1929	69.4	46.3	35.0	10.5	6.8	10.7	2.2	3.3	2.6	1.0	192.0
1930	64.0	38.1	34.2	11.5	6.5	8.7	1.5	2.5	3.0	0.8	175.1
1931	54.9	30.7	27.5	12.4	6.2	8.8	1.8	0.6	3.0	0.7	149.7
1932	29.7	20.6	15.7	9.3	7.1	4.3	2.1	1.1	3.2	0.7	98.9
1933	24.9	14.7	14.4	10.3	8.2	3.8	2.8	1.5	3.2	2.2	90.7
1934	34.1	20.6	18.7	10.6	7.9	5.0	3.0	2.0	4.1	4.6	115.8
1935	46.0	27.2	24.7	9.8	9.5	7.0	3.1	2.1	4.5	6.5	147.0
1936	66.8	24.1	31.7	12.7	10.5	9.6	3.0	2.1	4.5	7.3	180.4
1937	77.5	25.0	39.8	16.4	10.2	10.4	3.3	2.0	5.0	9.3	208.4
Totals	1,203.6	701.8	654.5	225.4	213.9	161.1	89.1	65.7	52.1	40.9	3,503.3
Per cent	34.4	20.0	18.7	6.4	6.1	4.6	2.5	1.9	1.5	1.2	100.0

[1] Includes Federated and Unfederated States, and Straits Settlement.   [2] Exports.   [3] Includes minor outputs not listed, averaging 3,800 tons per year, or 2.7 per cent of the total.

TABLE Ib.—APPROXIMATE WORLD PRODUCTION OF METALLIC TIN
(Thousands of long tons)

	Malaya	Great Britain	Netherlands East Indies	Nether-lands	China	Germany	Australia	Belgium	United States	Others	Total
1913	64.6	27.0	17.2	.....	8.4	11.8	4.7	.....	.....	1.5	135.0
1914	65.2	25.7	15.4	.....	7.1	9.6	3.1	.....	.....	1.3	127.4
1915	68.2	36.1	12.7	.....	7.9	1.1	4.2	.....	.....	1.3	131.5
1916	62.9	27.9	14.3	.....	8.3	1.0	3.9	.....	2.0	1.2	121.5
1917	62.6	32.7	12.9	.....	12.8	1.8	4.0	.....	5.4	1.3	133.5
1918	54.9	26.6	16.2	.....	8.7	2.2	4.6	.....	9.2	1.2	123.6
1919	51.9	22.9	13.2	.....	8.7	2.5	4.1	.....	10.9	1.1	115.3
1920	49.3	21.3	13.4	.....	11.3	3.0	4.1	.....	15.8	3.8	122.0
1921	41.9	12.1	13.3	.....	6.1	3.4	3.0	.....	10.3	0.8	89.8
1922	66.3	21.8	15.6	.....	9.0	3.8	2.7	.....	8.1	2.1	129.4
1923	69.9	30.9	15.0	.....	7.9	2.3	3.1	0.4	6.7	2.1	138.3
1924	80.7	35.5	15.5	.....	7.0	2.5	3.3	0.6	0.4	1.4	146.8
1925	79.1	38.7	14.5	.....	8.9	2.3	3.2	0.9	.....	0.7	147.5
1926	76.3	37.6	16.4	.....	6.5	2.3	3.0	0.8	.....	1.5	144.6
1927	83.5	38.1	15.6	.....	6.2	6.1	3.1	1.2	.....	0.8	154.5
1928	98.8	48.0	14.0	.....	7.0	4.6	3.1	1.0	.....	4.0	180.5
1929	105.7	55.2	13.3	1.3	6.8	2.6	2.3	0.9	.....	4.2	192.3
1930	96.8	45.4	14.6	1.9	6.5	2.8	1.5	0.7	.....	4.5	174.7
1931	87.4	35.6	12.9	2.8	6.2	3.7	1.7	0.2	.....	0.9	151.4
1932	49.9	28.5	8.2	4.0	7.1	3.9	2.0	0.8	.....	2.2	104.6
1933	46.9	23.0	8.9	5.1	8.2	0.8	2.4	2.7	.....	1.1	99.1
1934	49.6	25.4	10.5	13.6	8.5	0.6	2.5	3.9	.....	1.1	115.7
1935	60.5	30.0	11.3	15.0	9.5	0.8	2.8	4.0	.....	4.7	138.6
1936	84.5	34.0	12.9	21.2	10.5	0.9	2.7	5.1	.....	4.7	176.5
1937	95.2	34.5	13.9	26.8	10.5	3.9	3.0	5.5	.....	5.6	198.9
Totals	1,752.6	794.5	341.7	91.7	205.6	77.5	78.1	28.7	68.8	3,493.0	55,100
Percent	50.2	22.7	9.8	2.6	5.9	2.2	2.2	0.8	2.0	100.0	1.6
Mine Output	1,203.6	65.7	654.5		213.9		89.1		1.1	3,530.3	1,275,400
Deficit Imported		728.8		91.7		77.5		28.7	67.7		1,220,390
Surplus Exported	549.0		312.8		8.3		11.0				

the case with most of the other strategic metals.   The war period brought no phenomenal increases in output from countries favorably located, or from others not formerly producers, as has happened with other metals, and the increases during the inflation period were pretty well distributed.

Australia.—Although a producer of tin for nearly 100 years, Australia had no appreciable output until the early seventies, when in two years time it jumped from 100 tons to the position of leading producer.   In the decade from 1873 to 1882 Australia held the lead except in two years, with outputs ranging from 10,000 to 13,000 tons (23 per cent of the world total), gradually declining to less than 3,500 tons in 1898; this was followed by a recovery, reaching almost the former level, and a second decline that brought the output to 7,780 tons in 1913 and a low point of 1,451 tons in 1930, since when there has been marked improvement.   Production has amounted to 2.5 per cent of the world total since 1913 and 5.5 per cent since 1800.

Deposits of both lode and placer type have been worked in six states.   Production has been mostly from Tasmania, New South Wales, and Queensland, in about equal proportions, with small amounts from West Australia, Victoria, and Northern Territory.   Since 1918, New South Wales has replaced Tasmania as the chief producing State.

Bolivia.—Production of tin did not begin in Bolivia until about 1860, and did not reach outputs that made it of any great importance until the early years of the present century, when development became more rapid.   In 1906, Netherlands East Indies was surpassed, and Bolivia took second place in the production list, a position which has been held ever since except in six years.   In 1913, production was 26,300 tons, or 20 per cent of the world output, and during the early years of the war period, production declined here, as elsewhere.

Up to this time the Bolivian concentrates were smelted in Europe, mostly in England, but, during the war, shipping facilities were too much in demand to permit this, while, at the same time, the heavy United States consumption required cross-haul of metal, and in 1916 the smelting of Bolivian ores was begun in the United States; this continued until 1924, reaching the maximum in 1920, and was responsible for the war period increase in Bolivian production.   For a short time during the war, a small smelter was operated in Bolivia, and another in Chile, but conditions were unfavorable, particularly with respect to fuel supply, and they did not last long. With the cessation of smelting in the United States, England again took the lead in the handling of the Bolivian ores, with smaller amounts going to Netherlands and Germany.

The maximum output in 1929 was 24.1 per cent of the world total; the output since 1913 was 20.0 per cent of the world total, but the comparatively late entry of Bolivia as a producer cuts the proportion of the total since 1800 to 12.5 per cent.

The early production of tin in Bolivia was a byproduct recovery from ores mined primarily for their silver content. The development of the country into an important producer followed the completion of rail connections with the Chilean coast. The output is derived almost entirely from lode deposits situated in the higher levels of the Andes. At the present time operation is rather highly centralized, about half of the output coming from a single company, one-fifth from three others, and the remainder from some twenty small producers.

China.—China has been an important producer of tin for several centuries, but there is no record of output for earlier years, and records for recent years are confined to exports, with little or nothing known as to the amounts of metal involved in local consumption. Exports have been quite uniform, mostly at 6,000–8,000 tons, with some increase during the war and post-war periods, but with little change either in the inflation or depression periods. The ore is in lodes extending to considerable depths; one mine, now about 3,000 feet deep, has been operated for more than 500 years. About 95 per cent of the output is from the Kochiu district in southeastern Yunnan, near Mengtze, with small amounts from the neighboring provinces of Kwantung and Kwangsi. Mining and concentration are carried on by rather primitive methods and the concentrates are smelted at the mines to crude metal, which is refined in Hong Kong before exportation.

Nigeria.—Nigeria is one of the more recent additions to the list of producers, production having begun with 1 ton in 1904, increasing to 3,872 tons in 1913, and a maximum of 10,734 tons in 1929, with subsequent decrease in the depression period. Recent production has been maintained well enough to bring the total since 1913 up to 4.6 per cent of the world total, but the late start cuts the proportion to 2 per cent of the world total since 1800.

The bulk of the output is from alluvial deposits situated in the Bauchi Plateau, in the northeastern section of the Colony. Development has been hindered by shortage of water and inadequate transportation facilities, and recently by restriction measures. The ore is exported to the English smelters for treatment.

Great Britain.—Although now of comparatively minor importance, except that they furnish the only appreciable output in any of the major consuming countries, the tin deposits of Cornwall are among the oldest in the world. The records of these mines are more extensive than those of any others in the world, going back to 1156 A. D. It has been estimated that the total tin production from this area from 500 B. C. to date has been nearly 3,300,000 tons, of which more than 2,500,000 tons was previous to 1800; considering the relatively small amounts of metals required by the civilization of those days, this is a remarkably large figure. During the first three quarters of the nineteenth century the output was 30–40 per cent of the world total; later, decreasing outputs in Britain and large increases elsewhere cut the percentage heavily. Production since 1800 amounts to 10.2 per cent of the world total, and since 1913 to only 2 per cent. A maximum output in excess of 10,000 tons was reached in the sixties, and marked decline did not set in until the nineties; by 1913 production had declined to 5,288 tons, and in 1922 to only 370 tons. It is interesting to note that the English output since 1900 is almost identical with the corresponding figures of a century earlier.

The early Phoenicians recovered alluvial ore from streams and underground mining was not developed until later. Now all recovery is from lodes.

Burma (India).—The Malayan tin deposits extend up the peninsula through the lower portion of Siam and into Lower Burma. Production has been quite small until recent years, increasing from about 300 tons at the beginning of the war period to 5,000 tons in 1937, with few declines. India is one of the few producers which did not show a decrease in output during the depression period, but a constant increase. Part of the regular improvement in tin recovery in Burma is due to the fact that tungsten is associated with most of the ores in this northern section, thus adding to the value of the recovery.

Malaya.—The territory covered by this general term includes the Federated and Unfederated Malay States and the Straits

Settlements; the first two are producers of tin ore, most of which is converted into metal in smelters located in the latter.   Throughout the entire period for which production data are available, Malaya has been an important producer of tin, heading the list during most of the time, and consistently so since 1878, although the proportion supplied has decreased during recent years under the restriction program.   Malaya has produced 37.4 per cent of the recorded tin output since 1800, and 34.4 per cent since 1913; the maximum was 56.5 per cent in 1896, decreasing steadily as production increased in other countries, reaching 40.9 per cent in 1914, 30.2 per cent in 1920, and 26.6 per cent in 1933, although during the inflation period it had recovered to 36.6 per cent in 1928.   Since 1934 there has been a marked recovery, reaching 37.2 per cent in 1937.   Most of the output has been from the Federated States, only about 2 per cent of the total having come from the Unfederated States, and only a few hundred tons from the Straits.

In the Federated States, the deposits are located in Perak, Selangor, Pahang, and Negri Sembilan, the first two furnishing respectively 60 per cent and 30 per cent of the total.   In the Unfederated States, small tonnages have come from Johore, Kedah, Kelantan, Perlis and Trengganu, reaching about 2,000 tons shortly before the war period, attaining a war maximum of 4,400 tons, and then receding to the pre-war level.   The deposits are predominatingly alluvial; during the peak years of the inflation period about 5 per cent of the output was from lode mines. The original primitive methods of operating the alluvial deposits began to give way to more modern methods in 1912, when dredges were introduced; these, supplemented by hydraulic mining, now produced about one-half of the output.

Netherlands East Indies.—These islands were among the early producers of tin, and, lying as they do in the Oriental tin belt, the ores are of the same character and high grade as the adjacent deposits of Malaya.   During the third quarter of the last century, the output was almost as great as that of Malaya, but in the fourth quarter Malaya forged ahead.   From 1885 to 1905 the islands ranked as second producer, and then gave way to Bolivia. The consistent maintenance of output is evidenced by the fact that the output since 1800 is 18.4 per cent of the world total, while that since 1913 is 18.7 per cent.   Nearly two-thirds of the output is from the Island of Banka, and one-third from Billiton, with small amounts from Singkep, Sumatra, and the Riouw Archipelago. The Banka deposits are operated as a Government monopoly, but the others are in the hands of private companies, one on each island, paying royalty to the Government on their output. Operations on Banka are entirely alluvial, but on Billiton and Singkep there are also lode deposits. There is also a small recovery by dredging from the sea bottom near Singkep. Mining is mostly by open-pit methods, by hand, or with gravel pumps, but dredges are now being introduced.

Siam.—Although among the earlier producers of tin on a small scale, there are no statistical records of production until 1900. Estimates from export data indicate an output of about 2,500 tons in 1875, increasing gradually to about 3,900 tons in 1900, and 6,700 tons in 1913. Siam was one of the few countries in which production increased during the war period, and has shown comparatively small decreases during the depression. The deposits connect with those of Burma on the north and Malaya on the south, and are of the same general character, predominantly alluvial; they lie along the mountain range that forms the backbone of the peninsula, with the most productive areas on the western side, at Puket Island and Tongkah Harbor. Mining was originally in the hands of Chinese, but an English company began operations in 1880, and foreign companies now carry on dredging in the coastal region, and hydraulic mining in the interior. Except for small amounts taken by a native smelter for local consumption, the concentrates go to the smelters at the Straits.

Other Countries.—There are a number of minor producers, the most important of which are South Africa, with a maximum output of 1,900 tons; and Belgian Congo, with a maximum of 1,100 tons; Spain and Portugal have a combined output of 600–800 tons, and Indo-China and Japan each contribute about the same amount. Outputs of a few tons a year have been made more or less regularly by a number of others, chiefly Argentina, Austria, Czecho-Slovakia, Germany, Mexico, and the United States, but the combined outputs of all of them are so small that they are insignificant.

SMELTING

Table II*b* shows the approximate outputs of metallic tin from the more important countries in which smelting is done, from 1913 to date. These figures, particularly those before 1920, have been assembled from a number of different sources, with considerable variation between authorities for some years; in some cases results have been possible only by indirect methods; the table is therefore not presented as an absolutely accurate record, but as an approximation, which is believed to be close enough to the true figures to serve satisfactorily for the purpose of comparison in a general summary. A brief inspection of this table in comparison with Table I*a* makes it clear that smelting is even more highly concentrated than is ore production. Still further information on this line will be found in the subsequent section on *Political and Commercial Control*. The three leading ore producers, Malaya, Bolivia, and Netherlands East Indies, have supplied 73 per cent of the total mine production, while the three leading smelting countries, Malaya, Great Britain, and Netherlands East Indies, have produced 83 per cent of the metal; it is also to be noted that Bolivia, the second largest ore producer, does no smelting, and that Great Britain, a minor ore producer, takes second place in smelting, using imported ore for 83 per cent of the output. About 56 per cent of the total metal output has been smelted in the country of origin, and 44 per cent was exported to other countries. Of the ore exported for smelting, about 20 per cent originated in countries where the smelting capacity is not able to handle the entire ore output, and 80 per cent was from countries in which there is no smelting industry at all, or, as in a few cases, where smelting is done only on a scale to cover local consumption.

In addition to the smelters mentioned in the following discussion of the individual producing countries, which is based on 1934 reports, several small plants have been discontinued during the past few years, and others have been established.

Malaya.—Slightly over half of the output of metallic tin has been in Malaya, where at the present time there are four smelters, two at Penang and one at Singapore, Straits Settlements, and a smaller one at Selangor, Federated Malay States. The Malayan smelters have turned out 1,752,600 tons of metal, as compared with a local mine production of 1,203,600 tons, leaving a deficit of 549,000 tons, which has been supplied by imports, mostly from Siam, with smaller amounts from Burma, Indo-China, and other neighboring producers; the chief contributor from a distance has been South Africa. Most of the Alaskan ore has been shipped to Seattle, and thence to the Malayan smelters for treatment.

In 1929, Malaya produced 55 per cent of the total smelter output but, in 1937, only 48 per cent, largely as a result of the diversion of Netherlands East Indies ores to Netherlands.

Great Britain.—Although Great Britain has produced only 2 per cent of the ore output, the smelter output is 23 per cent of the total, as there are eight smelters in the country.   Metal production has totaled 794,500 tons, 65,700 tons from domestic ores, and 728,800 tons from imported ores, about two-thirds of which came from Bolivia, with Nigeria and other producing sections of the British Empire supplying most of the remainder.

Netherlands East Indies and Netherlands.—The 10 per cent of the total smelter output supplied by Netherlands East Indies represents only a portion of their ore output, as the smelting capacity has never been sufficient to handle all of it.   Of a total mine production of 654,500 tons, 341,700 tons has been smelted locally, and 312,800 tons has been exported.   Until recently the surplus went to the Straits, but in 1929 smelting was started at a new plant at Arnhem, Netherlands, which has grown until its 1934 output was greater than that of the island smelters while in 1937 it was almost double the island output.   In addition to the government smelters at Banka and Billiton and the privately owned plant at Billiton, the Government maintains a smelter at Batavia, Java.

China.—There is no information available on smelting in China for local consumption; the figures shown cover exports only. Most of this metal is handled in two small smelters in Yunnan, and four refineries in Hong Kong.   In addition, there are a number of small native smelters at the mines, which smelt for local consumption.

Germany.—The German smelting industry is based entirely on imported ores; the relatively large pre-war output rapidly dwindled during the war period, due to the inaccessibility of foreign ore supplies, and has never recovered to its former level, although there are six small plants, three of which are electrolytic.

Australia.—Two small smelters are still in operation at Sydney and three have recently been closed down in Tasmania.   Metal output has been fairly uniform, but with a slow downward trend, which has cut the total by about half since 1913.   A small surplus of ore has been exported.

Belgium.—A single plant in Belgium is of interest not so much from its past record, as for its future possibilities, in view of the increasing importance of its source of ore supply, the Belgian Congo.

Belgian Congo.—A small smelter has been handling about one-third of the ore output, the other two-thirds being exported to Belgium.

United States.—Although there have been other efforts of minor importance, there have been only two serious attempts to establish tin smelting in the United States, both of which have ended in failure, due to conditions over which the operators had no control. A plant with a daily capacity of 50 tons of metal was built in New Jersey in 1903, but was never put into operation, as it was unable to secure a satisfactory ore supply. The second attempt started in 1916, as a result of war conditions and demands, and lasted until early in 1924. Since the failure of these efforts was due to the manipulation of political and commercial control of the ore supplies, further details will be given later, under that heading.

All told, during the second attempt, eight plants were put into operation; the first and largest of these began operation in 1916, and also was the last to shut down, in 1924; others worked for shorter periods, some for less than a year. The ore supplies for these plants were drawn almost entirely from Bolivia, with only insignificant amounts from other sources, including the small domestic output. The total production during the period of operation was 68,800 tons, the maximum being 15,800 tons in 1920.

Other Countries.—Countries having smelters for local consumption, but not contributing to the world market, include Argentina, Portugal (2), and Japan. There is also a small plant in France, the output of which is negligible as compared with consumption.

UNITED STATES OUTPUT AND SUPPLY

The story of tin production in the United States is a short one, quickly told. There has been a small output since 1901, averaging 39 tons a year; the total output to date is about 1,450 tons, mostly from alluvial sources in Alaska; in only four years has the output exceeded 100 tons—1912, 1916, 1936 and 1937, the peak being 168 tons in 1937. Repeated attempts have been made to operate lode deposits in the Black Hills and the southern Appalachians, but the outputs have been small and soon discontinued.

Other attempts have been made in California, Nevada, New Mexico, and Washington, but with no success. All of the known deposits are too small and too low in grade to give any real promise

TABLE II.—AVAILABLE SUPPLY OF TIN IN THE UNITED STATES
(Thousands of long tons)

	Imports		Ex-ports	Avail-able New Sup-ply[5]	Total World Output (Mine)	Per Cent Con-sumed in U. S.	Sec-ondary	Avail-able Total Supply	Ratio Sec-ondary to New, Per Cent
	Metal[1]	In Ore[2]							
1913........	46.6	[3]	0.8	45.8	133.4	34	12.7	58.5	28
1914........	42.4	[3]	0.6	41.8	123.9	34	11.1	52.9	27
1915........	51.6	0.4	0.4	51.6	126.8	41	12.4	64.0	24
1916........	61.6	2.0	0.5	63.2	125.1	51	15.5	78.7	25
1917........	64.4	5.4	0.3	69.7	129.8	54	17.3	87.0	25
1918........	63.6	9.2	0.3	72.5	123.2	59	21.3	93.8	29
1919........	40.4	10.9	0.3	50.6	123.5	41	21.5	72.1	42
1920........	56.1	15.8	0.9	70.9	122.0	58	21.0	91.9	30
1921........	24.2	10.3	1.5	33.0	113.5	29	15.1	48.1	46
1922........	60.2	8.1	1.1	67.2	132.2	51	17.4	84.6	26
1923........	68.9	6.7	1.0	74.6	129.0	58	27.0	101.5	36
1924........	65.1	0.4	1.0	64.5	140.8	46	27.9	92.5	43
1925........	76.6	0.2	0.9	75.9	145.8	52	27.6	103.5	36
1926........	77.2	0.3	2.0	75.5	143.6	52	29.8	105.3	40
1927........	71.1	0.1	2.2	69.0	158.4	44	32.9	102.0	48
1928........	78.0	0.1	1.7	76.4	176.0	43	32.0	108.4	42
1929........	87.1	0.1	2.0	85.3	192.0	44	30.6	115.9	36
1930........	80.7	0.3	2.2	78.8	175.1	45	23.4	102.2	30
1931........	66.1	[4]	1.7	64.4	149.7	43	17.7	82.1	27
1932........	34.8	[4]	1.1	33.7	98.9	34	13.2	46.9	39
1933........	63.7	[4]	1.0	62.7	90.7	69	19.7	82.4	31
1934........	40.0	[4]	1.3	38.7	115.8	33	22.2	61.0	57
1935........	64.3	0.2	2.3	62.1	147.0	42	24.9	87.1	40
1936........	76.0	0.2	0.4	75.8	180.4	42	25.0	100.8	33
1937........	88.1	0.2	0.3	87.9	208.4	42	27.1	115.1	31

[1] Includes some scrap tin. [2] Metal content of ore not reported until 1924; previous figures are metal smelted from imported ore. [3] Not reported. [4] Less than 50 tons. [5] Does not include domestic production or changes in visible stocks, and hence will not check with apparent consumption figures in Table B.

of commercial development of any magnitude. It has been estimated that the imposition of a tariff of 100 per cent, or an equivalent price of $1 per pound, could not, even under the most optimistic viewing of conditions, result in the production of as much as 10 per cent of our consumption requirements. For all ordinary purposes, then, the possibilities of establishing tin production in the United States as a going industry can be ignored.

Lacking ore supplies capable of development, the United States has done the next best thing and has developed the recovery of secondary tin to a greater extent than any other country. Without these efforts, the consumption of new tin would have been decidedly increased, for, since 1913, the total amount produced is about 547,000 tons, making the United States in effect the fourth largest tin producer in the world.

The United States is the largest consumer of tin, all of which, outside of secondary recovery, must be imported from distant producers. The available supply of new metal since 1913 has varied from 29 per cent to 70 per cent of the world output, and has averaged 46 per cent for the entire period. Most of the imports have been in the form of metal, as smelting operations have been carried on only during the years 1916–1924. Table II gives a summary of the available supply of tin in the United States since 1913.

Imports.—Imports of metallic tin have been on a gradually increasing scale which almost doubled the amount between 1913 and 1929, and which has been interrupted three times: in the war period by the partial switch to ore imports, and in the post-war and depression periods by decreasing industrial demand. Previous to 1915, imports of ore and concentrates were so small that they were not separately reported; with the beginning of domestic smelting, imports of concentrates increased to a maximum in 1920, and then decreased, being only nominal in amount after smelting was discontinued in 1924. Table III shows the direct imports of metal from the leading countries where smelting is done, in addition to which there have been indirect imports through other countries, the sources of which are not known. These indirect shipments have not exceeded 2,000 tons, and average only 1 per cent of the total imports, so that, regardless of their source, they can not greatly affect the significance of the data for the more important countries, but in the case of some of the minor countries in the list, the figures may not be sufficiently complete to show the whole truth, if appreciable amounts of metal have eventually reached the United States through other countries. The total imports since 1913 include about 1,549,000 tons of primary metal from the various sources, plus 70,000 tons of metal content in concentrates, almost entirely from Bolivia, and 16,000 tons or more of scrap tin from unlisted sources (not included in the table).

Of the total primary metal imports, Malaya has supplied about 62 per cent, most of which was from ore of its own production. This percentage showed a maximum of 75 per cent in 1931, and a minimum of 37 per cent in 1917. Although the figures vary considerably from year to year between these two limits, in general, the proportion received from this source was increasing up to the peak of the depression. Great Britain supplied 22 per cent of the imports, mostly from Bolivian and Nigerian ores. China furnished 5 per.cent and Australia 1 per cent from domestic ores.

TABLE III.—IMPORTS OF METALLIC TIN INTO THE UNITED STATES
(Thousands of long tons)

	Ma-laya	Great Britain	China	Nether-lands East Indies	Nether-lands	Aus-tralia	Ger-many	Other Coun-tries	Total
1913	19.2	24.4	1	1	0.2	1	1.3	1.5	46.6
1914	16.9	22.7	1	1	0.3	1	1.4	1.2	42.4
1915	28.9	18.0	1,047	3.0		0.1		0.6	51.6
1916	30.9	18.5	2,328	9.1		0.5		0.3	61.6
1917	23.7	17.7	5,392	14.1		2.6		0.9	64.4
1918	32.2	8.1	8,476	9.5		3.4		2.0	63.6
1919	25.7	9.5	120	2.3		1.5		1.0	40.0
1920	34.6	10.8	5,973	1.5	0.9	1.4		0.8	56.1
1921	15.5	7.0	912	0.1		0.3		0.4	24.2
1922	42.3	9.0	4,601	2.9	0.4	0.5	0.1	0.5	60.2
1923	47.0	11.2	5,864	3.7	2	0.4	0.1	0.6	68.9
1924	45.5	12.4	2,163	1.0	2.5	0.6	0.6	0.2	65.1
1925	49.1	17.9	4,116	0.3	4.1	0.7	2	0.4	76.6
1926	42.8	20.8	2,764	1.8	7.2	0.9	0.4	0.5	77.2
1927	45.1	14.0	1,971	0.3	7.8	0.7	1.3	0.1	71.1
1928	52.3	12.2	2,224	0.3	7.2	0.8	1.8	1.2	78.0
1929	58.2	16.5	3,453	0.3	7.5	0.6	0.6	2	87.1
1930	55.7	12.1	4,955	0.2	7.4	0.2	0.1	2	80.7
1931	49.7	7.8	4,326	0.9	2.0	0.4	0.9	0.1	66.1
1932	21.8	5.4	3,852	0.5	2.7	0.2	0.2	0.1	34.8
1933	31.6	20.9	3,983	1.3	3.2	2	1.5	1.0	63.7
1934	24.8	8.5	2,854	1.7	0.8	2	0.9	0.3	40.0
1935	37.2	15.6	2,422	2.5	2.0	121	0.9	3.6	64.3
1936	54.4	8.4	1,029	2.7	4.5	25	0.2	4.8	76.0
1937	66.7	7.2	4,467	4.1	2.4	95		3.1	88.1
Totals	952.0	336.4	79,292	64.2	63.3	16,101	12.2	25.1	1,548.6
Per cent	61.5	21.7	5.1	4.1	4.1	1.0	0.8	1.6	100.0

[1] Not reported separately; included in Other Countries.   [2] Less than 50 tons.

The metal from the ores of Netherlands East Indies has shown considerable change; all told, 8 per cent of the imports have come from this source, one-half direct and the other half by way of Netherlands. Until 1929, metal received from Netherlands was re-exportation of receipts from Banka and Billiton, but since then smelting has been carried on in Netherlands, and the amount of direct imports from Netherlands East Indies has greatly decreased. Apparently a shift in the opposite direction is taking place between Belgium and the Belgian Congo; as shown in Table Ib, there has been some smelting done in Belgium since 1923, using ores from the Congo, and since 1933 the output has increased considerably. There have been frequent small imports of tin from Belgium into the United States, but in 1933 Belgian Congo appeared in the list as a source of a small amount of the imports, and in later years a considerable proportion of the imports listed from "other countries" has been from this source. Previous to the World War, imports from Germany were fairly large as compared with the local smelter production; these were entirely discontinued during the war period, but began again on a small scale in 1922. There is no information available to indicate how much of these imports is metal smelted in Germany from imported ores, and how much is re-exports of metal received from other sources.

TABLE A.—IMPORTS OF TIN BY GRADES
(Thousands of long tons)

	Straits	Banka-Billiton	Chinese	English	Undis-tributed	Total
1913	38.1	0.6	1.3	3.4	3.0	46.5
1914	35.5	0.3	0.9	3.4	2.5	42.5
1915	42.1	3.3	1.4	3.4	0.2	50.4
1916	43.0	7.6	1.5	5.7	0.5	58.5
1917	32.7	9.3	5.2	6.2	1.6	54.9
1918	34.2	7.6	6.0	6.6	3.6	58.0
1919	26.2	2.3	0.2	4.7	2.0	35.4
1920	37.5	3.7	4.5	3.2	1.6	50.6
1921	20.3	0.2	2.2	1.4	0.6	24.8
1922	48.3	3.4	4.9	2.4	0.5	59.5
1923	50.4	4.0	5.6	7.5	0.6	68.1
1924	52.9	1.8	2.7	6.7	1.4	65.3
1925	57.4	0.6	4.4	13.5	0.4	76.3
1926	55.2	2.0	3.4	15.6	1.1	77.3
1927	55.6	0.5	1.5	12.6	1.9	72.2
1928	66.2	0.4	1.2	9.7	2.2	79.7
1929	70.4	0.5	4.0	13.4	1.2	89.5
1930	65.5	0.2	3.4	10.9	0.2	80.1
1931	55.7	0.1	3.2	4.3	1.6	65.0
1932	25.4	0.5	3.6	4.7	0.5	34.6
1933	35.1	1.4	3.8	20.3	0.2	60.8
1934	27.5	1.9	2.9	7.9	1.1	41.3
1935	36.2	2.6	4.4	13.4	2.2	58.8
1936	56.9	2.8	4.1	7.9	5.1	76.8
1937	67.2	3.5	5.1	5.8	3.3	85.0

While from the standpoint of availability of an emergency supply, the country from which imports are received is of primary importance, from a purely industrial standpoint it is also necessary to take into account the grade of the metal received; this is particularly true of tin, as the larger proportion of the uses call for a high grade metal. Table A shows a distribution of imports by grades, which in most cases is determined by the source of the ore supply; these figures are only approximate, and in some years the total will not check with the official imports total. Straits ore is all smelted locally, though some of the metal imported by the United States may not reach here directly, but by re-export from some other country. Banka and Billiton tin is classed as such, whether it is smelted in the Netherlands East Indies, or is sent to Netherlands for smelting; United States imports include metal from both sources. English tin is not smelted exclusively from English ores, but from a mixture of ores, mainly from Nigeria and Bolivia.

In Table IV is given the distribution of the 1937 tin imports, classified according to source and port of entry at which they are received in the United States. This table shows several points of interest: (1) New York is the predominant port for the entry of tin, having handled 93 per cent of the 1937 total; (2) Baltimore and Philadelphia imports were presumably largely for local consumption; (3) entries to other eastern ports were small and widely scattered, half of them coming to New Orleans; (4) West Coast entries were 87 per cent at San Francisco, 6 per cent at Seattle, 3 per cent at Los Angeles, 2 per cent at Honolulu, and 2 per cent at Portland; (5) Malayan tin has the widest distribution, with entries listed at a dozen or more ports; (6) other major producers center mainly on New York, with small amounts to Philadelphia; minor producers shipped mostly to a single port, usually the most convenient one, and the same holds for Netherlands and Great Britain, among the larger producers.

TABLE IV.—DISTRIBUTION OF TIN IMPORTS IN 1937
(Long tons)

	New York	Philadelphia	Baltimore	Other Eastern[1]	West Coast[2]	Total
Malaya....................	61,660	175	2,885	84	1,964	66,768
China[3]..................	6,289	190	10	7	40	6,536
Neth. E. Indies.............	3,688	307			110	4,105
India.....................	200					200
Australia..................					95	95
Belgian Congo..............	190					190
Belgium...................	120					120
Netherlands...............	2,393				54	2,447
Great Britain..............	7,178		25			7,203
Mexico....................	17				183	200
Argentina.................	130					130
Bolivia[4].................	112					112
Total....................	81,977	672	2,920	91	2,446	88,106

[1] Includes Boston, Norfolk, Buffalo, Chicago and New Orleans. [2] Includes Los Angeles, San Francisco, Portland, Seattle and Honolulu. [3] Includes Hong Kong. [4] Includes a small amount from Chile, probably of Bolivian origin.

Exports.—Exports of tin from the United States have never been large; while domestic smelting was being carried on, there was a small amount of metal exported, and there has always been a small re-exportation of foreign metal. During 1926–1930 and again in 1935, re-exports reached their highest level, averaging about 2,000 tons, but have since declined.

Consumption.—Due to lack of complete data on invisible stocks (in the hands of consumers), full figures on consumption since 1913 can not be given, but the figures on available supply in Table II, and on apparent consumption in Table B give a fairly close approximation of the actual consumption. Figures on total stocks are available only since 1927, in Table V, which also includes pertinent data on other types of stocks for earlier years. Further details on consumption will be found in a later section on *Utilization.*

TABLE B.—APPARENT CONSUMPTION OF TIN IN THE LEADING COUNTRIES
(Thousands of long tons)

	United States	Great Britain	France	Russia	Germany	German Sphere[1]	Italy	Japan	World	World Output
1913......	45.0	24.7	8.2	2.7	19.0	?	2.9	?	126.5	135.0
1914......	41.6	17.9	6.2	2.5	14.8	?	2.5	?	105.8	127.4
1915......	51.6	30.8	7.9	4.3	6.0	?	4.4	?	123.6	131.5
1916......	62.2	21.1	8.7	1.9	5.5	?	2.8	?	121.0	121.5
1917......	70.8	16.4	12.0	4.9	3.5	?	3.3	?	127.7	133.5
1918......	74.0	15.0	9.3	?	2.2	?	2.1	?	117.4	123.6
1919......	47.4	19.2	8.5	.2	4.3	?	2.8	?	109.9	115.3
1920......	71.5	18.9	5.2	.2	7.2	?	2.1	?	125.1	122.0
1921......	34.3	7.6	6.5	.3	10.1	?	3.4	?	80.3	89.8
1922......	65.2	21.2	8.1	.4	10.0	?	2.9	?	129.6	129.4
1923......	76.6	16.7	9.1	1.2	6.4	2.5	2.9	3.8	134.5	138.3
1924......	63.1	20.7	10.8	1.2	8.3	3.8	3.8	3.9	133.9	146.8
1925......	76.1	25.0	10.9	2.0	11.0	3.4	4.2	4.0	151.2	147.5
1926......	76.2	16.6	10.7	1.8	7.6	3.6	4.1	4.1	146.4	144.6
1927......	69.4	19.3	8.0	3.8	13.4	4.6	4.0	4.4	150.9	154.5
1928......	75.6	27.8	10.7	4.6	12.8	5.0	4.0	4.7	170.6	180.5
1929......	84.9	24.2	11.7	5.0	16.0	5.5	4.9	4.8	183.6	192.3
1930......	76.9	22.6	11.5	4.8	13.5	4.8	4.3	4.1	168.0	174.7
1931......	62.9	20.9	10.1	4.4	10.7	4.1	3.4	4.2	140.5	151.4
1932......	35.5	18.5	8.5	3.8	9.0	3.6	3.6	4.4	104.6	104.6
1933......	59.7	20.0	9.8	4.1	10.2	3.0	3.9	4.4	132.5	99.1
1934......	43.6	21.1	9.3	5.8	10.0	3.7	4.1	5.2	123.1	115.7
1935......	62.5	21.4	8.2	7.3	10.4	4.1	6.6	6.2	149.2	138.6
1936......	73.0	21.9	9.7	9.7	8.5	5.2	3.6	6.4	159.8	176.5
1937......	86.7	26.0	9.3	25.1	11.6	5.2	3.6	8.2	198.3	198.9
Totals.....	1,586.3	515.5	228.9	102.0	241.6	62.1	90.2	72.8	3,414.0	3,493.0
Per cent...	46.5	15.1	6.7	3.0	7.1	2.8	2.6	3.2	100.0	....

[1] Includes Austria, Czecho-Slovakia, Poland, Hungary, Yugoslavia, Rumania and Bulgaria.

The apparent consumption of new tin by the various important consuming countries is shown in Table B. Of the total consumption since 1913, the United States has taken 46.5 per cent, or more than all of the other leading industrial nations combined. Data on secondary tin are not recorded except in the United States, but

TABLE V.—STOCKS OF TIN IN THE WORLD AND THE UNITED STATES
(Thousands of long tons)

	World Visible Supply[1]	United States Visible Supply												U.S. Invisible Supply[4]	U.S. Total Available at Year End	Week's Supply[5]
		In Warehouses			At Landings			Afloat			Total Visible					
		Max.[2]	Min.[3]	Year End	Max.[2]	Min.[3]	Year End	Max.[2]	Min.[3]	Year End	Max.[2]	Min.[3]	Year End			
1913	13.6	[6]	[6]	[6]	2.5[7]	1.2[7]	2.0[7]	[8]	[8]	[8]	[8]	[8]	[8]	[8]	[8]	[8]
1914	17.1	[6]	[6]	[6]	2.5[7]	1.1[7]	2.0[7]	[8]	[8]	[8]	[8]	[8]	[8]	[8]	[8]	[8]
1915	17.3	[6]	[6]	[6]	4.5[7]	0.9[7]	1.8[7]	[8]	[8]	[8]	[8]	[8]	[8]	[8]	[8]	[8]
1916	20.3	[6]	[6]	[6]	5.0[7]	1.3[7]	3.5[7]	[8]	[8]	[8]	[8]	[8]	[8]	[8]	[8]	[8]
1917	19.0	[6]	[6]	[6]	4.4[7]	0.5[7]	0.5[7]	[8]	[8]	[8]	[8]	[8]	[8]	[8]	[8]	[8]
1918	10.8	[6]	[6]	[6]	0.8[7]	0.1[7]	0.2[7]	[8]	[8]	[8]	[8]	[8]	[8]	[8]	[8]	[8]
1919	12.8	[6]	[6]	[6]	5.0[7]	0.1[7]	3.4[7]	[8]	[8]	[8]	[8]	[8]	[8]	[8]	[8]	[8]
1920	18.7	[6]	[6]	[6]	5.4[7]	1.9[7]	2.9[7]	[8]	[8]	[8]	[8]	[8]	[8]	[8]	[8]	[8]
1921	19.0	[6]	[6]	[6]	3.5[7]	1.7[7]	1.7[7]	[8]	[8]	[8]	[8]	[8]	[8]	[8]	[8]	[8]
1922	22.0	[6]	[6]	[6]	3.7[7]	1.2[7]	3.7[7]	[8]	[8]	[8]	[8]	[8]	[8]	[8]	[8]	[8]
1923	19.0	[6]	[6]	[6]	4.1[7]	1.7[7]	1.7[7]	[8]	[8]	[8]	[8]	[8]	[8]	[8]	[8]	[8]
1924	19.5	[6]	[6]	[6]	4.3[7]	1.8[7]	2.8[7]	[8]	[8]	[8]	[8]	[8]	[8]	[8]	[8]	[8]
1925	18.6	[6]	[6]	[6]	5.2[7]	1.4[7]	2.7[7]	[8]	[8]	[8]	[8]	[8]	[8]	[8]	[8]	[8]
1926	14.8	[6]	[6]	[6]	3.4[7]	1.3[7]	1.9[7]	[8]	[8]	[8]	[8]	[8]	[8]	[8]	[8]	[8]
1927	16.0	1.0	0.4	0.6	2.4	0.8	1.0	7.6	4.3	6.9	9.6	6.3	8.4	9.2	17.6	13
1928	19.9	1.2	0.2	0.7	3.9	0.6	1.7	9.6	6.3	9.6	12.0	8.8	12.0	8.5	20.5	14
1929	27.5	1.1	0.4	0.5	2.9	1.6	2.3	10.1	6.4	7.0	12.6	9.3	9.9	10.6	20.5	13
1930	42.7	3.7	1.4	2.0	3.6	1.7	2.6	9.1	6.2	8.2	14.2	10.0	12.9	15.5	28.4	19
1931	55.9	3.2	2.5	2.9	4.8	2.4	3.4	8.0	3.4	4.0	14.4	10.2	10.2	24.9	35.1	29
1932	58.3	2.6	1.7	1.7	2.8	1.5	2.8	4.5	2.2	2.9	8.4	6.2	7.4	20.6	28.0	41
1933	43.3	4.5	0.6	4.5	4.6	1.3	3.0	7.8	2.8	3.4	11.3	5.5	10.9	17.5	28.4	25
1934	21.6	5.1	1.1	1.1	3.3	0.9	3.6	4.8	2.0	4.0	10.3	6.6	6.6	16.9	23.5	28
1935	16.8	3.8	0.1	0.1	2.6	1.1	2.2	7.8	3.3	7.7	11.4	7.1	10.0	15.0	25.0	21
1936	17.5	3.3	0.1	0.1	5.0	1.5	5.4	11.9	5.9	10.9	16.0	9.1	16.0	18.0	34.0	24
1937	23.6	2.3	1.1	2.3	4.4	1.4	4.1	10.2	6.9	9.7	15.6	11.7	14.1	26.0	40.1	24

[1] Average of month-end figures, including stocks, metal afloat, and smelter carry-over. [2] Maximum month-end figure during the year. [3] Minimum month-end figure during the year. [4] Stocks in the hands of consumers. [5] Number of weeks the year-end total stocks would maintain consumption at the average rate during the year. [6] Included with Landings stocks. [7] Includes Warehouse stocks. [8] No data available.

the proportion in other countries is probably less than here, so that figures on total consumption would probably show an even higher percentage for the United States.

Stocks.—Complete figures on total stocks in the United States are available only since 1927, and are found in Table V, classified according to the location of the stocks—in warehouses, at landings, afloat en route for the United States, total visible, invisible (stocks in the hands of consumers), and the total available from all sources; for comparison a statement of world visible supply is included. For the years previous to 1927 the only figures available are world visible supply and the total of warehouse and landings stocks in the United States.

Normal stocks in the United States are usually quite small, as compared with the magnitude of the consumption, which means that in order to maintain supply, uninterrupted shipments must be maintained. The last two columns of Table V show the total stocks in the United States at the end of the year and the number of weeks this would last at the average rate of consumption during the year. For normal conditions, a stock covering 7 to 8 weeks' is about the minimum, but a larger stock would make one considerably more comfortable over the possibilities of maintaining an uninterrupted supply in the event of an emergency.

UTILIZATION OF TIN

Since 1913 the United States has consumed about 43 per cent of the world's output of new tin, practically the entire amount of

TABLE VI.—PERCENTAGE DISTRIBUTION OF TIN IN THE UNITED STATES BY USES

	1917	1928	1935	1937
As pure metal.............................	47.8	50.5	48.7	52.0
Coating iron and steel.....................	36.2	36.4	38.5	43.5
Coating other metals......................	3.6	3.4	2.9	2.9
Foil....................................	5.2	6.8	2.3	1.6
Collapsible tubes.........................	2.8	3.9	5.0	4.0
In alloys..................................	46.4	37.9	41.6	40.8
Solder.................................	22.3	18.7	23.5	22.0
Bearing metals..........................	14.2	11.0	7.3	7.5
Bronze.................................	6.3	5.8	6.7	7.2
White and type metals....................	3.6	1.6	2.0	2.0
Other alloys.............................	[1]	0.8	0.7	0.6
Terne plate.............................	[2]	[2]	1.4	1.5
Chemicals.................................	2.3	7.3	6.3	3.0
Unclassified..............................	3.5	4.3	3.4	4.2
Primary................................	?	74,369[3]	55,779	72,928
Secondary..............................	?	?	15,183	17,202
Total, tons............................	76,257	?	70,962	90,130

[1] Included under Unclassified.   [2] Included with Tinplate under Coating Iron and Steel.
[3] Primary tin only, so not directly comparable with other years.

which was imported, although about 2 per cent was imported as ore, and smelted in this country. A further amount equivalent to 36 per cent of the new supply was recovered as secondary tin, and put back into use. Data on the consumption by uses are not available over any great period of time, but surveys made by the United States Bureau of Mines during various years indicate the approximate distribution of the consumption of tin in the United States, as shown in Table VI.

By far the largest use of tin is in the coating of other metals for protection against oxidation and corrosion; this now accounts for a total of 46 per cent, most of which is in tinplate, which carries 1 to 2 per cent of tin as a rule. Other uses of the pure metal are comparatively small. In alloy form, solder bearing metals and bronze take the bulk of the supply. Since the most of the tinplate and the solder is used in the manufacture of cans, well over half of the tin consumption goes into the production of cans—which eventually end up on the garbage dump.

PRICES

The world market for tin is in London, and the price in New York, or any place else, for that matter, is based directly on the London quotation and the current rate of exchange. The accompanying graph, Fig. 10, shows the trend of the maximum, minimum, and average prices of tin on the New York market since 1913. A graph of the London prices, when compared with this would show some marked differences, particularly during the war period and the depression, but these arise, not from differences in the price trends, but from variations in the exchange rate between the pound sterling and the dollar.

At the time of the outbreak of the World War, tin prices were on the down grade, having declined from 50 cents to 38 cents during 1913, and to 31 cents during the first half of 1914. With the declaration of war there was some panic in the New York tin market, for supplies were at a low level, and were soon exhausted, and, while there was some increase in prices in anticipation of possible interruptions in supplies, the average price for August rose only to 50.595 cents, and dropped back to 32.79 in September with the arrival of fresh supplies. There were moderate increases in 1915 and 1916 but, when war demand got into full swing, prices doubled over their previous level. The post-

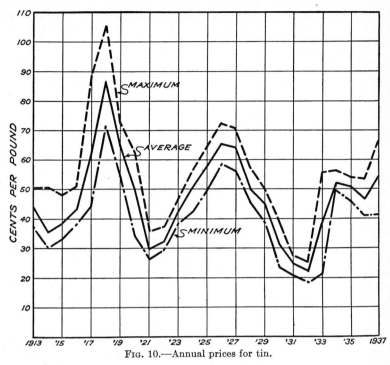

Fig. 10.—Annual prices for tin.

Table VII.—Tin Prices in the United States
(Cents per pound)

	Average Quoted Price	Commodity Index	Tin Index Price
1913	44.23	100.0	44.23
1914	35.70	97.6	36.58
1915	38.66	99.6	38.82
1916	43.48	122.5	35.49
1917	61.65	168.3	36.63
1918	86.80	188.1	46.15
1919	65.54	198.6	33.00
1920	50.36	221.2	22.77
1921	30.00	139.8	21.46
1922	32.58	138.5	23.52
1923	42.71	144.1	29.64
1924	50.20	140.5	35.73
1925	57.90	148.3	39.04
1926	65.30	143.3	45.57
1927	64.37	136.7	47.09
1928	50.46	138.5	36.43
1929	45.19	136.5	33.11
1930	31.70	123.8	25.61
1931	24.46	104.6	23.38
1932	22.01	92.8	23.72
1933	39.12	94.4	41.44
1934	52.16	107.3	48.61
1935	50.39	114.6	43.97
1936	46.42	115.8	40.09
1937	54.24	123.6	43.88

war deflation dropped prices to below the pre-war level, but the inflation period followed with steady increases up to 1926. Then over-production began to be felt, with resultant reaction on prices, and decreases followed which were soon supplemented by the depression, resulting in a minimum price of 18.35 cents and an average of 22.01 cents in 1932, a low point which had not been seen since 1898. At this time the restriction program began to make itself felt, and marked increases followed in 1933 and 1934. Since the establishment of restriction control, the price has been carefully controlled and stabilized, and the spread between the high and low prices in 1934 was the least since pre-war days.

Table VII presents data recently compiled by the U. S. Bureau of Mines, giving the average annual prices of tin, and the corresponding tin index prices, making the successive year's figures directly comparable.

TARIFF

Tin, either as metal or ore, has not been subject to a tariff duty in the United States since the McKinley Tariff, which placed a duty of 4 cents per pound on the metal, from July 1, 1893, to September 1, 1894. The same tariff placed the first duty on tinplate, which helped materially in the establishment of the domestic tinplate industry, but a duty on the tin necessary for the new industry was found to be a deterrent factor, and was soon removed. The present tariff law, in effect since 1930, provides protection for a potential domestic output by specifying a duty on the metal if and when the domestic production amounts to 1,500 tons, but as this limit is far above any present or future prospects, the provision is negligible. Most of the manufactured forms of tin now carry duty, and Table VII shows the tariff rates that have prevailed since the Payne-Aldrich Tariff of 1909.

In the case of tin, the domestic tariff is not the only one to be taken into consideration, for it was the imposition of an export duty of 40 per cent on tin concentrates shipped from British sources to points outside the Empire that blocked the attempt to smelt Straits ore in the United States in 1903. This duty is still in effect, and has accomplished the end for which it was designed, namely, confining to British territory the smelting of all tin ores from British sources. There are also export duties on concentrates from Bolivia and on metal from China, but these are flat rates regardless of destination, and do not discriminate against any country.

In the trade agreement signed with Great Britain on Nov. 17, 1938, tin was bound on the free list, and in return the export tax on ore exported from Nigeria was removed for exports to the United States.

TABLE VIII.—TARIFF RATES ON TIN
(Cents per pound or per cent ad valorem)

	1909–1913	1913–1922	1922–1930	1930—
Tin ore or concentrates.........................	Free	Free	Free	Free
Tin bars, blocks, pigs, granulated or scrap, and alloys	Free	Free	Free	Free
Tinplate, terne plate, and taggers tin.............	1.2c.	15%	1c.	1c.
Tinplate scrap...................................	Free	Free	Free	Free
Tin foil less than 0.006 inch in thickness..........	45%	20%	35%	35%
Tin powder, flitters and metallics.................	....	....	12c.	12c.
Bottle caps, collapsible tubes, and sprinkler tops,				
plain......................................	....	30%	30%	30%
decorated...................................	....	40%	45%	45%
Mineral water containers........................	15%	6⅜%	....	....
Chemicals.......................................	....	10%	25%	25%
Manufactures not specially provided for..........	45%	20%	40%	45%

POLITICAL AND COMMERCIAL CONTROL

While the manipulation of political and commercial control of important industries and sources of supply is a particularly valuable tool in military strategy, their use is not by any means confined to periods of war, but is applied whenever industrial and economic conditions warrant. This has been particularly manifest in the tin industry as it affects the United States. In 1903 a tin smelter was built in New Jersey, with the expectation of using Straits ore, but just about the time that the plant was completed, at a cost of some $300,000, the British Government placed an export duty on tin ores shipped outside the Empire, and the project had to be abandoned.

In 1916, under the pressure of war demand, the smelting of Bolivian ores was started, using improved methods of refining, to produce high grade tin, and was maintained for several years. At the low prices prevailing during the post-war period, operations became unprofitable, and the smaller plants closed down, leaving only the American Smelting and Refining Company and the Williams Harvey Corporation in operation. By 1923, the latter, which was a subsidiary of one of the large English smelters, found it to be more profitable to smelt in England than in the United States, and transferred all of its operations to the English plant. At the same time, the parent company was consolidating its position and improving its ore supply by securing an interest in the chief Bolivian producer, taking over the entire output. Since it was from this same Bolivian source that the American Smelting and Refining Company had been securing much of its ore, this move deprived them of an ore supply and the plant was closed down rather than face the problem of obtaining a new ore supply and continuing operation at increasing costs, which had already gone well beyond the treatment costs in English smelters.

Here then are good examples of the operation of political and commercial control factors in times of peace. Political control was responsible for the failure of the first attempt at domestic smelting of tin, and commercial control (along with the existance of unfavorable economic conditions) put an end to the second.

The distribution of political and commercial control is considerably different for ore and metal, though not so much now as before the consolidation of the British and Bolivian interests. Malaya is the only important producer smelting its ore entirely within its own territory. The tabulations of distribution of control given in Table IX are based on the output of 1929 as shown in the report of the Mineral Inquiry of the American Institute on Mining and Metallurgical Engineers; these data are supplemented by a comparative distribution of world output in 1937.

About two-thirds of the mine control is domestic and one-third foreign. Subdividing this by nationalities, control is found to rest predominantly in British, Chinese, Bolivian and Dutch hands. Smelter control is even more highly centralized, 85 per cent being in the hands of British capital, or of a combination of British and Bolivian, this latter combination being a development of the years immediately preceding the compilation of the table. Since 1929 there has been some readjustment in the Anglo-Bolivian and Dutch figures. In 1934 the metal output in Netherlands East Indies had increased to 9.1 per cent, and that in Netherlands to 11.8 per cent, a total of 20.9 per cent under Dutch control, as against 7.6 per cent in 1929. This increase was made largely at the expense of the Anglo-Bolivian output in Malaya, when ores that formerly went to the Straits for smelting were diverted to the new smelter in Netherlands. Another change is found in Belgian control, due to the increasing amounts of ore produced in Belgian Congo in the past few years. In 1934 the Belgian output was

TABLE IX.—POLITICAL AND COMMERCIAL CONTROL OF TIN PRODUCTION
(In percentage of 1929 world output)

	World Output		Control								
	1929	1937	Domestic	Foreign	British	Bolivian	Dutch	Chinese	German	French	United States
Ore											
Australia......	1.2	1.6	1.2	.....	1.2	.....	.....	.....	.....	.....	.....
Belgian Congo.	0.5	4.4	0.5	.....	.....	.....	.....	.....	.....	.....	.....
Bolivia.......	25.1	12.0	17.1	8.0	1.6	17.1	.....	.....	4.3	0.2	1.9
China........	3.5	4.9	3.5	.....	.....	.....	.....	3.5	.....	.....	.....
Great Britain..	1.8	1.0	1.8	.....	1.8	.....	.....	.....	.....	.....	.....
Burma (India).	1.4	2.4	1.4	.....	1.4	.....	.....	.....	.....	.....	.....
Indo-China....	0.4	0.7	0.4	.....	.....	.....	.....	.....	.....	0.4	.....
Japan........	0.4	1.1	0.3	0.1	.....	.....	.....	.....	.....	.....	.....
Malaya.......	37.8	37.2	17.6	20.2	17.6	.....	.....	18.4	.....	0.9	0.9
Netherlands E. Indies....	16.5	19.1	16.5	.....	.....	.....	16.5	.....	.....	.....	.....
Nigeria.......	5.8	5.0	5.8	.....	5.8	.....	.....	.....	.....	.....	.....
Portugal......	0.3	?	.....	0.3	0.2	.....	.....	.....	.....	.....	0.1
Siam.........	4.3	7.9	0.5	3.8	2.7	.....	.....	1.1	.....	.....	.....
South Africa...	0.7	0.3	0.7	.....	0.7	.....	.....	.....	.....	.....	.....
Total.......	99.7	97.6	67.0	32.7	33.0	17.1	16.5	23.0	4.3	1.5	2.9
Metal											
Australia......	1.2	1.5	1.2	.....	1.2	.....	.....	.....	.....	.....	.....
Belgium.......	0.4	2.8	0.4	.....	.....	.....	.....	.....	.....	.....	.....
China........	3.5	5.3	3.5	.....	.....	.....	.....	3.5	.....	.....	.....
Great Britain..	28.7	17.3	14.4	14.3	14.4	14.3	.....	.....	.....	.....	.....
France........	0.1	?	0.1	.....	.....	.....	.....	.....	.....	0.1	.....
Germany......	2.9	2.0	2.3	0.6	.....	.....	.....	.....	2.3	.....	0.6
Japan........	0.3	0.9	0.3	.....	.....	.....	.....	.....	.....	.....	.....
Malaya[1]......	55.0	47.9	39.7	15.3	47.4	7.6	.....	.....	.....	.....	.....
Netherlands...	0.7	13.5	0.7	.....	.....	.....	0.7	.....	.....	.....	.....
Netherlands E. Indies....	6.9	7.0	6.9	.....	.....	.....	6.9	.....	.....	.....	.....
Totals.....	99.7	98.2	69.5	30.2	63.0	21.9	7.6	3.5	2.3	0.1	0.6

[1] The smelters controlled by the Anglo-Bolivian combination are, in this table, divided equally between the British and Bolivian columns; the English output is entirely Anglo-Bolivian, while the Malayan is 39.7 per cent British and 15.3 per cent Anglo-Bolivian, making the totals 40.9 per cent British and 44 per cent Anglo-Bolivian.

3.4 per cent of the total. Full data are not available for 1934, but the apportionment to the leading interests, as compared with 1929, 1918, and 1913, is approximately as follows:

PERCENTAGE OF TOTAL OUTPUT

	1913	1918	1929	1934
British..	71	70	41	36
Anglo-Bolivian...................................	....	....	44	31
Dutch...	13	13	8	21
Chinese..	6	7	4	7
German..	9	2	2	0.5
Belgian..	....	....	0.4	3.4
United States....................................	....	7	....	....

In addition to the ordinary phases of political and commercial control, there has been in operation since 1931 an international cartel for the control of production and prices, which has been sanctioned and supported by Government authority in the majority of the leading producing countries.

GENERAL REVIEW OF THE DOMESTIC SITUATION

In spite of numerous attempts, the United States has never had an appreciable output of tin ore, and there seems little prospect that one can be developed under any conditions within the range of commercial possibility, as all known deposits of ore are too small in size and too low in grade to justify an attempt to work them on a scale that would produce an output of any appreciable magnitude.   To accomplish anything in this direction would require such a marked increase in the price of the metal as to be out of reasonable consideration.   Furthermore, a pile of old tin cans on a garbage dump would show a higher tin content than most of the available ore sources, so that any increase in supply resulting from increased prices is more likely to come from secondary recovery than from mining.

While tin is not highly important for primary military uses, it is extremely important as a secondary factor in any military program, and in the maintenance of the ordinary progress of industrial operations.   These are the justification for the agitation that has been raised at various times for the establishment of a reserve stock of tin.   Under normal conditions the stocks of tin maintained in the United States are comparatively small, and would last for only a few weeks, if over-seas shipments were interrupted. This happened in 1914, and for the entire month of August there was practically no tin on the market; similar conditions could bring about the same result again and, next time, we might not be so fortunate as we were the first time, when the interruption lasted for only a month.   A reserve stock is the only insurance against possible shortage, and its accompanying difficulties.

CONCLUSION

Considered as a strategic material, tin falls much into the same category as nickel, in that the possibilities of domestic production are practically zero, but different in that available sources are much more remote, and that the uses are less closely connected with the primary military program.   There is, however, not sufficient difference in the situation between the two metals, or for that matter, as to some of the others in the strategic list, to account for the amount of Congressional attention and investigation that tin has received during recent years. One of the fruits of the recent tin investigation in Congress is the regulation, of exports of tin-bearing materials from the United States. This is from many angles a desirable move; even though the restrictions on exports were not applied in normal times, they would be convenient to fall back on in time of emergency.

With no domestic production of tin and no prospect of developing one, and with these conditions prevailing not only in the United States, but throughout the entire continent of North America the domestic consuming industry is more completely dependent on remote sources of supply than is the case with any other strategic metal. The only possible protection against shortage of supply in the event of emergency demand, and against interruption in supplies, is a reserve stock pile containing sufficient metal to tide over the anticipated needs for one or two years.

CHAPTER VIII

ALUMINUM

Aluminum, which first appeared on the official critical list in 1932, was transferred to the strategic list in 1936, a move which probably should have been made sooner, as imports had been increasing for 10 years.

Although the official list includes only the heading aluminum, as with several of the other metals so included, it is primarily the ore of the metal with which we are concerned, as most of the imports are in that form. With nickel, platinum, mercury and tin, the deficiency in domestic supply is covered mainly by the importation of the metal itself, and imports of ores are comparatively small and unimportant; this was formerly also true of antimony, but during recent years there has been a shift toward the importation of ores for local smelting, and this practice now predominates. Imports of chromium, manganese, and tungsten are very largely in the form of ore, and aluminum also falls in this class, although metal imports rank considerably higher than with the other three metals.

The United States has extensive deposits of bauxite, the commercial ore of aluminum, but the demand for the metal has been expanding so rapidly during recent years that it became advantageous to the industry to import some of the higher grades of bauxite, of which large supplies have been developed in other countries. These imports began to assume material proportions in the early 'twenties, and now consumption is about evenly divided between imports and domestic production. While France is the leading producer of bauxite, with the United States second, several other countries have developed outputs of considerable size, but it is chiefly British Guiana and Dutch Guiana (Surinam) that are called on to furnish the United States imports.

REQUIREMENTS

The average annual world requirements of bauxite since 1913 have been approximately 1,310,000 metric tons, but, since production has increased nearly seven fold during that comparatively brief period, a more detailed statement is required, in order to give any real picture of the situation. Pre-war productions were of the order of half a million tons, increasing to a million tons during the period of the World War; after recovery from the post-war depression, production again doubled during the boom years of the 'twenties, but declined by half during the worst years of the industrial depression. Recovery from the depression low was at first slow, but later gained more speed, and 1936 made the remarkable return of an increase of 61 per cent over 1935, and a record world output of 2,876,000 tons, followed by an almost equally spectacular rise to 3,720,000 tons in 1937.

In terms of metal the figures have the same general relationship, except that during the boom period the proportionate increase was somewhat lower; this was probably due to two causes, but it is impossible to say just to what extent either of them has affected the results. The first of these is the fact that some of the bauxite mined in later years has been lower in grade, and hence would contain less metal, and the other is the extent to which uses have been developed for bauxite other than the production of aluminum. In general a pre-war production of 70,000 tons doubled during the war period, but failed in the second doubling, during the boom period, by about 20 per cent, and the 1937 total metal output was 74 per cent greater than the pre-depression high, while with bauxite the increase was 73 per cent.

USES

Some 13–15 per cent of the domestic consumption of bauxite is in abrasives, refractories, and a special type of alumina cement, characterized by its ability to develop its maximum strength more quickly than portland cement, and by its resistance to relatively high temperatures and to chemical attack; of these, abrasives takes the major proportion, in the production of the aluminous abrasives sold under the various trade names of alundum, aloxite, exolon, et cetera, all of which are the result of the fusion of bauxite or alumina in the electric furnace. In refractories, alumina brick or bauxite brick are made directly from bauxite, while certain high grade refractories are made from fused alumina. The amounts of bauxite used in cement in this country are comparatively small, but it is understood that in Europe appreciable amounts are used in this way.

Metallurgical Uses.—As a world average, European experts have estimated that about 60 per cent of the total bauxite output is used in the production of metal, but in the United States this figure runs as high as 70–75 per cent.   Aluminum is used as a pure metal and as an alloy, in castings and forgings, as well as rolled, pressed, extruded, spun, drawn, and stamped.   The compositions of the different alloys vary with the use, and the process of manufacture.   Die casting alloys carry Si, Si-Cu, or Si-Cu-Ni; permanent mold and sand casting alloys are more numerous and more complicated in composition.   Sand casting alloys include Cu, Si, Mg, Si-Cu, Cu-Fe-Zn, Cu-Fe-Mg, Cu-Mg-Ni, Cu-Fe-Si, Cu-Si-Mg, and Cu-Si-Mg-Ni-Mn in widely varying proportions, while permanent mold alloys include Si, Cu-Si, Cu-Fe-Zn, Cu-Fe-Si, Cu-Fe-Si-Zn, Cu-Fe-Mg, Cu-Fe-Si-Mg-Ni, Cu-Fe-Si-Mg, Cu-Mg-Ni, Cu-Si-Mg, and Zn-Mg.   Wrought alloys include Mn, Mn-Mg, Cu-Pb-Bi, Cu-Si-Mn-Mg, Cu-Mn-Mg, Cu-Mg, Cu-Mg-Ni, Cu-Si-Mg-Ni, Si-Mg, Cu-Mg, Cu-Mg-Ni, Cu-Si-Mg-Ni, Si-Mg, Si-Mg-Cr, Mg-Cr, Mn-Mg-Cr, and Cu-Mn-Mg-Zn.

Aluminum possesses three outstanding physical characteristics that are responsible for most of its popularity; lightness, high strength as compared with its weight; and resistance to atmospheric and many types of chemical corrosion; in addition it has a relatively high electrical conductivity, and hence can in many cases compete with copper as a conductor.   In some applications, only one of these properties is of prime importance, while in others more, or even all, are necessary considerations.   In cooking utensils and equipment used in the handling of milk, beer, and nitric acid, corrosion resistance is the controlling factor, though lightness may be a secondary item; in the materials used in many recently developed applications to various types of transportation equipment, both lightness and strength are of equal importance, and corrosion resistance may enter into the problem only to a minor degree, if at all; in the construction of a seaplane or a dirigible balloon, all three are prime requisites, while for use in a long-distance transmission line for the handling of electric power, conductivity must also be considered, in addition to the other three.

Any attempt to discuss the individual uses of the metal is precluded by limitations of space, for it is going into almost every conceivable type of use. Much of the recent increase in demand may be traced to the extensive applications where its combination of lightness and strength have made it possible to substitute aluminum for steel in power-driven machines and transportation equipment for the specific purpose of reducing the dead load and proportionately increasing the pay load; applications of this kind include such a wide variety of examples as railway passenger and freight cars, street cars, air craft, truck bodies, tank cars and trucks, mine cages, steam shovel booms, beer barrels, bridge floors, and wheelbarrows. Among the minor uses, two forms in particular have shown considerable expansion in recent years— foil and paint. The demand for foil is expanding in wrapping food products, and as a liner for bags for coffee and tea, and a quite recent development is the use of foil as a heat insulator; for this purpose crimped foil is used, the crimping providing a dead air space between the layers of foil, cutting down heat losses by conduction, while the reflecting surfaces of the metal foil reduce losses by radiation. In paint, aluminum powder gives a product that ranks high as a corrosion resistant, and, in addition, the reflecting power of the metal flakes also may serve a useful purpose in certain applications; aluminum paint is now almost exclusively used on outdoor storage tanks for volatile liquids, such as gasoline, due to its ability to reflect much of the sun's heat from the surface of the tank, and thus cut down volatilization losses due to the heat absorbed by the contents of the tank.

The use of aluminum metal as a deoxidation agent in the casting of other metals, particularly steel, is of importance, partly because of its pre-eminent value for this purpose, partly because of the appreciable amounts used in this way, and partly because the metal thus used is completely destroyed, instead of being added to the ever-increasing pool of metal in daily use, a large proportion of which will eventually return to the market as secondary metal when it is worn out in its first application.

Chemical Uses.—The production of various aluminum chemicals, particularly the chloride, sulfate, and complex sulfates (alums), takes about 15–20 per cent of the domestic bauxite supply; these salts are used chiefly in water purification, paper making, dyeing, and petroleum refining, besides minor uses.

Military Uses.—There are few if any uses that are specifically or exclusively of a military character; while the product as used may have only a military application, and while large numbers of various pieces of military equipment utilize aluminum in their make-up, this is usually only another example of the versatility of the usefulness of the primary qualities of the metal, lightness, strength, and corrosion resistance, which make aluminum preferable here over some other metal, just as is the case in its numerous commercial applications. Fundamentally, an aluminum mess kit is no different from the usual kitchen utensils, except that it is made in a size and shape to meet the specific conditions for which it is used, and that, since it has to be constantly carried in the soldier's pack, lightness is the primary consideration in the selection of the material, while with ordinary kitchen utensils, lightness is a secondary factor. The combination of lightness and strength are the fundamental reasons for the selection of aluminum for most of its military uses, since easy portability is of great importance.

There is, however, one point of importance in connection with the military use of aluminum, which is that, in order to secure the maximum combination of lightness and strength, only the best grades of primary metal can be used, while for many ordinary uses secondary metal is acceptable. This means that in time of emergency demand for military use, the supply of primary metal would be insufficient for both military and civilian needs, and it is partly this consideration that has resulted in the addition of aluminum to the strategic list.

SUBSTITUTES

Since no other metal has the peculiar combination of properties that has made aluminum so popular, there is little opportunity for substitution; there are, however, many commercial applications in which the use of aluminum is merely a convenience, and not a necessity, and such non-essential uses can, in case of shortage due to emergency demand, be replaced by other metals or alloys, with a considerable saving. Another type of replacement that also does not class as a true substitution is resulting from the development of alloys still lighter than those of aluminum, using magnesium as a base, which are being adopted for certain uses formerly confined to aluminum; since magnesium is more expensive than aluminum and is itself a critical material, the extent of such replacements is strictly limited, particularly in time of emergency.

ORES

Almost the only ore used for the commercial production of aluminum is bauxite, a hydrated oxide; mineralogically, there are two compounds, in bauxite, a mono-hydrate ($Al_2O_3.H_2O$), and a tri-hydrate ($Al_2O_3.3H_2O$). As mined in various localities, bauxite carries 10–30 per cent H_2O, 50–65 per cent Al_2O_3, and a number of impurities, mainly SiO_2, TiO_2, and Fe_2O_3. Each branch of the consuming industry has its own established ranges of composition that best fulfil its needs.

For metal production, at least 52 per cent Al_2O_3 and not over 4.5 SiO_2 and 6.5 Fe_2O_3 are preferred, but in some cases these limits are exceeded.

For chemicals, over 52 per cent Al_2O_3 and less than 3 per cent of Fe_2O_3 are preferred; there is no limit on SiO_2, but it is required that the physical condition of the bauxite be such that it be readily soluble in dilute sulfuric acid.

For abrasives, the limits for impurities are 3–5 per cent SiO_2, 2.5–4 per cent TiO_2, and 3–5 per cent Fe_2O_3; for refractories the requirements are similar to those for abrasives, except that the silica may be somewhat higher.

Some leucite ($KAlSi_2O_6$) has been used in Italy for the combined recovery of potash and alumina, but this has apparently been discontinued. In the past, experimental work has been done at different times on the treatment of alunite ($K_2O.3Al_2O_3.4SO_3.-6H_2O$) for the recovery of potash and alumina, and, since the completion of the Boulder Dam, this problem has again been taken up, this time by the United States Bureau of Mines, in view of the large deposits of this mineral that are known to exist within comparatively short distances from the dam site, as well as in Utah, Colorado and Wyoming.

Beneficiation.—In general, bauxites are sold as mined, except for a limited amount of washing and drying. Calcination would remove the large amount of combined water correspondingly reduce the freight charges, but since this renders the ore insoluble in the methods most used for its conversion into alumina or chemicals, this is seldom used except for ore intended for abrasive manufacture. Washing is usually used where the bauxite is accompanied by considerable amounts of clay, the removal of which by washing reduces the silica content. Attempts to apply flotation methods of concentration for the removal of silica and iron have shown promising results as to silica removal but have not been particularly successful in removing iron oxide. Magnetic methods for the removal of iron oxides have been successfully used by some producers.

The bauxite may be used as mined for the production of abrasives or refractories, but for metal production it must first undergo a rigid purification, since, otherwise, all the impurities present in the bauxite would appear in the finished metal. Various methods have been devised for this purification, but all coincide in the necessity for turning out as the finished product the oxide of aluminum, alumina or Al_2O_3, in as high a degree of purity as is practicable, in order to reduce to a minimum the amount of impurities in the finished metal.

The purification method most used is the Bayer process; the finely ground bauxite is digested in steam-jacketed autoclaves with a hot, strong solution of sodium hydroxide, dissolving the alumina as sodium aluminate, and leaving behind most of the impurities, which are removed by settling and filtering. Prolonged agitation of the solution in contact with some freshly prepared aluminum hydroxide causes the decomposition of the aluminate, and the precipitation of the metal as hydroxide, which is then filtered off, dried, and calcined, giving an alumina of high purity. Among other processes that have been used to a limited extent are the Hoopes-Hall and Haglund, both of which are dry processes, using electrothermic methods, and the Pedersen process, a combination of wet and dry methods, in which the bauxite is first used as a flux in the smelting of iron ore, producing a highly aluminous slag, which is then treated for the recovery of alumina by wet methods somewhat similar to the Bayer process.

Metallurgy.—The pure alumina produced in the purification process is converted to metallic aluminum by electrolysis, after solution in a bath of fused cryolite ($AlF_3.3NaF$) at a temperature of about 950° C.; the bottom of the cell, which is of baked carbon, and the liquid metal that accumulates on it serve as cathode of the cell, and several baked carbon anodes dip into the surface of the fused cryolite-alumina solution. In order to reduce the heat losses from the top of the cell, and at the same time to assure a continuous saturation of dissolved alumina in the cryolite, the surface of the liquid is kept constantly covered by a layer of fresh alumina, which is replaced periodically as it goes into solution.

Since it is impractical to produce alumina of 100 per cent purity, and, even if this were done, some iron and silica would be added to the bath from the ash of the carbon anodes (which are consumed at about the same rate at which the metal is reduced), the resulting metal ordinarily has a purity of better than 99.0 per cent, and more than 99.5 per cent may be secured if special precautions are taken as to the purity of the materials going into the cell. About 1925 a refining process was developed, similar in principle to the reduction process, by which liquid crude metal in the form of an aluminum-copper alloy was used as anode, the aluminum being electrolytically dissolved in the fused bath, and deposited on the cathode as high-purity liquid metal; in this way a purity of 99.99 per cent or better can be obtained. A similar process has recently been developed in France.

In general, taking into consideration the purity of the average run of materials, and the losses in treatment, it takes about 4 tons of bauxite to yield 2 tons of pure alumina, which will produce 1 ton of metal.

Secondary Recovery.—There is a well established secondary recovery system in operation that has grown up during the past 25 years to a point where it is now able to supply the market with one-half as much metal as the primary producers, about 40 per cent of which is returned as metal and 60 per cent as alloy. The total secondary recovery since 1913 has been 45 per cent of primary production, and 39 per cent of the available new metal supply, including imports, which is higher than with most metals. Fabrication scrap (sheet scrap, clippings, turnings, and similar material) and automobile scrap are large items in the bulk of reworked metal.

Forms in Which Aluminum Appears in the Market.—Ingot aluminum comes on the market in five grades, the high-purity refined metal, the selected 99.5+ grade, the ordinary 99+ grade, a lower 98–99 per cent grade, and a 93–98 per cent grade; the last is used chiefly as a deoxidizing agent in steel casting, while the others supply the demand for the cast, forged, rolled, and other types of finished and semi-finished material, either as pure metal or alloy.

Since all of the important consumers of domestic bauxite operate their own mines, only a comparatively small percentage of the bauxite production appears in the open market.

ORE RESERVES

Although information concerning many of the important bauxite deposits of the world is far from complete, and in some cases very little is known, sufficient data are at hand to insure a plentiful supply for many years to come. A probable estimate of the known sources is about one billion tons, and in addition there are large amounts in deposits yet unestimated, and in marginal and sub-marginal reserves.

British Guiana.—The reserves of British Guiana are similar in character to those of Surinam, but are apparently less extensive; no estimates have been published on the tonnage.

Czecho-Slovakia.—Deposits of bauxite are scarce in Czecho-Slovakia, but alunite deposits in the vicinity of Berehovo have an alumina content estimated to be equivalent to about 30,000,000 tons of good grade bauxite, and in addition there are large deposits of high alumina clay at Carlsbad and Znojmo, both of which at present rank as sub-marginal reserves.

France.—French bauxite reserves were estimated at 60,000,000 tons in 1925.

French Morocco.—Bauxite deposits of high quality in the Atlas Mountains have been reported at 20,000,000 tons from the upper layers; numerous waterfalls are available in the vicinity to furnish power for mining operations.

Gold Coast.—Although no production of bauxite has as yet been made in the colony, extensive deposits are known in several areas. In the Mount Ejuanema Kwahu district reserves have been estimated at 4,000,000 tons, and in the Sefwi Bekwai district 32,430,000 tons, with respectively 60 and 50 per cent of alumina. The Asafo deposits are estimated at 25,000,000 tons, and an area in the Yenahin district has been estimated at 168,000,000 tons of good ore; the four areas total 229,000,000 tons, and even though none of these ores have been commercially used as yet, there seems to be no doubt that Gold Coast will play an important part in the bauxite industry at some future time.

Greece.—Recent estimates have placed the Greek reserves at 10,000,000 tons of proven ore, and a possible total of 50,000,000 tons of all grades.

Hungary.—The reserves of bauxite in the Vertes district have been increased from 30,000,000 tons in 1925 to 250,000,000 tons; this area constitutes the largest reserve known in Europe, and one of the largest in the world.

India.—The bauxite deposits of India are known to be large, but have not been worked on any great scale, because of lack of local demand, and high shipping costs.

Italy.—Reserves of bauxite in Italy were estimated at 13,600,-000 tons in 1930, 8,100,000 tons in Istria and 5,500,000 tons in Abruzzi. The leucite deposits of Naples and Orvieto have an alumina content which has been estimated at some 30,000,000 tons; these deposits were worked for several years for the recovery of alumina and potash, and are still available as a potential reserve.

Nyasaland.—Bauxite has been found over an area of two square miles, with a thickness of 15–30 feet, and reserves have been estimated at 20,000,000 tons, with 57–60 per cent alumina.

Rumania.—Deposits in the Bihar Mountains have been variously estimated from 2,000,000 tons to 12,000,000 tons in sight, with possible extension to 20,000,000 tons.

Russia (U. S. S. R.).—A number of deposits in the Tikhvin region, originally reported at 8,000,000 tons, were later cut to 4,500,000 tons, and finally to 2,300,000 tons available for immediate use. Reserves in the Ural Mountains have been similarly altered, with figures varying from 35,000,000 tons to 8,300,000 tons. Totals have shrunk from 45,000,000 tons to 10,600,000 tons, with little of first rank in quality.

Surinam.—The numerous deposits along the Surinam, Cotica and Coermotibo Rivers vary in thickness up to as much as 20 feet, and average possibly 12 feet; large deposits are also known to occur as lateritic cappings on plateaus and hills in the interior. Enormous quantities are established in the reserves, but no figures of tonnage have been reported, and it is not known how much of the total is of commercial grade.

United States.—Moderate tonnages of bauxite are known to exist in Georgia, Tennessee, Alabama and Mississippi, but no data on tonnage have been found; it is likely that at present prices much of these reserves must be classed as marginal, although plentiful supplies of cheap power and some increase in price might make them a considerable factor in the market. Information on the Arkansas deposits is somewhat more specific; most of the known reserves are in the hands of the Aluminum Company of America. In 1900 the Arkansas reserves were estimated to contain 50,000,000 tons, since when some 8,500,000 tons has been mined; more recent consideration by geologists familiar with the region has led to the conclusion that the original estimate was too high. The United States Geological Survey has recently done some drilling in this area, resulting in an estimate of 11,600,000 tons of present commercial grade in Saline and Pulaski Counties, with much larger tonnages of marginal and non-commercial grades.

A large sub-marginal reserve, which may become available later, is found in the leucite and alunite deposits of Utah, Colorado, and Wyoming. The contained alumina in these deposits would amount to several hundred million tons, but their commercial utilization will require extensive developments in technology, and probably a marked increase in price of alumina and potash, before any definite progress could be made in this direction. Of the two, the possibilities for alunite are far more promising. The western leucites are much less favorable as a possible source of alumina than the Italian leucites, which have been tried and abandoned as uncommercial under present conditions.

Yugoslavia.—Estimates of reserves set at 50,000,000 tons in 1925 have since been increased to 80,000,000–100,000,000 tons.

WORLD OUTPUT AND SUPPLY

Although there are other uses for bauxite than as a source of aluminum, they are small in proportion, and the enormous increase in the demand has been largely due to the growth in the applications for the metal, practically all of which has come within the past 50 years. In this, aluminum holds a unique position. It is not by any means the only metal that has developed into commercial importance within that period of time; we do not have to go outside the strategic list to discover this, for 50 years ago tungsten was practically unknown in an industrial way, and its present commercial development did not begin until the early years of the present century. Aluminum stands alone, however, in the record made for speed and extent of development during this time, having increased from a production so small that it was usually measured in pounds, rather than tons, to a position in the group of major metals. For a long time there has

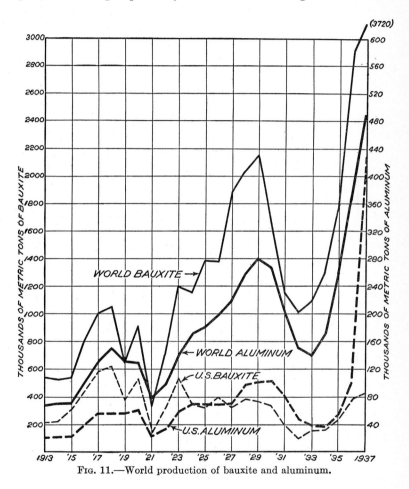

Fig. 11.—World production of bauxite and aluminum.

been a sort of conventional agreement that a metal could not be classed as a major metal unless its output equaled or exceeded that of tin, which was always considered the junior member of the group; aluminum reached this point during the war period, has led tin in production ever since, except for 2 years during the

TABLE Ia.—WORLD PRODUCTION OF BAUXITE
(Thousands of metric tons)

	France	United States	Hungary	Italy[1]	Suri-nam	British Guiana[2]	Yugo-slavia	Russia	Austria	Netherlands East Indies	Greece	Others	Total
1913	309	213	2	7			[6]		10[3]			9	550[3]
1914	200[3]	223		4			[6]		75[3]			9	520[3]
1915	57	302	58	7			[6]		100[3]			13	540[3]
1916	106	432	100[3]	9		2	[6]		142			11	800[3]
1917	121	578	129	8			[6]		163			16	1,000[3]
1918	140[3]	615	100	8		4	[6]		165			12	1,050[3]
1919	159	383	[4]	3		2	[6]		[4]			22	650[3]
1920	267	530	[4]	13[7]		32	28[7]		[5,7]			29	900[3]
1921	95	142	[4]	49		20	10		3			19	338
1922	236	315	[4]	67	19		31		[4]			30	702
1923	394	531	[5]	98	16	102	33		3			21	1,198
1924	389	353		141	63	157	18		[4]			29	1,150
1925	502	322		195	86	178	79		[4]			21	1,383
1926	508	399		91	44	189	132		[4]			12	1,379
1927	655	326	339	95	184	163	100		[4]			18	1,880
1928	636	381	396	162	214	168	49		[4]			24	2,030
1929	666	372	389	193	210	188	103		[4]			26	2,148
1930	609	336	32	161	265	121	95		[4]			8	1,627
1931	404	199	90	67	173	127	62	12	[4]			11	1,145
1932	404	98	112	87	127	64	67	37				10	1,006
1933	491	157	72	95	104	37	81	51	[4]			10	1,098
1934	528	160	185	131	103	51	85	61	[4]			9	1,313
1935	513	238	211	170	115	113	216	132	[4]	17	9	56	1,790
1936	649	378	329	262	234	213	292	200[3]	[4]	150	130	39	2,876
1937	688	428	451	386	392	367	358	250[3]	[4]	199	110	91	3,720
Totals	9,726	8,411	3,051	2,509	2,349	2,298	1,839	750	690	366	249	555	32,793
Per cent	29.6	25.6	9.3	7.7	7.2	7.0	5.6	2.3	2.1	1.1	0.8	1.7	100.0

[1] Not including small amounts of leucite, used for the recovery of alumina and potash. [2] Exports. [3] Estimated. [4] No data available. [5] Less than 500 tons. [6] Production included under Austria. [7] The former production of Dalmatia was transferred to Yugoslavia, and that of Istria to Italy at the close of the war.

TABLE Ib.—WORLD PRODUCTION OF ALUMINUM
(Thousands of metric tons)

	United States	Germany	Canada	France	Switzerland	Norway	Great Britain	Italy	Russia	Austria	Others	Total
1913	21	1	6	14	10	2.1	8	1		5		68
1914	26	1	7	10	10	2.9	8	1		4		70
1915	29	2	9	6	13	2.9	7	1		3		72
1916	40	8	9	10	15	4.5	8	1		5		100
1917	55	15	12	11	15	7.6	7	2		5		130
1918	57	25	15	12	15	6.8	8	2		8		149
1919	58	15	15	12.3	15	3.1	8	2		5		131
1920	62.6	12	12	8.4	12	5.6	8	1.2		2		128
1921	24.5	11	8		12	10	5	0.7		2		82
1922	33.6	16	10	7.5	13	12	5	0.8		2		100
1923	58.5	17	10	14.3	15	13.3	8	1.5		1.5		39.1
1924	68.3	20	12.5	18.5	19	20.0	7	2.1		2.2		69.6
1925	63.5	27.2	13.6	20.0	21	21.3	9.7	1.9		3.0		181.2
1926	65.8	30.6	17.8	24.0	21	24.4	7.3	1.9		3.0		195.8
1927	72.6	28.4	38.5	25.0	20	20.8	7.9	2.5		4.0		219.7
1928	95.5	31.7	40.0	27.0	19.9	24.8	10.7	3.6		4.0	1.0	256.2
1929	103.4	33.3	42.0	29.0	20.7	29.1	13.9	7.0		2.7	1.0	282.1
1930	103.9	30.7	34.9	26.0	20.5	27.4	14.0	8.0		3.0	1.3	269.7
1931	80.5	27.1	31.0	18.0	12.2	21.8	14.2	11.1	0.1	2.5	1.4	219.5
1932	47.6	19.2	17.9	14.5	8.5	17.8	10.3	13.4	0.9	2.1	1.2	153.6
1933	38.6	18.9	15.9	14.5	7.5	15.4	11.0	12.1	4.4	2.1	1.2	141.7
1934	33.6	37.2	15.6	16.3	8.2	15.3	13.0	12.8	14.4	2.1	2.3	170.9
1935	54.1	70.8	20.6	21.9	11.7	15.3	15.1	13.8	24.5	2.4	8.2	258.4
1936	102.0	97.5	26.2	26.5	13.7	15.4	16.4	15.9	37.9	3.3	10.9	365.7
1937	132.8	127.5	42.6	34.5	25.0	23.0	19.4	22.9	45.0	4.1	13.8	490.6
Totals	1,526	723	482	431	374	362	250	143	127	83	41	4,543
Per cent	33.6	15.9	10.6	9.5	8.2	8.0	5.5	3.1	2.8	1.8	0.9	100.0

post-war decline, and, in 1936, was practically double the output of tin.

Of the leading producers of aluminum, the United States is the only country with a material output of bauxite, but, even so, the supply of high grade ore is insufficient to meet the demand and must be supplemented by imports. Among the smaller metal producers, France and Italy have a large surplus of bauxite for export, while Russia is self-supporting; all others depend mainly on bauxite imported from countries with an export surplus, or from those with no established metal production.

Before the World War, France and the United States supplied practically the entire world output of bauxite, while now these two furnish only 40 per cent of the total, and five other producers have outputs in excess of 200,000 tons, and three others have reached or passed the 100,000 ton mark. War demand expanded the formerly negligible output of Austria and Hungary, to supply Germany, and was also responsible for the opening up of the British Guiana deposits. Both the Austrian and Hungarian outputs faded away with the cessation of war demand, but later Hungary staged a come-back of such proportions as to cover 13 per cent of the world total during the past 10 years. In the meantime, progress was being made in Yugoslavia, Italy, and Surinam (Dutch Guiana), although, in the first two, much of the production came from territory ceded to them by Austria at the close of the war; later, Russia developed an output sufficient to cover her own metal production, and in 1936 Greece and the Netherlands Indies came into prominence with greatly increased outputs.

For the period since 1913, France has led in bauxite production, with 29.6 per cent of the total, followed by the United States with 25.6 per cent; all others, because of their later entry into the list of producers, have less than 10 per cent. Considering only the past 10 years, in order to come more nearly to current production conditions, these figures change materially, with France 30 per cent, United States 15, British Guiana 13, Hungary 12, Surinam 10, Italy 10, and Yugoslavia 8 per cent.

For metal the United States is the leading producer, with 33.6 per cent of the total since 1913, followed by Germany with 15.9 per cent and Canada with 10.6 per cent; all others are below 10 per cent. Recent changes have made these figures somewhat different for the past 10 years, but not so much so as with bauxite;

this gives the United States 30 per cent, Germany 19 per cent, and Canada 11 per cent, with all others still below 10 per cent.

Table I*a* shows the annual country and world outputs, period totals and percentages for bauxite since 1913, while Table I*b* gives the same data for aluminum, for all countries furnishing a material proportion of the total. The production graph shows the trend of world output and United States output for both bauxite and aluminum. Many of the figures used in the tables are more or less approximate, particularly for the earlier years, as many reports are incomplete, and data from various sources sometimes differ by appreciable amounts.

In addition to the countries shown in Table I*b*, five others are producing aluminum in small amounts; Spain began in 1929, Japan and Sweden in 1934, Hungary in 1935, and Yugoslavia in 1937; Japan made an output of 7,500 tons in 1936, and Sweden 1,800 tons, while the others are 1,000 tons or less. Besides these, plans are under way for the construction of reduction plants in Australia and Czecho-Slovakia, and for increases in capacity in Italy, Japan, and Great Britain.

Austria.—Bauxite production in Austria has been of material proportions only during the war period, when it was the chief source of supply for the Central Powers. Immediately after the war, production declined to an insignificant amount, and most of the best producing territory was lost to Rumania, Italy, and Yugoslavia. Metal production, which has been 2,000–4,000 tons during recent years, and reached a maximum of 8,000 tons in 1918, is now entirely from bauxite imported from Yugoslavia or Hungary.

British Guiana.—Although started in 1917 under the pressure of war demand, the bauxite deposits of British Guiana got into production slowly, and it was not until after the post-war depression that the output reached material proportions. The only operating company is a subsidiary of Aluminium Ltd. The product is now exported to Canada, for treatment at the Arvida plant; previous to the installation of purification equipment at this plant, the ore was shipped to East St. Louis, Illinois, for purification, and the resulting alumina was then sent to Canada. Production rose to 189,000 tons in 1926, dropped to 37,000 tons in 1933, and recovered to new records of 213,000 tons in 1936, and 367,000 tons in 1937.

The deposits lie in small hills above the coastal plain, 60 to 80 miles from the coast, near the Demerara and Berbice Rivers. Most of the ore is beneficiated by washers and dryers to give a product better than 60 per cent Al_2O_3, and under 3 per cent SiO_2, but a small tonnage grading 50–60 per cent Al_2O_3 is shipped; a third grade, with less than 50 per cent Al_2O_3 is stocked at the mines. Average analysis of shipments is reported to be 61 per cent Al_2O_3, 2.75 SiO_2, 2.5 Fe_2O_3, 2.75 TiO_2, and 31 per cent H_2O.

Canada.—With no domestic production of bauxite, but with extensive water power developments for the supply of cheap power, Canada has built up the third largest aluminum production in the world, using bauxite from British Guiana. Up to 1927 no bauxite purification facilities were available in Canada, and imports were confined to alumina, the British Guiana shipments being routed through the United States for purification at East St. Louis. Since 1930 only bauxite has been imported, and alumina imports have almost disappeared. The two plants at Shawinigan Falls and Arvida (Quebec) are both owned by the Aluminum Company of Canada, a subsidiary of Aluminium Ltd. The Arvida plant is reported to be potentially the largest aluminum plant in the world.

France.—Except during the war and post-war periods, when production was abnormally low, France has held first place in bauxite production. After regaining the leading position in 1924, production continued to increase to a maximum of 666,000 tons in 1929, and 1937 saw a recovery from the depression decline to above the 1929 level. Domestic production of metal is comparatively small, and requires less than 10 per cent of the bauxite output; exports, chiefly to Great Britain and Germany, account for about 45 per cent, which would leave what seems to be an undue proportion of the total for domestic uses other than metal production, some of which may be going into emergency stocks.

The French bauxite and aluminum industry is located in the southeastern section, near the Swiss and Italian borders, at Var, Hérault, Bouches du Rhône, and Ariège. Var produces about 80 per cent of the ore. While there are a number of reduction plants, consolidations have brought them under the control of two large operating companies, which utilize a joint fabricating plant and sales agency.

Germany.—Bauxite production in Germany amounts to only a few thousand tons a year, and the consuming industry is practically entirely dependent on imported ores. Between recovery from the depression and the spur of an active campaign for self-sufficiency, metal production has quadrupled since 1933, placing the country as the second largest producer, and ore imports have increased proportionately. In 1933, France supplied nearly one-half of the imports, followed by Hungary, Yugoslavia, and Italy; in 1937, Hungary led with one-third, followed by Yugoslavia, Netherlands Indies, Italy, and France. Metal imports have been materially reduced, but have not yet been wiped out, amounting to 3,918 tons of ingot and manufactures, and 3,505 tons of scrap in 1937.

Incidentally, German imports of bauxite during 1932–1937 were 3,566,000 tons, as compared with a metal output of 371,000 tons, a ratio of 9.6:1; while a similar ratio for the United States was only 6.5:1; the difference seems to be more than might be explained by possible differences in the grade of bauxite used, or in uses other than for metal production, and would suggest the possibility of the storage of emergency stocks.

Great Britain.—British aluminum production is entirely dependent on imported bauxite, most of which comes from France. Production is being expanded, although it is now well above the 1929 level, since there is still a wide margin between production and consumption, and imports exceed the domestic output. There was formerly a small output of bauxite in northeastern Ireland, totaling about 100,000 tons from 1915 to 1928, since when it has been negligible.

Greece.—Increased demand and higher prices have stimulated the development of bauxite deposits in Greece. Exports were 13,150 tons in 1935, and 86,015 tons in 1936, principally to Germany, Great Britain, Norway, and Japan. The ores are of good grade, carrying 55–60 per cent Al_2O_3, although some are quite high in silica. Bauxite occurrences are being worked in several localities, but the most important one is near Mt. Parnassus, extending from the Gulf of Corinth near Itea on the south to Gravia and Bralo on the north.

Hungary.—The war production of bauxite with which Hungary supplemented the Austrian output to make up the supply of the Central Powers during the World War fell off with the close of war demand and was not revived until 1927, since when Hungary has ranked as a leading producer. Most of the output is from mines controlled by the German owned Bauxite Trust, and is exported to Germany. The principal deposits are located southwest of Budapest, at Gant and Halimba. The latter are the largest known in Europe, but are not yet developed, and practically all of the present output comes from Gant. The ore carries 50–63 per cent Al_2O_3, 15–30 per cent Fe_2O_3, and 2–4 per cent SiO_2. Two small deposits at Villany and Perepuszta, in southern Hungary, produce only small amounts.

The alumina plant at Magyarovar began operations in 1934; the reduction plant at Csepel Island, near Budapest, started in 1935, with a capacity of 1,200 tons, which is not quite sufficient to cover the local consumption, and expansion is planned.

Italy.—There is a considerable export surplus of bauxite in Italy, Germany being the largest buyer, taking 60 per cent of the 1936 output. About one-third of the output is required for the domestic metal reduction plants, which had expanded to a point where there was a fairly large export surplus of metal (6,000 tons in 1935), with further expansions under way doubling the output. Local demand, however, expanded so much that with a metal output of 22,900 tons in 1937, as compared with 15,100 tons in 1937, exports practically disappeared, and imports jumped to 3,600 tons. The bauxite deposits are located in Abruzzi and Istria; leucite deposits in Naples and Orvieto were worked on a small scale for several years for the recovery of potash and alumina, but no production has been reported since 1932.

Netherlands East Indies.—The Islands of Bintang and Batam are rapidly developing a large output of bauxite; the 17,000 tons produced in 1935 increased to 150,000 tons in 1936 and 199,000 tons in 1937, most of which went to Germany. The ore is reported to carry 53 per cent Al_2O_3, 2.5 SiO_2, 13.5 Fe_2O_3, and 1.2 per cent TiO_2.

Norway.—The Norwegian reduction plants depend entirely on foreign materials; bauxite, mainly from Italy, and alumina from France, Great Britain, Germany and the United States, are each imported to the extent of about 25,000 tons. Most of the metal output, which has as yet not fully recovered from the depression decline, is exported to the United States and Germany.

Russia (U. S. S. R.).—Russian production is of comparatively recent origin, but has expanded rapidly, and the 1936 metal output stood in third place. Bauxite deposits occur in the Leningrad, Sverdlovsk, and Chelyabinsk regions, but the ore carries only 36–50 per cent Al_2O_3. Four alumina plants supply their product to three reduction plants, and further expansion of the industry is planned.

Surinam (Dutch Guiana).—Since the Surinam production is mined by a subsidiary of the Aluminum Company of America, practically the entire output is shipped to the United States, for conversion into alumina at East St. Louis. The 1936 output was still somewhat below the pre-depression high but 1937 reached a new high record of 392,000 tons, and fourth place in the list of producers. The ore deposits are at Moengo, and are reported to contain 59 per cent Al_2O_3, 2 per cent SiO_2, 6 per cent Fe_2O_3, 3 per cent TiO_2, and 30 per cent H_2O.

Switzerland.—The Swiss metal production is entirely from imported ores, and the bulk of the product goes into export trade. Production declined seriously during the depression, and did not fully recover until 1937. There are several reduction plants, whose control, ore supply, and distribution are closely associated with French, German, Italian, and Austrian operations.

United States.—Emergency demand during the war period, when domestic production of bauxite was trebled, depleted the reserves to such a point that later production has never been able to equal the war-time peak, although the 1936 output recovered to the pre-depression level. Beginning with the recovery from the post-war decline, there has been an increasing dependence on imports, which during the past five years have exceeded production by a small margin.

In metal production, the United States ranks first, though the 1936 and 1937 figures show only a small margin over the rapidly increasing output of Germany.[1] While the period totals since 1913 give the United States 33.6 per cent against 15.9 per cent for Germany, the 1936 and 1937 distribution was 27 per cent to the United States and 26 per cent to Germany.

Bauxite mining in the United States began in Georgia in 1889, followed by Alabama in 1891; production began in Arkansas in

[1] Preliminary figures for 1938 give Germany first place in aluminum production.

1896, but did not reach significant proportions until 1900; shipments from Tennessee appeared in 1907, but operations here were discontinued in 1928. Arkansas produced 95 per cent of the 1936 output, and 87 per cent of the total since the beginning of operations. The ores vary considerably, with 50–65 per cent Al_2O_3, 7–21 SiO_2, 1–10 Fe_2O_3, 1–4 TiO_2, and 29–33 per cent combined water.

Bauxite for metal production comes largely from Arkansas, while the output of the smaller deposits in Alabama and Georgia is mainly used for other purposes. Mine operation was formerly entirely by open-pit methods, but more recently underground work has been expanding.

Yugoslavia.—A new metal reduction plant started operations in June, 1937, with a capacity of 880 tons annually. This will consume only a small proportion of the bauxite output and will not disturb the established export trade, which is mostly to Germany. Most of the bauxite deposits occur in a belt extending along the Dalmatian coast. The more northern deposits carry 48–53 per cent Al_2O_3 and 1–4 per cent SiO_2. The Drnis mine, which produces over 500 tons daily, lies in this section. In central Dalmatia, ores of somewhat higher grade, 55–62 per cent Al_2O_3 and 1–5 SiO_2, have recently come into production from a number of mines. Deposits in Herzegovina have contributed increasing proportions of the output in recent years.

Other Countries.—A company has been organized for the production of aluminum in Australia, but the source of bauxite has not yet been determined; small amounts have been mined in Victoria and New South Wales, but these total only about 1,000 tons annually.

Important deposits have been developed in Malaya, near Singapore, and are being actively exploited by Japanese interests.

Bauxite occurs in several states in Brazil, and in 1936 some 7,000 tons was shipped to Argentina for the production of aluminum sulfate.

Bauxite production in India rose from 2,500 tons in 1930 to 7,700 tons in 1935, but declined to 3,700 tons in 1936.

Several districts in Rumania, formerly part of Austria, contributed to the Austrian war output, but have since been worked on only a small scale. Recent increases in demand have expanded the 1934 output of 1,460 tons of bauxite to 10,800 tons in 1936.

UNITED STATES OUTPUT AND SUPPLY

Even through during the heavy demand incident to the World War, the United States was able to maintain self-sufficiency, with little dependence on imports of either ore or metal, and with exports in excess of imports, this position could not be maintained except under war pressure, and from 1920 imports of both ore and metal increased, the former quite heavily. At the same time exports increased, since much of the Canadian supply of alumina was being received through the United States, but the amount of imports going into domestic consumption also increased. In 1925 imports of bauxite exceeded domestic production, and although production has been greater than imports in five of the 13 years since then, the amounts of excess have been small, and the total imports for the period have exceeded production by 7 per cent; even after deducting the amounts of imports that were re-exported, the imported bauxite consumed domestically constituted 43 per cent of the available supply, against 57 per cent from domestic production.

Although domestic bauxite production has not been able to keep pace with the rapidly increasing demand for the metal, domestic reduction capacity has made a better record, and imports of metal have decreased; at the same time, increasing secondary recovery has helped to fill the gap, so that while in 1913 and 1921–1922 imported metal supplied 30 per cent or more of the total domestic supply (including secondary metal), during recent years the proportion has been much lower, ranging from 6 to 10 per cent.

Table IIa shows the data concerning the available supply of bauxite in the United States, while Table IIb covers the same ground for the metal. Combining the data from the two tables, to give the total metal content available in both forms, we find that in 1915–1919, the period of domestic self-sufficiency, production of bauxite totaled 2,331,000 tons, imports 21,000 tons, exports 94,000 tons, and available supply 2,237,000 tons; production then exceeded consumption by 3 per cent; at the same time metal production totaled 239,000 tons, imports 14,000 tons, exports 18,000 tons, and total new supply 235,000 tons, leaving metal production 2 per cent greater than consumption; this gives a total surplus of both ore and metal amounting to 5 per cent. During the five years 1925–1929, after bauxite imports had grown

TABLE IIa.—AVAILABLE SUPPLY OF BAUXITE IN THE UNITED STATES
(Thousands of metric tons)

Year	Production	Imports	Exports[1]	Available Supply[1]	Per Cent of Available Supply in Production	Per Cent of Available Supply in Imports	Per Cent of Available Supply in Exports	World Output	Per Cent of World Output in Domestic Production	Per Cent of World Output in Domestic Imports	Per Cent of World Output in Domestic Exports	Per Cent of World Output in Domestic Consumption
1913	213	22	[2]	235	91	9	.....	550	39	4	.....	43
1914	223	25	5[3]	243	92	10	2	520	43	5	1	47
1915	302	3	16	289	105	1	6	540	56	1	3	54
1916	432	4	18	414	104	.....	4	800	54	.....	2	52
1917	578	8	22	564	103	1	4	1,000	58	1	2	56
1918	615	4	20	599	102	1	3	1,050	59	.....	2	57
1919	383	6	18	371	103	2	5	650	59	1	3	57
1920	530	44	23	550	96	8	4	900	59	5	3	61
1921	142	28	6	164	87	17	4	338	42	8	2	48
1922	315	24	20	318	99	7	6	702	45	3	3	45
1923	531	121	80	573	93	21	14	1,198	44	10	7	48
1924	353	205	78	480	73	43	16	1,150	31	18	7	42
1925	322	359	80	601	53	60	13	1,383	23	26	6	43
1926	399	286	89	596	67	48	15	1,379	29	21	7	43
1927	326	362	124	564	58	64	22	1,880	17	19	6	30
1928	381	356	115	622	61	57	18	2,030	19	18	6	31
1929	372	387	136	623	60	62	22	2,148	17	18	6	29
1930	336	416	106	646	52	64	16	1,627	21	26	7	40
1931	199	311	90	421	47	74	21	1,145	17	27	8	37
1932	98	209	29	278	35	75	10	1,006	10	21	3	28
1933	157	152	22	286	55	53	8	1,098	14	14	2	26
1934	160	169	52	277	58	61	19	1,313	12	13	4	21
1935	238	203	84	357	67	57	24	1,745	14	12	5	20
1936	378	328	86	620	61	53	14	2,760	14	12	3	22
1937	425	518	125	818	52	63	15	3,400[4]	13	15	4	24
Total	8,408	4,546	1,444	11,509	73.1	39.5	12.6	32,310	26.0	14.2	4.5	35.8

[1] The figures for both exports and available supply are lacking in accuracy, due to the inclusion of refined alumina in the exports, as explained in the text. [2] Not reported. [3] From July 1, 1914. [4] Estimated.

TABLE IIb.—AVAILABLE SUPPLY OF ALUMINUM IN THE UNITED STATES
(Thousands of metric tons)

Year	Production	Imports	Exports	Available New Supply	Secondary Recovery	Available Total Supply	World Output[2]	Per Cent of Total Supply in Domestic				Per Cent of World Output in Domestic				
								Production	Imports	Exports	Secondary	Production	Imports	Exports	New Supply	Total Supply
1913	21	11	1	32	4	36	68	58	31	.....	11	31	16	.....	47	53
1914	26	8	1	34	4	38	70	68	21	.....	11	37	11	.....	49	54
1915	29	4	1	33	8	41	72	71	10	.....	19	40	6	.....	46	57
1916	42	3	1	45	17	62	100	68	5	.....	27	42	3	.....	45	62
1917	55	.....	5	50	15	65	130	85	.....	8	23	42	.....	4	38	50
1918	57	1	11	47	14	61	149	93	2	18	23	38	1	7	32	41
1919	58	8	2	64	17	81	131	72	10	3	21	44	6	2	49	62
1920	63	18	4	77	14	91	128	69	20	4	15	49	14	3	60	71
1921	25	14	2	36	8	45	82	55	31	4	18	31	17	2	45	55
1922	34	18	4	48	15	63	100	54	28	6	24	34	18	4	48	63
1923	59	20	5	74	19	93	139	63	21	5	21	42	14	3	53	67
1924	68	13	6	76	25	100	170	68	13	6	25	40	8	4	44	59
1925	64	20	7	76	40	117	181	55	17	6	34	35	11	4	42	65
1926	66	34	4	96	40	136	196	49	25	3	29	34	17	2	49	69
1927	73	33	8	97	42	138	220	53	23	6	30	33	15	4	44	63
1928	95	17	8	105	43	147	256	65	11	5	29	37	7	3	41	57
1929	102	22	9	115	43	158	282	65	14	6	27	36	8	3	41	56
1930	104	11	9	106	36	142	270	73	8	6	25	39	4	3	40	53
1931	81	6	3	84	27	111	219	73	5	3	24	37	3	1	38	51
1932	48	4	2	49	22	72	154	67	6	3	30	31	3	1	33	46
1933	39	8	3	44	30	74	142	53	11	4	40	28	6	2	31	52
1934	34	8	2	40	42	82	171	41	10	2	51	20	5	1	24	48
1935	54	10	2	62	51	113	258	48	9	2	45	21	4	1	24	43
1936	102	11	1	112	51	163	366	63	7	1	31	28	3	1	30	44
1937	133	20	4	150	55	204	491	65	10	2	27	27	4	1	30	42
Total	1,532	322	101	1,752	682	2,433	4,543	63	13	4	28	34	7	2	39	54

[1] Not reported.   [2] New metal only.

to exceed production, exports were consistently increasing, while metal imports were also increasing. In this period bauxite production dropped to 60 per cent of supply, and metal production to 82 per cent of new supply. Combined, this gives a domestic output of only 49 per cent of the required supply. During 1930–1937 bauxite production dropped to 54 per cent of supply, and metal production increased to 92 per cent of the new supply, increasing the combined domestic output to 50 per cent of the consumption requirements. The combined figure reached 57 per cent in 1935, but had declined to 46 per cent in 1937.

Imports.—Imported aluminum, which, as has been indicated, has during recent years supplied one-half of the domestic consumption, is now received mainly in the form of bauxite, net imports of metal having been reduced to comparatively small amounts. Just how much of the reduction in metal imports since 1929 has been due to depression conditions, and how much to changes in the trend of the industry, it is impossible to determine, but indications seem to point to the latter, rather than the former, in spite of the fact that metal imports have been increasing steadily since 1934.

The bulk of the metal imports listed in Table II*a* (usually about 98 per cent) is ingot metal, the remainder being plate, sheet, and hollow ware; in addition to the amounts covered in the table, there are imports in a number of other forms which are reported only by value, the estimated weight of which is of the order of 300–400 tons annually. Although the metal imports are small in bulk as compared with the ore imports, their true industrial importance is far greater than these comparative figures would indicate, as the value of the metal imports is about double that of the total ore imports.

Bauxite imports are almost entirely from British Guiana and Surinam, the former ratio of approximately 1:2 had changed to 1:5 in 1937; imports from other countries usually do not exceed 3–4 per cent of the total, but occasionally run double these amounts. Canada formerly supplied about half of the metal imports, followed by Norway, Switzerland, United Kingdom, and Germany; in 1937 the order was Canada 56 per cent, Norway 21, Switzerland 13, United Kingdom 5, France 2, and Spain 2 per cent.

Exports.—The export figures for bauxite, as shown in Table II*b* include both bauxite and alumina (listed in the export returns as bauxite and bauxite concentrates). From 1923 to 1927 much of the Canadian supply of alumina was imported from bauxite purification plants in the United States, using bauxite imported from British Guiana, and the export figures shown were largely alumina, rather than bauxite; the bauxite equivalent of these figures would probably be more nearly double the figures given; the true export figures and the corresponding supply available for consumption in the United States are distorted to this extent. In 1928 bauxite purification was established in Canada, and since then little alumina has been exported, although during the past two or three years the amount has been increasing; in 1937 about 30 per cent of the total exports was alumina, and the remainder was calcined bauxite, one ton of which is equivalent to 1.65 tons of crude bauxite. Here again true export and available supply figures are distorted, and this should be borne in mind in using these figures. There is little bauxite or alumina exported to countries other than Canada.

The comparatively insignificant exports of metal are mostly ingots, but plates, sheets, tubes and utensils have been increasing in importance lately.

Consumption.—Approximate figures on the amounts of bauxite consumed annually are shown in Table II*a*, and on aluminum in Table II*b*, but it must be pointed out that since no information is available on stocks, the figures can be based only on the supply available for consumption, rather than on the actual consumption. Further data on bauxite will also be found in a subsequent paragraph on utilization.

Stocks.—No record is available on stocks, either of bauxite or aluminum.

SMELTING

The distribution of the reduction of aluminum by countries is shown in Table I*b*. Although the domestic bauxite supply is definitely insufficient, as is evidenced by the extensive imports of recent years, the domestic smelting capacity has been built up to a point where metal imports are comparatively small and secondary recovery is well established. There are four reduction plants in the United States; the largest is at Massena, N. Y., the next largest at Alcoa, Tenn., and smaller ones at Badin, N. C., and Niagara Falls, N. Y.

The smelting operation is somewhat complicated by the character of the ore, which carries a large percentage of combined water, and impurities of such a nature as to require the conversion of the bauxite into pure alumina before it can go into the reduction cell. Since the removal of the moisture and the impurities reduces the weight by about one-half, it is desirable to do this at the mine, so as to save transportation charges, but in most of the producing localities industrial conditions are not favorable, and in the long run it is cheaper to ship the ore as mined, or with only drying to remove moisture. Only in a few cases are the purification plants at or near the mine; in others, purification is done at the smelting plant, or at some convenient intermediate point.

UTILIZATION OF BAUXITE AND ALUMINUM

The distribution of the available supply of bauxite among the consuming industries since 1916 is shown in Table VI. Abrasives and refractories have used an average of 13 per cent of the supply, while chemicals have taken 15 per cent; the annual demand for abrasives and refractories has varied between rather wide limits, while that for chemical material has been much more uniform in character. Ore for reduction to metal has averaged 72 per cent of the supply, of which 43 per cent was domestic and 29 per cent imported. Since imports did not reach material proportions until 1924, the division between domestic and imported material before and after this date will differ considerably from the average value; previous to 1924 the supply of metallurgical ore was almost exclusively domestic, while since then the division has been 42 per cent domestic and 58 per cent imported. It is to be noted in this connection that all of the imports are entered as metallurgical material, while the abrasive and chemical supplies are credited entirely to domestic ore; actually, this is not strictly true. Probably the chief error is the assignment of the entire imports to metallurgical use, since quite appreciable amounts of British Guiana bauxite are known to have been consumed in the production of chemicals, but since the amounts are not known, no correction can be made in the table to allow for this. It must also be borne in mind that the figures for available supply, as carried over from Table IIa are subject to correction on account of exports. Between these two items of error, it is admitted that the value of the table is questionable, and it is used only as a rough approximation of data not otherwise obtainable.

A table supplied by the Aluminum Company of America, based on domestic consumption of new metal during the past few years, gives the following distribution by types of use, in percentage of the total consumption:

Transportation.. 33
Cooking utensils....................................... 16
Electrical conductors.................................. 12
Machinery and electrical appliances.................... 11
Building construction.................................. 6
Chemical... 6
Foundry and metal working............................. 5
Iron and steel metallurgy.............................. 4
Food and beverages.................................... 4
Miscellaneous... 3

TABLE VI.—ESTIMATED DOMESTIC UTILIZATION OF BAUXITE
(Thousands of metric tons)

| | Available Supply | Abra- sives | Chemi- cals | Metallurgical[1] | | | Metal Pro- duced |
				Domes- tic	Im- ported	Total	
1916..............	414	46	81	287	[2]	287	40
1917..............	564	114	83	367	[2]	367	55
1918..............	599	125	65	409	[2]	409	57
1919..............	371	37	69	265	[2]	265	58
1920..............	550	53	87	389	21	410	63
1921..............	164	7	42	93	22	115	25
1922..............	318	20	80	215	4	219	34
1923..............	573	74	70	387	41	428	59
1924..............	480	68	56	229	127	356	68
1925..............	601	75	68	179	279	458	64
1926..............	596	74	79	246	197	443	66
1927..............	564	73	63	190	238	428	73
1928..............	622	74	85	222	241	463	95
1929..............	623	108	88	176	251	427	102
1930..............	646	84	69	183	310	493	104
1931..............	421	55	59	85	221	306	81
1932..............	278	6	63	29	180	209	48
1933..............	286	19	91	47	130	177	39
1934..............	277	36	68	56	117	173	34
1935..............	357	56	67	114	119	233	54
1936..............	620	87	75	215	242	457	102
1937..............	818	128	77	215	393	618	133
Totals............	10,742	1,319	1,585	4,598	3,133	7,741	1,454
Per cent..........	100.0	12.3	14.7	42.8	29.2	72.0	....

[1] All imported material is entered as metallurgical, although small but unknown amounts may have gone into other uses. These figures are the difference between imports and exports in Table IIa, and are unavoidably too high, due to the fact that in some years the exports include a considerable amount of refined alumina, and actually represent larger amounts of bauxite. [2] When exports exceed imports (1916–1919), the amounts are deducted from the metallurgical material.

PRICES

Almost the entire domestic output of bauxite is for direct consumption by the producer, or is sold under a long term contract

and the same is true of imported ore; for this reason very little
bauxite appears in the open market, and price quotations consequently do not represent market conditions in the same way
that they would in the case of most other similar products.
Lacking significant price quotations, the accompanying graph
of bauxite prices, Fig. 12, is based on the producers' valuation
at the mines in the case of domestic ore, and on the shippers'
declared valuation at the port of shipment for the imported

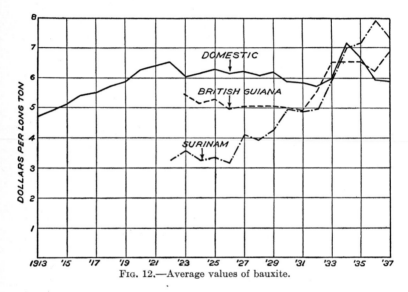

Fig. 12.—Average values of bauxite.

ore.   It is significant to note that while there is a consistent
rise in the valuation of domestic bauxite from 1913 to 1922,
there is scarcely a trace of the war inflation that trebled the price
of the metal.   This may presumably be accounted for by the
fact that there were almost no sales in the open market.   Under
these conditions one is led to infer that as a matter of simplification in accounting the cost of bauxite was maintained on its
former basis, and that all of the results of the increased price of
the metal were attributed to the metal alone, instead of a due
portion of the increase being allocated to the ore.

A comparison of the declared valuation of the ores imported
from British Guiana and Surinam also shows some peculiar relationship.   These two sources supply nearly all of the imported

material, and in both cases production is made by an affiliated company of the Aluminum Company of America, and the imports are consigned to another affiliated company, so that again valuations are largely a matter of internal accounting methods. Nevertheless it is interesting to note the comparative values of ore from these two sources, and their relation to the domestic values, and particularly the consistent rise in the value of Surinam ore. It is possible, however, that at least part of this increase may have been due to gradual increase in the grade of the product as continued operation led to improvements in the productive operations, while much of the rise from 1931 to 1933 may be attributed

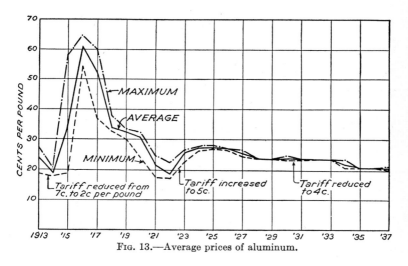

Fig. 13.—Average prices of aluminum.

to the devaluation of the dollar, and the consequent relative increase in the value of the foreign currency.

Prices of aluminum are more specific, and the accompanying graph, Fig. 13, shows the trend of the maximum and minimum monthly averages, and the annual averages, since 1913, for the open market prices for 99 per cent ingot. Prices for 98 per cent ingot are usually 1–2 cents less, and secondary metal is still lower. During the war period there was considerable disturbance in the market, and there was at times a large margin between the open market price for imported metal and the contract price established by the sole domestic producer. The two prices were practically the same in 1914, but with the open market price slightly lower. By June 1915 the war demand began to manifest itself in the open market, which rose to 65 cents by the end of 1916. The domestic price, however, was under the complete control of the producer, and was held at a more reasonable level, the average being 26 cents in 1915, 37 cents in 1916, and 38 cents in 1917; during 1918–1920 the two prices were again at approximately the same level, in the neighborhood of 33 cents, but in 1921 the domestic price dropped only to 27 cents, while the open market price dropped to 21 cents, with quotations at the end of the year as low as 17.5 cents. This differential decreased by about half in 1922, and after the increase of the tariff on aluminum from 2 cents to 5 cents per pound in 1922, the prices gradually equalized themselves. Since 1924 there has been only one price, which is accepted as the open market price, although it is set by the domestic producer, and not by the market for imported metal.

Table VII presents data recently compiled by the U. S. Bureau of Mines, giving the average annual value at the mines for domestic bauxite, the average quoted price for aluminum, and the corresponding index prices, after applying the commodity index for the year.

TABLE VII.—BAUXITE AND ALUMINUM PRICES IN THE UNITED STATES

	Bauxite Dollars per Long Ton		Commodity Index	Aluminum Cents per Pound	
	Average Value	Index Price		Quoted Price	Index Price
1913.................	$4.75	$4.75	100.0	23.63	23.63
1914.................	4.88	5.00	97.6	18.59	19.05
1915.................	5.10	5.12	99.6	34.13	34.27
1916.................	5.40	4.41	122.5	60.75	49.58
1917.................	5.48	3.26	168.3	51.25	30.45
1918.................	5.69	3.03	188.1	35.60	17.86
1919.................	5.85	2.95	198.6	32.14	16.18
1920.................	6.23	2.82	221.2	30.61	13.84
1921.................	6.38	4.56	139.8	21.21	15.17
1922.................	6.50	4.69	138.5	18.68	13.49
1923.................	6.04	4.19	144.1	25.41	17.63
1924.................	6.15	4.38	140.5	27.03	19.24
1925.................	6.28	4.23	148.3	27.19	18.33
1926.................	6.16	4.30	143.3	26.99	18.83
1927.................	6.20	4.54	136.7	25.41	18.59
1928.................	6.06	4.38	138.5	23.90	17.26
1929.................	6.19	4.53	136.5	23.90	17.51
1930.................	5.83	4.71	123.8	23.79	19.22
1931.................	5.82	5.56	104.6	23.30	22.28
1932.................	5.69	6.13	92.8	23.30	25.11
1933.................	5.99	6.35	94.4	23.30	24.68
1934.................	7.15	6.66	107.3	21.58	20.11
1935.................	6.65	5.80	114.6	20.50	17.89
1936.................	5.91	5.10	115.8	20.50	17.70
1937.................	5.81	4.70	123.6	20.08	16.25

TARIFF

As is the case with most materials covered by a tariff, the number of headings covered by successive tariff acts has gradually increased, until now there is a fairly complete coverage of the industry, although with items that carry through two or more acts, there is more of a tendency to decrease the rate than to increase it, except for the Act of 1922, where new entries and increased rates predominate. In general, the downward trend in rates is found in crude and semi-finished goods, while more highly manufactured goods show a rising trend in rates.

TABLE VIII.—TARIFF RATES ON ALUMINUM
(Cents per pound or per cent ad valorem)

	1909–1912	1913–1922	1922–1930	1930—
Crude bauxite	....	Free	$1/ton	$1/ton
Refined bauxite				
Less than 64 % Al_2O_3	4/10c.	15 %	½c.	½c.
Over 64 % Al_2O_3	6/10c.			
Alums	Included with alum cake		¾c.	¾c.
Sulfate (alum cake)				
Less than 15 % Al_2O_3	¼c.	15 %	3/10c.	⅕c.
Over 15 % Al_2O_3	⅜c.		⅜c.	⅜c.
Salts, n.s.p.f.[1]	....	....	25 %	25 %
Metal, scrap and alloys, crude	7c.	2c.	5c.	4c.
Silicon alloys	....	....	....	5c.
Ferrosilicon alloys, 20–52 % Al	....	....	....	2½c.
Ferrosilicon alloys n.s.p.f.[1]	....	....	....	5c.
Plate, sheet, bars, rods	11c.	3½c.	9c.	7c.
Tubes, moldings, castings, n.s.p.f.[1]	....	....	40 %	....
Wire	....	15 %	15 %	....
Utensils, hollow and flat ware	....	25 %	11c. + 55 %	8½c. + 40 %
Leaf	....	25 %	0.06c./leaf	0.06c./leaf
Foil (less than 0.006 inch thick)	....	....	35 %	40 %
Powder and powder in foil	....	....	12c.	12c.
Powder in leaf	....	....	....	0.06c./leaf + 10 %
Manufactures n.s.p.f.[1]	45 %	20 %	40 %	45 %

NOTE: These are basic rates, some of which have been changed by reciprocal trade treaties with various countries.
[1] N.s.p.f., not specially provided for.

POLITICAL AND COMMERCIAL CONTROL

Among the more important producers of aluminum, only France and Italy have supplies of bauxite in excess of their own needs; Russia is self-supporting, and the United States is dependent on imports for half of the requirements; all others are completely dependent on imported ore, or are so nearly so that the home supply is negligibly small. The only case in which this dependence is varied in any way is that of Great Britain, which has plentiful supplies of bauxite in the colonial possessions, but these are so much more distant from the centers of consumption that thus far most of the British imports have been drawn from the more readily accessible deposits in southern Europe, rather than from the more remote colonial sources. Japan and Russia have ambitions looking toward heavy increases in their metal outputs; Japan is entirely dependent on outside sources for ore, while such limited supplies as are known in Russia are of low grade, so that any extensive expansion can be made only with great difficulty, unless outside ores are used.

On the other side of the picture, both France and Italy have a considerable surplus of ore over their own needs, and have exported large amounts. Hungary and Yugoslavia have only small metal outputs, leaving most of their large ore outputs available for export, while British Guiana and Surinam export their entire production.

Of the 1936 metal production, only about 35 per cent was made from bauxite produced in the same country, while 65 per cent had been made from ore imported from some other country. This extensive dependence on imports by nearly all of the metal producers affords opportunity for a wide variety of political control, but aside from minor barriers of tariffs and import quotas, thus far only three regulations of major importance have been imposed. After the World War a British ruling limited the exploitation of mineral resources on Crown lands in British territory to British capital, but in the case of the British Guiana bauxite deposits a concession was granted to American capital with the proviso that the metal reduction plant must be located in British territory; it was this condition that led to the establishment of the large plant at Arvida, Quebec, although for several years the conversion of the bauxite to alumina was done in the United States.

A French decree dated April 16, 1935, prohibited the exportation of bauxite or aluminum, except under government license; this, however, has not as yet affected the amount or the destination of the exports, which continued in 1936 and 1937 in about the same way as before, but it affords a means by which exports may be readily and speedily restricted or diverted from any particular destination, should occasion demand such action. At the time it was anticipated that this decree might be used as a means of restricting exports of bauxite to Germany, but this has not yet been the case, at least not to any great degree, as German imports from France in 1936 and 1937 exceeded 95,000 tons, as compared with 120,450 tons in 1934.

Both the British and the French moves have been of a restrictive character, the former actively and the latter thus far only potentially, but a German regulation has served to stimulate the bauxite industry in a remarkable degree. In order to encourage aluminum production and utilization in Germany, even though the ore had to be imported, and at the same time to effect a saving of copper through the substitution of aluminum, the German Control Office issued a decree in May 1934 restricting the use of other base metals. This action resulted in an increase of aluminum production in each of the succeeding years to date, in amount approximately equal to the 1934 output, so that the outputs for these years have been roughly double, treble and quadruple that of 1934. This has of course required a corresponding increase in the demand for bauxite, most of which has been obtained from mines in Hungary and Yugoslavia that are controlled by German capital, with smaller amounts from Italy and France; the German imports in 1937 reached the unprecedented figure of 1,313,152 tons, or about 60 per cent greater than the United States used in the same year for about the same metal production.

Turning to the commercial angle of the problem, the factors involved in the commercial control of the industry with respect to both ore and metal are so complicated that it is difficult to give an adequate picture of the situation in the brief space available; this difficulty may be appreciated more fully when it is stated that a recent book on the international control of non-ferrous metals devoted 67 pages to the subject of aluminum, and later the same author expanded this to a book of 600 pages. Probably the largest amount of information that can be given in the same space may be obtained from a somewhat condensed version of the tabulation of control as it existed in 1929, as published in the report of the Mineral Inquiry of the American Institute of Mining and Metallurgical Engineers, as shown in Table IX. According to these data, only 30 per cent of the bauxite output is under the control of domestic capital, that is capital native to the country in which the deposits are located, but over 75 per cent of the metal output is in the hands of domestic companies. To show the relative shift in output of both ore and metal between 1929 and 1937, the table is supplemented by a comparative distribution of output in 1937.

American capital is by far the largest in the group, controlling 44 per cent of the bauxite and 52 per cent of the metal output; besides the United States and Canada, the bauxite operations under American capital include British Guiana, France, Italy, Surinam, and Yugoslavia, while metal interests outside of the home territory are confined to small amounts in Italy and Norway. Next in importance comes the combination of German and Hungarian capital in the Bauxite Trust and the German domestic interests, which are concerned primarily with the supply of ore and metal for Germany; these interests control 29 per cent of the bauxite and 12.5 per cent of the metal output. It is to be noted that American control is much higher with metal than with ore, while the German-Hungarian group have the excess on the ore side.

TABLE IX.—POLITICAL AND COMMERCIAL CONTROL OF ALUMINUM PRODUCTION
(In percentage of 1929 world output)

Bauxite	World Output		Control								
	1929	1937	Domestic	Foreign	North American[1]	British	French	German	Swiss	British-French-American[2]	Bauxite Trust[3]
British Guiana	10.1	9.9	....	10.1	10.1	....	....	....	....	....	....
France	30.6	18.5	11.8	18.8	4.6	6.6	11.7	....	7.7	....	....
Germany	0.3	?	0.3	....	....	....	....	0.3	....	....	....
Great Britain	0.1	?	0.1	....	....	0.1	....	....	....	....	....
Greece	0.3	3.0	0.15	0.15	....	....	....	0.15	....	....	....
Hungary	17.8	12.1	....	17.8	....	....	....	....	....	....	17.8
India	0.4	?	0.4	....	....	0.4	....	....	....	....	....
Italy	8.8	10.4	....	8.8	2.3	....	....	6.55	....	....	....
Surinam	9.6	10.5	....	9.6	9.6	....	....	....	....	....	....
United States	17.0	11.5	17.0	....	17.0	....	....	....	....	....	....
Yugoslavia	4.8	10.1	....	4.8	0.5	....	....	2.3	....	....	2.0
Others	0.2	?	0.1	0.1	....	....	....	....	....	....	0.1
Totals	100.0	86.3	29.85	70.15	44.1	7.1	11.7	9.3	7.7	....	19.9
Aluminum											
Austria	1.4	0.8	0.7	0.7	....	....	....	....	0.7	....	....
Canada	10.8	8.7	....	10.8	10.8	....	....	....	....	....	....
France	10.8	7.0	10.8	....	....	....	10.8	....	....	....	....
Germany	12.2	26.0	11.8	0.4	....	....	....	11.8	0.4	....	....
Great Britain	5.2	4.0	5.2	....	....	5.2	....	....	....	....	....
Italy	2.8	4.7	1.5	1.3	0.4	....	....	0.9	....	....	....
Norway	10.1	4.7	....	10.1	2.0	3.3	....	....	....	4.8	....
Spain	0.4	?	....	0.4	....	....	....	0.4	....	....	....
Switzerland	7.7	5.1	7.0	0.7	....	....	....	0.7	7.0	....	....
United States	38.6	27.0	38.6	....	38.6	....	....	....	....	....	....
Totals	100.0	88.0	75.6	24.4	51.8	8.5	10.8	12.5	9.4	4.8	....

[1] North American control is predominantly United States, but involves some Canadian capital, and to this extent somewhat overlaps on British capital. [2] Ownership of the Norwegian plants is somewhat complicated; two companies are believed to be owned by British capital, one by a combination of British and North American, one by Norwegian and North American, while that of the fifth is uncertain. [3] The Bauxite Trust is an international organization financed largely by German and Hungarian capital.

It is impossible to determine just how much if any change has been made in ownership and control between the various national groups since 1929, but entirely disregarding this possibility, considerable change will have ensued from the changes in output that have taken place since then. Bauxite production in 1936 was 34 per cent greater than in 1929, and in 1937 was 73 per cent greater, and much of this increase has been in countries that were among the smaller producers in 1929; hence the proportionate control will have been materially altered, even though actual ownership of operating companies remains unchanged. For the same reasons similar changes are to be expected on the metal side, where increases in output are even greater than with bauxite, although fewer countries are involved. The most important changes in bauxite output have been in British Guiana, Hungary, Italy, Yugoslavia, Greece, Netherlands East Indies, and Russia; these countries produced 40 per cent of the 1929 total, but 58 per cent of the 1937 total, nearly half of which was from countries not in the list in 1929. Malaya has also become a producer, and in 1938 is expected to show a material output, possibly as much as 100,000 tons, under Japanese control. With the metal, the chief changes are in Germany and Italy, which have increased from 15 per cent of the 1929 total to over 30 per cent in 1937.

In addition to a large amount of interlinkage in ownership and control through consolidations, holding companies, and other affiliations, the commercial control has been still further complicated by the maintenance since 1926 of an international cartel by the leading European producers, which controls production quotas, markets, and prices.

GENERAL REVIEW OF THE DOMESTIC SITUATION

Aluminum was first placed on the critical list in 1932, and was transferred to the strategic list in 1936. During the war period the United States was completely self-supporting with respect to both bauxite and aluminum; imports were reduced to almost nothing, and exports were greater than imports, and in 1918 the bauxite production reached an all-time high of 615,000 tons. The war effort skimmed much of the cream from the Arkansas deposits, and in the recovery from the post-war depression and the beginning of the boom period of the 'twenties, the rising output was halted at 531,000 tons in 1923, and ever since then production has been at a definitely lower level, and imports have supplied a growing deficiency. The peak output of the boom period was 399,000 tons in 1926, and 1937 showed the highest figure since 1923, with 425,000 tons. New metal production and secondary recovery have almost kept pace with increasing demands, and have between them accounted for 93–98 per cent of the available supply since 1930. While metal imports have dropped, net ore imports have ranged from one-third to two-thirds of the available supply, and it is chiefly this factor which led to the transfer of aluminum to the strategic list.

Another factor which made this transfer advisable was the fact that secondary metal makes up such a large proportion of the supply. While production capacity is sufficient to supply the normal demand for new metal, this is true only because the new metal supply is supplemented by such a large amount of secondary metal. While secondary metal is entirely satisfactory for many ordinary commercial uses, it is not satisfactory for most of the military uses, and in case of an extensive increase in the demand for virgin metal, such as would inevitably occur in the event of a major emergency, the new metal supply would not be sufficient to meet the combined needs for this and ordinary commercial uses. Much of this overload could be relieved by a wider commercial use of secondary metal, and the remainder would have to be obtained by expanding domestic production or from imports from accessible sources of supply in friendly countries.

In the event of a blockade in sea traffic, the only available source would lie in the Canadian output, which should be sufficient to cover any ordinary shortage, unless by chance British interests were opposed to our own in the emergency. In any case, a rigid control of the industry would be required, but a serious deficiency in supply, while possible in theory, is remote in probability.

CONCLUSION

All angles considered, aluminum is not so important as a strategic material as many others in the list, nor does it involve so many or such complicated problems as some of the others. Except under extreme conditions, no serious complications are to be anticipated in maintaining, if not a plentiful, at least a measurably adequate supply. While domestic reserves of ore are such that they do not support the demand under ordinary commercial conditions, and it is more profitable to import ores, emergency conditions would increase prices sufficiently to offset this, and there is no question of the ability of the reserves to meet even emergency demands if prices are scaled to suit the conditions; the only adverse factor is the time element required to step up production to the level demanded. On the metal side, even less difficulty is to be expected, since present plant capacity is more nearly in line with possible emergency demand, but on the other hand, any expansion of smelting capacity will require more time than a corresponding change in mine capacity.

All told, emergency problems in connection with aluminum bid fair to be the cause of fewer headaches than possibly any other item in the list of strategic mineral supplies, and the addition of the metal to the strategic list may be viewed as largely a precautionary measure, to be on the safe side, rather than as an urgent necessity. Some of the anticipated difficulties could be avoided by the establishment of a reserve stock of either metal or ore, to tide over the emergency, until domestic production could meet the demand, as it is rather evident that Germany is now doing, when one compares the magnitude of their bauxite imports with the metal output over the past few years.

CHAPTER IX

ANTIMONY

Antimony has more uses of a direct military character than any other member of the strategic group and possibly more important uses than any of the others except mercury. The production of antimony in the United States has never been large; even during the war period the output was only a small fraction of the requirements. While China is the predominant producer, the general distribution of the metal is somewhat better than in many other cases. While the extensive deposits in China are able to produce at a lower price than any of the others and hence have contributed about three-quarters of the world supply during normal times, other countries, particularly Bolivia, were able to produce material amounts under the high prices prevailing during the war period; at that time the Chinese output dropped to less than half of the total; in fact, in 1916, the year of maximum output, China produced only 37 per cent of the total, against 27 per cent from Bolivia, 16 per cent from Algeria, and 30 per cent from all other countries. During the past few years, China has again dropped well below its former level, due to competition from Mexico and Bolivia.

At the outset, a word of explanation is needed on the nomenclature of certain antimony products, for there still prevail in the industry some terms that originated in the middle ages, which are contradictory to the modern accepted use of these terms. Current literature may now be followed with little danger of confusion, but if one dips into that of only a few years past, particularly from European countries, the unfamiliar terms are liable to be misleading. Antimony metal was given the name, "regulus," by the ancients, and the term still persists to some extent in the trade, particularly in England. The highest grade of refined antimony was called "star antimony," because of the characteristic spangled appearance of the surface of the ingot. "Needle antimony," "crude antimony," "antimony crude," or simply "crude," does not refer, as might be inferred, to a crude or unrefined metal, but to the liquated sulfide, a comparatively pure form of Sb_2S_3, which is also sometimes called, quite properly, "antimony matte." Greater progress is being made in the United States in the elimination of these obsolete terms than in any other country.

REQUIREMENTS

The average requirements for antimony, as measured by production since 1913, have been 27,200 metric tons annually. This figure approximately coincides with the normal average industrial demand, as the high figures during the war period have been offset in the average by the years when the industrial consumption was subnormal. The war maximum rose to 61,500 tons, while the post-war minimum dropped to 11,000 tons, and then held quite steady at about 17,000 tons through 1924. The inflation period saw a gradual increase to a high of 30,800 tons in 1929, and the depression minimum, as was the case with most of the strategic metals, held above that of the post-war period. Recovery did not reach the 1929 high until 1936, and 1937 increased to 34,500 tons.

USES

Although in general the uses of antimony are moderately diversified, both as to the form in which the metal is used and the type of use requiring it, yet in the final analysis it will be found that the major proportion of the metal, regardless of the specific requirement, is employed for the purpose of imparting hardness and stiffness to some type of lead alloy. The uses for pure antimony, as such, are extremely limited, about the only one of any importance being in the manufacture of various types of ornamental castings, such as coffin plates, candle sticks, and small bric-a-brac, particularly of Oriental origin. Chemical uses are more varied, but are largely centered in the oxide and sulfide.

Metallurgical Uses.—From 75 to 80 per cent of the total antimony consumption, including almost the entire amount used in the metallic condition, is in the form of an alloy with lead (and sometimes other metals), the primary objective being the imparting of a sufficient degree of hardness and stiffness to the lead to enable it to be used for purposes which would not be possible in its normally soft state.   Hard lead, or antimonial lead, containing from 4 to 12 per cent of antimony, produced either by alloying the two metals or, more often, by the smelting of antimonial lead ores or a mixture of antimony and lead ores, is applicable to a wide variety of uses, the most important of which are: storage battery plates; sheet and pipe in the chemical industry, particularly where resistance to sulfuric acid is required; and the sheathing of cables for telephone, telegraph, and other uses.   The lead used in sheet, foil, and collapsible tubes is usually strengthened by the addition of 1 to 4 per cent of antimony, and many solders contain small percentages of antimony.

Until the recent extensive use of storage batteries in automobiles and the partial substitution of other types of alloys for bearings, the production of bearing metals was the heaviest consumer of antimony.   These alloys vary considerably in composition, depending on the service to which they are to be subjected, and the price for which they are to be sold, and may carry from as low as 3 per cent to as high as 20 per cent of antimony with varying amounts of tin, lead, copper, and sometimes other metals.

Its use in type metal is probably the most important service which antimony has rendered to mankind, although the amounts used are far less than in some other applications.   With the modern development of printing, several different compositions of type metal are used, depending on the service required, but all are fundamentally alloys of antimony and lead, with usually small amounts of some other metals.   Metal to be used in the backing of electrotype plates may have as little as 2 per cent antimony, for here the brunt of the load is borne by the copper surface rather than by the type metal itself.   For linotype and monotype metal, which is used only for one printing and is then melted for re-use, 10 to 15 per cent of antimony is used, but for hand-set type, which is to be used repeatedly, or for small type, where the load is heavy on a small printing surface, 18 per cent or more of antimony will be needed.   Stereotype plates require still more antimony, up to 23 per cent, as they are much thinner than the standard type height, and require greater stiffness.

Other alloys of wide variety use small amounts of antimony in their make-up.   These are chiefly the so-called white metal alloys, but they also include some types of brasses and bronzes. Among the more important white metal alloys are: Brittania metal (lead-antimony-copper); pewter (lead-tin-antimony); Queen's metal (tin-antimony-copper-zinc); and sterline (copper-antimony-zinc-iron).

Chemical Uses.—The most used compounds of antimony are the oxides and sulfides. The white trioxide (Sb_2O_3) and the red trisulfide (Sb_2S_3) are used as paint pigments, as are also small amounts of other compounds. Fusible enamels may be made from the trioxide or the tetraoxide (Sb_2O_4), but if the enamel is to be used in contact with foods, only the pentoxide (Sb_2O_5) should be used, as food acids may dissolve small amounts of metal from the lower oxides and cause poisoning. The oxides and sulfides are also used as coloring agents in glass. Safety matches use about 3 per cent of the trisulfide in the match head and about 8 per cent in the striking surface.

One of the earlier methods of vulcanizing rubber was with the pentasulfide (Sb_2S_5); during vulcanization this broke down, liberating sulfur, which accomplished the vulcanization, and the red trisulfide, which gave the rubber a characteristic red color. With the development of cheaper methods of vulcanization, the same color may be secured with other pigments, but some antimony is still used in rubber work.

A number of salts of antimony are used medicinally, both externally and internally, the most important being the tartrate of antimony and potassium, commonly known as tartar emetic.

Military Uses.—In addition to the many ordinary industrial uses which also serve military needs, such as bearing metals, storage batteries, and cable coverings, there are several specific military uses which make antimony of primary importance from a military standpoint. Shrapnel balls and bullet cores of lead are hardened with varying percentages of antimony. The bursting charge of shrapnel shells contains antimony sulfide, which produces a dense white smoke on explosion, thus enabling the location of the burst to be observed. Another important use of the sulfide is in the priming mixture for the detonating caps of rifle and artillery cartridges.

SUBSTITUTES

The most extensive substitution that has been made is in the use of antimony in bearing metals, which has about been cut in half. This movement started during the war period and its accompanying shortage of antimony with the development of Frary metal, an alloy in which the hardening action on the lead is accomplished by small percentages of barium and calcium. Later, other similar alloys were developed, and the field of this type of hardening agent for lead has been extended to other uses where antimony was formerly used, such as cable covering. This type of substitution may be of very considerable importance in any future emergency shortage of antimony, as its use can, in case of necessity, be expanded beyond its present status, including the military requirements for shrapnel and bullet cores.

More recent advances in bearing metals have made further inroads on the use of antimony, as cadmium alloys are now being extensively used by several automobile manufacturers. So far as is known, little, if any, progress has been made in developing substitutes for antimony in battery plates and other chemical uses of hard lead where resistance to sulfuric acid is required; there are definite possibilities in this direction, using alloys of the type of Frary metal, but under ordinary conditions there is little incentive to push the substitution. A considerable degree of substitution is possible and, in case of extreme emergency, possibly almost complete substitution in the requirements of antimony for enamels, paints, chemicals, and rubber.

Ordinarily antimony is to be considered as a cheap metal, available as a substitute for others more expensive; for example, the use of antimony in cable covering is a substitute for tin, which was formerly used for this purpose. The substitution of other materials in bearing metals mentioned above is the chief exception to this rule; but, under emergency conditions, with high prices and shortage of supply from remote sources, the tide of substitution tends to flow in the other direction.

ORES

The chief ore of antimony is stibnite, the trisulfide, also known as gray antimony or antimony glance; when pure it contains 71.8 per cent antimony. There are a number of other antimony minerals, but they are found only in small quantities, associated with stibnite, and are not of any particular commercial importance, as they are never found alone in paying quantities and, in association with stibnite, they do not materially affect the treatment processes.   In the primary deposition of all pure antimony ores, the antimony mineral is stibnite, which continues predominantly unchanged in the ore as mined in the most important deposits of China in Hunan province, in most of the South American deposits and many other antimony deposits.   The antimony deposits of southern China however consist mainly of oxidized ore, and this is also true of most of the antimony deposits of Mexico though many of the deposits of Oaxaca, Queretaro and Sonora consist of partly oxide and partly sulphide ore.   Since 1931 the antimony smelter at Laredo Texas has successfully used the low grade oxide ores of Mexico as its largest source of antimony. The ores vary widely in richness, and the subsequent treatment depends much on the grade of the ore and on the final product desired, which may be one of the three oxides, the pure sulfide, or the metal.   An antimony content in excess of 60 per cent is preferred, but lower grades are usable if low in harmful impurities and, in some cases, ores are worked as low as 10 per cent.

Of greater domestic importance is the occurrence of small amounts of antimony in many sulfide ores of lead; if the antimony content of the ore is high enough, these ores may be smelted directly to a hard lead; or if small, the antimony content is removed from the lead in the refining process, and is recovered separately.

Beneficiation.—Very little information is available on the extent to which modern ore dressing methods are applicable or are being used in the beneficiation of antimony ores, probably because the major share of the output is in remote districts where more or less primitive methods are still in use.   One of the chief methods of improving the ore is by the liquidation process, in which advantage is taken of the low melting point of antimony sulfide, which may be separated from the gangue by heating the ore sufficiently to fuse the sulfide, allowing it to drain away from the gangue. This is not a particularly economical process, as recoveries are 85 to 88 per cent at the best, decreasing with the metal content of the ore.

Ores with 90 per cent or better of sulfide content are rated as crude antimony, and may be sold as such or smelted.   Ore with 90 per cent down to 40 or 45 per cent sulfide may be liquated for the production of crude antimony; with lower grades, the losses are heavy and the ore is usually subjected to a roasting process, producing a volatile oxide, which may be condensed and sold as such or smelted to metal.

Both the liquation and the roasting processes serve as a combined beneficiation and a preliminary step in the metallurgical treatment. Being simple, they can be handled fairly satisfactorily with native labor, and the more recent methods of ore dressing have been little used.

Metallurgy.—Antimony metal may be produced by the direct smelting of ore, of liquated sulfide (crude), or of the oxides obtained from the roasting process. The bulk of the output comes from the last two processes. Most of the antimony metal production at Laredo is the result of blast furnace smelting of oxide ores without roasting.

Direct smelting of the ore is carried out in blast furnaces and is best applicable to ores containing 25 to 40 per cent of metal, as these are too low in grade for the best results in liquation and are too high in grade for best work in roasting. Blast furnace smelting is still in a more or less experimental condition, and is little used.

The oxides may be smelted in blast furnaces, reverberatory furnaces or crucibles, using charcoal or some other form of carbon as a reducing agent; or in some cases liquated sulfide may be used for most of the reduction, the sulfur combining with the oxygen of the oxides, leaving behind the antimony from both the sulfide and the oxide. In furnace smelting, the ease with which the antimony compounds volatilize necessitates the use of condensation chambers in the flue to recover the volatilized portions of the charge.

The liquated sulfide, or crude, may be roasted to oxide and smelted as such, but, due to the high grade of the crude, that process is little used. It is usually smelted with oxides, as mentioned above, or may be reduced to metal by fusion in a crucible with scrap iron, giving antimony metal and a residue of iron sulfide.

Various attempts to develop wet extraction or electrolytic methods have not as yet proved commercially successful.

A pure ore and careful technique may give a product sufficiently pure for the market, but the presence in the metal of impurities, which consist chiefly of sulfur, iron, arsenic, copper, and lead, is generally sufficient to necessitate a refining process for their removal, either in a reverberatory furnace or a crucible, fusing the metal with an oxidizing slag. The volatilization losses in the refining operation are high, and reworking the condensed flue dust adds materially to the cost of refining.

The "starring" of the ingot, which is demanded by many buyers because it is considered an indication of high purity (although this is not necessarily the case), is accomplished by slowly cooling the metal in the ingot mold under a cover of a specially prepared slag with a melting point lower than that of the metal.

Secondary Recovery.—Many of the leading uses of antimony are permanent in character, and leave material susceptible of secondary recovery. A large proportion of the metal in cable coverings, storage batteries, and chemical equipment comes back into the market. Monotype, linotype, and stereotype metal is remelted repeatedly by the user, without coming back through market channels, and, even after frequent remeltings have changed the composition, is doctored to restore approximately the original composition, by adding antimony to replace that lost by oxidation; half-tone metal is contaminated by the copper facing, and must go back through the smelter, although the quantity of metal returned is sometimes materially reduced by "sweating" the plates, that is, heating them above the melting point of the lead alloy, thus recovering most of it, and sending to the smelter only the copper shell with a thin film of adhering alloy. Hand set type, when worn out, are sold as scrap, for recasting by a type foundry, as the printing plant does not have facilities for this work, unless it uses the monotype and has the desired matrices available. Recoveries of bearing metal and the white metal alloys are not so extensive, as the individual units are small, and in many cases the recovery would cost more than the value. Ammunition is completely lost, as is also all of the antimony going into chemical uses. The secondary turnover in storage batteries is probably the best among the larger uses, considering both the time element and the proportion recovered; it has been estimated that about 75 per cent of the worn out automobile batteries come back for secondary recovery in from 1 to 5 years. The proportionate return with chemical equipment and cable covering is probably equally high, but the time interval is usually greater.

The statistics of secondary production show that the total recovery since 1913 has averaged 35 per cent of the available supply, or 55 per cent of the new metal supply. In pre-war days the figure was less than 20 per cent of the available supply, but a gradual improvement has been maintained, as the use of automobile storage batteries increased, and during several recent years the recovery has been 50 per cent or better; in other words, the amount of secondary antimony coming into the market was equal to or greater than that of new metal, and, without the secondary recovery, the demand for antimony in the United States would have been more than doubled.

Forms in Which Antimony Appears on the Market.—Domestic antimony is made in cakes of about 10 by 10 by $2\frac{1}{2}$ inches, weighing about 56 pounds. These are shipped direct to consumers in carloads unboxed, and are available for small lot purchases from warehouses at principal consuming centers in boxes containing 224 pounds net or 10 boxes to the long ton. Imported antimony is usually in somewhat smaller cakes weighing 30 to 40 pounds. Chinese antimony is sold in cases containing 224 pounds and English metal is sold in casks containing 672 pounds. Ordinary brands have a guaranteed purity of 99 per cent, while special brands run 99.6 to 99.8 per cent. The usual impurities are those mentioned in the discussion of refining, reduced to below the minimum amount covered by the guarantee of the grade in question.

There is a limited market for crude or needle antimony (liquated sulfide), for the three oxides, and for various chemicals.

ORE RESERVES

Probably less is known concerning antimony ore reserves than of those of any other strategic metal. This is largely due to the primitive character of a large portion of the operations, particularly in China and Bolivia, and to the generally undeveloped condition of the smaller deposits in other countries where production is sporadic and largely dependent on price levels. The two main veins of the Panchi mine, one of the largest in China, were originally estimated to contain 175,000 tons of ore, of which about 13 per cent had been mined by the end of 1919, since when no further information is available, though it is probable that later work has increased the known reserves. The largest producing area is at Hsi-Kuang-Shan, where reserves are thought to be in excess of 1,000,000 tons. The reserves of low grade ore in Bolivia are known to be of considerable extent but, so far as is known, no specific figures have been published.

In terms of actual tonnage of reserves available, little more is known concerning deposits of the middle class group of producers, such as Mexico, Algeria, France, and Czechoslovakia, than of the large group of minor producers, except the generalization that the larger outputs that have been maintained would indicate more plentiful sources of supply. Among the numerous minor producers, in which the United States is unfortunately to be classed, information is limited to the recognized fact that certain amounts of metal appear in the market when prices are high enough to cover production costs, but, when production is small and intermittent, there is little incentive to the development of a small deposit and the blocking out of ore reserves. In the United States, deposits that have been worked, mainly during the war period, and give promise of possible commercial exploitation if prices rise to a sufficiently high level, are found in the following states: Alaska, Arizona, Arkansas, California, Idaho, Nevada, Oregon, South Dakota, Utah, and Washington. The bulk of the recent output has been from Idaho.

WORLD OUTPUT AND SUPPLY

The first authentic records of antimony date from the 15th century, but the metal was known and had limited but well recognized uses long before that time. In spite of this long history and the opportunity that has been provided for the development of additional uses through several centuries, the uses are confined to a comparatively small number of applications, the demand is still only moderately large, and outside of the war period, the total output has exceeded 30,000 tons only in 1929, 1936 and 1937, although the war peak was more than double that amount.

Although a number of countries have antimony deposits that have contributed varying amounts, some consistently and others intermittently, depending on the extent of the demand and particularly on the prevailing price, China has been outstandingly the foremost producer, with Bolivia a poor second; these two countries have supplied three-quarters of the output since 1913, and China alone has furnished almost two-thirds of the total. The world output has varied widely with changing economic conditions; starting with about 25,000 tons in the years immediately preceding the World War, it grew rapidly under war demand to a maximum of 61,500 tons in 1916, dropped to 11,000 tons in 1919, and, from 1920 to 1924, was quite uniform at slightly over 17,000 tons. It was not until 1925 that demand began to increase and production came back to the pre-war level, this increase continuing until 1929 with a maximum of 30,800 tons. The depression minimum was 17,800 tons in 1931, and 1937 saw a recovery to 34,500 tons.

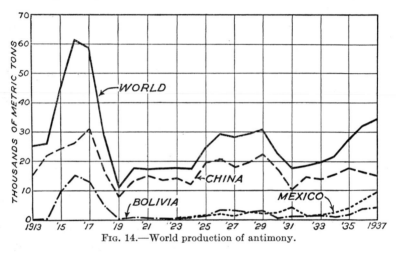

Fig. 14.—World production of antimony.

Table I shows the annual output since 1913 for all countries that have contributed appreciable amounts to the supply, the annual totals, the period totals for each country, and the percentage of the period total that has been supplied by each country. The world production graph, Fig. 14, shows the trend of production in the world, and separately for China, Mexico and Bolivia, the principal producers. Many of these figures, particularly for the earlier years, are more or less approximate, as statistics are incomplete, and, in many cases, the amounts reported by different agencies vary considerably; the data given in the table represent a reasonably close estimate of the available supply.

Another difficulty encountered in the compilation of complete statistics on antimony arises from the variations in the methods of reporting in different countries. While most countries report the antimony content of the ore produced, China, the most important of all, reports only the quantities of final products exported, any figures on actual production, either of ore or of final products, being largely estimates, except during the past few years, when reports have been made on metal production. In order to put the production figures on ore content on as nearly the same basis as those of China, the outputs are reported on an estimated basis of recoverable metal in the ore produced, assuming an average recovery of 80 per cent of the metal in the ore. This method of handling the data gives figures that are more nearly directly comparable than any other that could be applied.

China is the only country having a material amount of exportable surplus; home consumption is so small as to be negligible, and practically the entire output is exported. Bolivia, Mexico, Algeria, and Australia are in much the same position as to consumption, but the amounts produced for export are much smaller; of these four, Mexico has been the most consistent producer, operations in the other countries being largely confined to periods of heavy demand and high prices. In Czechoslovakia domestic demand is somewhat larger than in the other countries, but leaves a moderate surplus for export. France and Italy produce mainly for home consumption, any exports of domestic output being more than offset by imports.

Production conditions are such that costs are considerably less in China than in other countries; with only a few favorably situated producers in each country outside of China able to operate except at periods of high prices, production in these countries is low at other times, and expands only when prices go above the level of the operating costs of any particular deposit. While this condition prevails to a greater or less extent in all of the countries concerned, it is particularly true in those capable of making the best showing when prices permit, namely, Bolivia and Algeria. Conditions are such in both of these countries that production is very low when the price of the metal is less than 10 cents per pound, becomes moderate in amount at 10 to 15 cents, and may be increased heavily at still higher prices. Past experience has demonstrated that these two are capable of producing material amounts of metal at high prices, but they can not be counted on for any great amounts at normal prices, although

Bolivia seems to have made some improvement in this respect, and, during 1930–1934, made a better showing than during the post-war depression.

The correlation between prices and production is shown in Fig. 15, both for the world total *ex* China, and for the combined outputs of Bolivia and Algeria. The production curves follow the price curve quite closely, and emphasize strongly what has already been said about the influence of prices on production. This condition can be improved only by improving the more or less primitive methods of mining and treatment that are used in many localities, and thus reducing costs.

Variation of production with price changes is, of course, met with in every commodity, and particularly so in the mineral

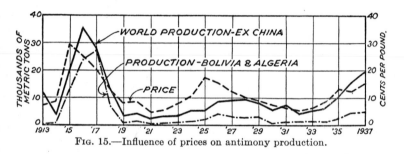

Fig. 15.—Influence of prices on antimony production.

industries, where production costs may vary widely with the size, character, and richness of the deposit; with the location, and the extent to which transportation costs enter into the final costs; and with the efficiency and plentifulness of the labor supply available. But it is somewhat exceptional to find these conditions combined in such a way as to make quite such a marked differentiation in production ability as is found in the case of antimony, where one country alone may furnish almost the entire supply at low prices, but less than half when prices are high.

Algeria.—Antimony production in Algeria, small in pre-war times, increased under war demand to a maximum of 8,900 tons in 1916, but declined rapidly after the war, to hundreds rather than thousands of tons. Since 1933 there has been a marked revival, and the 1,000-ton output in 1936 was the largest since 1920. There is an extensive mineralized zone extending across the entire northern area of Algeria from Morocco to Tunis. The principal

TABLE I.—WORLD PRODUCTION OF ANTIMONY[1]
(Thousands of metric tons)

	China[2]	Bolivia	Mexico	Algeria	France	Czecho-Slovakia	Australia	Italy[3]	United States	Others	Total
1913	15.0	[4]	2.3	0.2	5.4	[5]	1.0	0.1	......	0.3	25.2
1914	22.0	0.1	1.6	0.3	0.6	[5]	0.9	0.1	......	0.3	25.9
1915	24.0	9.9	0.2	2.7	0.9	[5]	1.7	0.5	1.8	2.0	43.7
1916	26.3	15.1	0.8	8.9	2.5	[5]	1.7	0.7	1.4	4.1	61.5
1917	31.4	12.9	2.6	4.5	2.3	[5]	1.2	0.5	0.3	2.3	59.2
1918	15.7	4.8	3.3	2.2	1.3	[5]	0.7	0.4	[4]	0.3	28.7
1919	7.7	0.1	0.5	0.7	1.0	0.2	0.6	[4]	......	0.2	11.0
1920	13.0	0.5	0.6	1.0	1.1	0.3	0.5	0.2	......	0.2	17.4
1921	14.7	0.3	[4]	0.1	1.3	0.4	0.2	0.1	......	[4]	17.1
1922	13.9	0.2	0.4	0.6	0.8	0.1	1.0	0.2	[4]	0.1	17.3
1923	14.3	0.3	0.4	0.5	0.7	0.5	0.4	0.3	[4]	0.2	17.6
1924	12.1	0.6	0.6	0.9	1.0	1.1	0.1	0.4	[4]	0.6	17.4
1925	19.5	1.4	1.1	0.5	0.6	0.5	0.1	0.4	[4]	0.3	24.8
1926	20.9	3.5	2.1	0.7	0.7	0.9	0.1	0.4	......	0.6	29.8
1927	18.0	3.2	1.5	0.1	0.9	1.6	[4]	0.3	......	1.6	27.1
1928	19.3	2.8	2.9	0.1	1.0	1.0	0.1	0.3	[4]	1.8	29.2
1929	22.4	3.0	2.2	0.1	1.0	0.6	[4]	0.3	......	1.2	30.8
1930	17.4	0.9	2.4	0.1	1.1	0.3	[4]	0.5	......	0.2	22.9
1931	10.1	1.1	4.4	0.1	0.7	0.5	[4]	0.3	......	0.6	17.8
1932	14.5	0.2	1.0	0.2	0.5	0.5	[4]	0.3	0.3	0.4	18.9
1933	13.8	1.7	1.8	0.1	0.3	1.1	[4]	0.3	0.5	0.6	20.2
1934	15.5	1.1	2.4	0.5	0.2	0.9	[4]	0.3	0.3	0.5	21.8
1935	17.7	1.9	4.1	0.8	......	1.6	[4]	0.4	0.5	0.8	27.8
1936	16.3	3.6	6.7	1.0	......	0.8	0.1	400	0.6	2.6	32.1
1937	14.7	3.9	9.8	0.9	......	0.9	0.2	500	1.1	2.8	34.5
Totals	430.2	74.1	55.7	27.9	25.9	13.8	10.6	8.2	6.8	24.6	679.7
Per cent	63.3	10.9	8.2	4.1	3.8	2.0	1.6	1.3	1.0	3.6	100.0

[1] Approximate recoverable metal content of ore produced or exported, unless otherwise stated; based on an estimated recovery of 80 per cent of the metal content of the ore; does not include antimonial lead ores. [2] Metal content of all exports. [3] Metal, crude and oxide produced. [4] Less than 50 tons. [5] Data not available.

antimony deposits are in the eastern section, in the department of Constantine, near Ain Beida. Several other occurrences have also been worked at various times, notably at Djebel Taya and Ain Kerma. The ore goes to France for smelting. As is indicated by the war output, the Algerian deposits are capable of a considerable output but only in periods of high prices.

Australia.—Production in Australia has been confined to the Costerfield district of Victoria and the Hillgrove district of New South Wales. The ore is a complex gold-antimony mixture, the treatment of which has given considerable difficulty due to low recoveries. There are several antimony occurrences known in Western Australia, but these have not been worked to any appreciable degree. Antimony is also present in some of the gold ores of this territory, especially at Wiluna, but, so far as is known, there has been no attempt made to recover the antimony. The Australian concentrates go to England for smelting. Production has never been large and has not exceeded 100 tons for many years.

Bolivia.—Little is known about the extent of the antimony occurrences in Bolivia beyond the fact that they are numerous and widely scattered. The chief producing centers are in the vicinity of Uncia and Porco. Mining was on a small scale until stimulated by war demand and high prices; the post-war decline took things back to about the pre-war basis until rising prices again brought new life during 1925–1929 and 1935–1937. Most of the output seems to be from small workings by native operators rather than by organized mining companies. Production costs are therefore high and only a few of the deposits can be worked during periods of low prices. Operations during the war period indicated that, for Bolivian production to reach any appreciable figure, the price of the metal must be at least 10 cents per pound. Antimony is present in some of the Bolivian gold ores but is not recovered in the treatment; antimonial lead ores are also known but have not been mined. The ores produced are fairly high in grade, usually about 60 per cent, and are all exported for smelting, formerly mostly to Belgium and England, with smaller amounts to the United States and France, but since 1935 most of the output has come to the United States. Bolivian ore as exported averages around 60 per cent. Lots of ore are commonly sold as high as 65–67 per cent and as low as 50–55 per cent.

China.—Although antimony is found widely distributed throughout China, the principal deposits are in the provinces of Hunan, Yunnan, Kwenchow, Kwangtung, Szechwan, and Kwangsi, with Hunan far in the lead; about 90 per cent of the entire output comes from the region around Changsha. China has held predominance as an antimony producer since early in the present century, having supplied 63 per cent of the total world output since 1913.

Only a few of the operations are conducted on a large scale, and much of the work, both in mining and smelting, is done in a primitive fashion, with little in the way of modern equipment or technical supervision. In addition, the entire antimony industry, as well as that of tungsten, is the plaything of the various warring factions that have over-run China for so many years, and, at times, the conduct of the industry has been seriously hampered both by the military activities in the vicinity of the mines and by the various attempts that have been made to control the industry by whatever faction happened to be in power at the moment, with the object of bleeding as much revenue as possible from the industry.

A still further difficulty has been encountered at times in the exchange situation. Although the Chinese ores average better in grade than those of any other country, and production is affected less by low prices for the product, there are many mines with working costs too high to operate at very low prices, particularly if the period of low prices for antimony happens to coincide with a period of high prices for silver, the main currency basis of the country; for this makes the returns to the producer still less than they would otherwise have been. Conversely, if silver prices are low when antimony prices are low, the returns to the producers may be satisfactory in spite of the low prices in the consuming countries. This angle will be discussed more fully later, in the section on prices.

In spite of all of these difficulties the antimony output has been maintained at a remarkably high level and with not as much disturbance and fluctuation as might be expected under the circumstances. The industry has, however, undergone a considerable degree of transition in the period under review. During the pre-war period, only small amounts of metal were exported; some ore was exported, but the bulk of the shipments was crude antimony (liquated sulfide).   During the war period, ore exports were greatly reduced and much of that exported went to Japan for smelting.   (In this connection, it might be well to point out that Japan has little domestic antimony production; most of the imports received by the United States and other countries as coming from Japan actually originated in China; this material was re-exported as received, or was treated and the resulting crude or metal exported.)   Since the close of the war period, exports both of ore and crude have been small and metal exports have predominated.

During recent years, Great Britain has been the chief buyer of Chinese antimony, followed by Japan, United States, and Germany.   This does not mean that either Great Britain or Japan are heavier consumers than the United States, but merely that they do more re-exporting.

Czecho-Slovakia.—There are several small antimony mines in Slovakia and Ruthenia, three or four of which have been working fairly regularly.   The ore is low in grade (10 to 15 per cent), but is concentrated to 50 or 60 per cent and smelted locally.   The output supplies the domestic consumption, with a small surplus for export.   Minor occurrences in Bohemia, which contributed to the former Austrian output, seem to have dropped out of the picture.

France.—Antimony deposits are numerous in France but are mostly small.   The chief producing districts are in the departments of Mayenne, Vendée, Cantal, Haute-Loire, and Bouches-du-Rhône, the first being the most important and, during late years, the only active producer.   The French output was formerly the largest in Europe but has declined heavily in recent years and has not yet shown any signs of the post-depression recovery that has been manifested in other countries.   The ore is smelted locally along with imported ore, chiefly from Algeria, producing crude, oxide, and metal, only small amounts of which are exported.

Italy.—The chief Italian deposits are in the Iglesias district of Sardinia, which have been working continuously on a small scale. The Sienna district of Tuscany has made intermittent production, and, during the war period, there was a small output from Sicily and the Ivrea district of Piedmont.   The ore is treated in local smelters, producing mainly metal with small amounts of crude and oxide, which are sufficient to supply about half of the national demand.

Mexico.—The Mexican deposits are more important than their average production figures indicate. While Mexico stands third in the list of producers, it was only the heavy war output that gave Bolivia rank ahead of Mexico, and, since 1918, the Mexican total has been greater than that of Bolivia, since production is more consistent and somewhat less subject to price fluctuations. Furthermore, Mexico is the only source of antimony directly accessible to United States territory; advantage has already been taken of this fact, through the establishment of a domestic smelter at Laredo, Texas, which depends largely for its supply upon Mexican ores.

The chief deposits are situated in San Luis Potosi, Oaxaca and Sonora with other important productive deposits in Queretaro, Durango, Zacatecas and Guerrero; deposits of possible commercial importance are known in Chihuahua, Coahuila, Lower California, Hidalgo, Mexico and Puebla. Previous to the establishment of the Laredo smelter, about three-quarters of the ore output was smelted locally, mostly to metal, although some was produced as antimonial lead, as well as small amounts of crude; the remainder was exported as ore, chiefly to the United States. Since then one of the larger local smelters has been dismantled and its ore supply diverted to Laredo.

Since 1931 when the antimony smelter was established at Laredo Texas, the production of Mexican ores has increased considerably in spite of unsettled conditions in Mexico. With more settled conditions, Mexico may well prove to be a reliable source of antimony ore supply for the United States at all but very low price levels.

United States.—Under the pressure of war demand and high prices, work on antimony production was carried on in Alaska, Arizona, Arkansas, California, Idaho, Montana, Nevada, Oregon. Utah, and Washington, with a small output during the years 1915–1918. Production since then has been intermittent, and has not exceeded 100 tons, except since 1932. Most of the recent output has been from Idaho. The total production in the United States since 1913 has been less than 1 per cent of the world total, although this proportion would be increased slightly if one included the antimony content of hard lead smelted from domestic antimonial lead ores.

Other Countries.—A number of other countries have produced minor amounts of antimony, some quite regularly, and others only intermittently. Among the latter are Argentina, Borneo, Canada, Germany, India, Indo-China, Rhodesia, and South Africa. Countries having larger and more consistent outputs, varying from a few tons to a few hundred tons, include Austria, Greece, Hungary, Japan, Yugoslavia, Peru, Portugal, Spain, Spanish Morocco, and Turkey. The combined output of these minor countries varies from year to year but has averaged only 3.6 per cent of the total since 1913; only in 1915–1917 and 1927–1929 has the amount exceeded 1,000 tons.

UNITED STATES OUTPUT AND SUPPLY

The production of antimony ores in the United States has been so scanty and irregular as to be insignificant. Even in 1915, the year of maximum war output, the production was only a shade over 1 per cent of the available supply, although this figure might possibly be doubled by the inclusion of the antimony content of hard lead smelted from domestic ores. Since 1913 there has been no production in 9 years, while in 8 years the outputs were less than 50 tons, and amounted to less than 200 tons all told; in the remaining 6 years the outputs varied from 300 tons to 1,800 tons, and totaled 4,500 tons. Table II gives the data on the supply available from all sources. From 1932 to 1935 the metal obtained from secondary recovery exceeded that which was received from all other sources, both foreign and domestic.

Imports.—Although there has consistently been some importation of antimony in ore, except in 1922, the amounts were comparatively small until since 1930, when the opening of the Laredo smelter increased the demand for ore. Imports of crude and compounds have been fairly stable, but ore and metal have changed radically from time to time. During the period 1913–1930 the distribution of the imports of antimony for consumption was 70 per cent metal, 13 per cent in ore, 4 per cent in crude (liquated sulfide), 6 per cent in compounds, and 7 per cent in alloys; during 1931–1937 metal has dropped to 27 per cent while ore increased to 65 per cent; the ore ratio has been increasing almost every year and, in 1937, reached 83 per cent. The difference in these figures can not all be attributed to the establishment of a domestic smelting industry, however, as the heavy decrease in consumption during the depression period had some influence, as did also the increasing rate of secondary recovery.

The distribution of the imports received from the various producing sources is shown in Table III, so far as it can be determined. These figures are not available previous to 1915. In many cases the countries from which shipments arrive in the United States are not the actual producers, the material having been re-exported. So far as is known, all of the shipments coming from Chile, as well as most of those from Argentina and Peru, originated in Bolivia, and are so entered in the table; likewise the figures for China include all shipments received from Hong Kong and Japan, as the ore from which this metal was smelted came from China. Most of the ore received from "Other Countries" originated in the country from which it was shipped, but a considerable proportion of the metal was smelted from ore obtained from China or Bolivia, so that the figures given for these two countries are known to be too low; but, since the amounts given for Bolivia, China and Mexico account 93 per cent of the total, the discrepancy can not be very large.

Until 1931, when ore shipments for the new Laredo smelter began, imports of ore were comparatively small. (Shipments for the Laredo smelter actually began late in 1930, from ore mined during 1929 and 1930, but for some reason these imports did not appear in the official statistics until early in 1931.) Even including the war period imports, the amount received in ore up to 1930 was only 13 per cent of the total, about half of which was in the war period; since 1931, however, the combination of reduced demand for metal under depression conditions, and the increased demand for ore to supply the Laredo smelter has swelled the ore imports heavily, at the expense of the metal imports.

It will be noted that, in most years, the total of the general imports is greater than that of the imports for consumption, carried over from Table II for comparison; these differences cover changes in stocks, re-exports, and also the discrepancy involved by the fact that the general imports figures for metal include some if not all of the imports of crude, the exact conditions being uncertain.

TABLE II.—AVAILABLE SUPPLY OF ANTIMONY IN THE UNITED STATES
(Metric tons)

	Imports for Consumption, Sb Content of					Total Imports	Production in		Exports	Total New Metal	World Total	Percentage Consumed in U.S.	Secondary	Total Available Supply
	Ore	Crude	Metal	Compounds	Alloys		Ores³	Alloys						
1913	1,800	¹	5,700	700	¹	8,200		2,300	²	10,500	25,200	42	2,500	13,000
1914	1,100	¹	5,900	900	100	8,000		2,500	700	9,800	25,900	38	2,400	12,200
1915	1,400	...	6,600	300	200	8,500	1,800	4,900	1,400	12,000	43,700	27	2,800	14,800
1916	4,200	...	6,400	200	100	10,900	1,400	3,200	1,400	12,700	61,500	21	4,100	16,800
1917	5,300	500	10,200	¹	...	16,000	300	2,500	400	18,100	59,200	31	4,500	22,600
1918	1,300	600	12,700	¹	¹	14,600	¹	2,300	600	16,300	28,700	57	4,800	21,100
1919	400	200	6,500	100	1,100	8,300	...	1,800	200	9,900	11,000	89	4,000	13,900
1920	600	900	8,900	200	1,900	12,500	...	1,800	400	13,900	17,400	80	5,100	19,000
1921	100	200	9,200	100	3,700	13,300	...	1,400	100	14,600	17,100	85	4,300	18,900
1922	...	500	8,500	300	5,000	14,300	1	1,300	100	15,500	17,300	89	6,400	21,900
1923	1,000	600	6,100	1,500	800	10,000	1	2,000	¹	12,000	17,600	68	7,300	19,300
1924	800	400	6,200	800	100	8,300	1	2,500	100	10,700	17,400	62	8,500	19,200
1925	700	500	8,900	1,200	800	12,100	1	2,400	100	14,400	24,800	58	9,900	24,300
1926	1,400	1,400	10,400	1,500	700	15,400	1	2,400	200	17,600	29,800	59	14,700	32,300
1927	1,800	700	9,000	1,200	100	12,800	...	2,500	300	15,000	27,100	55	11,300	26,300
1928	2,000	800	8,800	1,800	400	13,800	1	3,100	500	16,400	29,200	56	10,800	27,200
1929	1,700	1,200	10,100	1,500	300	14,800	...	2,800	500	17,100	30,800	56	10,100	27,200
1930	800	500	7,000	500	100	8,900	...	1,500	400	10,000	22,900	44	7,300	17,300
1931	4,400	400	3,400	600	100	8,900	...	900	600	9,200	17,800	52	7,200	16,400
1932	1,200	300	1,400	300	¹	3,200	400	1,000	100	4,100	18,900	21	5,900	10,000
1933	1,900	500	1,800	500	300	5,000	500	800	100	5,700	20,200	28	6,700	12,400
1934	2,600	300	1,600	200	500	5,200	400	1,500	400	6,300	21,800	29	6,900	13,200
1935	4,200	900	1,100	400	200	6,800	500	1,000	300	7,500	27,800	27	8,700	16,200
1936	9,600	750	1,100	900	300	12,600	700	1,300	400	13,500	32,100	44	9,000	23,200
1937	12,500	500	900	800	400	15,100	1,100	1,500	400	16,200	34,500	47	11,200	28,500
Totals	62,800	12,650	158,400	16,500	17,200	267,500	7,100	51,200	9,700	309,000	679,700	...	176,400	485,400
Per cent	12.9	2.6	32.7	3.4	3.5	55.2		10.5	2.0	63.6	...	46.5	36.4	100.0

¹ Less than 100 tons.   ² Not available.   ³ Not included in total, as it is duplicated under alloys.

TABLE III.—IMPORTS OF ANTIMONY INTO THE UNITED STATES[1]
(Metric tons)

	China[3]		Mexico		Bolivia[2]	Other Countries		Total		Total General Imports	Imports for Consumption
	In Ore	Metal[4]	In Ore	Metal[4]	In Ore	In Ore	Metal[4]	In Ore	Metal[4]		
1915	850	7,500	150		450	100	450	1,550	7,950	9,500	8,000
1916	650	8,700	500		2,500	650	250	4,300	8,950	13,200	10,600
1917	1,850	14,000	650	1,850	2,600	300	300	5,450	16,150	21,550	15,500
1918	100	9,800	550	2,700	[5]	[5]	100	1,250	12,600	13,850	14,000
1919	150	4,950	100	350	200	200	1,200	600	6,500	6,850	6,900
1920	200	11,150			600	100	150		11,300	11,900	9,500
1921	50	9,450			500		150		9,600	9,700	9,300
1922		8,000	250		600	100	50	950	8,050	8,050	8,500
1923		6,050	150		500		1,050	800	7,100	7,400	7,100
1924		5,350	400	200	300		1,050	700	6,600	7,400	7,000
1925		7,200	700	1,450	700	50	2,400	1,450	9,700	10,400	9,600
1926		10,550	650	1,100	1,150		2,750	1,800	13,350	14,800	11,800
1927		9,000	650	1,250	1,350		1,700	2,000	11,200	13,000	10,800
1928		7,400	400	200	1,300	[5]	1,450	1,700	10,300	12,300	11,800
1929	200	9,600	100	50	500	[5]	1,500		12,200	13,900	7,800
1930		6,000	4,250	100	150		450	4,400	7,700	9,100	2,600
1931		4,400	1,100	100	100		100	1,200	4,700	3,000	3,700
1932		1,700	1,600	450	350		50	1,950	1,800	4,250	4,600
1933		2,200	2,200	300	400		50	2,300	2,300	4,600	6,700
1934[5]	[5]	1,800	3,150	400	1,000		50	4,150	2,000	4,600[6]	6,700
1935[5]			6,350		3,100		50	9,600	2,350	6,700[6]	10,600
1936[6]	100	650	8,250		4,100	50	50	12,500	1,050	10,600[6]	13,400
1937[6]	100	400					150		950	13,400[6]	
Totals	4,250	147,650	32,150	11,150	22,000	1,650	15,450	60,150	174,400	234,600	208,400
Per cent	1.8	64.8	13.7	4.8	9.4	0.7	6.6	35.6	74.4	100.0	

[1] Not available previous to 1915. [2] Includes shipments from Argentina and Chile, most of which originated in Bolivia. [3] Includes shipments from Hong Kong and Japan, most of which originated in China. [4] Contains small amounts of antimony (liquated sulfide). [5] Less than 50 tons. [6] Imports for consumption; general imports not published.

The distribution of the 1937 antimony imports, classified as to source and port of entry into the United States are shown in Table IV. The Texas Border ore shipments would indicate that the Laredo smelter is using only Mexican ores. Ore shipments from Mexico and South America to East and West Coast ports is presumably for the production of antimonial lead and oxide. Practically all of the crude came from China and went to New York. Most of the Mexican metal entered the United States by rail through the Border ports of San Antonio and Nogales, beyond which the distribution can not be followed, but it was presumably for western use, or it would have been sent to New York by boat. Chinese metal and scattered small amounts from European smelters mostly came to New York, with a small amount of Chinese diverted to the West Coast.

TABLE IV.—DISTRIBUTION OF ANTIMONY IMPORTS IN 1937
(Short tons)

	New York	Other Eastern[1]	Mexican Border[2]	West Coast[3]	Total
Ore[6]					
Mexico...........................	191	9	8,768	143	9,111
Bolivia[4].........................	3,518	....	....	28	3,546
Argentina[5].......................	981	....	....	....	981
China............................	128	....	....	....	128
Japan............................	17	....	....	....	17
Great Britain....................	36	....	....	....	36
Total.....................	4,871	9	8,768	171	13,819
Crude[7]					
China............................	604	133	....	....	737
Belgium..........................	20	....	....	....	20
Germany.........................	14	....	....	....	14
Total.....................	638	133	....	....	771
Metal					
Mexico...........................	6	....	359	....	365
China............................	331	6	....	80	417
Great Britain....................	29	....	....	....	29
France...........................	73	....	....	....	73
Belgium..........................	61	....	....	....	61
Total.....................	500	6	359	80	945

[1] Includes Philadelphia, Baltimore, Cleveland and Omaha. [2] Includes San Antonio and Nogales. [3] Includes Los Angeles, San Francisco, Portland and Seattle. [4] Includes shipments from Chile and Peru, presumably of Bolivian origin. [5] Probably largely of Bolivian origin. [6] Metal content. [7] Gross weight.

Exports.—As indicated by the figures in Table II, exports have never been large enough to affect the supply to any appreciable degree, even during the war period.

Consumption.—Specific figures for consumption for a few isolated years are given later in the discussion of utilization. Aside from these, the only guide to consumption is the data on available supply given in Table II.

Stocks.—No record has been published covering industrial or smelter stocks. Stocks in bonded warehouses vary considerably; although these have lately averaged around 1,000 tons, in September, 1922, they completely disappeared, and at times during the war period they were in excess of 4,700 tons.

SMELTING

While China, the leading ore producer, has also led in the smelting industry, a number of other countries have maintained a smelting industry on a smaller scale, including Australia, Great Britain, France, Japan, Yugoslavia, Mexico, Italy, Czecho-Slovakia, and recently the United States. Unfortunately insufficient figures are available from these countries to compile a table of metal production, and little specific information can be found concerning the present status of the industry except in isolated cases. The largest producers of metal after China have been Great Britain and France, the former entirely from imported ores, and the latter partly from domestic ores and partly from imported ores, chiefly of colonial origin. In both cases, production has declined heavily, from several thousand tons annually to a matter of hundreds of tons. Japan reached productions in excess of 10,000 tons during the war period, mostly from Chinese ores, but recent outputs are apparently comparatively small. Metal production in Czecho-Slovakia and Italy has never been large, usually of the order of a few hundred tons. The Mexican production of 2,000–3,000 tons during the war period has been reduced to a few hundred tons, partly by reduced demand and partly by the transfer of some of the smelting operations to the United States with the opening of the Laredo smelter.

For two or three years during the war period there was some emergency smelting of antimony ores in the United States, but this ceased at the close of the war, and, until the end of 1930, the only smelting carried on in this country was that of antimonial lead ores. The smelter at Laredo, Texas, started operations on a moderate scale at the beginning of 1931. So far as can be determined, there is at the present time no regular smelting of antimony ores carried on in the United States, outside of the Laredo plant, although there may be minor amounts of metal recovered by lead refining plants. On request, production figures for the Laredo plant have been furnished for the years 1931–1937, and a brief comparison shows the extent to which domestic smelting is meeting the demand.

The Laredo plant, since the beginning of operation, has smelted 52 per cent of the ore imported, 41 per cent to metal and 11 per cent to oxide; has produced 35 per cent more metal and 9 per cent more oxide than has been imported; and has furnished 29 per cent of the total new metal made available during the period. Since the turn of the depression, conditions have been markedly improved over these averages, so much so that in 1937 metal production was four times imports and oxide production was a half larger than imports. As a result of improved industrial conditions and increased demand, the plant was doubled in capacity during 1935, to a maximum monthly output variable according to demand between 900 short tons of metal and 600 tons of metal and 300 tons of oxide, and the production rate has been still further increased.

TABLE A.—DOMESTIC ANTIMONY STATISTICS
(Metric tons)

	Imports for Consumption			Domestic Production[1]				
	In Ore	Metal	In Oxide	Metal[2]	In Oxide[3]	Total Antimony	Available Supply[4]	Per Cent
1931	4,400	3,400	600	1,990	1,490	3,480	9,200	37
1932	1,200	1,400	300	1,610	660	2,270	4,100	55
1933	1,900	1,800	500	1,090	1,270	2,360	5,700	40
1934	2,600	1,600	200	1,630	1,910	3,540	6,300	56
1935	4,200	1,100	400	1,930	2,940	4,870	7,500	65
1936	9,600	900	900	3,130	3,580	6,710	13,500	50
1937	12,500	1,000	800	3,680	5,140	8,820	16,200	54
Totals	36,400	11,200	3,700	15,060	16,990	32,050	62,500	51

[1] Almost entirely from imported ores. [2] Laredo production only. [3] Of these totals, Laredo has produced about 25 per cent. [4] Total new metal available, as shown in Table II.

In addition to the operations at Laredo, there has been a heavy increase in oxide production at other plants; this has been so pronounced that in 1937 metal constituted 29 per cent of the current supply, and oxide 37 per cent, as compared with 73 per cent and 23 per cent respectively in 1932.

UTILIZATION OF ANTIMONY

Estimates of the percentage distribution of the antimony used for various purposes are available for two years in the war period, 1917 and 1918, and for two more recent years, 1926 and 1928. These emphasize strongly the heavy predominance of the lead-hardening uses of antimony, which account for 80 per cent or more of the total consumption, for, in addition to the uses classified under this heading, a considerable proportion of the unsegregated uses under "Other Alloys" and under "Miscellaneous" also fall into this category. The percentage distribution to the various uses is shown in Table VI.

TABLE VI.—UTILIZATION OF ANTIMONY

	1917	1918	1926	1928
Bearings	36.3	34.6	31.5	18.0
Batteries	6.1	4.8	14.0	28.0
Cable coverings	2.7	1.1	3.0	3.5
Soft metal alloys	8.9	10.2	12.0	5.0
Hard lead	11.1	11.2	10.0	3.5
Type metal	8.7	6.8	8.0	11.5
Ammunition	7.0	11.7	0.5	5.5
Total lead hardening	80.8	80.4	79.0	75.0
Enamels	4.6	3.3	4.0 ⎫	15.0
Pigments and chemicals	2.5	2.3	3.5 ⎬	
Rubber	7.1	8.4	7.0 ⎭	
Other alloys	3.1	2.5 ⎫	8.5 ⎫	10.0
Miscellaneous	3.9	3.1 ⎭	⎭	
Total tonnage[1]	22,600	21,100	32,300	27,200

[1] Available supply, as shown in Table II, which somewhat exceeds actual consumption.

The figures in Table VII give a general idea of the distribution of antimony to its various uses during past years, but it will be noted that the 1928 data differ widely from that of preceding years. The data presented in the discussion of smelting indicate that in the 10 years following 1928 further marked changes have taken place, especially with respect to metal and oxide, and this is substantiated by the following tabulation of the amounts and percentages of antimony which have been used in the various primary forms. The amounts shown here are the sum of domes-

PRIMARY FORMS IN WHICH ANTIMONY IS USED
(Short tons of antimony content)

	Metal		Oxide		Crude		Alloys		Total
	Tons	Per Cent	Tons	Per Cent	Tons	Per Cent	Tons	Per Cent	Tons
1928	9,684	59	2,114	13	846	5	3,884	23	16,528
1929	11,073	63	1,778	10	1,264	7	3,347	19	17,462
1930	7,700	73	626	6	499	5	1,738	16	10,563
1931	5,954	61	2,305	24	455	5	964	10	9,678
1932	3,283	57	1,112	19	304	5	1,086	19	5,785
1933	3,138	46	1,962	29	495	7	1,228	18	6,823
1934	3,562	42	2,341	28	292	3	2,261	27	8,456
1935	3,382	36	3,732	40	946	10	1,345	14	9,405
1936	4,622	38	4,915	40	829	7	1,780	15	12,146
1937	5,101	36	6,572	46	540	4	2,136	15	14,349

tic production (if any), plus imports, for the four primary forms in which antimony is placed on the market; in this connection, it should be said that the column headed "Alloys" is not intended to cover the amounts of antimony ultimately consumed in alloy form, but only the hard lead produced directly from antimonial ores and such antimony alloys as are imported.

Disregarding sporadic fluctuations, it is evident that the proportion of antimony used in the form of crude has shown little change, while that in alloys has dropped somewhat. The chief differences, however, are found in metal and oxide, the former having dropped heavily, while the latter has seen an even more marked increase, to such an extent that during 1935–1937 both the tonnage and percentage of antimony going into use as oxide was greater than that used as metal. This radical change with respect to metal and the smaller one for alloys is probably traceable largely to the heavy increase in the turnover of automobile batteries for secondary antimony. Thus far, no information is available which will account for the rapid and heavy expansion in oxide production and consumption. How much of it is going to cover increases in former uses, and how much to new uses, still remains to be seen. It is highly desirable that a thorough canvass be made of current uses, especially of metal and oxide, for without better knowledge of the current uses it is impossible to analyze any potential emergency demand.

PRICES

In earlier years most of the imported antimony entered the United States at the port of New York, and the New York price was the ruling one. The establishment of domestic smelting has changed the marketing centers somewhat, but the New York price still remains the basic price. Imported metal is sold either in bond *ex* dock, or duty paid, f.o.b. cars, port of New York, but the New York quotations are uniformly on a duty paid basis, and the price of domestic metal is largely controlled by that of imported metal. An accompanying graph, Fig. 16, shows the maximum and minimum monthly averages and the annual averages of the New York price for antimony since 1913.

There are two outstanding features of the antimony market: (1) the wide fluctuations in price, particularly in times of active demand; (2) the rapidity with which these fluctuations occur.

These seem to be due not so much to speculative activity in the market as to the long time required for the shipment of Chinese metal and the consequent uncertainty in the time of arrival; the stocks of metal maintained in the United States have never been large, and if a temporary shortage of metal occurs when buying is active, prices are liable to rise abruptly and, with the arrival of new stocks, to drop just as quickly. The ordinary uncertainties of long distance shipping have at times been supplemented by the effects of the local activities of the Chinese military factions in the producing districts and by governmental interference with the normal tenor of the industry.

In 1916, at the height of the war demand, the maximum price for the year was about four times the minimum, or, put in another

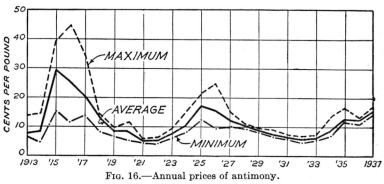

Fig. 16.—Annual prices of antimony.

fashion, the spread between the high and low prices for the year was three times the year's minimum; at the peak of the inflation period, in 1926, this spread, as compared to the year's low, had decreased by half, and in the current price increase, which has been under way since 1932, the high of 1935 was only one-third greater than the low of the year. Compared on the same basis, the high and low monthly averages for the period since 1913 are 44.71 cents and 4.32 cents, while the actual maximum and minimum prices were 46.00 cents and 4.13 cents. No market in which the spread between high and low prices ranges as widely as ten or more times the low can be said to be in a healthy condition, and greater stability would be welcome to both producers and consumers.

It will be noted that, since domestic smelting has become established in the United States, and the dependence on Chinese shipments has been materially decreased, the market has been somewhat more stable than before.   The rapidity and the wide range of the fluctuations have been materially reduced, but the tendency has not been entirely removed, as is evidenced by the

TABLE VII.—ANTIMONY PRICES IN THE UNITED STATES
(Cents per pound)

	Average Quoted Price.	Commodity Index.	Antimony Index Price.
1913	7.52	100.0	7.52
1914	8.76	97.6	8.98
1915	29.64	99.6	29.77
1916	25.37	122.5	20.70
1917	20.69	168.3	12.29
1918	12.58	188.1	6.69
1919	8.19	198.6	4.16
1920	8.49	221.2	3.84
1921	4.96	139.8	3.55
1922	5.47	138.5	3.95
1923	7.90	144.1	5.48
1924	10.84	140.5	7.71
1925	17.50	148.3	11.80
1926	15.99	143.3	11.16
1927	12.39	136.7	9.06
1928	10.31	138.5	7.44
1929	8.96	136.5	6.56
1930	7.67	123.8	6.19
1931	6.72	104.6	6.42
1932	5.59	92.8	6.02
1933	6.53	94.4	6.92
1934	8.90	107.3	8.30
1935	13.62	114.6	11.88
1936	12.24	115.8	10.47
1937	15.36	123.6	12.43

fact that the 1935 high of 16.75 cents was more than three times the 1932 low.

Supplementing the graph of annual average prices in Fig. 16, Table VII gives the annual average price in cents per pound for ordinary grades of antimony, as reported by the *Engineering and Mining Journal*, and the antimony index price derived from these by the use of the corresponding annual commodity index.

It is particularly to be noted that during the latter years of the war period the price of antimony was dropping, while the commodity index was increasing heavily, so that the index price at the end of the war was at a low level; also that the index price in 1937 was the highest since 1916.

It has already been pointed out in the discussion of *World Output and Supply* how, at the low prices ordinarily prevailing, the bulk of the output has been furnished by China, but when prices rise above the ordinary levels, other countries, particularly Bolivia and Algeria, are able to supply a material proportion of the total.   These are the usual fluctuations of supply and demand, with the price reacting upward with increased demand or shortage of supply, and downward with increased output or decreased consumption; of course these fluctuations affect the Chinese production to some extent as well as that of other countries, but to a lesser degree because of richer and more plentiful ore supplies, and consequent lower production costs.

There is considerable reason to believe that long continued price much above 13 or 14 cents brings sufficient overproduction to result usually in rapid fall to excessively low prices that shut down production in most countries.   The more systematic antimony

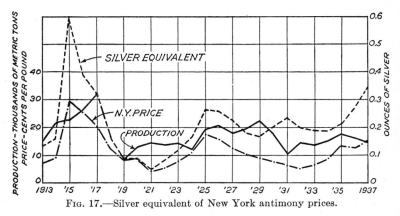

Fig. 17.—Silver equivalent of New York antimony prices.

operations of the last ten years may enable rapid increase in production with increased demand, without excessive price, and systematic curtailment with decreasing demand without the inefficiency of wide spread shut down forced by excessively low price.   However, the effects of the Japanese invasion of China to the vicinity of the principal antimony district, the recent laws and policies in Mexico that make flexibility of production most difficult and endanger the safety of industrial investments, and the trade policies and currency policies of authoritarian governments introduce great uncertainties into the future of the world antimony industry.

As has been mentioned under *China*, the fact that the monetary system of the country was on a silver basis adds an additional complicating factor in the fluctuating price of silver.   During the early years of the war period the price of antimony was high and that of silver was low, so that, in 1916, the price of 1 pound of antimony in New York would purchase 0.6 ounce of silver, but during the succeeding years, the price of antimony declined while that of silver rose, and, in 1921, the silver equivalent of a pound of antimony had dropped to 0.05 ounce; although the New York price of antimony had itself dropped to about one-sixth of the former high, the effective purchasing power of this price in China was down to one-twelfth.   On the other hand, in 1929–1931 the declining price of silver more than offset the drop in the price of antimony, and the purchasing power of the price of a pound of antimony in terms of silver increased by more than one-third.

Ordinarily, general price trends that affect one metal will also affect the other, and a decrease in the price of silver would mean a practically proportionate drop in the price of antimony, except to the extent that the decline might be offset by increased production costs resulting from advanced commodity prices (in terms of silver) of materials necessary for the smelting and refining operations, particularly those imported and purchased with foreign exchange.   Sometimes other conditions intervene to disturb the equilibrium and cause the two prices to work in conjunction or opposition.   As a result, when the combination works in favor of the Chinese producer, the output tends to increase beyond the normal proportion of the world total, but when it works adversely, the production may be expected to lag below normal.

An accompanying graph, Fig. 17, shows the fluctuations in the amounts of silver purchased by the price of 1 pound of antimony at the average prices of each since 1913, which serves as a rough indication of the Chinese purchasing power of income received by producers from the sale of antimony.

TARIFF

The comparatively low grade of the antimony ores known in the United States means working costs so high that little can be done in the way of production of domestic ore under any except extraordinarily high prices; hence the present tariff on antimony is designed for the protection of the smelting branch of the industry rather than the mining branch.   The various tariff rates that have been in effect since 1913 are shown in the following table.

In order to assist in the establishment of a domestic smelting industry, and to foster the development of oxide production, efforts were made in 1929 to increase the duties on metal and oxides, using a sliding scale which would provide a duty of 4 cents per pound when the New York price was not over 7 cents per pound, gradually decreasing to no duty when the price exceeded 14 cents, but this failed of adoption, as did also an attempt on the part of the domestic smelting interests for an increase in tariff rates in 1931.

TABLE VIII.—TARIFF RATES ON ANTIMONY
(Cents per pound, or per cent ad valorem)

	1909–1913	1913–1922	1922–1930	1930—
In ore.........................	1c.	Free	Free	Free
Needle or crude (Liquated sulfide)	1c. lb. Sb	10%	¼c.	¼c.
Regulus or metal...............	1½c.	10%	2c.	2c.
In alloys......................	Free	Free	Free	Free
Oxides........................	1½c. + 25%	25%	2c.	2c.
Tartar emetic..................				6c
Other salts....................	Free	25%	1c. + 25%	1c. + 25%

POLITICAL AND COMMERCIAL CONTROL

The 1933 report of The Mineral Inquiry on The Nationality of Commercial Control of World Minerals unfortunately did not include any data on antimony, so that the information at hand is rather scattered, is not at all complete, and, in addition, may be so old as to be obsolete in some respects, particularly in China, where there has been so much governmental interference with the industry in the past few years, with little publicity as to the exact status of affairs. The chapter on Antimony in *Political and Commercial Geology*, published in 1920, summarized the situation in the various important producing countries as follows:

Algeria.—The leading interests in Algeria were French and Belgian.

Austria.—During the war period, the operation of the mines in Austria-Hungary was in the hands of the government.

Bolivia.—The bulk of the Bolivian shipments during the war period went to England, with small amounts to the United States and still less to France, but no information is given on the nationality of ownership of the deposits.

China.—The Chinese mines were mostly native owned, and the smelting industry was largely in the hands of a single Chinese company.

France.—The leading French producer controlled not only the main local deposits, but others in colonial and foreign territory as well, while some output was controlled by Italian capital.

Italy.—The chief Italian producer was controlled by German interests before the war, and the ore was shipped to Germany for smelting. (While no specific information is available, it is likely that the former German interests were appropriated by the Italian government after Italy entered the war.)

Japan.—Although considerable amounts of Chinese ore have been smelted in Japan, this ore has been mostly bought in the open market, and there is little Japanese ownership in Chinese mines.

Mexico.—Ownership of mines, inactive deposits, and smelting plants in Mexico was largely in the hands of United States and British capital, with a minor French interest.

Although Chinese production is largely under the control of local mine owners and smelters, the sale and shipment of the product has been handled mostly by brokers and exporters of other nationalities. In 1925, the control of the foreign shipping was reported to be distributed as follows: German, 57 per cent; British, 18 per cent; French, 12 per cent; Japanese, 5 per cent; Chinese, 4.5 per cent; Danish, 2.5 per cent. Several successive governmental agencies have been formed to exercise control over the industry, but their object has been to limit production, set prices, and levy taxes, and there has apparently been no effort made to control the ownership or operation of the mines and smelters.

GENERAL REVIEW OF THE DOMESTIC SITUATION

The domestic situation with regard to antimony is similar in many respects to those of other metals of the strategic group; as is the case with most of the others, the United States is the world's heaviest consumer of the metal; as with nickel, chromium and tin, there is normally no appreciable domestic output; there was a slight increase in output during the war period, somewhat greater in proportion than with nickel and tin, but less than with chromium; as with tin, there has been a transition from metal shipments to a partial replacement by ore for domestic smelting, but, where with tin this was a war measure that ceased shortly after the close of the war, with antimony it has been a peace-time development that gives promise of permanence; as with nickel, though to a less degree, there are available supplies in adjacent territory, and the problem of transportation is much less than with chromium and tin.

While there are some antimony deposits in the United States, they are of such a grade and character that they give no promise of any appreciable production at normal price levels; even at the inflated prices of the war period the total output of the entire period was only 3,500 tons. Domestic consumption has therefore been almost entirely dependent on imported material. The most important development in recent years was the establishment of a domestic smelter, which started operation in Laredo, Texas, at the beginning of 1931.

As has been pointed out in Tables II and III and in the discussion on "Imports," the imports have changed radically as a result of the establishment of domestic smelting, ore imports having largely replaced the former metal imports, and Mexico has supplanted China as the chief source of supply.

While 72 per cent of the general imports during 1913–1930 was metal and only 13 per cent in ore, the demand for ore for domestic smelting in 1931–1935 shifted the proportions to 49 per cent in ore and 32 per cent in metal; in 1935, the proportion had risen to 83 per cent in ore, against only 6 per cent of metal. Equally important is the shift in the sources from which the antimony is obtained; ore receipts from China have been insignificant except during the war period, and the increased ore supply to cover the requirements of the Laredo smelter has all come from Mexico, with the result that, while China furnished two-thirds of the ore and metal requirements during 1913–1930, nearly all as metal, in 1931–1935 the figure dropped to 40 per cent, and the corresponding Mexican figures increased from 7 per cent to 45 per cent, nearly all in ore. In 1937, imports from China had dropped to 8 per cent, while Mexico had risen to 57 per cent and Bolivia to 27 per cent.

From a strategic standpoint, this shift in antimony supply is an item of considerable importance, since it has led to the accomplishment of a number of desirable ends, all directly or indirectly the result of the establishment of domestic smelting.

First, the accessibility of the domestic antimony supply has been materially improved, in drawing on the adjacent Mexican deposits, rather than on the more remote Chinese deposits, while the Bolivian deposits, also more accessible than the Chinese, are coming into more importance as a secondary source of supply, thus leading to a simplification of the problems inherent in transportation over long distances.

Second, the existence of a domestic smelting industry has made possible the production and utilization of small amounts of domestic ore, and has materially increased the possibility of future utilization of our scanty reserves in the event of emergency demand.

Third, the maintenance of the necessary ore stocks at the smelter, and of finished metal stocks, has made a relatively large increase in the stocks of antimony in the country, available for emergency demand. Previously these stocks have been far too small, and any move to increase them is one in the right direction.

From a strategic standpoint it would be more desirable to have the domestic smelting industry located at a more inland point, rather than on the extreme border of United States territory, but this factor has been outweighed by the economic advantages of a location as close as possible to the sources of ore supply. The question has also been raised as to the economic desirability of maintaining a domestic smelting industry, on the score that the tariff protection that permits its operation increases the price of antimony to all consumers by 2 cents per pound, and that the increased price more than offsets the advantage of domestic smelting when the industry is operated on such a small scale, particularly since foreign ore is used, and the benefits of the tariff are confined to such a small producing group at the expense of all consumers. While this argument may have some economic justification, just as it does with manganese and tungsten, it is much weaker in the case of antimony than with the others, since the proportion of the total consumption that is covered by the domestic smelting industry is quite high and is constantly growing, in spite of the fact that there is only a single plant involved; also, the situation is not complicated by the problematical question of the depletion of domestic ore reserves by current operations to a point where they would not be sufficient to cover possible future emergency demand, as is the case with both manganese and tungsten; and, finally, the purely economic side of the argument does not take into consideration the recognized strategic value of the maintenance of domestic smelting, as cited above, which can not be evaluated on a dollars and cents basis.

CONCLUSION

While inspection of Table II shows that, since 1913, the United States has been dependent on imports for more than half of its antimony supply, as against 11 per cent of primary domestic output and 36 per cent of secondary recovery, the situation at the present time is better than would be inferred from these average figures. In the first place, since 1930, domestic supply has increased through higher secondary recoveries; and, in the second place, the establishment of domestic smelting has materially increased the possibilities for primary production, although thus far the general depression in industry has prevented an actual increase in production over the former levels. Furthermore, the shift in the sources of supply to the more accessible Mexican and Bolivian ores reduces the liability to shortage of supply due to possible interruptions in long distance transportation or shortage of shipping facilities. When we add to these factors the savings that may be made by restriction in nonessential uses, substitution, and increased secondary recovery, it does not seem likely that any very serious shortage can result, even under emergency conditions, although stringent economy might be required. This conclusion, however, must not be taken as any argument against the desirability of establishing and maintaining a war reserve stock of sufficient size to avoid any possibility of difficulty from shortage of supply.

CHAPTER X

MERCURY

In mercury we have a metal that stands out from all of the other strategic mineral products in several different ways. Of this group it is the only one of which the United States has at any time been a leading producer; in the late seventies and early eighties of the last century, the United States was not only the world's foremost producer of mercury, but it supplied more than half of the total, and, in 1877, the proportion reached two-thirds, with an output of 2,755 metric tons. Since that time the United States' output has fluctuated considerably between rather wide limits but with a general downward trend. During the period with which we are concerned, the maximum was 1,237 tons in 1917, and the minimum 216 tons in 1921. In spite of this pronounced decline, the United States has, since 1913, produced 65 per cent of its requirements, although it is the heaviest consumer, absorbing 25 per cent of the world supply.

The only other metal of the strategic group of which the United States has produced any material proportion of its needs is tungsten, of which the domestic output has furnished one-third of a consumption requiring 29 per cent of the world supply. Although the average annual rate of tungsten production has been about 100 tons higher than that of mercury, the fluctuations in output have been much less for mercury, and the country has been a producer of mercury for nearly a century, while the tungsten industry did not reach material proportions until the period of the World War.

As with all the other strategic metals, there is a marked concentration of production that fails to coincide with the centers of consumption, not only in the United States, but in other countries as well. Of the major industrial countries, only the United States has any appreciable domestic supply, and, among the other producers of mercury, only Italy has an appreciable domestic consumption, and this is small, amounting only to some 100 tons a year, or about 5 per cent of the normal output.

REQUIREMENTS

Although mercury is a key metal in any munitions program, from its use as a detonator for explosives of all kinds, this is by no means a use which is limited to war times alone, for during times of peace, the requirements for sporting ammunition and for blasting work consume proportionately about as much mercury as is demanded during a war period. Mercury then is not primarily a munitions metal, but, as is the case with all of the others, it is primarily an industrial metal, with certain of its ordinary industrial uses accentuated and expanded by war demands.

We have, in the discussion of manganese, chromium, tungsten, and tin, because of the close association of their consumption with the production of steel, presented in the graph of world production a curve for world steel output, to emphasize the relation between these metals and steel. There is no direct connection whatever between the consumption of mercury and that of steel, but, nevertheless, the production curves (Fig. 18) show about as close a correlation with each other as was found with the metals directly associated with steel. The graph of world steel production is generally accepted as one of the best available gages of general industrial activity, and the fact that there is a marked degree of correlation between it and the corresponding curve for mercury, with which there is no direct connection from a consumption standpoint, emphasizes the degree to which mercury enters into the framework of the general industrial structure of the world.

From an average annual world total of just under 4,000 metric tons during the World War period, the output of mercury dropped by almost half during the post-war depression. This was followed by a rapid expansion of output from 1922 to 1929, broken only in 1923, 1924 and 1928 by the failure of Spain to maintain its share, and reaching to a maximum of 5,600 tons. A depression minimum of 2,040 tons was reached in 1933, followed by improved outputs, reaching 4,980 tons in 1937. The production curve for the past 10 years, however, is not a true representation of consumption requirements; during this period there was heavy over-production which built up unsold stocks to the extent of several thousand tons, and which required stringent restriction of output to enable them to be dissipated. These stocks are now reduced to reasonable amounts, and the average output of 3,680 tons annually over the entire period since 1913 is probably fairly representative of the average requirements; the maximum consumption during the boom period was probably not over 4,000 tons.

USES

As with other metals, the industrial uses of mercury may be classified according to whether the use requires the metal, or one of its chemical compounds, but with this marked difference, that, in the case of mercury, all the compounds used are produced from metallic mercury, so that fundamentally all uses require the reduction of the ore to metal, while most of the compounds of other metals used industrially are made from the oxide or some other natural mineral form of the element, without its having to be reduced to the metallic form.

With mercury the uses requiring a compound predominate, and comprise about 70 per cent of the total consumption, against 30 per cent used in metallic form. Another important point is that, while all of the compound uses of mercury are final, and result in the complete eventual loss of the metal, nearly all of the metal uses are what might almost be called static uses, in that the metal is subject to continued and repeated use with little or no losses beyond those due to accidental leakage or spillage. On the other hand, it must be borne in mind that, while a thermometer or a contact switch may be used for years without any loss whatever of mercury, the probabilities are that when it eventually is broken the contained mercury is either lost or is too small in amount to justify the bother of saving it, so that, in the long run, a large proportion of the metal used in apparatus of this sort is liable to complete loss; but, with the larger types of equipment, like a barometer or a mercury vapor lamp, the metal content is greater and the chances of its being saved are greater.

These metal uses may be classified under the following descriptive headings: (1) Continuous uses, in which the metal undergoes continuous or repeated use without appreciable loss; (2) repeated uses, in which the metal goes through repeated cycles of use, with a small loss by leakage, absorption or chemical attack, which must periodically be made up with new metal; (3) ephemeral uses, in which the metal is entirely lost. Incidentally, it might be stated that approximately 1,000 different uses for mercury in various forms are listed in the literature, only a few of the most important of which are mentioned here.

Metallurgical Uses.—One of the oldest, and one of the most important uses of mercury, not so much from the standpoint of the amount used, but of the economic importance of the product, is in the recovery of gold and silver from their ores by amalgamation, either in the milling of lode ores or the washing of sands and gravels by placer mining, hydraulicking, or dredging. In the early days of gold mining in the recently discovered Western Hemisphere, this was the main method of securing gold and silver, and in fact the demand for mercury for this purpose was the main incentive for the search for mercury; it was a common saying during the California gold rush that in order to work a gold mine you had to have a mercury mine.

The development of more modern methods, particularly the discovery of the cyanide process for the recovery of gold and silver, materially reduced the demand for mercury, and improvements in the amalgamation process reduced the mercury losses, so that the consumption was much less, but, during the past few years, there has been a swing back toward the use of amalgamation methods for gold, and at the present time nearly two-thirds of the gold produced in the United States is recovered either by amalgamation or placer methods. While most of the mercury is recoverable, and can be used repeatedly, there are small losses which must be replaced.

A large amount of metallic mercury is consumed in the manufacture of various types of electrical apparatus, particularly mercury vapor lamps and rectifiers, and contacting and switching devices for electric signs and traffic control lights. Scientific and industrial instruments such as thermometers, barometers, thermostats, pressure gages and controls, flow meters, and vacuum pumps also utilize large amounts. Smaller amounts are used in bearing metals and solders, in certain types of electric batteries, in the temperature compensation of clock pendulums, and in a host of other devices.

Several types of electrolytic cell for the production of chlorine and caustic soda utilize mercury cathodes, but here again, as with amalgamation, the bulk of the metal lasts indefinitely, and the only steady consumption is in the replacement of some small losses.

One of the most promising prospective uses for mercury is in the mercury boiler, which has been under development for a number of years. This is the most economical method known for the generation of power from fuel, but thus far has been confined to a few large installations. There are now three units in operation, two of 20,000 kilowatts each, and one of 10,000 kilowatts, with two smaller units under construction or recently completed. These units require 13 to 15 pounds of mercury for each kilowatt of installed capacity, so that the three working units contain 750,000 pounds of metal; replacements to cover leakage and losses amount to about 1 per cent per year. It is hoped eventually to make this system of power generation satisfactory for units as small as 1,000 kilowatts, and, if this comes to pass, it will open up an extensive new market for mercury. How this may affect the situation may be judged by the fact that the average output of mercury in the United States would supply metal for only 85,000 kilowatts of new installations each year. To what extent this would benefit the domestic market remains to be seen, as it is possible that price considerations might favor the use of imported metal, rather than domestic.

Chemical Uses.—The largest item in the list of uses in compound form is for drugs and chemicals, including such as pharmaceuticals, chemical and dental preparations, and seed disinfectants. The second largest is mercury fulminate, used as a detonator in ammunition and blasting caps. These two items alone account for well over half of the total consumption.

The pigment known as vermilion, extensively used in paints and printing inks, owes its brilliant color to the sulfide, HgS, and antifouling paint for marine use contains the oxide, HgO. Together, these account for much of the consumption.

The fourth large item in the list is the use of mercury nitrate in the manufacture of felt, this compound being required to soften the hairs so that they will stick together. Among the minor chemical uses are boiler compounds, fireworks, wood preservatives, and as a catalyst in the preparation of various chemicals, one of the most important of which is acetic acid.

Military Uses.—There are no specific military uses that differ from the ordinary industrial ones. The foremost one is, of course,

the use of fulminate as a detonator, but much of the fulminate
needed in the munitions program of the World War was diverted
from ordinary industrial lines, so that the total mercury used in
this form was not increased as much as might be expected. In
1917, fulminate took 17 per cent of the total mercury consumption, while the corresponding figure for 1928 was 19 per cent;
specific figures for 1918 are lacking, but apparently the percentage increased above that of 1917. The next important item under
this heading is antifouling paint for naval use. A third item that
might be of considerable size is the requirement for felt. If the
military hats needed for a major army mobilization were made in
the usual way, this would call for something like 10 per cent of the
total mercury requirements. The military program would also
call for many scientific and electrical instruments in which mercury plays a part, and consumption along these lines would be
increased.

SUBSTITUTES

In the general industrial field there is little tendency toward
substitution in normal times, since most of the usual incentives
are lacking. The particular properties which make mercury
applicable for its various uses, particularly its liquid condition
at ordinary temperatures, are not found in other metals, so that
the possibilities for substitution are restricted. But under
emergency conditions, with a shortage of supply as the controlling
factor, there are certain substitutions and eliminations that can
be utilized.

From a military standpoint the most important use is in detonators, for which there is no satisfactory substitute. A number of
other detonating materials are known, and have been used to some
extent, but none has as yet proved as reliable as mercury fulminate. None of them have yet been standardized to a degree that
they are considered satisfactory for military use, but lead azide
has been used to some extent in commercial work, and its use
could doubtless be extended considerably in case of necessity.
The amount of fulminate needed in the detonation of high explosives has been materially reduced by the use of "boosters";
high explosives are difficult to detonate, and require considerable
power in the detonating charge; by interposing the booster
between the fulminate and the high explosive, a small amount of

fulminate can be used to detonate the booster, which in turn detonates the high explosive.

The use of mercury in military felt hats is not an absolute essential; if substitutes can not be found for mercury in the production of felt, a different type of headgear can be used, in case a shortage in mercury makes it necessary. There are antifouling paints containing no mercury; while, in general, they are not considered as effective as the mercurial paints, they can be utilized to a considerable degree. The use of vermilion in paints and pigments is not at all essential, and it can be replaced by other materials or dispensed with entirely if the emergency demands. The same is largely true of seed disinfectants, which can mostly be replaced by a nonmercurial poison if they can not be temporarily dispensed with entirely.

The use of the mercury boiler is purely a matter of economy of operation, which could be dispensed with in case of necessity, thus freeing a large amount of mercury for more essential uses, providing the power facilities thus put out of commission can either be spared or replaced by other power. The same condition prevails with respect to the use of mercury cathodes in electrolytic cells for the production of caustic soda and chlorine. There are numerous types of cells which use other kinds of electrodes, and it is easy to say that the mercury cells can be shut down and the mercury used for more essential purposes, but, before this can be done, we must be assured that the plant capacity available from other types of cells is sufficient to supply the demand put upon them. If it were necessary to construct new cells of a different type to take the place of the mercury cells in order to maintain the required output, the cost involved in both time and money would probably make the project unfeasible when balanced against the small amount of mercury thus liberated for other uses.

There is a possibility for some restriction in the use of mercury in electrical and scientific apparatus, and the same is true of many other applications, but such restrictions as could be made along the usual industrial lines would probably be offset by the increases that would be called for in the same lines by the generally increased industrial activity that accompanies a war effort.

ORES

While a small amount of mercury is found in the native condition, as a fairly pure metal, most of it occurs in the form of the sulfide, HgS, known as cinnabar, normally a brilliant red or scarlet mineral with a specific gravity of about 8, and containing, when pure, 86.2 per cent Hg; when contaminated by impurities the color varies through a reddish brown to black. The Spanish ores are, on the average, the richest mined in large quantities, running 5 to 7 per cent. The Italian ores usually average somewhat less than 1 per cent, but, in 1934, a considerable tonnage was mined containing 9 per cent. The ores of the United States are still lower in grade, the average in 1934 being 0.4 per cent, although some mines run several times this amount. Some of the Mexican ores carry as much as 8 per cent, but the amounts of high grade ore are small.

Ordinarily an ore must carry at least 0.3 per cent Hg, or 6 pounds per ton, in order to be workable, but, in times of top price, ores have been worked with as low as 1 to 3 pounds per ton. It is interesting to contrast this statement of present day conditions with the fact that at the largest and oldest mine in California the question was raised in 1863 as to whether the mine should be abandoned, because, since 1850, the ore grade had dropped from 37 per cent to 18 per cent. By 1892 the ore had dropped to 1 per cent, and now even that would be considered fairly high grade.

Beneficiation.—With low grade material, beneficiation may be used to improve the tenor of the ore before it goes to the furnaces. In the early days of the industry the concentration of mercury ores was considered impossible, for while the cinnabar has a high specific gravity, which would seem to make it readily amenable to gravity concentration, it is also highly friable, so that in crushing the ore large amounts of fines are produced, which are lost in suspension in the water used. For this reason little ore dressing was done beyond hand picking the ore. Later, by taking more care with the crushing operations, so that less fines were produced, ordinary wet gravity methods were applied, tables being used in most cases. Results varied considerably with the character of the ore, both as to its physical nature and its mercury content. Concentrates ran from 15 per cent to 60 per cent or more; under favorable conditions recoveries of 80 per cent or more were possible, but, with poor conditions, they might be as low as 50 per cent. Recently flotation methods have been applied in several localities; these have the advantage of saving the fines, but the cost of operation is greater.

The chief reason why concentration methods have not been more widely adopted is that the furnace treatment of the ore is so cheap, and the losses in concentration are so high, that the losses more than offset the cost of furnacing the larger volume.

Metallurgy.—The underlying principles of the reduction of the ore to metal are extremely simple. When the mercury sulfide is roasted in contact with air the sulfur burns, leaving the mercury as vapor in the gases, from which it is recovered by cooling and condensation. A modification of the method that is much used for small scale work heats the ore in a closed retort, lime or iron being added to combine with the sulfur and leave the mercury free to distil out. The chief difficulties encountered are the losses of mercury uncondensed in the gases, fine mercury mist carried out by the gases and the condenser water, and mechanical losses through leakage or absorption into the material of the condenser system.

Secondary Recovery.—There are probably quite appreciable amounts of secondary mercury recovered from various sources, but no statistics have ever been collected, so that the actual amounts are unknown. Certain types of amalgamation tailings from gold or silver ores have been treated in considerable quantities for the recovery of the mercury retained in them. Also many of the larger electrical and scientific instruments contain sufficient mercury to justify recovery when the apparatus is worn out or broken. One of the large paper companies using mercury cathode cells in the production of electrolytic bleach solutions is planning to construct a small plant to recover the mercury absorbed in the body of the concrete cells, when they are torn down for reconstruction, and other similar recoveries of metal are possible. The possibilities of secondary recovery are confined to the metal uses, as all of the compound uses result in such a wide dissemination of the mercury that profitable recovery is impossible.

Forms in Which Mercury Appears on the Market.—As has been pointed out, all mercury ores are reduced to the metallic condition, and compounds needed are then produced from the metal; all mercury then appears on the market primarily as metal. Due to its weight, it requires a substantial container, and the one which has been developed and is universally used is a "flask" of wrought iron fitted with a screw plug; this is heavy enough to stand handling and shipping without boxing or crating. The standard flask used in the United States contained 76½ pounds up to June, 1904, 75 pounds to June, 1927, and 76 pounds since; the standard European flask contains 34½ kilograms, equivalent to 76.07 pounds. The flask is so thoroughly standardized in the mercury industry that it is extensively used as a unit of quantity, and many of the statistics are given in flasks, rather than in pounds, kilograms, or tons.

ORE RESERVES

The ore reserves in the various producing districts vary widely in amounts and richness, and in few cases are reserves actually blocked out sufficient to cover future operations for any great length of time. This, however, does not mean that plentiful supplies can not be assured for many years to come. Although it has already been in operation for more than 2,000 years, the Almaden mine in Spain still has the largest known reserves, reported to be sufficient to cover the entire world consumption for at least 100 years at the maximum rate of consumption thus far realized.

Italian reserves at the leading mines, Monte Amiata and Idria, are also moderately large, although they do not compare in magnitude with the Almaden. In 1926 the developed ore reserves of Monte Amiata were estimated to contain about 18,750 metric tons of metal, while those of Idria were estimated at 20,000 tons in 1920. Subsequent production has used up much of the reserves as established at these dates, and no data are available on the amounts that have been added since.

In the United States, mining conditions are such that reserves as a rule are blocked out only for from 1 to 5 years in advance of active mining, although the "probable" reserves are much more extensive. In a few of the larger and older mines, reserves of considerable magnitude have been developed. During the past 10 years new territory has been added both to active production and to the reserves in Oregon, Washington and Arkansas. The bulk of the domestic reserves, while indefinite in amount, is quite large, but the ores are of such low grade that many mines can be worked only in periods of high prices.

Reserves in excess of 5,000 tons of metal were reported in Algeria in 1929, from which only a small subsequent production

has been made. The Nikitovka deposits in Russia were estimated to contain 8,300 tons of metal, of which about one-sixth has
gone into subsequent production.

WORLD OUTPUT AND SUPPLY

Mercury was one of the seven metals known to the ancients,
with a history going back into the pre-Christian era. But despite
its ancient history, and a fairly wide distribution in small quantities, we have here again an example of extreme concentration of
occurrence, for of the total mercury output since 1913, more than
85 per cent has come from three countries, Spain, Italy, and the
United States, and curiously enough almost 85 per cent of the total
of these three countries has come from three mines, one in each
country. Previous to the close of the World War there was a
fourth producer; at that time Austria was producing amounts
almost as great as the United States, but the territory including
the mercury mines was lost to Italy in the war settlements, and it
is the addition of the former Austrian output that placed Italy
in the position of leading producer during most of the years since
the war.

As soon as conditions settled down after the post-war depression, Italy began consistently to increase her mercury production,
reaching a maximum of 2,000 tons in 1929. Spain took up the
challenge and made an even greater increase, reaching 2,500 tons
in 1929. Both disregarded the fact that from 1926 on they were
producing more than enough mercury to supply the entire world
demand. As a result, they were not able to sell their entire
output, and excess stocks began to accumulate in both countries.

In 1928, after something like 2,000 tons of unsold stocks had
accumulated in the two countries, they joined interests to form a
cartel for the control of the industry. Although the cartel was
supposed to control both production and marketing, and to maintain production at a restricted rate, divided proportionately
according to the production capacity of the mines, actually the
production control was not maintained. The mines did not
reduce their outputs until 1930, and even then, although the
Spanish cut their production by about two-thirds, the Italian
mines still continued at a rate far out of proportion to the
current demand, which had in the meantime suffered heavily
from the industrial depression and was at an abnormally low level.

As a result, it was not until 1933 and 1934 that appreciable reductions in stocks began to take place.   The increased home demand resulting from the Italian-Ethiopian war absorbed most of the remaining Italian stocks, and, with the action of economic sanctions on Italy restricting her exports, and with generally unsettled European conditions making future supplies somewhat uncertain,

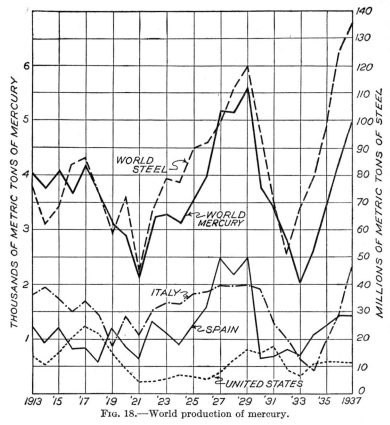

FIG. 18.—World production of mercury.

the whole world turned to Spain for mercury.   The 1935 Spanish exports were far in excess of any previous figure and served to reduce the unsold stocks by more than 1,000 tons.

Table I shows the annual outputs since 1913 for all countries that have contributed appreciable amounts, the annual totals, the period totals for each country, and the percentage of the period total that has been supplied by each country.   The world production graph, Fig. 18, shows the interrelationship between the outputs of the leading countries. These emphasize the outstanding importance in the mercury industry of the three leading countries, Italy, Spain, and the United States, and the comparative insignificance of other producing countries. In fact, in none of the other countries is the production of appreciable importance except as a source of supply for local consumption.

TABLE I.—WORLD PRODUCTION OF MERCURY
(Metric tons)

	Austria	Italy	Spain	United States	Mexico	Russia	China	Czecho-Slovakia	Total[2]
1913..............	819	1,004	1,245	670	166	[3]		2	89	4,020
1914..............	878	1,073	952	536	162	[3]	60	75	3,770
1915..............	760	985	1,222	716	94	[3]	211	68	4,080
1916..............	410	1,093	795	1,018	53	[3]	178	85[4]	3,665
1917..............	648	1,071	827	1,237	33	[3]	261	95	4,195
1918..............	420	1,038	567	1,119	164	[3]	293	85[4]	3,705
1919..............	[1]	845[1]	1,226	738	119	[3]	80	80[4]	3,100
1920..............	.....	1,401	861	455	77	[3]	45	67	2,910
1921..............	.....	1,071	635	216	46	[3]	98	57	2,135
1922..............	.....	1,541	1,318	217	42	22	17	6	3,240
1923..............	.....	1,656	1,144	270	45	51	2	51	3,270
1924..............	.....	1,641	899	343	37	66	3	78	3,130
1925..............	.....	1,834	1,277	312	39	10	3	73	3,560
1926..............	.....	1,871	1,594	260	45	127	2	82	3,990
1927..............	.....	1,996	2,493	384	81	74	74	55	5,170
1928..............	.....	1,988	2,195	616	87	102	68	72	5,140
1929..............	.....	1,998	2,476	817	83	130	20	65	5,600
1930..............	.....	1,933	663	743	171	120	25	71	3,800
1931..............	.....	1,298	682	860	251	150	22	77	3,400
1932..............	.....	1,016	816	435	253	200	22	45	2,800
1933..............	.....	607	676	333	155	232	13	7	2,040
1934..............	.....	441	1,096	532	158	267	102	26	2,650
1935..............	.....	972	1,226	604	216	300[4]	45	69	3,460[4]
1936..............	.....	1,473	1,461	571	183	300[4]	85	65	4,200[4]
1937..............	.....	2,302	1,452	569	170	300[4]	60	95	4,980[4]
Totals...........	3,935	34,138	29,798	14,573	2,930	2,451[4]	1,791	1,638	91,990
Per cent..........	4.3	37.1	32.4	15.9	3.2	2.7	1.9	1.8	100.0

[1] The former Austrian output is included under Italy after 1918. [2] Includes small amounts from countries not listed. [3] Not available. [4] Estimated.

Austria.—Austria was for many years the third largest producer after Spain and the United States but was surpassed by Italy in 1908 and, in the redivision of territory that followed the World War, the district of Trieste, which included the mercury mines, was ceded to Italy, and Austria practically disappeared from the list of producers. Such small production as remains, usually less than 5 tons a year, is a byproduct from ores worked for other metals.

The Idria mine is one of the older European mines, dating back to 1470.

China.—China has at times had a moderate output, but the statistics are unreliable, and probably incomplete. The industry is retarded by antiquated methods of mining and smelting, political disturbances, and labor troubles, or the country might be able to make better use of the resources available and reduce the amounts imported.

Czecho-Slovakia.—There is only one mine in Czecho-Slovakia, with a small and fluctuating output.

Germany.—The only mercury mine in Germany, the Pfalz mine in the Rhine Palatinate, was reopened in 1934 after lying idle for nearly a century. No statistics have been reported as yet, but it is understood that an output of about 120 tons annually is expected. This move was partly for the purpose of aiding unemployment and partly to assist in the program of self-sufficiency, as Germany is a heavy importer of mercury.

Italy.—There are a number of small mines in Italy, but the chief ones are the Monte Amiati, in Tuscany, and the Idria, in Trieste, which was acquired from Austria at the close of the World War. The Italian output did not reach a magnitude of any great importance until the early years of the present century, surpassing that of the United States and Austria in 1908 and becoming of major importance only after the absorption of the Austrian mines.

Italy is the only country of even second rank industrially which has a sufficient mercury output to supply her own needs. All of the more important Italian mines are operated under a government monopoly.

Mexico.—Mexico has been a consistent producer of small amounts of mercury over a long period, mostly from the States of Guerrero and San Luis Potosi, with minor amounts from several other states. The figures of Mexican production are somewhat misleading, since material proportions of the output reported in many years was secondary metal, recovered by treatment of old amalgamation tailings. The maximum output was about 350 tons in 1898.

Russia (U. S. S. R.).—Mercury is mined only at Nikitovka, in the Donetz Basin; the production has not been large, but is being expanded gradually. Other deposits are known, but are not yet being worked, so far as is known.

Spain.—The Almaden mine, in the Province of Ciudad Real, was the first large discovery of mercury, and is one of the oldest mines in the world, having been worked for more than 2,000 years. In spite of this long period of active working, the mine still has the largest known reserves, which are estimated to be able to supply the entire world demand at its past maximum rate for the next 100 years. The ore is rich, some being as high as 20 per cent, but the annual average of all produced by the mine during the past 10 years has declined from 7 to less than 5 per cent. The working of the mine and smelter has been along primitive lines, and it is only within the past few years that attempts have been made to modernize the procedure. For example, smelting furnaces dating back to the sixteenth century were still in use up to 1931, and, up to 1925, only hand labor was used in the mine.

In addition to the Almaden mine, there is a small production from the Provinces of Granada and Oviedo, but these amount to less than 1 per cent of the total.

With the decline of United States output, Spain became the leading producer in 1883, a position which she continued to hold in most years up to the close of the war, when Italy took precedence through the acquisition of the Austrian mines. Spain again took the lead in 1927, when improved methods of mining and smelting increased the output, and has maintained it ever since, except for the years when the production was restricted for the purpose of disposing of accumulated stocks, and since the outbreak of the Spanish Civil War.

United States.—The New Almaden mine, in Santa Clara County, California, one of the world's greatest mercury mines, discovered in 1824, was first considered a silver mine, and it was not until 1845 that the ore was identified as cinnabar and the true nature of the mine became apparent. This was the start of mercury mining in California and, ever since, the state has been the leading producer in the country. The discovery of gold in California a few years later, and the need for mercury to work the gold ores by amalgamation, gave the new industry a boost which kept it in the forefront. Later, other mines were discovered in the state, and in other states, and production increased to a maximum of 2,755 metric tons in 1877, or two-thirds of the world total.

The early ores were exceedingly rich, but gradually became leaner as the mines were worked deeper, with a resulting heavy shrinkage in output. The old records of the New Almaden mine showed a yield of 37 per cent in 1850, 20 per cent in the early sixties, 10 per cent in 1866, and, in 1892, slightly under 1 per cent. At the present time the average tenor of all ore treated in the country is about 0.4 per cent. This gradual decrease in ore grade is the primary reason why the United States has dropped from its original position as the world's foremost producer of mercury.

The chief states now contributing to the supply are, in order of importance, California, Oregon, Texas, Nevada, Washington, and Arkansas, with small amounts from Arizona, Alaska, and Utah. With the exceedingly low grade of ore worked, few mines can operate at a profit except when prices are high, so that production has fluctuated widely from year to year. The number of mines working has varied from as low as 10 in 1922 to 95 in 1932.

Other Countries.—Other countries that have small outputs, usually of only a few tons a year, are approximately in order of importance: New Zealand, Turkey, Japan, Algeria, Rumania, Chosen, Bolivia, Australia, and Chile.

The following list of countries have reported the existence of deposits of cinnabar, in most cases too small or of too low grade to be of commercial importance; where the name is given in italics it indicates that at some time there has been some production, which has been discontinued: Argentina, Borneo, Brazil, *Canada*, *Colombia*, Dutch Guiana, Ecuador, Ethiopia, France, Haiti, Java, Madagascar, Paraguay, *Peru*, Portugal, Serbia, South Africa, Sumatra, Uruguay, and Venezuela.

Only in the case of Peru has the production been of any importance. The Santa Barbara mine was opened in the Province of Huancavelica in 1566 and closed in 1839, after having produced over 51,000 tons of mercury, making it one of the foremost mercury mines in the world, second only to the Almaden mine in Spain, with the New Almaden mine in California third. An attempt was made during the war period to reopen this mine, but the venture was unsuccessful and was eventually abandoned.

UNITED STATES OUTPUT AND SUPPLY

The United States has declined from its former position as a leading producer of mercury, although it still retains third place, and, since 1913, has furnished about one-sixth of the world output. Ever since the peak in 1877 the production curve has been

quite irregular but with a general downward trend, due largely
to the decreasing metal content of the ores with increasing depth,
and the gradual depletion of the mines. By 1914, production
had declined to 536 metric tons, but the heavily increased demand
of the war period more than doubled the output, which reached
1,237 tons in 1917, and again declined to a minimum of 216 tons
during the post-war depression.

The heavy drain that had been put on the mines by the war
demand made the post-war recovery a slow matter, and the pro-
gressive decline in the metal content of the ore made it impossible,
even at the peak of the inflation period, to attain outputs much
above the pre-war level. With the advent of the 1929 depression,
production began to decline, but an increase in foreign prices in
1931 made it impossible, for the first time since the war, to export
domestic mercury at a profit, with the result that 1931 showed the
highest output since the war. This condition, however, lasted
only a short time, but, even then, the effect of the depression on
production was much less pronounced than in many other industries, the 1933 low being 40 per cent of the 1929 high. Subsequent recovery has also been better than the average, the 1935
output being 74 per cent of the 1929 high, while the general level
of recovery in the mineral industries was only 50 per cent, but
this was followed by declines in 1936 and 1937.

The restricted output has been consistently less than consumption demand, and the deficit has been supplied by imports. The
data on available supply given in Table II show that, since 1913,
the United States has produced 16 per cent of the total world
output, but has consumed 25 per cent; domestic production
amounted to 63 per cent of the available supply, of which 7 per
cent was exported and 56 per cent consumed, the remainder of
the consumption being imported.

Imports.—Imports have fluctuated rather widely, in response
to the changes in current conditions of supply and demand, attaining a maximum of nearly 2,000,000 pounds in 1926, and almost
disappearing in 1931. In addition to the metal, smaller amounts
are imported in the form of fulminate, vermilion, and other
compounds, chiefly calomel and corrosive sublimate. The origin
of the imports, as shown in Table III, also was variable; of the
two major sources, Spain was in the lead, supplying 53 per cent
of the total imports since 1923, against 34 per cent from Italy;

TABLE II.—AVAILABLE SUPPLY OF MERCURY IN THE UNITED STATES
(Thousands of pounds)

	Domestic Production	Imports[1]	Exports	Available Supply	World Total	Per Cent Consumed in U. S.	Produced in U. S.	
							Per Cent of Supply	Per Cent of World Output
1913...............	1,516	171	86	1,601	8,863	18	95	17
1914...............	1,241	615	107	1,749	8,311	21	71	15
1915...............	1,577	422	253	1,746	8,995	19	90	18
1916...............	2,245	424	666	2,003	8,050	25	112	28
1917...............	2,712	391	808	2,295	9,248	25	118	29
1918...............	2,466	504	232	2,738	8,164	34	90	30
1919...............	1,606	798	683	1,721	6,834	25	93	23
1920...............	1,004	1,063	116	1,951	6,415	30	51	16
1921...............	475	795	30	1,240	4,707	26	38	10
1922...............	478	1,269	22	1,725	7,143	24	28	7
1923...............	595	1,355	24	1,926	7,208	27	31	8
1924...............	756	988	16	1,728	6,900	25	44	11
1925...............	688	1,564	15	2,237	7,849	28	31	9
1926...............	573	1,948	9	2,512	8,796	29	23	7
1927...............	846	1,516	2	2,362	11,398	21	36	7
1928...............	1,358	1,107	2	2,465	11,332	22	55	12
1929...............	1,800	1,134	2	2,934	12,368	24	61	15
1930...............	1,638	183	2	1,821	8,378	22	90	20
1931...............	1,897	42	379	1,560	7,496	21	122	25
1932...............	959	295	16	1,238	6,173	20	77	16
1933...............	735	1,544	2	2,279	4,497	51	32	16
1934...............	1,174	775	2	1,949	5,842	33	60	20
1935...............	1,321	594	2	1,915	7,628	25	69	17
1936...............	1,259	1,375	20	2,614	9,259	28	48	14
1937...............	1,255	1,438	35	2,658	10,979	24	47	11
Totals............	32,174	22,310	3,517	50,967	202,833	25	63	16

[1] Imports for consumption.   [2] Not reported.

TABLE III.—IMPORTS OF MERCURY INTO THE UNITED STATES
(Thousands of pounds)

Year	Spain	Italy	Mexico	Others	Total
1923....................	801	472	86	210	1,569
1924....................	81	583	87	155	906
1925....................	732	843	74	60	1,709
1926....................	1,059	883	80	124	2,146
1927....................	1,025	682	138	4	1,849
1928....................	464	429	136	140	1,169
1929....................	715	68	92	211	1,086
1930....................	213	....	11	....	224
1931....................	27	....	....	....	27
1932....................	346	262	....	9	617
1933....................	1,293	244	156	21	1,714
1934....................	536	49	188	1	775
1935....................	521	69	4	....	594
1936....................	775	492	26	82	1,375
1937....................	535	747	117	39	1,438
Totals............	9,123	5,823	1,195	1,056	17,198
Per cent............	53.1	33.9	6.9	6.1	....

Note: General imports to 1933; imports for consumption from 1934; data not reported previous to 1923.

the only other producer exporting direct to the United States was Mexico, with 7 per cent of the total. The remaining 6 per cent was re-exported from a number of different countries, and the real source of this metal is unknown. Although, during the past few years, imports have been confined almost entirely to Spain, Italy, and Mexico, in earlier years indirect shipments frequently reached as much as 15–20 per cent of the total imports, so that the exact amounts obtained from the different prime sources were somewhat reduced, but, on the average, it may be said that the imports have been roughly divided between Spain and Italy in the proportion of about 2:1.

The general distribution of the 1935 exports of Spain and Italy was affected by the operation of economic sanctions against Italy in connection with the Italo-Ethiopian war. Italian shipments had to be confined to those countries not a party to sanctions agreements, while Spain supplied the demands of the sanctionist group. The receipt of imports from Spain and Italy was disturbed in 1936 and 1937 by the Spanish Civil War, resulting in a marked increase of imports from Italy.

TABLE IV.—DISTRIBUTION OF MERCURY IMPORTS IN 1937
(Thousands of pounds)

	New York	Boston	Philadelphia	New Orleans	Total
Italy......................	747.4	....	....	....	747.4
Spain.....................	423.3	45.6	14.0	55.1	538.0
Mexico....................	115.9	....	....	....	115.9
Great Britain..............	38.8	....	....	....	38.8
Total...................	1325.4	45.6	14.0	55.1	1440.1

As is indicated by Table IV, practically all of the mercury imports are handled through the port of New York. Spanish shipments were scattered somewhat, and a few hundred pounds from Mexico went to El Paso. The shipments from Great Britain were probably of Spanish origin.

Exports.—Except during the war period and in 1931, the exports of mercury from the United States have been insignificant in amount. In 1916, 1917, and 1931 exports exceeded imports, and the country was self-supporting. In the earlier case this was the result of the war expansion, while, in 1931, exportation was made possible by the rise of European prices to a level higher than the domestic. All told, exports since 1913 have taken 11 per cent of the domestic output, more than three-quarters of which was during the years 1915–1919. In this period of 5 years the total exports exceeded the total imports; although this condition actually prevailed for only two of the five years, the surplus in these two years was great enough to cover the deficits of the other three years. During the post-war years, exports declined to a nominal amount and finally, after 1926, the figures were no longer reported, except when the temporary revival in 1931 brought exports again into prominence for a short time, until 1936, when publication was again resumed.

Consumption.—Specific data on consumption of mercury have been collected only in a few isolated years, details of which will be given in the discussion of utilization. Aside from these figures, the only guide to current consumption is found in the figures on available supply in Table II.

Stocks.—No record is kept of industrial stocks, and lacking this we can not convert the data on available supply into true consumption figures. Imported stocks in bonded warehouses has varied during recent years from almost none up to 5,370 flasks.

UTILIZATION OF MERCURY

Estimates of the amount of mercury used in the United States for various purposes are available for only 2 years, 1917 and 1928, as shown in Table VI.

TABLE VI.—UTILIZATION OF MERCURY

	1917		1928	
	Pounds	Per Cent	Pounds	Per Cent
Drugs and chemicals.................	638,000	32.2	1,042,000	39.3
Fulminate...........................	364,000	18.4	501,000	18.8
Vermilion...........................	235,000	11.9	186,000	7.0
Felt................................	128,000	6.5	131,000	4.9
Amalgamation.......................	64,000	3.2	34,000	1.3
Electrical apparatus.................	202,000	10.2	194,000	7.3
Instruments.........................	47,000	2.4	228,000	8.6
Miscellaneous.......................	300,000	15.2	340,000	12.8
Totals...........................	1,978,000	100.0	2,656,000	100.0
Available supply.....................	2,295,000	....	2,465,000	....

The figures for available supply for the same years, taken from Table II, indicate that, in 1917, there was a surplus to be added to stocks, while, in 1928, it was necessary to draw upon existing stocks in order to supply a deficit.

PRICES

Being a liquid, mercury can not be handled like other metals, but must be placed in a container, and this container has become so thoroughly standardized in the industry that it is frequently used as a unit of measurement; mercury prices are regularly quoted, not per ounce, pound, or ton, but per flask.

The chief marketing centers for mercury are London and New York City; formerly San Francisco was also an important feature in the market, but since much of the western metal originally sold in San Francisco by the producers was later re-sold in New York, the San Francisco quotations gradually receded in importance, and now are seldom reported, except as the basis of local retail sales.   The New York price was usually higher than the San Francisco quotation by approximately the cost of transportation, but this was not always the case, and occasionally the San Francisco price was the higher.

The domestic price was theoretically based on the European price set by the Cartel composed of the Spanish and Italian producers, plus tariff and transportation, but here again many variations were found.   These variations from the normal price differential between the different markets hinged mainly on two factors—current conditions of supply and demand, and the effect of speculation.   Mercury is a metal which, by its very nature, lends itself readily to the manipulation of speculators; it has small bulk for its value; is conveniently packed for storage; is not subject to loss or deterioration; and, finally, the total output, although relatively small in amount, is required for a wide variety of uses.   For these reasons the price of mercury has always been subject to a considerable amount of fluctuation, sometimes within short periods of time, and over a wide range.

Figure 19 shows the maximum and minimum monthly averages and the annual averages of the New York price for mercury since 1913; in making this graph, prices preceding 1927, when the 75-pound flask was used, have been adjusted to a 76-pound basis, so as to be directly comparable with the later prices, based on the current 76-pound flask.   These curves emphasize what has already been said as to the wide range of the price fluctuations and the spread between the maximum and minimum prices, particularly in times of war or economic stress.

In 1913 prices were low and market conditions were abnormally quiet, the spread between the high and low for the year being less than $2, but as soon as war demand became manifest the market became highly disorganized, with rapid fluctuations in price and with an increasing spread between high and low in each succeeding year, reaching a climax in 1916, when the high price for the year was four times the low. The excessively high prices of late 1915 and early 1916 were the combined result of

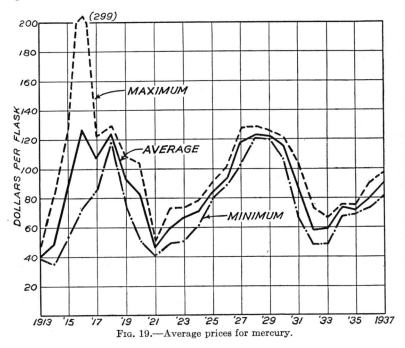

FIG. 19.—Average prices for mercury.

heavy buying, restricted imports under foreign embargoes, excessive freight rates, with probably a seasoning of panic and speculation. This condition was broken by increased imports and careful market manipulation, avoiding depletion of the domestic supply; later, government stabilization of prices further eased the situation.

During the post-war period prices dropped almost to the pre-war level, and then, during the inflation period, climbed back to an average equal to the war peak but without the wide spread between high and low. During the depression, prices gradually declined by about half and, as was to be expected, showed an increase in the spread between high and low.   Reaching a minimum in 1932, there was a slight improvement in 1933 and more in 1934, while 1935 showed a small decrease.   The gradual settling of the market during recent years is indicated by the successive decreases in the price spread, which was $36.88 in 1931, $23.63 in 1932, $17.83 in 1933, $10.19 in 1934, and $6.20 in 1935.   Since

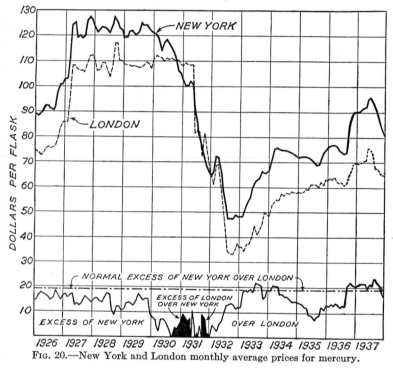

Fig. 20.—New York and London monthly average prices for mercury.

1935 the disturbance caused by the Spanish Civil War caused the spread to increase again.

The character and extent of the fluctuations in price are shown in the graph of monthly average prices of both New York and London for the past 12 years (Fig. 20), the London prices being converted into dollars by the current average exchange rate for the month in question.   During the present recovery period it will be noted that the market has been more regular than in previous years, when two, or even three marked advances and recessions were common within the year.

Normally the New York price should exceed the London price by the import duty of 25 cents per pound and transportation charges, a total of slightly more than $19 per flask; however, the full margin is seldom found to be in effect, and, due to changing market conditions, it fluctuates considerably from month to month. As shown by Fig. 20, there have been only a few months in the past 12 years when the price differential between New York and London exceeded $19, and during much of the time it was well below this level; in fact, there was a period from late 1930 to early 1932 when the London price was higher than New York, and considerable domestic metal was exported to Europe.

TABLE VII.—MERCURY PRICES IN THE UNITED STATES
(Dollars per flask of 76 pounds)

	Average Quoted Price	Commodity Index	Mercury Index Price
1913	$ 40.07	100.0	$ 40.07
1914	48.95	97.6	50.15
1915	88.17	99.6	88.52
1916	127.16	122.5	103.80
1917	107.72	168.3	64.00
1918	125.12	188.1	66.52
1919	93.38	198.6	47.02
1920	82.20	221.1	37.16
1921	46.07	139.8	32.95
1922	59.74	138.5	43.13
1923	67.39	144.1	46.77
1924	70.69	140.5	50.31
1925	84.24	148.3	56.80
1926	93.13	143.3	64.99
1927	118.16	136.7	86.44
1928	123.51	138.5	89.18
1929	122.15	136.5	89.49
1930	115.01	123.8	92.90
1931	87.35	104.6	83.51
1932	57.93	92.8	62.42
1933	59.23	94.4	62.74
1934	73.87	107.3	68.84
1935	71.99	114.6	62.82
1936	79.92	115.8	69.02
1937	90.18	123.6	72.96

Note.—Prices for the 75 pound flask, standard to 1927, have been adjusted to correspond with the 76 pound flask now used.

Supplementing the graph of annual average prices in Fig. 19, Table VII gives the annual average price in dollars per flask, as reported by the *Engineering and Mining Journal*, and the mercury index price derived from these by the use of the corresponding commodity index.

The mercury index price rose during the early years of the war period, but dropped after 1916; from the post-war low of 1921 the index price increased steadily each year to a peak in 1930.

TARIFF

Due to the high cost of working the low grade of ore that prevails in most of the domestic mercury deposits, tariff protection is necessary in order to maintain prices at a sufficiently high level to permit operation, and, as the ore grade progressively decreased, the tariff rate has been increased in each of the recent tariff acts except that of 1930, when the rate was retained unchanged.

TABLE VIII.—TARIFF RATES ON MERCURY
(In cents per pound or per cent ad valorem)

	1909–1913	1913–1922	1922–1930	1930—
Mercury	7c.	10 %	25c.	25c.
Fulminates	Free	Free	12½c.	12½c.
Vermilion	10c.	15 %	28c.	35c.
Other forms	35 %	15 %	45 %	22c. + 25 %

POLITICAL AND COMMERCIAL CONTROL

The situation with regard to political and commercial control of mercury production is radically different from that of other metals in several ways:

1. Fewer countries are involved. In 1929, three countries, Spain, Italy, and the United States, produced 88 per cent of the world total, and, in 1935, these same three produced 87 per cent of the total. Since 1913, these three have produced 85 per cent of the total, and, if one includes the former Austrian output along with Italy, where it has been since the close of the war, the proportion becomes 90 per cent. Platinum is the only other metal which approaches these conditions.

2. In the case of mercury, political control is much more effective, because in most of the countries we are concerned not merely with the general control such as any political subdivision may exert on production within its area, but with actual governmental ownership and operation of the mines. The Almaden mine has been owned and operated by the Spanish government since 1645. Up to the end of the World War, the Idria mine was owned by the Austrian government. In pre-war years German capital was predominant in the Italian mines in the Monte Amiata district, but, with the entry of Italy into the war, these mines were seized by the Italian government, and, at the close of the war, the Idria

mine was acquired from Austria, so that the bulk of the Italian production* is under direct government ownership and control. The small Russian and Turkish outputs also fall into the same category.

It thus appears that over 70 per cent of the mercury output since 1913 has been under government ownership, and that a still higher percentage prevails for the present potential capacity. Only the 16 per cent produced in the United States and the 7 to 8 per cent from Mexico, China, Czecho-Slovakia, and other minor producers are privately controlled.

3. In addition to governmental ownership of Spanish and Italian mines, sale of the product was for several years controlled by a Cartel formed in 1928 by the two governments. Before then each had made its own sales arrangements, as has also been done since shortly before the Spanish Civil War, Italy being favorable to the Insurgents, while the mercury mines remained in Loyalist territory to the end of the struggle.

4. The commercial control of the output not under government ownership is practically entirely in the hands of domestic capital of the country concerned. So far as is known, the United States mines are entirely owned and controlled by home capital. In Mexico there seems to be some ownership by United States and British capital, although the prevailing control is Mexican. No information is available on other countries.

GENERAL REVIEW OF THE DOMESTIC SITUATION

Mercury is the only strategic metal of which the United States has ever been a leading producer and domestic production still contributes an average of two-thirds of the consumption demand. During the war period the United States was self-supporting, for, while considerable amounts were imported, still more was exported. During the years 1915–1919, inclusive, the exports of mercury exceeded the imports by more than 100,000 pounds. The imports of these years can then be attributed to such factors as speculation, market manipulation, and convenience in distribution, rather than to the absolute necessity for the metal for domestic consumption. It having been demonstrated that the country could have been independent of outside sources in the last war, the question then arises as to whether the same condition is still possible in a future emergency of the same character. Examination of the various facts available seem to indicate an answer in the affirmative, but it is evident that this will be possible only under certain conditions, and might possibly entail even greater economies and restrictions in the use of the metal than those prevailing during the World War.

There are very considerable reserves of ore available, but they are of such low grade that the problem largely resolves itself into

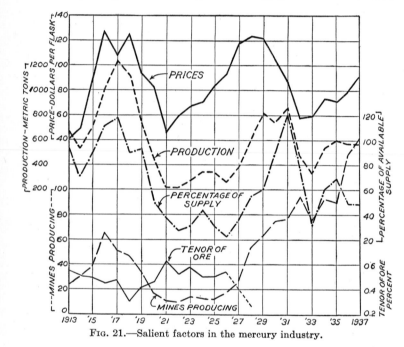

Fig. 21.—Salient factors in the mercury industry.

one of price. It seems certain that, if price is not taken into consideration, sufficient supplies can be provided from domestic sources, but it is quite possible that the prices necessary to accomplish this would be higher than the world price, even under emergency conditions, and that, if and when the time comes, it would be desirable to gage the domestic production effort with respect to the availability and price of foreign metal, and to produce at home only such amounts as the prevailing conditions might warrant or demand.

There are several factors to be taken into consideration in order to get a proper picture of the situation. In order to make them all readily accessible for direct comparison, they are combined in

the accompanying graph of salient factors in the mercury industry (Fig. 21). The various items involved are prices, past
production, the percentage of the available supply produced by
domestic mines, the number of producing mines, and the tenor of
the ore. The main factor is price, and it will be noted in the
graph that there is a fairly close correlation between this and
all of the other factors. In general, in periods of high prices, the
number of mines working, the resulting output, and the percentage of the available supply produced, all increase; during low
prices, they all decrease. While the correlation is not perfect,
it is sufficiently close to emphasize the interdependence of these
factors. Aside from the irregularities due to the figures of a
single year, the chief variations to be noted are:

1. While production followed prices quite closely during the
war, there was a marked lag during the period of increasing prices
following the post-war depression, with a break from 1924 to
1927, and the peak of the production curve was not reached until
1931, although prices had then been on the decline since 1928.

2. This same lag and break was even more pronounced in the
percentage of available supply contributed by domestic production.

3. In spite of the heavy pressure for maximum output during
the war period, the maximum number of mines operated was
sixty-six in 1916, while in 1932, a year of comparatively low
production, ninety-five mines were working. The bulk of the
output is produced by only a few mines; for example, in 1935
nine mines turned out 77 per cent of the total, and 81 mines the
other 23 per cent. Only a few of the larger mines, with ore better
than the average, can operate during periods of low prices. As
prices increase, more of the smaller mines come in, and also, in
some cases, the larger mines are able to work ore of a lower grade.
A gradual improvement in technology, and a reduction in mining
and treatment costs furnish the explanation for the increasing
number of mines remaining in operation since prices began to
decline in 1928, when the number would normally be expected to
decrease.

4. The tenor of the ore treated in the United States averages
far lower than with any of the other producers of any consequence. In general it will be noted that, as prices increase, the
tenor of the ore decreases, indicating the ability to work lower
grades of ore at high prices. During and immediately following
the post-war depression, when prices were low and only a dozen

mines were working, the ore tenor crept up to the highest figure
that it has attained since pre-war days, and probably higher than
will ever be seen again unless some new deposits of exceptional
richness are discovered. During the war period, under the
demand for high production, many of the larger mines made
heavy inroads on their better grade reserves, and such discoveries
as have been made since have failed to replace them. The gradual decrease in ore tenor that has been under way since the beginning of the industry reached a level averaging only 0.5 per cent
during the years 1913–1926, since which date these figures have
not been regularly published. A separate report covering 1928,
when the number of mines working had materially increased,
showed a drop to 0.27 per cent, and later, with 90 to 95 mines
working, the figure was probably still lower. Ore tenors as low
as 0.15 are reported to have been worked at a profit.

At hearings before the United States Tariff Commission in
1934, evidence was given that about 8,500 flasks (about 300 metric
tons) could be produced at a cost of $75, and that, at $90, the
domestic market could be satisfied. Then follows the statement
that "about 80 per cent of the normal output is produced at a cost
of around $90 or less per flask." These claims raise five questions,
outlined as follows:

1. What is *normal* output? The war maximum was 1,237 tons,
and the post-war maximum 860 tons; the average since 1913 was
583 tons, and for the past 10 years 608 tons. This indicates that
the normal output would be about 600 tons, but whether this
was the figure referred to in the report is not clear.

2. How about the divergence between output and consumption?
The maximum consumption during the war was 1,250 tons, and
the post-war maximum 1,330 tons; average consumption since
1913 has been 924 tons, and for the past 10 years, 1,027 tons,
figures that are, respectively, 58 per cent and 69 per cent greater
than the average outputs for the same periods.

3. Are these cost figures complete? It is a common practice
to calculate production costs on the basis of current operation, and
in many cases such items as capital charges, taxes, and deprecia-
tion are not included. For this purpose, the cost figures should be
complete.

4. Next comes the question as to how long a producer could
remain in business with both costs and selling price at $90.

Between these two must be a margin for producers' profit and marketing costs.

5. And finally, if a price of $75 is required to produce 300 tons, increasing this to $90 seems a rather small margin to boost production to our assumed normal output of 600 tons, let alone to full consumption requirements, whether these figures be on the basis of 1,027 tons for the past 10 years, or on the 1929 maximum of 1,330 tons.

However, let us turn to the record of past performance for further light on the subject. In this we find so many irregularities and inconsistencies that it is difficult to draw any hard and fast conclusions, so we can speak only in general terms. First, can a $75 price furnish an output of 300 tons? The prices for 1924, 1934, and 1935 were less than this (averaging $71.65 for the 3 years), but brought a minimum output of 343 tons, a maximum of 595 tons, and an average of 490 tons; in addition, prices less than $60 brought outputs of 333 tons in 1933 and 435 tons in 1932. On the other hand, a price of $93 brought only 260 tons in 1926, and $118 yielded 384 tons in 1927. On the whole, we may safely say that $75 will probably supply considerably more than the 300 tons estimated, and it seems quite possible that $90 can assure our assumed normal of 600 tons. The average of the prices for 1919, 1926, and 1931 was $90.50, and the average output for the three years was 619 tons. Since the high was 860 tons in 1931, at $87.35, it is even possible that, under favorable conditions, $90 might produce the 900 tons average.

When we come to the question of supplying the maximum demand of 1,330 tons or more, we are facing a problem for which there seems to be no definite answer; it can be done, of course—at a price; but what that price might be is difficult to say. During 1927–1930, prices ranged from $115 to $123, and averaged $119.85, but the total output for the 4 years was only 3,416 tons, or an average of 854 tons—less than a price of $87.35 produced in 1931. There are so many factors to be taken into consideration when we get into these upper brackets of price and production that there is endless room for speculation as to the outcome, and no definite answer can be given until we have available for study more information on present and probable future costs than has yet been accumulated.

From the standpoint of possible emergency demand, the fact that past production has averaged 63 per cent of demand, and that the chief factor limiting the expansion of present production is that of price, makes the situation more favorable than that of most of the strategic group.   Otherwise the comparatively small stocks that are ordinarily maintained in the country would be more of a drawback than they are.   In a general way, we may figure that the average annual output that has been maintained will have to be increased by about half to equal the previous average industrial consumption, by an approximately equal amount to cover the maximum industrial demand, and by a third similar increment to meet possible emergency demands for military purposes.   It is considered possible to accomplish this if prices are set at the proper level, and that probably $150 per flask would be sufficient.   Failure to meet the needed output would necessitate the covering of the deficit by economy, diversion from less essential uses, and substitution, if it could not be obtained from foreign sources.

CONCLUSION

Having behind it the experience and equipment of a long established industry that once led the world in production, conditions with respect to the future supply of mercury are probably better than with any other strategic metal, but the handicap of a constantly decreasing ore tenor is a very real one. While emergency requirements would possibly exceed the probable supply, the resulting deficit does not seem likely to be greater than could reasonably be expected to be coverable by imports, economy, diversion, and substitution.   The establishment and maintenance of a war reserve stock, sufficient to cover such a prospective deficit would obviate the necessity for much pinching to make ends meet, would make the situation much more comfortable, and deserves serious consideration.   Lacking future discoveries of ore deposits richer in grade than the present average, mercury seems destined to remain a strategic metal from a general industrial standpoint, although to a lesser degree than most others, while, from a purely military standpoint, its strategic character is even less marked; in fact it is so near the border line that, like platinum, it might, under the most favorable conditions, be considered outside the strategic group.

CHAPTER XI

PLATINUM

As a strategic material, platinum lies near the border line; at the time of the World War it was highly strategic in character, but since that time there have been marked changes in industrial uses, with increased domestic production, reduced demand in many directions, and at the same time an extensive development of substitutes, fostered by the high price of the metal; as a result, at the present time, although platinum has been removed from the official list of strategic materials, and transferred to the critical list, it still remains in the industrial strategic list, since domestic production remains at a comparatively low level, and 95 per cent of the new metal supply has consistently been imported.

There has also been a radical change in the centers of production. Before the World War about 92 per cent of the total output was from Russia and 7 per cent from Colombia, with about half of the remaining 1 per cent from the United States, and the other half from other small producers. Russia almost ceased producing during the revolutionary period following the war, and has not since attained more than about one-third to one-half of her pre-war output, while Colombia has trebled her previous figures; South Africa has come in as a new producer of considerable amounts, supplemented by Ethiopia and Sierra Leone with smaller amounts, and Canada has risen from an insignificant producer of a few hundred ounces, and now stands at the head of the list.

As is characteristic of the strategic materials, there is a wide discrepancy between centers of production and consumption, but not so pronounced as with some of the other metals. The United States, Germany, Great Britain, and France are the chief consumers; none of these have any domestic production except the United States, where until lately the proportion was so small as to be almost negligible; but although there is no production in Great Britain, a large percentage of the world output is now

305

produced in British territory—Canada, South Africa, Australia, and Sierra Leone—and most of it goes to England for refining, making this country a leading center in the marketing of the metal.

REQUIREMENTS

Platinum has a large number of important industrial uses, but it happens that a number of these are capable of restriction or substitution in case of shortage of supply; this fact, taken in conjunction with the heavy use of platinum in jewelry, which can be entirely dispensed with in case of necessity, has resulted in wide fluctuations in the requirements, depending upon the availability of the metal and its price. During the period since 1913, world production has been as low as 44,000 ounces (1921), and as high as 268,000 ounces (1927), a figure more than six times the former, and with only six years between; and by 1937 the total had increased to 382,000 ounces. In addition, the accompanying graph of world production (Fig. 22) and the figures in Table I show other wide variations in supply. In general, the pre-war output fluctuated around 250,000 ounces annually, mostly from Russia; this decreased rapidly during the war period, as the Russian industry became disorganized, and still more when the revolution practically stopped mining operations. This heavy reduction in the Russian supply forced requirements to drop correspondingly, and was a large factor in the search for sources of supply in other countries, the development of substitutes, and the recovery of secondary metal. In no other strategic metal was the war supply so low, as compared with the pre-war, or the fluctuations between maximum and minimum supply so great. The fact that this country was able to proceed as well as it did with its World War program, which involved extensive new applications of platinum in the production of ammonia and nitric acid, was a monument to the careful balancing of requirements and to conservation of supplies.

USES

Although there are a number of minor uses for the metal, the leading ones are found in the jewelry, chemical, electrical, and dental industries. These practically all fall in the category of metallurgical uses, as nearly all call for platinum in the metallic form; although the chemical industry demands large amounts of platinum, very little of it is in the form of a chemical compound; truly chemical uses, which demand the platinum in the compound form, rather than the metallic, consume very little of the metal, but such amounts as do go into these uses are eventually largely lost, as little of it is in a form susceptible of secondary recovery, while with most of the metallic uses, the recovery is quite high.

An interesting early use of platinum was in coinage. In 1828 Russia authorized the coining of 3, 6, and 12 ruble pieces from platinum. At this time the price of the metal was low, but the commercial value of the metal in the coins soon rose to above the face value of $7 per ounce, and inside of 20 years coinage had to be stopped, because the coins were being exported and melted down for their metal content. All told, nearly half a million ounces of platinum was coined, but few of the coins escaped the melting pot, and they are now quite rare. A few years ago some consideration was given to the possibility of again using platinum in coinage in Russia, but due to the wide fluctuations in the price of the metal, the proposal was dropped.

The credit for the original use of platinum in coinage, however, apparently goes to certain ingenious individuals who utilized the platinum that was recovered from certain South American gold placers in the early years of the Spanish occupation for the production of spurious coins. The close similarity of platinum to gold in all of its physical characteristics except that of color made it possible to use the metal to make a coin that would pass anything but a careful examination, if it was covered with a thin facing of gold to deceive the unwary receiver. Incidentally, it may be remarked that many of these coins remained undetected in circulation for so long that by the time their true character was discovered, the value of platinum had increased to such a degree that it was much greater than that of the gold which it had originally replaced in the coin, and the discoverer of the fraud was rewarded by having a coin worth more than its face value.

Metallurgical Uses.—The jewelry industry has accounted for 60 per cent of the platinum consumed in the United States since 1918, the first year in which consumption figures were collected. This material has gone into rings, bracelets, necklaces, brooches, earrings, and other types of ornamental jewelry, particularly as a setting material for diamonds. The white color of the platinum improves the color of the diamond which is set in it, while the yellow of gold in a setting tends to impart this color to the stone; at the same time, the greater hardness and strength of the platinum alloys used for this purpose, as compared with gold, make it possible to use less metal in the setting, and thus produce a better effect, with the stone in greater prominence.

Platinum has also been used extensively in the manufacture of accessories such as hand bags, cigarette cases, pocket lighters, knives, and other similar items, where utility is combined with adornment, and during the past few years the lower prices for platinum have considerably increased uses of this type.

The electrical industry has accounted for 13 per cent of the consumption since 1918. In the form of wire, ribbon and sheet, platinum is used for resistance material, contacts and lead-in wires in many types of electrical instruments and devices such as telephones, magnetos, signs, automatic switches, X-ray tubes, and radio tubes, to mention only a few items in the list. Electrical uses declined heavily through substitution of less expensive materials, particularly during the period of extremely high prices inaugurated during the World War, and since 1929 have dropped to an average of 8 per cent.

The chemical industry finds a place for platinum in a wide variety of uses; although chemical uses total 13 per cent since 1918, the same as for electrical uses, there has been little change in the demand for chemical uses, as there has been with electrical, and the chemical field now consumes about twice as much platinum as the electrical industry, although the ratio was formerly 2:1 in the other direction.

Among the earlier chemical uses were laboratory apparatus of a wide variety of kinds—in crucibles, dishes, sheet, gauze, foil, wire, and a number of special forms, such as weights, muffles, triangles, filter cones, spatulas, and electrodes for electrochemical analysis. In the manufacturing industry a considerable amount was utilized in stills for acid distillation, particularly for sulfuric acid. Later, with the advent of the so-called contact process for the production of sulfuric acid, large amounts of platinum, in the form of platinum black, were required as a catalytic agent; other processes followed, using platinum as a catalyst, the most important of which were the synthesis of ammonia from nitrogen and hydrogen, and the oxidation of ammonia to nitric acid. Another important use in the chemical industry is in spinnerets for the spinning of fibers of rayon, or artificial silk, and certain branches of the electrochemical industry use platinum as an electrode material in their electrolytic processes. In addition to these major uses, there have been a multitude of minor ones, too numerous to detail.

Among the first uses of platinum in dentistry were anchor pins in artificial teeth, and posts for post teeth, and a number of other less important uses have been developed in prosthetic dentistry. Although dental uses have consumed less platinum than any of the other major uses, only about 9 per cent since 1918, the demand has been more constant than in any of the others.

A wide variety of miscellaneous uses have accounted for 5 per cent of the total consumption. Among the more important of these are thermoelectric and resistance pyrometers for the measurement of high temperatures; heating coils for small high-temperature electric furnaces for laboratory use; tips for fountain pen points; hypodermic needles; tips for lightning rods; cautery tips for surgical work; and parts for scientific and engineering instruments, where permanence is a factor.

Many in this extensive, but still far from complete list of uses, require pure platinum, while others take alloys of various compositions. Pure platinum is fairly soft, and where only hardness is to be imparted to the alloy, iridium is the usual alloying agent, in amounts from 5 to 20 per cent, and occasionally more. For other purposes, other metals are used, including rhodium, palladium, silver, gold, copper, and nickel, and an extensive list of standard alloy compositions are available on the market for the various uses for which they are best fitted.

Chemical Uses.—The chemical uses of platinum, that is, uses requiring the metal in the form of a chemical compound, as distinguished from the use of the pure metal in the chemical industry, account for only a very small percentage of the total consumption. These include fluorescent screens for X-ray work; photographic paper; pigments for pottery decoration; chemical reagent for certain types of analytical work; and platinum salts for use in electroplating platinum.

Military Uses.—There are no specific military uses for platinum, but in the event of war, many of the ordinary industrial demands would be heavily increased, particularly for catalysts in the production of sulfuric acid, ammonia, and nitric acid; laboratory equipment; dental material; and those phases of the electrical industry connected with signal transmission—telegraph, telephone, and radio.

SUBSTITUTES

Except for a temporary increase at the time of the Russian-Japanese War, when the price reached $38 per troy ounce, the price of platinum, up to the end of 1909, had been so little if any above the price of gold (the only metal that up to that time had been much used as a substitute), that there was practically no incentive for a search for substitutes for platinum. But beginning in 1909 there was a consistent increase in price, largely due to increasing demand for use in jewelry, and by the outbreak of the World War the former price level had been more than doubled. This increase led to considerable substitution, and when war demand led to another doubling in price, the development of substitutes was promoted still more actively, with the result that many of the former uses for the metal were almost wiped off the list. The high prices of the war period were repeated in 1923–1926, followed by a decline extending over several years, which eventually reached a low point of $23 in 1931; although later prices were somewhat higher, the revaluation of gold in 1933 automatically reduced the price of platinum to less than that of gold; these low prices during the past several years have removed, at least temporarily, much of the incentive toward substitution.

The uses of platinum are so varied, and involve so many different physical characteristics, that the development of substitutes has been a complicated problem. In most cases substitutes have had to be devised for each of the typical individual uses, since that applicable in one case is not suitable in another, no substitute having been developed which has *all* of the desirable properties of platinum. The field of substitutes for platinum is therefore more complicated than that of any other strategic metal. Most of the substitutes thus far developed are to be classed as:

Partial, in that a modification is made which permits a reduction in the amount of platinum required, but not a complete replacement;

Incomplete, in that the substitute gives the desired properties, but to a lesser degree; or

Imperfect, in that it fulfils the main requirements, but may lack some minor features which are not important enough to rule it out of consideration.

Few of the current substitutes can be classed as *perfect*, in that they perform the work of platinum even for any one particular application, with equal or better results in every way, at equal or less cost. A large percentage of the possible substitutes are not entirely acceptable, but are tolerated only because of the savings in cost which their use permits.

The first extensive substitution was the replacement of platinum as a lead-in wire in electric light globes. Platinum had been used for this purpose from the inception of the electric light because it had the same coefficient of expansion as glass, and hence could be sealed into the glass; a metal that contracted from the heat of the sealing-in more slowly than the glass would crack the glass, and one that contracted faster would separate from the glass and leave a leak that would destroy the vacuum in the lamp. About 1911–1912 an alloy of nickel and iron was developed that had the same coefficient of expansion as glass, and this rapidly and completely replaced platinum for this use. From the standpoint of economy and conservation in the use of platinum, this is one of the most important substitutions that has been made; and at the same time, it is one of the few *perfect* substitutions. Had this or some other similar substitution not been devised, the present output of light globes would require practically the entire platinum output to satisfy the demand of this one industry alone, and the metal would be so widely disseminated, and in such a small state of division that there would be little secondary recovery possible.

Another reduction of considerable magnitude was made in the electrical consumption of platinum by the use of tungsten contact points in magnetos and other types of equipment; in some cases where the wear is less severe, contacts of silver or graphite may serve the purpose.

Nickel-chromium alloys are now used as a resistor in electric furnaces for moderate temperatures, and molybdenum for high temperatures. Nickel-chromium and other base metal alloys are also used for thermocouples for moderate temperatures.

In the chemical industry the massive acid stills, some of which contained as much as 2,000 ounces of platinum, have largely been replaced by fused silica, and an even more important step has been the development of vanadium oxide catalysts, which may entirely replace platinum in the manufacture of contact sulfuric acid, and of platinized silica gel, in which the amount of platinum required is greatly reduced.   In laboratory apparatus, depending on the particular purpose for which it is needed, we find in use as substitutes a wide variety of metals and alloys, including tantalum, tungsten, gold, nickel, palladium, palladium-gold, nickel-chromium, iron-chromium, and chromium-tungsten-cobalt.   In other fields we find such alloys as platinum-tantalum; and platinum-gold, where substitution is only partial.

In jewelry the possibilities for substitution are much more restricted, for much of the demand is in the extreme luxury trade, where cost is not an item to be considered.   When platinum reached such a high degree of popularity in jewelry, there was considerable fraudulent substitution of cheaper products by unscrupulous manufacturers, not for the purpose of lowering the price of the product, but to reduce its cost of production and so increase the profit.   This led to the passage of stamping laws in many countries, and in various states of the United States, prohibiting the sale of metal under the designation of "platinum" unless the composition conformed to certain minimum specifications as to actual platinum content.   This, however, does not prevent the manufacturer who wishes to produce a cheaper product from using substitutions which have the appearance of platinum, providing they are not labeled and sold as platinum.   White gold, an alloy of gold, nickel and zinc, is much used to simulate platinum, as is also palladium in the form of various alloys. While originally used largely as a cheapening agent in platinum jewelry, there has gradually developed a considerable demand for palladium under its own name, due to its lower cost and close similarity to platinum.

The whole field of platinum substitution is a complicated one, and examples of only the more important types can be cited here; in addition to those listed, there are many more of less importance.

ORES

While platinum is found in a number of countries in small amounts, in only four has it been found in appreciable quantities —Russia, Canada, Colombia, and South Africa.   The ores fall into three groups:

Native ores, in which the platinum occurs in the metallic condition, alloyed with varying amounts of other metals of the platinum group, palladium, iridium, osmium, rhodium, and ruthenium, with small percentages of iron, copper, and gold. The platinum content of the crude metal varies from 60 to 85 per cent, depending on the source; iron is usually next in amount, with 4 to 20 per cent; the amounts of the other platinum group metals are usually small, totaling 5 to 15 per cent, with the exception of Australia, where the osmium-iridium content runs higher (25 per cent); the gold content is 1 to 3 per cent, and copper varies from zero to 4 per cent. The non-metallic gangue in the crude metal is usually not over 1 to 4 per cent, but metal has been found in Spain with as high as 36 per cent of gangue.

Compound ores, in which the metal is present in the form of a chemical compound with one or more other elements. Ores of this type have thus far been found in commercial quantities only in South Africa, where compounds of platinum with arsenic and sulfur are found associated with native platinum, in the ratio of about four parts of native metal to one part in combination.

Byproduct ores, usually ores primarily of gold, copper or nickel, from which the platinum is recovered solely as a byproduct in the smelting of the ores and the refining of the primary metal. The nickel-copper ores of the Sudbury district of Canada carry about one ounce of platinum to 20 tons of ore, the recovery of which, with the recent improvement in the nickel market, has put Canada in the lead as a platinum producer. Refiners of copper and gold, in the course of the refining operation, recover small amounts of platinum from the anode slimes of the electrolytic refining process.

In addition to the types of ore listed above, there is a small amount of platinum found in a native alloy known as osmiridium, which, as its name indicates, is primarily an alloy of osmium and iridium. The only localities in which this alloy is found in any quantity are Tasmania and South Africa. The former are placer deposits that have been worked for some time, but the product contains little if any platinum. In South Africa an alloy containing 11 to 12 per cent platinum is associated with gold, and is recovered from the concentrators of several of the large gold mines.

The mining of the straight native ores is by placer methods, washing, hydraulic mining, or dredging, depending on the character and location of the ore, and the magnitude of the operation.

It is only in South Africa that the native metal and the compound ores are found *in situ* in the mother rock, and rock mining methods have to be utilized.

Beneficiation.—None of the ores carry more than a fraction of an ounce of the platinum metals to a ton of ore, and extensive ore dressing is required for the separation of the metal. The high specific gravity of the crude metal (18 to 19) makes this fairly simple, by use of some type of gravity concentration. The chief difficulty encountered is due to the fact that some of the platinum particles are so small that they tend to remain in suspension in the water current, and so pass out with the tailings. With gold ores this is overcome by the use of mercury, which amalgamates with the gold particles and holds them, but this procedure is of no value with platinum ores, as the metal does not amalgamate freely with mercury. For this reason, unless proper precautions are taken, a considerable proportion of the finely divided platinum that usually accompanies placer gold in small quantities, is likely to be lost. With the South African ores the presence of mineral compounds of platinum complicates the concentration process, and even with the use of flotation the recoveries are low with some types of ore.

Metallurgy.—Since the product of the mining and concentration of the native ores is an alloy of the mixed metals of the platinum group, with comparatively little gangue to complicate the further procedure, the metallurgy of the metals boils down to the separation and refining of the constituent metals of the crude alloy.

Carrying, as no other platinum ores do, a mixture of crude metal and metallic compounds in a massive rock matrix, the treatment of the South African ores presented radically new problems, complicated by the fact that the crude metal content could not be separated in the usual high degree of purity, with respect to the associated gangue, and that the minerals involved were new ones, that had never before been handled metallurgically.

The crude metal recovered by gravity concentration carries about 26 to 42 per cent of metal, mostly platinum and palladium, with a small percentage of gold, and still less of the other platinum metals. The further treatment of this product for the recovery of the metal is not particularly difficult. The mineral concentrates, as distinguished from the metal concentrates, carry only about

10 ounces of platinum metals per ton, and a long and complicated process is required for their treatment.

The smelting and refining of crude platinum is centered in three localities. Much of the Russian output is handled in local refineries, though the product was for a time shipped to Germany for sale through a selling agency; some crude metal is exported direct to the United States, and Great Britain. The bulk of the Canadian and the South African outputs are sent to England for refining. The International Nickel Company, controlling most of the Canadian production, operate their own refinery in England, while other plants handle the South African shipments. The Falconbridge Nickel Mines produce about one-eighth of the Canadian nickel output, smelt to matte at the mine, and ship the matte to Norway for finishing. No information is at hand as to the disposition of the platinum-bearing slimes recovered in the nickel refinery, but probably they go to England also. The refineries in the United States handle the small domestic output, practically all of the Colombian, moderate amounts from Russia, and small amounts from South Africa.

All of the platinum recovered from nickel ores is obtained as a slime in the electrolytic refining of the nickel, and goes directly to the platinum refinery. The byproduct platinum recovered by copper and gold refiners is usually refined to pure metal at the point of recovery.

Secondary Recovery.—Due to its high price, the recovery of secondary platinum has always been maintained at a high level, from the scrap and waste produced by the manufacturer to the worn out or damaged product in the hands of the final consumer. There is probably proportionately less loss in the recovery of used platinum for secondary use than is the case with any other metal, including gold. Although a large proportion of the uses are quite permanent in character, and the life runs into several years, there is a steady return of secondary metal, amounting to approximately half of the supply of new metal available for consumption. Data on the amounts of secondary metal recovered will be found in a table in a later section.

Forms in Which Platinum Appears on the Market.—Platinum may be purchased in the open market as pure metal, or in the form of the various standard alloys required by the consuming industries, as ingot, semi-finished, or finished product. The common forms of semi-finished material are sheet, foil, wire, ribbon, rods, tubing, and screen, either woven from wire or perforated from sheet. In the finished material each specific use requires a special size, shape and composition of metal, making the possibilities too numerous to mention.

ORE RESERVES

Ore reserves of platinum in the different producing countries are known to be extensive, but are indefinite in quantity. The Russian deposits have been studied at various times, and reserves for future development are known to be considerable, but no recent figures are available. Definite data on Colombian reserves are likewise lacking but it is known that for several years the yield from the dredging areas is decreasing. There are more than 200,000,000 tons of nickel ore definitely blocked out in the Canadian mines, but the average platinum content is not known; at the present rate of recovery this would represent over 10,000,-000 ounces of platinum, but even though it is questionable as to whether the entire amount averages as high in platinum content as the ores now being worked, it is evident that the potential supply is plentiful. It has been pretty well established that the South African deposits probably carry more platinum than is to be found in all of the other known deposits of the world, but the grade of the ore is so low, and the costs of recovery so high, that these reserves will be of much more significance in later years when the richer deposits are more nearly worked out, when prices are higher, or when recovery methods have been improved and cheapened. Little information is as yet available on the Alaskan deposits.

The present potential world production is well above the consumption demand, and there is no immediate prospect of a shortage of supply except under such emergency conditions as may interfere with the long ocean shipments that are necessary to bring the metal to the centers of consumption.

WORLD OUTPUT AND SUPPLY

Platinum first began to come into prominence less than 200 years ago, although it was known previous to 1600. Curiously enough, attention was first attracted to the metal by the fact that its specific gravity was so close to that of gold that the early

Spanish gold seekers of South America found difficulty in separating from their gold the small amounts of platinum associated with it. Since the platinum at that time had almost no value, it was looked on only as a nuisance. This attitude was strengthened when, as a result of a growing use of the metal for the debasement of gold coins, the Spanish government prohibited the export of platinum from the colonies, a move which materially retarded the spread of knowledge of the metal and the development of uses for it, and it was not until 1751 that it came to the attention of the scientific fraternity. Subsequent progress was steady but slow, due to the difficulties met in working the metal, since there was at that time no known means of producing a temperature sufficiently high to melt it.

Platinum was discovered in the gold mines of the Ural Mountains in 1819, and three years later rich deposits of the metal were found that soon were able to supply the bulk of the world's demand. From this time, for more than 100 years, Russia continued to be not only the world's leading producer of platinum, but also almost the only producer, the output from other sources being so small as to be almost negligible. By 1913 the world output had grown to 227,000 ounces, of which Russia produced nearly 93 per cent and Colombia nearly 7 per cent, with less than 1 per cent from other sources. The leading minor output at this time was 1,000 to 1,500 ounces annually from the United States, mostly as a byproduct from gold and copper refining.

The Russian output suffered heavily during the war and the revolutionary period that followed, and again during the depression period; at no time since has the output reached its 1913 level. The Colombian output gradually increased from the beginning of the war period, when the declining Russian supply was not sufficient for the demand, as did also the minor outputs, but only in Canada was the increase of major proportions. Later South Africa entered the field as a new producer.

The decline in production that was manifest in Russia and Colombia in 1928 and 1929, just preceding the general industrial depression, the effect of which would not be perceptible before 1930, was largely due to the heavy production of 1927. Increasing outputs in all four of the leading countries resulted in a total in 1927 that was in excess of demands, and a sharp decline followed. The 1927 total was about on a par, or possibly slightly in

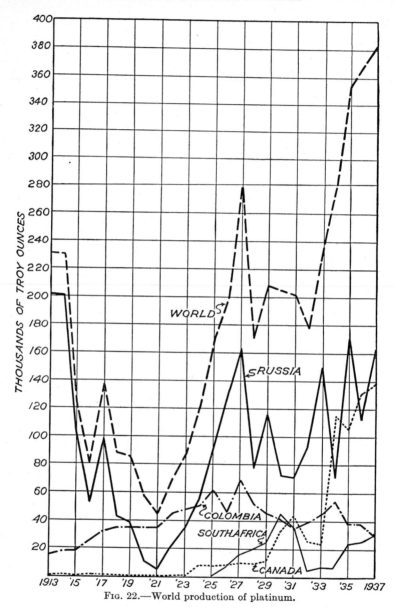

FIG. 22.—World production of platinum.

excess of the pre-war maximum, and the high prices that had prevailed in the interim had fostered the substitution of other metals and alloys for so many of the former uses of platinum that the world was no longer capable of consuming an output of this magnitude. In 1934 production had again expanded to near this same level, and in spite of efforts to develop new uses, there is still an appreciable surplus, and prices remain comparatively low.

Table I shows the annual outputs since 1913 of all countries making an appreciable contribution to the total, the annual world totals, the period totals for each country, and the percentage of the period grand total that has been supplied by each country. These, and Fig. 22 show clearly the wide fluctuations that have disturbed the industry during the past 25 years. Although statistics for the early years are quite uncertain, even down to the beginning of the war period, estimates have been made of the total platinum output of the various countries since the beginning of their production, according to the best information available, for comparison with the corresponding figures for recent years.

Canada.—Platinum production in Canada previous to 1923 was only a few hundred ounces annually, about 50 ounces of which was from British Columbia placers, and the remainder was byproduct recovery from the nickel ores of the Sudbury district of Ontario. Beginning in 1923, new smelting methods, with better recovery of the platinum, combined with the mining of ores with an increasing platinum content as new areas were opened up in the mines, increased production considerably, and by 1931 the output had reached 45,000 ounces. The next two years showed a decrease, due to the restricted demand for nickel, but in 1934 nickel sales increased heavily, and the recovery of the associated platinum kept pace with it, and exceeded 116,000 ounces, putting Canada in the position of leading producer, with a later increase to nearly 140,000 ounces in 1937.

The Canadian nickel ores contain on the average 0.05 ounce of platinum per ton, and about three-quarters of that amount of other metals of the platinum group, mostly palladium. The nickel ore smelted in 1937 would carry about 175,000 ounces of platinum, but, as there is a considerable time lag in the recovery of the platinum, the 1937 recovery was 139,400 ounces. There is every reason to assume that the demand for nickel will continue to

TABLE I.—WORLD PRODUCTION OF PLATINUM[1]
(In troy ounces)

	Russia[6]	Colombia[2,3]	Canada	South Africa[4]	United States[12]	Ethiopia[2,4,9]	Belgian Congo	Australia[2,5]	Sierra Leone[2]	Japan[2,3]	Total
1913	210.0	15.0	0.2	......	1.0	......	......	0.4	......	[11]	227.0
1914	202.0	17.5	0.7	......	1.5	......	......	0.2	......	[11]	222.0
1915	104.0	18.0	0.5	......	1.2	......	......	0.1	......	[11]	124.0
1916	53.0	25.0	1.0	......	2.8	......	......	0.1	......	0.1	82.0
1917	98.5	32.0	1.0	......	6.3	......	......	0.3	......	0.1	138.0
1918	43.2	35.0	0.7	......	9.7	......	......	0.6	......	0.1	89.0
1919	39.4	35.0	0.7	......	10.5	......	......	0.2	......	0.2	86.0
1920	11.3	35.0	0.6	......	11.5	......	......	0.8	......	0.3	57.5
1921	5.5	35.0	0.3	......	2.9	......	......	0.2	......	0.2	44.0
1922	22.5	45.4	0.5	0.1[10]	2.0	......	......	0.1	......	0.2	70.0
1923	34.7	48.3	1.2	0.2[10]	2.1	......	......	0.6	......	0.1	87.0
1924	56.9	51.5	9.2	9.5[10]	3.5	......	......	0.6	......	0.1	122.0
1925	94.8	62.0	8.7	0.6[10]	4.3	......	......	0.4	......	0.2	171.0
1926	131.8[7]	46.7[7]	9.5	8.4	4.4	0.5	......	0.4	......	0.2	202.0
1927	163.1[7]	70.1[11]	11.2	16.8	4.6	2.2	......	0.4	......	[12]	268.0
1928	78.9[7]	53.5	10.5	20.2	4.6	3.2	......	0.4	[13]	0.1	171.5
1929	115.8[8]	45.6	12.5	25.4	5.6	3.8	......	0.1	......	0.1	208.9
1930	72.8[8]	42.4	34.0	45.5	5.3	3.8	......	0.2	0.5	0.1	205.6
1931	71.8[8]	35.8	44.8	36.1	5.6	6.2	......	0.3	0.5	0.3	201.4
1932	93.7[8]	40.5	27.3	5.8	1.9	8.2	0.1	0.3	0.5	0.3	178.7
1933	150.4[8]	46.0	24.8	6.9	1.3	6.7	......	0.1	0.4	0.2	235.9
1934	70.7[8]	54.8	116.2	7.5	3.0	5.6	1.3	0.2	0.5	0.1	279.9
1935	170.9[8]	38.6	105.4	4.9	6.6	5.4	1.0	0.1	0.8	0.5	353.9
1936	113.6[8]	38.3	131.6	26.0	7.4	8.0	3.2	[13]	0.5	[13]	328.7
1937	161.8[8]	29.3	139.4	31.2	9.3	?	2.6	[13]	0.3	?	382.2
Totals	2,375.4	996.3	692.9	276.1	114.3	53.7	8.1	7.7	4.0	3.2	4,537.0
Per cent	52.3	21.9	15.3	6.1	2.6	1.2	0.2	0.2	0.1	0.1	100.0

[1] Official figures, in ounces of fine platinum, unless otherwise noted; figures in round numbers are partly estimated. [2] Crude platinum, usually containing about 80-85 per cent platinum. [3] Figures of Imperial Institute, London. [4] Estimated platinum content of total platinum group metals produced. [5] Does not include platinum content of osmiridium. [6] Figures on Russian platinum are more or less uncertain, and vary somewhat, depending on the source; those quoted seem to be as reliable as any available. [7] Exports; production figures not available. [8] Known exports; not complete. [9] Registered output; probably not complete. [10] Platinum content of osmiridium output; other production did not begin until 1926. [11] Not available. [12] Platinum of domestic origin recovered by domestic refineries. [13] Less than 50 oz.

increase, as new uses are constantly being developed and old uses are expanding, and, so long as this is true, Canada seems destined to remain in the lead as a platinum producer. Another important factor in the situation is the fact that the Canadian output is entirely a byproduct, which can be recovered at a cost far below that incurred in the mining and treatment of an ore for its platinum content alone.

Colombia.—Although the Choco district of Colombia, near the head waters of the Atrato and San Juan Rivers, has been known as a platinum producer since the early days of the Spanish conquest, it is only during the period under review that the production has reached important levels. Colombia exported platinum at an early date, when little was known about the metal, or the proper methods of working it. The metal had little actual value (35–40c per ounce), and in 1823 when exportation was prohibited, as has been cited in a previous section, this price was cut in half; consequently the natives frequently threw it away if the traders objected to buying it. In comparatively recent years, when platinum was well established as an article of commerce, at a relatively high price, those who could locate the position of one of the ancient trading posts carefully washed the ground in the vicinity and recovered comfortable amounts of platinum that had been discarded by the natives, possibly 100 years before, when the trader refused to buy it.

After Russia became an important producer through the discovery of richer deposits, the poorer deposits of Colombia did not offer any great attraction, although production continued slowly to increase as the demand for the metal grew. In 1913 the Colombian output was about 15,000 ounces. War demand soon pulled this up to an estimated 35,000 ounces, and production continued to expand fairly steadily until curtailed by the overproduction of 1927, and the industrial depression that followed shortly after. The low point in production was reached in 1931, at about half of the previous maximum of 70,000 ounces, and subsequent recovery brought the 1934 output back to about 55,000 ounces. Production has since declined heavily, to less than 30,000 ounces in 1937, due to a lowering of the platinum content of the gravels in the leading dredging area.

Most of the Colombian output is recovered by mining companies using modern dredges on the rivers in the producing district, although small amounts are brought in by natives using primitive methods.

Russia (U. S. S. R.).—From the time of the discovery of the rich Ural deposits until the internal disorganization resulting from the World War and the subsequent revolution, this district produced the lion's share of the world's supply. By 1921 production had almost ceased, but the following years saw the industry reestablished, and again in the lead, though not with its former outstanding lead over other producers. The 1927 output, the highest since 1913, was only 78 per cent of the 1913 figure, and decreasing demand during the depression and increasing outputs in other countries again made serious inroads, with only a partial recovery since.

The Russian contribution to the total output shrunk from 93 per cent in 1913 to 13 per cent in 1921, increased to 61 per cent in 1927, and again dropped to 36 per cent in 1931. Statistics from Russia have been incomplete for a number of years past, due to the adoption of a policy of suppressing the figures on platinum output, so that, after 1926, only exports have been available, and, since 1929, even these have not been complete, but cover only the imports of other countries that can be traced to Russian sources. The current information available is too uncertain to justify any definite statements of comparison, but the indications are that in 1934 Russia lost its position as leading producer, which had been held for more than 100 years, except during the disorganization of 1920–1923.

South Africa.—Although there had been since 1921 a byproduct recovery at various of the large South African gold mines of a few thousand ounces a year of osmiridium, containing several hundred ounces of platinum, the direct mining and recovery of platinum did not begin until 1926. During 1922–1925 discoveries of platinum lodes were made in several different localities, particularly in the Waterberg, Lydenberg, Potgietersrust and Rustenburg districts of the Transvaal. Enormous quantities of ore were shown to exist in these various deposits, and it was estimated by competent authorities that there probably existed here more platinum than was contained in all the rest of the world's known deposits. This naturally gave a big boost to the promotion of platinum mines, and companies were organized almost in wholesale quantities, and development was begun on several of the more promising properties.

As so frequently happens, however, especially in the mining industry, entirely too optimistic an attitude had been held, and insufficient attention had been given to the technical and commercial difficulties that were beyond the rosy glow of the immediate horizon. As has already been pointed out in the discussion of ores, this was the first time that platinum had ever been mined from a lode deposit, or in the form of a compound ore, rather than a native ore, and entirely new metallurgical procedures had to be developed. Although this was eventually accomplished, it was only after long and expensive research, and in the meantime many of the companies had gone into liquidation. Another difficulty that had not been sufficiently appreciated was the effect that a prospective large new supply would have on the price of platinum, a factor which was magnified by the simultaneous expansion of the Canadian output. Successive reductions in price year after year from 1927 to 1931 cut returns to less than operating costs, resulting in the closing down of one plant after another, and from June, 1932, to August, 1933, all operations were suspended. Out of a total of some forty or fifty companies registered, only five actually produced metal; one of these closed in 1927, a second in 1930, and eventually the three survivors were merged into a single company.

For a time, while prospects were at their rosiest, South Africa was hailed by the enthusiasts as the world's coming foremost producer; this has failed to materialize, and probably never will, or at least not for a long time to come, for the reason that though enormous platinum reserves are known to exist in these deposits, the grade of the ore is too low, and the production costs too high for effective competition against the other established producers, especially Canada, with her low-cost byproduct recovery.

United States.—Platinum is recovered in the United States from placer deposits in the Goodnews Bay district of Alaska, south of the mouth of the Kuskokwin River, and from beach sands near Cape Blanco, Curry County, Oregon, as well as from various gold placers in California and Alaska. This production of crude platinum, amounting to 500 to 1,000 ounces in most years, is considerably exceeded by the byproduct recovery from gold and copper refining. Production since 1913 has averaged about 4,400 ounces annually, and has materially exceeded this amount only during the years of excessively high prices during the war period.   This production averages less than 4 per cent of the consumption.

Previous to 1932 the domestic production of platinum from native ores averaged only about 500 ounces annually, but during the past few years this has been increasing; in 1934 the mine output of crude was 3,730 ounces, equivalent to about 3,000 ounces of platinum, the largest output on record.   Most of this came from the Alaska placers.   Since 1934 the Alaskan output has been expanded, giving a total mine output of 10,000 ounces of crude in 1937, and preliminary estimates place the 1938 figure at about three times this amount, so that for the first time in history the United States output will be a material proportion of the world total.   The gradually increasing output of gold, that has marked the depression period, has increased the recovery of platinum both from gold placers and from gold refiners, but at the same time copper production has been so low that the decrease in byproduct recovery from this source has more than offset increases in other types of byproduct recovery.

Other Countries.—The most important of the minor producers in Ethiopia, where production began in 1926, and has grown to an average output of some 6,000 ounces of crude metal.   In 1929 the production of crude metal began on a small scale in Sierra Leone, and, in 1934, the recovery of 1,261 ounces was reported as a byproduct recovery from the copper refinery recently established in the Belgian Congo.   Australia has long been a producer of small amounts of crude, mostly from New South Wales, although small amounts have been found in Victoria and Queensland.   The production of crude platinum in Japan is quite small, but there is some recovery of byproduct metal from copper refining, the amounts of which are not definitely known. Other sections of the Orient that have supplied small amounts are India, Papua, New Zealand, Philippine Islands, and Sumatra; Borneo was, in the early days, a producer of moderate amounts, but in recent years has almost disappeared from the production lists.

UNITED STATES OUTPUT AND SUPPLY

Platinum production in the United States has never been large, the average output since 1913 has been less than 3 per cent of the available market supply, and the highest point reached was

20 per cent, when production was at its war peak, and production in Russia had almost ceased. In the years immediately preceding the war period, about half of the output was mine production of crude metal, largely a byproduct recovery from gold placers, and the other half was byproduct recovery from copper and gold refiners. Almost no metal was produced as a true primary product. During the war period production increased considerably, mostly through increased byproduct recoveries by copper refiners. During the post-war years production declined almost to its pre-war level, gradually increasing again during the inflation period. Another decline in the depression period was followed by marked increases from new sources, rather than from expanding recoveries from former sources. The location of these various sources is discussed in the previous section on world output and supply. The production since 1932 has been characterized by several new features: (1) a recovery of output from the 1932 minimum; (2) heavy increases in output from new sources; (3) greater outputs in crude metal than in refinery byproducts; (4) increased recoveries of crude from placers that are worked primarily for their platinum content.

The United States is the world's largest consumer of platinum, 97 per cent of which has come from outside sources or from secondary recoveries. The importance of secondary recovery is probably greater with platinum than with any other metal. In eight of the nine years between 1916 and 1924 the United States consumption was greater than the entire world output by about 50 per cent, a condition which could not have been possible except through extensive and systematic secondary production to supply the difference. Table II gives a summary of the available supply of platinum in the United States since 1913, as well as data on consumption and stocks.

Imports.—Although Russia has predominated in production during most of the time, imports into the United States direct from Russia have totaled only about 6 per cent of the aggregate imports since 1913. Before the war much of the Russian metal was refined in France or England before being forwarded to the United States. During the war the industry was disorganized to such an extent that there were no direct imports. The post-war reorganization of the industry established a sales agency in Berlin, and for a time this handled most of the exports. It is

TABLE II.—AVAILABLE SUPPLY OF PLATINUM IN THE UNITED STATES

(Thousands of troy ounces)

Year	Domestic Production[1]	Imports[2]	O.P.M.[3] Recovered	Exports[2]	Available New Supply[4]	Secondary	Stocks[5]	Apparent Consumption[6]	Sales Reported[7]	Percentage of World Output in	
										New Supply	Apparent Consumption[11]
1913	1.0	118.5	[8]	[8]	118.0[9]	40.0	[8]	158.0[11]	[8]	52	70[11]
1914	1.5	72.0	[8]	[8]	72.0[9]	40.7	[8]	113.0[11]	[8]	32	51[11]
1915	1.2	61.4	2.1	[8]	60.0[9]	42.1	[8]	102.0[11]	[8]	48	82[11]
1916	2.8	53.6	3.6	1.9	50.9	45.5	[8]	96.1[11]	[8]	62	117[11]
1917	6.3	30.3	5.8	4.0	26.8	59.0	[8]	85.8[11]	[8]	19	62[11]
1918	9.7	55.0	5.3	0.3	59.1	40.4	51.5	99.5[11]	100.8	66	112[11]
1919	10.5	54.6	4.9	1.0	59.2	54.5	29.2	146.0	133.7	69	170
1920	11.5	81.7	5.5	2.6	85.1	51.3	46.7	118.9	123.1	148	207
1921	2.9	62.2	4.6	4.0	56.5	39.1	38.5	103.8	151.1	128	236
1922	2.0	95.0	3.6	2.0	91.4	40.1	41.9	128.1	156.8	130	183
1923	2.1	86.5	3.0	1.7	83.9	39.2	36.6	128.4	152.4	96	148
1924	3.5	95.7	8.2	7.1	83.7	45.5	40.5	125.5	130.4	68	103
1925	4.3	106.5	8.3	19.8	82.7	35.6	44.0	114.8	137.3	48	67
1926	4.9	115.0	8.8	13.5	97.6	38.8	64.2	116.2	138.8	48	58
1927	4.4	128.6	4.9	21.5	106.6	46.1	68.8	148.1	122.6	40	55
1928	4.6	108.5	7.6	11.2	94.3	47.2	45.7	154.6	149.7	55	90
1929	5.6	115.2	6.2	4.0	110.6	33.6	51.9	138.0	145.3	53	67
1930	5.3	106.2	5.7	1.8	104.0	33.8	52.9	136.8	83.5	51	67
1931	5.6	91.7	4.9	2.4	90.0	33.4	51.2	125.1	77.0	45	62
1932	1.9	33.2	3.0	22.1	10.0	21.6	38.0	44.8	54.6	6	25
1933	1.3	111.3	3.0	25.0[10]	84.6	35.1	41.2	116.5	76.2	36	49
1934	3.0	133.3	3.9	2.7[10]	129.7	35.5	41.4	165.0	61.1	46	59
1935	6.6	122.6	4.8	5.2[10]	119.2	47.1	50.3	157.4	87.4	34	45
1936	7.4	157.3	7.2	58.0	99.5	56.0	56.9	148.9	112.4	30	45
1937	9.3	148.8	9.1	62.4	86.6	55.9	60.2	139.2	96.0	23	36
Totals	119.2	2346.4	127.2	276.2	2062.2	1056.9	......	3110.5	......	......	......
Per cent	3.8	75.4	4.1	8.9	66.3	34.0	-0.3	100.0	......	45	68

[1] Refiners' production traceable to domestic sources. [2] Not including jewelry. [3] This deduction covers other platinum-group metals recovered by refiners from crude platinum treated. [4] Production plus imports, less O.P.M. and exports. [5] Refiners' and dealers' stocks only; does not include consumers' stocks. [6] Available new supply plus secondary, plus or minus changes in stocks. [7] Sales reported by refiners; these cover the bulk of consumption, but are not complete. [8] Not reported. [9] Estimated. [10] Incomplete, as exports reported from July 1, 1933, to Dec. 31, 1935, did not include shipments by parcel post. [11] Disregarding changes in stocks.

TABLE III.—IMPORTS OF PLATINUM INTO THE UNITED STATES
(Thousands of troy ounces)

Year	Great Britain	Colombia	Germany	Russia	France	Others[1]	Total	Ore	Crude	Refined
1913	21[3]	13[3]	54[3]	1[3]	29[3]	1[3]	118.5		48.9	69.6
1914	15[3]	14[3]	27[3]		15[3]	1[3]	72.0		31.2	40.8
1915	25.9	16.3	0.5		17.9	0.8	61.4		55.7	5.7
1916	24.7	24.8			2.0	1.9	53.5		41.2	12.2
1917	3.6	23.9			1.9	0.9	30.3		26.1	4.2
1918	0.4	30.5		21.0	0.4	2.6	55.0		45.8	9.1
1919	21.0	26.0	0.1	0.4	5.4	1.7	54.6		47.9	6.6
1920	34.2	29.9	0.2	0.8	12.5	4.3	81.7		57.8	23.9
1921	17.4	31.8			7.5	5.3	62.2		44.8	17.4
1922	35.0	37.2	12.0	0.5	11.4		95.0		94.9	
1923	22.5	32.3	0.2		7.8	11.5	86.5	4.1	46.7	35.7
1924	37.3	43.5	0.5		8.0	6.8	95.7	1.9	2.0	31.9
1925	63.6	33.6	2.3	4.2	1.7	7.2	106.5	0.8	58.7	47.1
1926	55.4	39.0	26.6	6.0	11.4	7.8	115.0	1.2	87.2	26.6
1927	41.1	52.0	23.2	15.0	2.3	2.4	128.6		90.5	38.1
1928	23.1	52.8	12.8	14.4		3.4	108.5	0.7	78.4	29.4
1929	36.4	45.8	0.4	5.8		5.2	115.1	0.6	74.1	40.6
1930	45.9	43.2	0.3	0.1		2.7	106.2		81.2	25.0
1931	44.0	41.5		21.9		1.2	91.7	1.1	67.1	23.6
1932	14.6	16.4		11.5		2.2	33.2	0.2	25.4	7.6
1933	63.1	15.6		22.4		10.7	111.3		71.5	39.8
1934	63.4	48.8		4.5		9.5	133.3		119.5	13.8
1935	62.7	31.4		15.0		6.1	122.6	0.7	61.2	60.7
1936	119.8	29.1				3.885	157.3	2.204	103.1	52.0
1937	104.0	24.1		15.0	0.1	5.657	148.8	1.186	85.6	62.1
Totals	995.1	796.1	160.8	144.1	134.1	117.1	2,345.1		1,622	723.1
Per cent	42.4	33.9	6.8	6.1	5.7	5.0	100.0		69.2	30.8

[1] This column, from 1923 to 1934, contains small amounts of manufactured platinum, the sources of which were not available. Previous to 1923 manufactured material was listed in the import returns by value only, and the amounts can not be included in the table; the values varied from a few hundred dollars to more than $100,000, so that in some years the amounts would materially increase the totals as given. [2] Not available. [3] Approximate.

only during recent years that direct imports to the United States have been made in any appreciable quantity. The only marked exception to this was the receipt of 21,000 ounces so late in 1917 that it was not recorded in the import figures for that year, but was included in those for 1918; this, however, was not a regular shipment, but had been collected by United States agents in Russia, and was shipped out of Russia secretly, to supply United States war needs.

Amounts about equal to those from Russia have been received from France and Germany, most of which apparently originated in Russia, as did also a considerable proportion of the heavy receipts from England, until this became the refining center for Canadian and South African metal. During 1932–1934 shipments of Russian metal to England were comparatively small, but since 1935 have increased to more than half of the total Russian exports.

About one-third of the total imports since 1913 have been from Colombia, although previous to the war period Colombia was a poor second to Russia as a source of imports; practically the entire Colombian output is regularly sent to the United States.

The total imports of Russian origin can not be determined, as the majority of them have come through other countries. The imports from England have been approximately 42 per cent of the total; during the earlier years most of this metal originated in Russia, but since the development of the industry in Canada and South Africa these countries have supplied most of the raw material for the English refineries, and eventually much of the refined product has reached the United States. Direct imports into the United States from Canada and South Africa have been negligible.

The bulk of the imports is crude metal, for refining in the United States. Previous to the war the greater proportion of the imports was refined metal, but war conditions reversed this, and in general, the proportion of crude imports has increased ever since, while that of refined has decreased. Almost the entire imports of refined metal are now in the form of ingots, bars, sheets or plates—that is, semi-finished material. Although in 1909 as much as 14 per cent of the total value of the platinum imports was manufactured products (the weights of manufactured products were not reported previous to 1919), this had declined to less than 2 per cent in 1913, and since then has been negligible in amount; the total imports of manufactured platinum, except jewelry, during the past 10 years has been only 110 ounces.

Exports.—Exports in a few isolated years, exports of platinum from the United States have been of the order of 1,000–4,000 ounces per annum; during 1925–1928, 1932–1933 and 1936–1937 exports were on a considerably heavier scale, as is indicated in Table II, with a maximum of 62,400 ounces in 1937. During these eight years the aggregate exports were 75 per cent of the total since 1913.

Consumption.—Figures on available supply, as calculated from production, imports and exports, are usually considered a fair guide to consumption of a product, if adjusted for changes in stocks. A comparison of the figures on available supply of platinum with those for sales consumption as reported by the refiners of platinum, all shown in Table II, makes it evident that there is a decided lack of coordination, the reason for which, however, can not be definitely determined. A moderate amount of variation is to be expected in approximate data of this kind, but differences of the magnitude found here are difficult to explain.

Table VI gives a break-down of consumption by consuming industries, since 1918, reference to which was made in the discussion of uses.

Stocks.—The figures on stocks, given in Table II, are those in the hands of refiners at the close of the year. Were records available on invisible stocks, in the hands of consumers, it is possible that some of the discrepancies between the figures on available supply and consumption might be eliminated.

UTILIZATION OF PLATINUM

The best data we have on the ultimate utilization of platinum is found in Table VI, in the breakdown of United States consumption by the various consuming industries. Unfortunately no information has been published along similar lines in other countries, but consumption in the leading industrial countries is doubtless along somewhat the same lines as in the United States. It would also be both interesting and useful to have more detailed data on the amounts of platinum required for some of the more important specific uses, but nothing of this kind has ever been collected.

It will be noted that there have been wide variations in the consumption in the different industries from year to year. Jewelry has ranged from a low of 13.4 per cent in 1918, when uses of this type were restricted, to 70.1 per cent in 1927; in general, the proportion runs about 65–70 per cent in prosperous years, and 50–60 per cent in off years. Aside from a high war consumption in 1918, chemical uses have taken 6–15 per cent of the total platinum in most years, with a marked recent tendency to increase, largely due to the development of platinum-clad

TABLE VI.—CONSUMPTION OF PLATINUM BY INDUSTRIES IN THE UNITED STATES
(Thousands of troy ounces)

	Jewelry		Chemical		Dental		Electrical		Others		Total
	Ounces	Per Cent	Ounces	Per Cent	Ounces	Per Cent	Ounces	Per Cent	Ounces	Per Cent	Ounces
1918...	13.5	13.4	45.4	45.0	11.5	11.4	25.0	24.8	5.4	5.4	100.8
1919...	82.4	61.6	10.8	8.1	11.0	8.3	23.9	17.7	5.6	4.2	133.7
1920...	77.3	62.8	13.2	10.7	6.4	5.2	23.0	18.7	3.1	2.5	123.1
1921...	101.3	67.0	12.3	8.1	13.2	8.7	20.6	13.6	3.8	2.5	151.1
1922...	108.5	69.2	8.8	5.6	11.7	7.4	25.0	15.9	2.8	2.1	156.8
1923...	105.7	69.4	8.6	5.7	16.3	10.7	18.6	12.2	3.2	2.1	152.4
1924...	87.2	66.4	10.5	8.0	11.9	9.1	16.6	12.7	5.0	3.8	130.4
1925...	93.3	67.9	12.6	9.2	9.3	6.8	18.8	13.7	3.4	2.4	137.3
1926...	85.9	61.9	10.3	7.4	8.5	6.1	16.8	12.1	17.4	12.5	138.8
1927...	86.0	70.1	11.0	9.0	7.5	6.1	14.9	12.1	3.2	2.6	122.6
1928...	93.5	62.4	18.5	12.4	11.0	7.3	21.3	14.2	5.4	3.6	149.7
1929...	84.0	57.8	20.3	13.9	13.1	9.0	20.7	14.3	7.2	5.0	145.3
1930...	44.8	53.6	15.0	18.0	11.8	14.1	8.5	10.2	3.3	4.0	83.5
1931...	41.3	53.6	11.5	14.9	10.1	13.2	8.2	10.7	5.9	7.7	77.0
1932...	33.4	61.2	5.2	9.5	8.7	15.9	3.5	6.3	3.9	7.1	54.6
1933...	41.3	54.2	14.1	18.5	11.1	14.6	3.4	4.5	6.3	8.2	76.2
1934...	33.0	53.9	14.7	24.0	6.8	11.1	3.6	5.9	3.1	5.1	61.1
1935...	56.2	64.0	13.4	15.3	9.7	11.1	5.9	6.7	2.5	2.9	87.7
1936...	50.9	45.3	21.0	18.7	14.5	12.9	8.8	7.8	16.3	14.5	112.4
1937...	49.8	51.9	18.3	19.1	11.1	11.6	9.5	9.9	7.2	7.5	96.0
Total..	1369.1	59.4	295.4	12.9	215.2	9.4	296.6	12.9	113.0	4.5	2290.5

equipment. Dental uses show much less variation in weight than other lines of consumption, which throws an abnormal emphasis on the percentage variations, making it appear, curiously enough, that dental uses are low in prosperous times and high in adverse times, since the percentage of the total was 6–9 per cent in 1924–1929, while since 1930 it has been 11–16 per cent. In electrical uses there has been a marked and quite consistent tendency to decline, as substitutes have been developed for so many of the former uses for platinum in the electrical industry.

PRICES

There is no basic world market for platinum, as there is for tin and some other metals. There are three leading market centers, which are determined by the location of the centers of refining and consumption; London handles the output of the British refiners of Canadian and South African metal; the sales agency of the Russian state monopoly was for some time in

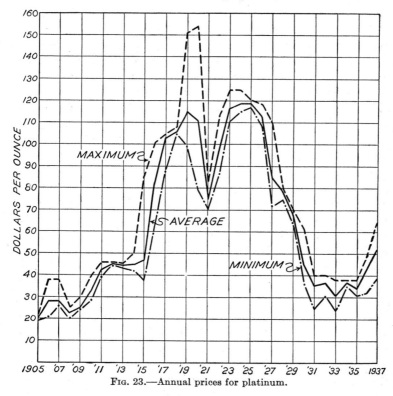

Fig. 23.—Annual prices for platinum.

Berlin, but this has apparently been discontinued; and domestic sales are based on the New York quotations. Formerly Paris was also a market center, much of the Russian output being handled in France and Germany, but after the establishment of the Russian selling agency in Berlin, the Paris market became a subordinate one. Prices in all of these centers are usually closely linked together, although occasionally one market or another breaks away from the established prices, in an attempt to push sales ahead of other markets.

In the marketing of platinum we have at various times had to consider a factor that is not encountered in connection with any of the other strategic metals, except recently with tin, namely an international syndicate to control marketing and maintain prices. In several other strategic industries price control has been maintained to some extent, but more through closer control of production than of the marketing itself, this being made possible through a closely localized production. In the case of nickel, production is largely in the hands of a single producer; natural nitrates and iodine are controlled by a closely organized group of producers in a single country; for several years past the production of tin has been limited by an international agreement, legalized by the governments of the chief producing countries, but the control in the case of platinum has been maintained at the marketing end, rather than at the producing end, by agreement between the sellers and producers in the countries concerned. For a number of years the market was controlled by a British firm, which at the time was the leading refiner, but in the early years of the present century an international syndicate was formed, which included the leading refiners in the various countries. As is shown by the accompanying price graph, Fig. 23, this syndicate was able to maintain a fairly stable market, up to the time of its disruption by the World War. Soon after the close of the war another syndicate was organized, and operated until 1927.

The method of operation of these syndicates was to allot production quotas to the leading producers, and to purchase these quotas at an agreed price, on condition that the producers sold no metal to outside buyers. In 1927 a disagreement between the syndicate and the Soviet authorities over the size of the Russian quota resulted in the withholding of the Russian output, and the establishment of a separate selling agency for Russian platinum in Berlin, in competition with the syndicate. Prices were already being forced slowly downward by increasing outputs, and this move broke the price from $108 to $72 in three months.

Increasing outputs among the old producers and new production in South Africa and Canada made it highly desirable that a new agreement be made, including these new producers, and bringing the Russian output back under control, and after long negotiation a new syndicate was formed in 1931, but only after prices had dropped to about one-third of those preceding the Russian secession from the agreement. For reasons which have not been made public, this latest syndicate remained in active control of the market for only a short time, but nevertheless stable market conditions have been maintained, although at prices not seen in the industry since 1910.

Figure 23 shows the maximum and minimum monthly averages and the annual averages of the New York price since 1905, the years preceding 1913 being included to complete the picture of the rise in the price of platinum from the level of gold, which began in 1905. The price increase inaugurated by the Russian-

TABLE VII.—PLATINUM PRICES IN THE UNITED STATES
(Dollars per troy ounce)

	Average Quoted Price	Commodity Index	Platinum Index Price
1913	$ 44.88	100.0	$44.88
1914	45.14	97.6	46.24
1915	47.13	99.6	47.31
1916	83.40	122.5	68.08
1917	102.82	168.3	61.12
1918	105.95	188.1	56.34
1919	114.61	198.6	57.72
1920	110.90	221.2	50.11
1921	75.03	139.8	53.68
1922	97.62	138.5	70.46
1923	116.54	144.1	80.90
1924	118.82	140.5	84.59
1925	119.09	148.3	80.30
1926	113.27	143.3	79.04
1927	84.64	136.7	61.91
1928	78.58	138.5	56.73
1929	67.66	136.5	49.56
1930	45.36	123.8	36.63
1931	35.67	104.6	34.08
1932	36.46	92.8	39.29
1933	30.99	94.4	32.83
1934	36.47	107.3	33.98
1935	34.15	114.6	32.67
1936	42.93	115.8	37.06
1937	51.77	123.6	41.88

Japanese war in 1904–1905 was halted by reduced demand resulting from the financial panic of 1907, but another more gradual increase followed almost immediately, which was stabilized during 1911–1915. During and immediately after the World War prices went to unheard-of levels and although there was a drop during the post-war depression, recovery was prompt, with steady increases in price up to the latter half of 1925. For 10 years there was an almost continuous series of falling prices, resulting from over-production, dissension within the industry, and general industrial depression. Only since late in 1933 has there been any material improvement in prices. The annual averages are shown in Table VII, along with the platinum index prices derived from them by the use of the corresponding commodity index.

Although at the time, it was thought that the war period prices were high, the averages for several later years were higher than the war years, though the maximum was not so great. In the platinum index price, many of the seemingly high prices are brought down to much lower levels, and from 1922 to 1926 the index price was higher than any during the war years. The recent industrial depression is seen to have had little effect on the index price, and all of the heavy drop since the peak of 1924 has been due to increasing production and the breakdown of the former price control agencies in the industry.

TARIFF

There has never been any tariff duty imposed on platinum, either in crude form, or as unmanufactured refined metal. Various forms of manufactured platinum have been subject to duty in the different tariff acts, and there has been a gradual paring down of forms permitted duty-free entry with each of the recent revisions of the tariff rates. The Underwood tariff, in effect during 1913–1922, provided the following rates:

Ores of Platinum, Free.

Platinum, unmanufactured, or in ingots, bars, plates, sheets, wire, sponge or scrap, and vases, retorts, and other apparatus, vessels, and parts thereof composed of platinum, for chemical purposes, Free.

Articles or wares not specially provided for, composed wholly or in part of platinum, and whether partly or wholly manufactured, 50 per cent *ad valorem.*

The preceding tariff acts, although worded slightly differently, provided substantially the same conditions, except that the tariff rate was slightly lower on manufactures—45 per cent in the acts of 1883 and 1890, 35 per cent in 1894, and 45 per cent in 1897 and 1909. The Fordney-McCumber Tariff, in effect in 1922–1930, and the Smoot-Hawley Tariff, from 1930 to date, restricted free entry to platinum, unmanufactured or in ingots, bars, sheets or plates not less than one-eighth inch in thickness, and to sponge and scrap. This threw all types of manufactured material into the dutiable list, the rate being increased to 60 per cent by the former act, and to 65 per cent by the latter, while platinum jewelry and ornamental goods were increased to 80 per cent.

POLITICAL AND COMMERCIAL CONTROL

The report on political and commercial control of minerals by the Mineral Inquiry, organized by the American Institute of Mining and Metallurgical Engineers, did not cover platinum, but a brief summary of the situation may be made from such information as is available.

The ownership and operation of the Russian deposits is a state monopoly, and the bulk of the output is refined in the two refineries operated by the Soviet precious metals syndicate.

About half or more of the Colombian output is made by a company owned and controlled in the United States; the control of the remainder is unknown. Practically the entire Colombian output is exported to the United States for refining.

The bulk of the Canadian output is made by the International Nickel Company, owned and controlled in the United States. The platinum output of the company goes to its plant at Acton, England, for refining, in accordance with the British policy of smelting ores of British origin in British territory. A minor producer, Falconbridge Nickel Mines, is a Canadian company, but while the preliminary smelting of the ore is done in Canada, the matte produced is shipped to Norway, where it is reduced and refined in a plant owned and operated by the same company. In 1935 this company established its own plant for the separation and refining of the precious metal slimes from the nickel refinery.

The South African output is, so far as is known, controlled by local and British capital, and the output goes to England for refining.

GENERAL REVIEW OF THE DOMESTIC SITUATION

The domestic output of platinum has never been large, and although the Alaskan production has increased considerably during the past few years, there is no prospect that it will ever supply more than a fraction of the demand, and dependence must still be placed on foreign sources. As it turned out, the only opportunity that we have had to improve the accessibility of the supply was wrecked several years before it was recognized as a material factor in the situation, by the imposition of political control from within the British Empire, which resulted in the transfer of nickel smelting from New Jersey to Canada, and the refining of the resulting platinum recoveries in England. Had it not been for this interference of political control, as dictated by nationalistic interests, it is probable that the smelting of the nickel would have continued in New Jersey, and the resulting platinum recovery, which has now reached a point sufficient to supply the entire United States demand, would have greatly simplified the problems of supply.

From an ordinary industrial standpoint, the platinum situation is not particularly difficult, as such of the necessary supply is not available from Colombia, is readily obtainable from England. Although the intervening distances are considerable, the transportation problem is simplified by the small bulk of the product, so that cargo space is not a consideration; the amounts of platinum ordinarily imported into the United States in the course of a year would, exclusive of packing, occupy no more space than one or two tons of manganese ore. During normal times there is no lack of accessibility, and with the increases in output that have developed during recent years there is no prospect of scarcity of supply.

From a military standpoint, the strategic character of platinum has undergone considerable change since the war period. During the World War operations were handicapped by extreme scarcity, and later, when the official War Department list of strategic materials was compiled, platinum was well toward the top of the list. Since then conditions have changed so radically that in 1936 platinum was transferred from the strategic to the critical list. While this is largely true for emergency demands, it does not in the least affect the situation from a general industrial standpoint.

Platinum is the only metal of which the United States holds a war reserve stock to cover military requirements. Substitutes have been developed for many former uses, and in case of necessity the substitution program could be pushed still farther. Although byproduct recovery from copper refining is now at a low level, this would automatically increase with an emergency demand for copper, and placer outputs have expanded considerably during recent years. Under emergency demand and higher prices, secondary recovery might be expected to increase by about one-half over recent figures, if we may judge from World War conditions. On the basis of present conditions, a two-year emergency supply would be made up about as follows, assuming complete cessation of imports, excepting those en route at the outbreak of the emergency.

	Ounces
War reserve stock	27,000
Refiners' stocks[1]	60,000
Two years' domestic output[2]	65,000
Two years' secondary recovery[3]	110,000
En route[4]	12,000
	274,000

[1] Figures for 1937.
[2] Based on estimated 1938 output.
[3] Secondary recovery in the four years 1917–1920 was 205,000 ounces.
[4] One-twelfth of 1937 imports.

This estimate gives us an available supply of about 137,000 ounces per year, which would undoubtedly be increased by current imports, as it is hardly likely that conditions would be such as would prevent all imports. The supply will also be increased somewhat by unreported stocks in the hands of producers and consumers. A supply of even 200,000 ounces is sufficient for a two-year program of essential uses, as the deficit between this and the usual industrial consumption could easily be covered by restriction of the amounts to be used in jewelry, and, if necessary, by extended substitution in other lines; and in case extreme measures were required, there is an enormous stock of platinum in jewelry and other ornamental objects which could be drawn on. Thus it is seen that even under extreme conditions, the situation is not serious, and under anything less than complete isolation from all sources of supply, an emergency could be handled without serious complications; in fact, the difficulties to be overcome would probably be considerably less than were encountered during the World War.

Extreme conditions are to be anticipated only in the unlikely event of a war in which we find ourselves opposed to the British Empire. No serious difficulty is likely with England neutral, and with England as an ally the military program would take precedence over ordinary commercial considerations, and any needed supplies of platinum could be diverted from Canadian sources to the United States refiners, instead of to the British refiners, as is now the regular procedure.

CONCLUSION

As has been shown in the preceding section, although platinum is industrially a metal for which there is a pronounced domestic deficiency, which would ordinarily cause it to be classed as strategic, this classification now holds only from an industrial standpoint; the trend of developments during the past few years have combined in such a way as to make it unlikely that platinum need any longer be considered as a strategic metal from a purely military standpoint, hence the transfer from the strategic to the critical list in 1936. The reasons for this change center around a number of different factors, such as changing uses, the extensive development of substitutes, the discovery of new sources of supply, and last, but not least, the existence of a war reserve stock, held over from the World War, sufficient to cover the more pressing military needs for any ordinary munitions program. The situation might be made even more favorable, however, by increasing the size of the reserve stock.

CHAPTER XII

MICA

The non-metallic group of strategic minerals stands out from the other two groups (ferro-alloy and non-ferrous), not only from the fact that they are non-metallic minerals while all of the others are metallic, but also because each of the three members of the group are marked by special conditions of occurrence, properties, or uses. In this respect, mica is more exceptional than the other two members of the group, nitrogen and iodine. Mica is a mineral used exclusively in its original form, and not for the extraction of a metal or for conversion into some other form of compound. Among the eight members of the metallic groups, only chromium is used to any appreciable degree in mineral form. Strictly speaking, "mica" is not the name of a mineral, but of a group of nearly a dozen minerals, all of the same general type, but only two of these are of any great commercial importance. The outstanding feature from a strategic standpoint is that, while low grade micas are abundant and widely distributed, high grade micas are of extremely limited occurrence, and since most of the strategic uses require the high grade types, the strategic position of mica in the United States is pronounced.

Before entering into the discussion of the purely strategic phases of the mica situation, it is necessary to state briefly the characteristics of the different types of mica, in order to differentiate between the non-strategic low grade types and the highly strategic high grade micas. Mineralogically, "mica" is the name applied to a group of complex silicate minerals which are characterized by their property of crystallizing with such pronounced cleavage planes that the mineral may be readily split up into thin sheets, giving a product that is transparent, almost colorless in the best grades, flexible, tough, highly resistant to temperature and atmospheric and chemical corrosion, and a good non-conductor of heat and electricity. Roughly speaking, commercial mica may be classed in four groups:

"Waste" or "scrap" is a term which covers all material so imperfect in formation or so small in size as to render it useless for any purpose other than the production of ground mica; this covers both mine scrap and shop scrap. Mine scrap consists of the imperfect, discolored and small size material sorted from the higher grade products at the mine. Shop scrap is composed of the trimmings from high grade material in the course of converting the rough sheets into the desired shape or size for any particular use, and hence is of considerably better quality than mine scrap, except in size. Since 1930, fine mica recovered from clay washing has been included in the statistics of waste and scrap production, accounting for 1000–2000 tons annually; and since 1935, mica recovered (in ground form) from mica schists has been included. These two sources have more than trebled the tonnage of scrap produced in recent years, but neither one has the slightest connection with the production of sheet mica.

"Splittings" are an intermediate size, at least $\frac{3}{4}$ square inch in area and 0.001–0.0012 inch in thickness. These are mainly split from material too small to make the smallest standard sheet, or from waste and scrap, although small amounts are obtained in the course of the removal of flaws from larger sheets. They are used in built-up material, using a cement to hold the splittings together, thus making it possible to build up sheets of any desired size or thickness, as well as a wide variety of special shapes. The terms films and splittings are sometimes used synonymously, but strictly, there is a clear difference. As used in India, the home of the industry, sheets of mica not over 0.001 inch in thickness are called splittings; between 0.001 and 0.009 inch in thickness they are called films; and over 0.01 inch in thickness, blocks or thick sheet.

"Punch" is a classification covering the smallest size of sheet material, large enough to punch into washers and other small shapes, but too small for the smallest standard sheet size.

"Sheet" covers a range of sizes from $1\frac{1}{2}$ by 2 inches up to 8 by 10 inches. The rough sheets are sized according to the largest standard rectangle that can be cut from them, and due to the irregular shape of the sheets as split from the blocks, the average area of the rough sheet must be considerably greater than that of the cut sheet.

The wide range of variation in these grades and sizes is best illustrated by the range of prices of the products. Scrap mica varies widely in price, depending on the variety, quality, and market conditions, but the general average is in the neighborhood of 1 cent per pound, with some types as low as \$7 per ton and others as high as \$25. Punch mica may run as low as 2–3 cents per pound or as high as 10–15 cents. Sheet mica prices vary even more widely, increasing rapidly from 10–35 cents per pound for $1\frac{1}{2}$ by 2 inches, up to as high as \$3–\$8 per pound for 8 by 10 inch sheets. It is solely with sheet mica that we are here concerned. The term "sheet mica" correctly includes splittings, the thinnest form. These are all imported, India furnishing about 93 per cent of the world's supply, Madagascar 5 or 6, and Canada and small remainder. India's supply is all muscovite, while Madagascar and Canada furnish phlogopite only. The United States imports its entire requirements of splittings. This is for two reasons: (1) The country has never given any evidence that the necessary tonnage of good quality, well-splitting sheet mica could be produced; only a little of the necessary grade and quality could be recovered from our scrap. (2) Even supposing that five times our hitherto maximum output of sheet could be produced, steadily and unfailingly, the prohibitive cost of splitting with workers receiving 40 cents an hour and working only 40 hours a week, as against the 1 cent an hour for a 75 hour week which prevails in India and Madagascar, is evident.

REQUIREMENTS

The world requirements for sheet mica and splittings, as measured by production since 1913, have varied between a minimum of 5,600,000 pounds in 1921 and a maximum of 38,300,000 pounds in 1935, with an average of 12,720,000 pounds, only 10 per cent of which was supplied by the United States. The war period output was slightly in excess of 10,000,000 pounds, a figure which was considerably augmented immediately after the post-war depression, with a peak of 17,400,000 pounds in 1929; the depression minimum in 1932 was 6,600,000 pounds, considerably better than the post-war low. By 1935 production rose to a new high record of 19,300,000 pounds, due largely to heavy increases in India and Madagascar, and by 1937 this figure had almost been doubled; these high figures are open to some doubt, however, as it appears that the recent Indian exports include undeterminate amounts of scrap mica. Of these totals, by far the largest proportion (about 80 per cent) is splittings.

USES

Its unique combination of physical properties make mica so exceptionally well adapted for certain uses that it is practically indispensable, while for others it is employed simply because it is at the same time the best and cheapest available material, although others may be substituted. The chief uses for mica center around its high insulating and dielectric properties, inertness to high temperatures, low heat conductivity, flexibility, cleavage toughness, and transparency. While there are some places where it is used for its mechanical properties alone, probably 90 per cent of the modern uses of sheet and punch mica are in the electrical industry; as an insulator against high voltages, especially at high temperatures, there has been no known substitute for mica, but the new bentonite films discussed under *Substitutes* promise relief in this direction.

The purely mechanical uses include lamp chimneys and shades, windows or peep-holes in ovens, furnaces, stoves and stereopticons, eye protectors, gas masks, and other similar uses where transparency is required in combination with resistance to heat and shock. Mica diaphragms have been used in phonograph reproducers and telephone headsets, but these are now usually of metal. The major electrical uses require flat insulation in a wide variety of shapes and sizes, both as straight insulation, such as separators for commutator bars, discs, washers, and bushings, and as a form on which to wind heating elements of irons, toasters, and numerous other items of domestic and industrial heating equipment. The small shapes are made from punch mica, and the larger ones from sheet. Formed insulation may be made from sheets if the shape is not too large or complicated, and the cost is justified, but a large proportion of the special shapes, such as plates, tubes, rods, cones, and large bushings, are formed by cementing splittings together under pressure, making a product known as micanite; originally shellac was used as a bond, but later this has been largely replaced by special cements of a more permanent character. In this way all sorts of complicated shapes may be formed, with results not greatly inferior to sheet mica, and at a much reduced cost. Another important electrical use of mica, of a slightly different character, is as a separator between the leaves of an electrical condenser; this requires an exceptionally high quality of mica, absolutely without flaws, but makes a condenser with better characteristics than any other dielectric. The development of the radio and of the internal combustion engine for the automobile and airplane have made an enormous increase in the demand for condensers. High grade mica is also used as a support for the elements in certain types of radio tubes.

Military Uses.—There are no specific military uses for mica, but war demand would greatly increase the ordinary electrical uses; many military requirements are identical with specific industrial requirements, as for example, radio sending and receiving sets, airplane spark plugs, motors and generators; and the Army and Navy, particularly the Navy, carry large stocks of mica of both the natural sheet and the micanite type, in addition to hundreds of cut-to-shape parts, all furnished to them under very strict service specifications.

SUBSTITUTES

For many of the uses of mica, in which high dielectric strength is required, particularly under high temperatures, there is no known substitute. In some cases, where the requirements are not so strenuous, sheet mica has been replaced by micanite, and in case of necessity still further substitution could be made in this direction, but only at an increased cost if Oriental splittings were not available, and domestic splittings had to be provided. Other uses are of a type that could be classed as non-essential in a time of emergency demand, and some saving could be made by substituting porcelain or some type of synthetic insulation for many of the mechanical and electrical uses, and by using waxed paper in condensers where the requirements would permit. It is an unfortunate fact, however, that the bulk of the possibilities for the substitution of other products for mica lies in the field of low grade mica, of which there is a plentiful supply, rather than in the uses of sheet mica, with its restricted possibilities for domestic production.

Within the past year there has been developed a proposed substitute for mica which gives promise of a substantial usefulness, but the product is still too new to permit any definite evaluation of the extent to which it may serve to reduce the demand for mica by replacing it in any of its various uses. This product is a tough, flexible film, formed by drying thin layers of a colloidal suspension of bentonite in water; after heating under pressure, these films are reported to have an electrical resistance comparable with mica. Films of various thickness can be produced, and if a laminated product is desired, it may be made by combining several thinner films. Should further development of this product demonstrate it to be a suitable substitute for mica for electrical uses, many of the problems connected with the strategic position of mica will be solved.

ORES

Chemically, the micas are highly complex silicates of aluminum and one or more other bases, the specific characteristics of the mineral being determined by the variable second base metal in the composition. The leading mica of commerce is the potash mica, muscovite, or white mica, while the second in importance is the magnesium mica, phlogopite, or amber mica. These two cover the bulk of the commercial mica mined, although small amounts of other varieties are sometimes used. Muscovite occurs associated with granite pegmatites, and phlogopite with the type of basic magnesian rocks known as pyroxenites. Muscovite is found in a number of localities, but phlogopite comes almost entirely from Canada and Madagascar.

It is a characteristic of mica to occur in irregular, pockety bodies, the mining of which involves the removal of a large amount of barren rock. In general, the "ore" carries not over 10 per cent of mica, of which 7 per cent is suitable only for scrap, 2 per cent is of punch size, and 1 per cent or less is of sheet size, with the smaller sheet sizes in heavy predominance. This is the explanation of the greater supplies of small sizes, and the scarcity of the larger sheet sizes.

Preparation.—After a preliminary sorting at the mine, discarding all material unsuitable for the production of sheets, the rough mica goes to the cobbing shed, where the crystals or "books" are cleaned of adhering rock and split into sheets.

Very little mica is sold in the run-of-mine condition. The books are first split into slabs about ¼ inch thick (rifting), for convenience in handling, and after hammering the edges to loosen the laminae, the splitting knife is used to separate sheets about ¹⁄₁₆ inch in thickness, discarding all faulty material. Some producers sell these split sheets, while others proceed further with the preparation. The next step is the trimming of the sheets, for the removal of all imperfections from the edges of the sheets. If this is done simply by breaking away the imperfect edges with the fingers, the product is said to be "thumb trimmed"; when the trimming is done by power driven knives or shears, the result is "knife trimmed" sheets; "sickle trimmed" sheets have had the imperfect edges removed by hand, with a knife or sickle. Thumb trimmed and sickle trimmed sheets have approximately the same shape as the original sheet, since only the edges have been removed; thumb trimming leaves a rough, ragged edge, while sickle trimming leaves a smooth cut edge, with a bevel, since the sheet can be cut readily only when the knife is held at an angle. Knife trimmed sheet differs in two ways; the edge produced by the power knife or shears is square, instead of beveled, and the original irregular outline of the sheet has been replaced by the straight shear cuts, giving a more or less regular polygon. The chief object of the trimming is to facilitate the further splitting, as well as to remove the imperfections. The trimmed sheets are known as "uncut" or "unmanufactured" sheet mica, and are mostly sold in this form, although some producers carry the operations through the final stage of cutting the sheet to standard market sizes and shapes, giving what is known as "cut" sheet.

All of the various stages in the preparation of sheet mica are carried on almost entirely by hand labor, since none of the operations are of such a purely mechanical character that they can dispense with human skill and judgment. It is only in the making of splittings that there seems to be much opportunity for the mechanization of the process. This is an important phase of the industry, in view of the increasing importance of built-up mica products, for without machine production of splittings the low cost of Oriental labor will continue to control the production. Many attempts have been made to build machines that would automatically produce splittings of a specified thickness, but without any success thus far. Over 80 per cent of the mica imports of the past 15 years have been splittings, partly for lack of raw material at home, but chiefly because of the labor cost in making the splittings. If this difficulty could be solved by machine splitting, it would open up a new field in the domestic industry, that would be of marked strategic impórtance aside from its purely industrial aspects, although the raw material available would not suffice to meet more than a fraction the demand.

Grading and Classifying.[1]—As produced in the United States, mica is classified under three heads as to quality: clear, slightly stained or spotted, and heavily stained or spotted. The Indian grading covers clear, slightly stained, fair stained, good stained, stained, and black spotted, with sometimes other designations. While these classes serve a definite useful purpose, they are unsatisfactory, in that there is no definite boundary line between them, as there is between sizes, and improper classification may easily result.

The methods of grading the sheets for size differs in each of the leading producing districts. The basis of the grades most used are shown in Table A. The main difference in the various methods of grading is that in the United States and Canada the sheets are sized according to the largest standard rectangle that can be cut from them, while in other countries they are graded according to the area of the sheet, in square inches in India, and in square centimeters in countries using the metric system of measurement. In the table, the metric sizes are converted to the corresponding area in square inches, to facilitate comparison. When the foreign sizes vary materially from the next lower standard United States size, it is liable to cause some loss in the use of imported sheet, particularly since intermediate dimensions are not recognized in the United States standards, and a sheet measuring $2\frac{1}{2}$ by $3\frac{1}{2}$ inches would be classed as 2 by 3.

It should also be noted that the standard sizes are used not only for the sheets that are actually cut to these specified sizes, but also to designate trimmed sheets suitable for cutting to these sizes, and in this connection attention is called to the fact that due to the irregular shapes and sizes of the trimmed sheets,

---

[1] In the mica trade, grading refers to the sizing of the material, and not to the quality.

they must have a considerably greater area than that of the cut size. Figures given in a later table indicate that in average United States practice, the waste in cutting is about two-thirds, since a trimmed sheet suitable for a cut sheet $1\frac{1}{2}$ by 2 would probably have to measure more nearly 3 by 4. This waste is available for the production of ground mica, and under pressure might supply some material suitable for punch mica and splittings.

Sheet mica is sold by the pound, and the price increases rapidly with the increasing size and quality of the sheet; further details of these variations will be given later in the discussion of prices.

TABLE A.—STANDARD SIZES OF SHEET MICA IN VARIOUS COUNTRIES

Bihar		Madras		United States	Canada	Madagascar		Argentina	
Grade	Sq. In.	Grade	Sq. In.	Inches	Inches	Grade	Sq. In.	Grade	Sq. In.
....	......	IX	96–112	....	......	......	......	......	......
Extra Extra Specials.....	80 up	VIII	80–96	8 by 10	......	......	......	......	......
Extra Specials.	60–80	VII	64–80	....	......	......	......	......	......
Specials.....	48–60	VI	48–64	6 by 8	......	......	......	......	......
A-1............	36–48	V	32–48	6 by 6	5 by 8	......	......	A	35–47
No. 1.........	24–36			4 by 6	4 by 6	1	Over 24	1	24–34
No. 2.........	15–24	IV	16–32	3 by 5	3 by 5	......	......	2	14–23
No. 3.........	10–15	III	8–16	3 by 4	......	2	6–24	3	10–13
No. 4.........	6–10	II	4–8	3 by 3	2 by 4	......	......	4	6– 9
No. 5.........	3–6			2 by 3	2 by 3	3	1–6	5	3½– 5
No. 5½.......	2½–3	I	Under 4	2 by 2	1 by 3	......	......	......	......
No. 6.........	1–2½			1½ by 2	1 by 2	......	......	......	......
No. 7.........	Under 1			....	1 by 1	4	Scrap	......	......

Secondary Recovery.—While there is no organized secondary recovery of mica, scrap produced in trimming sheets, is available for punch mica, splittings, and ground mica.

Forms in Which Mica Appears on the Market.—Mica comes on the market as uncut and cut sheet of various classes, thicknesses and sizes, including punch and splittings, as well as in various forms of built-up material made from splittings.

ORE RESERVES

The character of the mineralogical occurrence of mica is such that little is or can be known of the extent of the deposits being worked; hence there is almost no specific information as to reserves. It has been estimated that micas constitute 4 per cent of the igneous rocks of the world, which would make the total tonnage a figure of almost astronomical proportions, but unfortunately most of this is in a form not recoverable on a commercial scale, and, even if it were recoverable, the product would be suitable only for ground mica, of which there is already a plentiful supply. Growth of the mica crystals to a size suitable for the production of commercial sheet sizes is comparatively rare.

Mica deposits are worked in a hand-to-hand fashion, with almost no information as to the amount of material at hand in the deposit, other than what can be judged from the surface or the point of operation. Many deposits are comparatively small in size, are soon worked out, and operations are then transferred to another deposit. On the other hand, some deposits have been worked continuously for many years and may last for many more, but none have the life characteristics that are expected in a typical metal deposit.

WORLD OUTPUT AND SUPPLY

Production figures for mica from many producing countries are more or less incomplete and inaccurate; in several cases only total output is recorded, and only estimates are available as to the proportion of the total that is sheet mica; in others figures that purport to be for sheet may include small amounts of scrap; a third uncertainty is incorporated in the figures by the fact that mica is sold by the original producer in all stages of preparation. One sells mine-run material, and reports the tonnage. A second sells untrimmed sheets, and a third trimmed sheets, the outputs of which are reported as such. A fourth sells cut sheets, the weight of which is only a fraction of that of the uncut form, the remainder going into scrap. For a true picture of the mica output, reports should all be on the same basis, for as it is now the results lose a considerable degree of their accuracy and usefulness, due to their composite form. For these reasons the production table can not be claimed to have the accuracy that might be desired, but it is the best summation of world production that can be compiled under the circumstances.

Out of a total output since 1913, varying from as low as 4,600,000 to as high as 38,300,000 pounds, and averaging about half way between these extremes, 75 per cent has come from India; the addition of the United States, Canada, and Madagascar increases the proportion to 93 per cent; Rhodesia, Argentina and Brazil have furnished over 4 per cent, with the remaining 2.4 per cent scattered among a number of minor producers.

The last four producers named have entered the list with material outputs only since the war period. On the other hand, during the same time, Canada has declined heavily, and is now producing only a fraction of its former output.

TABLE I.—WORLD PRODUCTION OF SHEET MICA[1]
(Thousands of pounds)

	India[2]	United States	Cana-da[1]	Mada-gascar[2]	Argen-tina	Bra-zil	Rho-desia	Others[3]	Total
1913	6,998	1,701	1,100	13	13	22	......	280	10,100
1914	4,536	557	600	6	......	33	......	130	5,900
1915	3,404	554	400	2	......	113	......	90	4,600
1916	6,126	866	1,200	6	13	119	......	80	8,400
1917	7,006	1,277	1,200	26	139	214	......	190	10,050
1918	6,714	1,644	750	8	378	325	......	125	9,950
1919	6,792	1,546	1,294	40	320	318	11	570	10,900
1920	7,983	1,683	1,540	110	603	150	197	500	12,800
1921	3,465	742	398	340	325	102	170	30	5,600
1922	6,702	1,078	395	204	141	148	148	70	8,900
1923	9,330	2,063	910	363	224	124	181	225	13,400
1924	7,850	1,461	1,363	630	264	174	300	325	12,400
1925	11,166	1,794	960	631	262	143	293	760	16,000
1926	10,074	2,172	613	728	186	115	374	480	14,700
1927	8,678	1,512	781	756	168	86	428	360	12,800
1928	10,694	1,682	116	888	265	97	423	350	14,500
1929	13,002	2,035	120	838	262	99	386	450	17,200
1930	9,284	1,465	132	758	220	115	370	480	12,850
1931	5,934	962	87	518	112	119	150	380	8,200
1932	5,266	339	5	309	121	93	29	400	6,600
1933	6,344	365	135	382	165	51	13	350	7,800
1934	10,454	584	229	638	386	132	7	320	12,700
1935	15,888	937	186	1,155	496	242	13	420	19,300
1936	19,938	1,319	184	904	462	522	27	110	23,400
1937	33,288	1,695	546	1,346	?	728	45	150	38,300
Totals	236,916	32,033	15,244	11,575	6,025	4,384	3,565	7,625	317,400
Per cent	74.6	10.1	4.8	3.6	1.9	1.4	1.1	2.4	100.0

[1] Figures in round numbers are estimated. Figures from some countries are incomplete, and those from others include some scrap. [2] Exports; post-depression figures apparently include some scrap mica. [3] Does not include U. S. S. R. (Russia) since 1927, the figures being incomplete, with no data as to the proportion of sheet in the totals.

Table I shows the annual outputs since 1913 for all countries that have contributed appreciable amounts to the total, the annual totals, the period totals for each country, and the percentage of the grand total that has been supplied by each country. One of the interesting facts shown in that the 1935 total output was a new high record, which was doubled by 1937, but it must be remembered that the figures for India during recent years have included scrap mica amounting to possibly one-quarter or more of the total output reported. The Rhodesian output also includes more scrap than sheet. The accompanying world production graph, Fig. 24, shows the trend of world production,

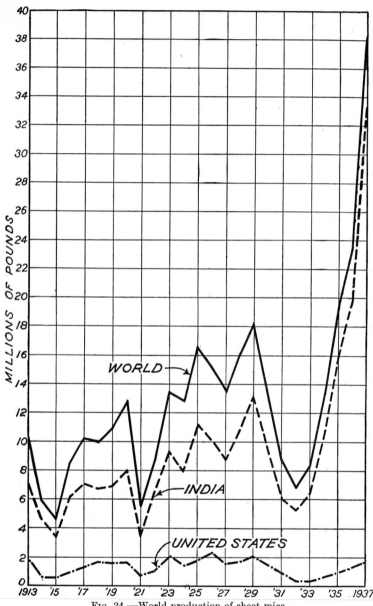

FIG. 24.—World production of sheet mica.

as well as that of the two major producers, India and the United States.

Of the countries producing sheet mica, only the United States and Canada have an appreciable domestic consumption; all others export practically the entire output, with the possible exception of Russia, where adequate data are lacking on both the production and the exports.

Argentina.—There are numerous deposits of mica known in the provinces of San Luis, Cordoba, San Juan, Salta, and Catamarca, but in spite of the many occurrences, mining has been done only on a small scale, chiefly in the first two localities.

Canada.—The production of phlogopite, or amber mica, has declined materially in Canada in recent years, chiefly due to the inability to compete with the output of low priced labor, though possibly a madagascan decline in the former insistence on amber mica for electrical insulation may have had some effect. This reduction was so intensified during the depression years that the sheet output was only 5,000 pounds in 1932, against a maximum of 1,540,000 pounds in 1920, and while post-depression recovery has raised the outputs to better than the 1929 level, they are still low in comparison with earlier years.

Production is fairly evenly divided between the provinces of Quebec and Ontario. Before the marked decline that has been under way since 1927, about 13 per cent of the total output was sheet mica, a somewhat better figure than had been maintained in the United States, but since the decline, the proportion of sheet has decreased by about one-half.

From records covering several years at one of the leading Canadian mines, about 35 per cent of the product was marketable sheet, all phlogopite, distributed by sizes as follows:

Sizes	Per Cent
1 by 1 inch	44
1 by 2 inches	26
1 by 3 inches	15
2 by 3 inches	9
2 by 4 inches	4
Larger	2

These figures run somewhat lower than those of the United States for the smaller and larger sizes, and somewhat better for the intermediate sizes.

The Lacey mine is probably the largest body of phlogopite yet discovered, but the cost of producing sheet, and splitting it, is too high to compete with the Madagascan splittings, though amber mica is much more easily split than white mica. Price aside, phlogopite would probably be preferred to muscovite for nearly all electrical insulation uses, and for this reason Canadian deposits (owned largely by United States nationals), form a valuable back log to depend upon in any emergency that would make price relatively unimportant. Amber mica can not be used for condensers, however, and probably not in radio tubes, the power loss being usually over 1 per cent, as against the maximum permissible of 0.04 per cent.

India.—India has long been a heavy producer of mica, about 80 per cent of which comes from the state of Bihar, and the remainder from Madras, except for a few tons annually from Rajputana. Practically the entire output is exported, as the domestic consumption is estimated at not more than 1–2 per cent of the production. During recent years these exports have been distributed to the following consumer countries: 38 per cent to the United States, 36 per cent to the United Kingdom (much of which is re-exported to United States and Germany), 9 per cent to Germany, 4 per cent to France, and 13 per cent to other countries; of the total, 18 per cent was sheet, locally known as block mica, and 82 per cent splittings.

There are no accurate statistics of mine production in India, as there is evidence of extensive theft from the mines, and the stolen material does not appear in the official production reports; also, some small producers in remote districts fail to report their product. For example, the official production reported for the period 1919–1935 was 794,000 cwt. (of 112 pounds), but for the same period exports were 1,317,000 cwt. There is a small amount of mica imported into India, for splitting and re-export, but as this has seldom reached as much as 5 per cent of the total exports, has averaged about 2 per cent, and during recent years has dwindled to well under 1 per cent. There is such a heavy discrepancy between production figures and exports that the exports are usually accepted as more nearly representing the true status of the industry, rather than the obviously incomplete production figures. An average discrepancy of 42 per cent during the 'twenties had increased to 59 per cent in 1929; agitation for legislation to remedy the situation, and its final accomplishment in 1932 caused a recession of the discrepancy to about 30 per cent in 1930–1933, but lack of funds to police the affected territory properly prevented further improvement, and in 1934–1935 the discrepancy was back to its 1929 level. The proper handling of this illicit trade in mica is one of the outstanding problems in the Indian industry.

The Indian production leads in the extent to which it has recovered from the 1932 depression minimum, the 1935 output being considerably above that of 1929, which was the high point of previous production.

With a comparatively small domestic consumption, and that confined to sheet mica, there has been until recently no incentive for the production of scrap mica, as its value was too low to stand the heavy transportation costs over long distances to the consuming countries, so that the local industry was confined almost entirely to the production of sheet mica. There is a heavy loss in the preparation of the finished sheets from the rough blocks, so that large amounts of scrap are available, with little demand for it; during the past few years it is evident that some of this scrap is being exported, though it is not shown separately in the returns. Although the official Indian export statistics show only sheet and splittings, since the last change in tariff in 1930, an increasing amount of scrap mica has appeared in the Indian imports entering the United States. Out of total Indian imports of 44,846,000 pounds since 1930, some 23,225,000 pounds is listed as scrap mica; the Indian exports to the United States for the same period was 50,912,000 pounds, so it is apparent that this figure includes scrap, and that the Indian outputs for recent years, as shown in Table I, include material amounts of scrap, and are too high, but by just how much they are too high it is impossible to determine with any degree of accuracy. It is also difficult to see why there is such a wide discrepancy between the Indian exports and the domestic imports from India.

According to official reports from the mine operated during the war period by the Indian Government, the results from which were fairly representative of other operations, the rock mined averaged about 6 per cent of rough mica, and mining was at the rate of about 55 long tons daily, containing about 7,500 pounds of rough mica; preliminary sorting at the mine reduced this to 5,000 pounds, which went to the splitting and trimming sheds, where a loss of 80 per cent cut the yield to 1,000 pounds of unsorted sheet. Further loss in the sorting and grading amounted to about 10 per cent, one-half as waste, and the other half as films removed to take a flaw out of a sheet. Based on a representative month's output, this daily output after sorting and grading gave the yields in the different grades and sizes as shown in Table B.

TABLE B.—AVERAGE GRADING DISTRIBUTION OF INDIAN MICA

Grade	Area, Sq. In.	Pounds of Sorted Grades and Sizes				
		Clear	Slightly Stained	Fair Stained	Stained	Totals
Specials...................	36–48	....	0.05	0.1	0.05	0.2
No. 1......................	24–36	0.15	0.4	0.2	0.45	1.3
2......................	15–24	0.35	0.9	0.55	2.0	3.9
3......................	10–15	0.8	1.6	10.0	2.6	15.0
4......................	6–10	3.8	8.0	4.8	13.8	30.4
5.......................	3– 6	11.0	20.0	9.0	60.0	100.0
5½......................	2½– 3	6.4	13.0	0.2	42.0	61.6
6......................	1– 2½	16.0	47.0	2.0	655.0	720.0
Totals...................	....	38.5	90.95	26.85	775.9	932.4

This table illustrates better than almost anything else that could be given the preponderance of the low grades and small sizes produced, and justifies the relatively high prices for the better grades and sizes. A number of changes have been made in the Bihar scheme of grading. In addition to the numbered sizes listed above, A-1 covers 36–48 square inches; Special, 48–60; Extra special, 60–80; and Extra extra special, 80 and over. Formerly Number 5 was the smallest size utilized, but war demand placed Number 5½ and Number 6 on the list, and subsequent expansion in the uses for built-up micanite created a demand for Number 7, less than 1 square inch. Incidentally, with large amounts of small mica at hand, and with India the chief producer of shellac, it is difficult to understand why the country did not take a prominent place in the production of micanite in the earlier days when shellac was the only cementing agent used in its manufacture.

Madagascar.—Like Canada, Madagascar produces mainly phlogopite, or amber mica. It will be noted from Table I that the expansion of the Madagascar production coincides fairly closely with the decline in Canadian production, indicating the trend of competition between the two sources, and the gradual shift to the cheaper source of supply. Exports go chiefly to France, with small amounts to the United States and England. More Madagascan mica reaches the United States in re-exports from France than is received directly. The distribution of the exports by grades in 1926 was as follows:

Size	Per Cent
No. 1, over 155 sq. cm. (24 sq. in.)	2.4
No. 2, 40–155 sq. cm. (6–24 sq. in.)	7.8
No. 3, 6–40 sq. cm. (1–6 sq. in.)	79.2
No. 4, scrap	10.6

Russia (U. S. S. R.).—Mica occurs in numerous localities in both European and Asiatic Russia and mining was carried on on a small scale up to the past 10 years, since when it has increased to several thousand tons annually, but no information is available to give any very accurate idea as to the proportion of sheet mica in the total. An official estimate made at the time production began to expand placed the proportion of sheet at 10 per cent, but with later heavy increases in output, it is possible that this no longer applies. Since production figures are available for only a few scattered years, and since the proportion of sheet is uncertain, no attempt has been made to incorporate any figures in the world production table.

Rhodesia.—The bulk of the Rhodesian output is from the Lomagundi district of Southern Rhodesia, with a few tons a year from the Susaka district of Northern Rhodesia. Beginning in 1919, production reached a maximum of 428,000 pounds in 1926, but almost ceased during the depression period, and has not yet shown much recovery; the greater part of the output is reported to be scrap, and it is questionable as to whether the figures should have been included in the world table.

South Africa.—Except for a small expansion during the war period, mica production in South Africa was insignificant up to 1924. Deposits are known in Transvaal, Cape Province and Natal, but production has been confined to Transvaal. In a study of mica published in England in 1927 it was estimated that not more than 20 per cent of the South African production was sheet mica; however, recent more detailed official figures indicate that in 1935 and 1936 the sheet output did not exceed 1,000–2,000 pounds, so that in view of the considerable degree of uncertainty as to the South African figures, they have been omitted from the table of world production.

United States.—Although the United States holds second place as a mica producer, it is a rather poor second, with India at 75 per cent of the total, and the United States only 10 per cent. On the whole, the industry in the United States is comparatively small, even when the scrap production is included, rarely exceeding a total of 8,000 short tons, of which, as a rule some 5–15 per cent is sheet mica; but the value of even this small proportion usually exceeds that of the much larger bulk of scrap mica by a considerable margin.

The production of sheet mica in the United States began to show an upward trend in the middle 'nineties, and reached a maximum of 2,476,000 pounds in 1910, since when production has been highly variable; only three other years have shown outputs in excess of 2,000,000 pounds, and the general trend has been so low that the average since 1913 is only 1,280,000 pounds. Almost one-half of the total output has come from New Hampshire, and one-third from North Carolina, but during recent years of low production these proportions have been approximately reversed.

Figures supplied by several of the larger producers during 1916–1918, covering a total output of about 2,500,000 pounds, gave the following distribution of material reaching the trimming benches:

		Per Cent
Trimming scrap	....	65
Uncut sheet	....	9
Cut sheet	3	....
Cutting scrap	6	....
Uncut punch	....	26
Cut punch	8	....
Punch scrap	18	....

Supplementing the figures already given on the distribution of sizes in Canada and India in Tables A and B, Table C presents an official estimate of the distribution of sizes in the sheet mica output of the United States in five different years. This distribution agrees fairly well with the Indian figures, taking into consideration the differences in the standard sizes used in the two countries.

TABLE C.—AVERAGE SIZE DISTRIBUTION OF UNITED STATES MICA
(A, per cent of sheet mica; B, of total output)

	1918		1922		1923		1924		1925	
	A	B	A	B	A	B	A	B	A	B
Punch..................	62.7	16.55	85.2	6.40	86.4	9.82	80.4	10.79	77.0	6.52
Circle.................	...	...	...	...	2.3	0.26	6.1	0.82	4.6	0.39
1½ by 2...............	11.6	3.06	3.8	0.29	3.2	0.36	4.2	0.56	5.2	0.44
2 by 2...............	9.3	2.46	3.0	0.23	2.5	0.28	3.4	0.46	5.4	0.46
2 by 3...............	8.6	2.27	3.9	0.29	2.6	0.30	2.7	0.36	4.0	0.34
3 by 3...............	3.0	0.79	1.3	0.10	1.0	0.11	1.2	0.16	1.1	0.09
3 by 4...............	1.8	0.48	0.9	0.07	0.7	0.08	0.7	0.09	1.2	0.10
3 by 5 ⎫					0.9	0.10	0.8	0.11 ⎫		
4 by 6 ⎬..............	3.0	0.79	1.9	0.14	0.4	0.05	0.4	0.05 ⎬	1.5	0.13
6 by 8 ⎭							0.1	0.01 ⎭	...	...
Totals................	100.0	26.40	100.0	7.51	100.0	11.36	100.0	13.42	100.0	8.47

Other Countries.—There are a number of small producers,
with outputs ranging from 50,000 to 250,000 pounds, but production is usually quite variable; in this class we find Australia,
Brazil, Chosen, Norway, Sweden, and Tanganyika. Producers
on a smaller and still more intermittent basis include Bolivia,
Ceylon, Eritrea, Guatemala, Italy, and Mexico. Many more
countries are known to have mica resources but little is known
about their character and possibilities; among these are Austria,
Chile, China, Cochin India, Costa Rica, Ethiopia, Kenya, New-
foundland, New Zealand, Papua, Peru, Rumania, Switzerland,
and Tibet.

UNITED STATES OUTPUT AND SUPPLY

The production of sheet mica in the United States since 1913
has averaged 10 per cent of the world output, and 26 per cent of
the apparent domestic consumption, leaving 74 per cent to be
supplied by imports. Production has varied from a minimum
of 339,000 pounds in 1932 to a maximum of 2,172,000 pounds in
1926, with an average of 1,281,000 pounds; as compared with
the world output, the minimum was 5 per cent in 1932–1935, the
maximum 17 per cent in 1913, and the average 10 per cent; the
percentage of the total domestic supply produced in the United
States varied from a low of 15 per cent in 1933 to a high of 43 per
cent in 1913, and averaged 26 per cent; and the proportion of
the world output consumed in the United States has ranged from
24 per cent in 1932 to 56 in 1923, with an average of 39 per cent.

Domestic production declined heavily during the early years
of the war period, and, though it increased materially after the

TABLE II.—AVAILABLE SUPPLY OF SHEET MICA IN THE UNITED STATES
(Thousands of pounds)

	Imports for Consumption					Produc- tion	Available Supply	World Output	Per Cent Consumed in U. S.	Produced in U. S.	
	Untrim- med and Trimmed[1]	Cut[2]	Splittings[3]	Manu- factures[4]	Total Imports					Per Cent of Supply	Per Cent of World Output
1913	2,048	5	200[5]	5	2,250	1,701	3,951	10,100	39	43	17
1914	361	5	1,000	5	1,360	557	1,917	5,900	32	29	10
1915	434	5	1,200	5	1,640	554	2,194	4,600	48	25	12
1916	704	5	1,700	5	2,410	866	3,276	8,400	39	26	10
1917	656	5	2,700	5	3,360	1,277	4,637	10,050	46	28	13
1918	741	5	2,000	5	2,750	1,644	4,394	9,950	44	37	17
1919	723	5	2,100	5	2,830	1,546	4,376	10,900	40	35	14
1920	1,299	5	3,200	5	4,500	1,683	6,183	12,800	48	27	13
1921	328	5	1,320[6]	5	1,660	742	2,392	5,600	43	31	13
1922	386	46	3,000[6]	10	3,450	1,078	4,528	8,900	51	24	12
1923	1,044	80	4,302	37	5,463	2,063	7,526	13,400	56	27	15
1924	672	94	3,619	75	4,460	1,461	5,921	12,400	48	25	12
1925	605	41	3,240	65	3,951	1,794	5,745	16,000	36	31	11
1926	818	52	5,230	78	6,178	2,172	8,350	14,700	57	26	15
1927	776	66	2,588	29	3,459	1,512	4,971	12,800	39	32	12
1928	542	53	3,496	14	4,105	1,682	5,787	14,500	40	29	12
1929	1,283	119	5,053	19	6,473	2,035	8,508	17,400	49	24	12
1930	873	75	3,326	8	4,282	1,465	5,747	13,000	44	26	11
1931	420	21	1,524	4	1,969	962	2,931	8,300	35	33	12
1932	250	24	945	14	1,233	339	1,572	6,600	24	22	5
1933	616	40	1,343	18	2,017	365	2,382	7,900	30	15	5
1934	678	69	2,145	10	2,902	584	3,486	12,800	27	17	5
1935	594	94	3,041	40	3,769	937	4,706	19,300	24	20	5
1936	860	58	4,467	51	5,436	1,319	6,755	23,400	29	20	6
1937	1,005	139	7,933	73	9,150	1,695	10,845	38,300	28	16	4
Totals[7]	18,716	1,071	70,672	545	91,047	32,083	123,080	318,000	.....	.....	10
Per cent[7]	15.2	1.2	57.4	0.6	74.0	26.0	.....	.....	39	26	10

1 Includes all mica except scrap classed in the import schedules as unmanufactured; mostly uncut, trimmed sheets. 2 Includes stamped shapes, mostly washers and disks. 3 Includes films and splittings of all classes. 4 Includes mica plates and other forms of built-up mica, and manufactures in which mica is the component of chief value. 5 Data not available previous to 1922; cut mica and splittings were reported together, but only in terms of value; judging from the imports of splittings estimated from consumption, the amounts of cut mica imported during these years was comparatively small, while that of manufactures was almost negligible. 6 Splittings were not reported separately until 1923; figures for previous years are estimates based on consumption during the year. 7 Totals and average percentage based on 1922–1937 only.

TABLE III.—Imports of Mica into the United States
(Thousands of pounds)

	India				Canada			Great Britain[2]			France[3]		Madagascar	Grand Total[4]
	Untrimmed and Trimmed	Cut	Splittings	Total[1]	Untrimmed and Trimmed	Splittings	Total[1]	Untrimmed and Trimmed	Splittings	Total[1]	Splittings	Total[1]	Total[1]	
1923	[7]	[7]	[7]	3,393	[7]	[7]	3,080	[7]	[7]	411	[7]	50	.....	7,189
1924	134	47	2,997	3,189	246	519	767	80	162	264	123	156	.....	4,671
1925	196	26	2,736	2,975	41	456	498	127	209	354	198	251	.....	5,308
1926	298	43	4,828	5,181	88	634	728	171	174	358	235	262	8	7,003
1927	211	5	1,810	2,043	336	224	597	64	157	230	212	156	39	3,289
1928	159	9	2,381	2,551	81	109	190	83	300	396	205	267	138	3,690
1929	562	32	4,508	5,105	282	179	461	279	328	638	442	561	62	7,009
1930	358	26	1,283	1,669	286	70	356	127	138	270	163	188	86	3,671
1931	60	10	823	894	211	33	244	47	70	123	130	141	116	1,650
1932	133	14	616	763	2	97	99	50	10	70	100	104	51	1,089
1933	423	31	852	1,310	47	57	104	90	5	105	37	41	41	1,669
1934⁵	442	48	1,750	2,240	38	94	133	104	39	152	130	136	134	2,903
1935⁵	365	37	2,616	3,012	42	59	102	71	24	117	135	141	130	3,780
1936⁵	391	42	3,888	4,321	62	69	131	120	51	191	104	106	342	5,437
1937⁵	376	118	6,904	7,399	122	120	242	101	182	303	107	109	634	9,150
Total⁶	4,108	488	37,992	44,665	1,884	2,720	4,652	1,514	1,829	3,571	2,321	2,619	1,781	60,590
Per cent⁶	6.8	0.8	62.8	73.8	3.1	4.5	7.7	2.5	3.0	5.9	3.8	4.3	3.0	100.0

1 Includes built-up mica and other manufactured forms, and in some cases small proportions of scrap mica. 2 Re-exports, chiefly from India. Re-exports, chiefly from Madagascar. 4 Includes other countries supplying minor quantities, totaling an average of 5 per cent of the total. 5 Imports for consumption; previous years, general imports. 6 For 1924–1937 only. 7 Data not available previous to 1924.

entry of the United States into the war, the war peak was still below the 1913 figure, which has since been exceeded in only four scattered years. The recent years of industrial depression seriously reduced the domestic production, and, while the 1937 output shows a comfortable recovery from the 1932 low, the figure is still under 1926 maximum. Table II gives the data on the available supply from various sources since 1913, broken down into the more important types of product, so far as figures are available.

Imports.—Until the passage of the Fordney-McCumber Tariff Act in 1922, the statistics on the imports of mica into the United States were indefinite, as only uncut mica was reported by weight; all other forms were lumped together and reported by value only, and, except for the cut mica, the import figures shown in Table II for years previous to 1922 are estimates based on consumption and declared values. Table III shows the imports since 1923, broken down by countries and types of material, for all countries supplying more than 1 per cent of the total. Of these imports, 74 per cent came from India, 8 per cent from Canada, 6 per cent from England, 4 per cent from France, and 3 per cent from Madagascar. Neither England nor France are producers, and all of their shipments originated elsewhere, most of the English from India, and the French from Madagascar. Totaling the imports on this basis gives 80 per cent from India and 7 per cent from Madagascar. About three-quarters of the total imports were splittings, and only one-quarter sheet sizes. No distribution is available of the various sizes of sheets imported.

Exports.—Exports of mica of all kinds are reported in bulk, and have varied from less than 100,000 pounds during the war period to over 6,000,000 pounds in 1929. No data have been published on the various grades included in the exports, but since the average value has been only about 5 cents per pound, it is evident that most of it is ground mica, and that the sheet sizes that could be included in this low valuation would be negligible in quantity.

Consumption.—Except for splittings, the only data available on the consumption of mica are those found in the table of available supply. The most highly strategic form of mica is splittings, and, for these, approximate consumption data have been collected since 1917, and are shown in Table D. These figures indicate that three-quarters of the supply came from India, the annual proportions varying from 57 per cent in 1919 to 87 per cent in 1936. From Canada the trend has been in the opposite direction, declining from a maximum of 32 per cent in 1920 to a minimum of 4 per cent in 1937, with an average under 16 per cent. This decline in Canadian shipments was due in part to the Indian increases, and partly to the entry of Madagascar into the market with gradually increasing amounts, reaching 18 per cent in 1933. The domestic supply of splittings has never been large, the highest figure on record being less than 7 per cent in 1918, and during recent years the production of splittings has practically disappeared as an integral part of the domestic industry, the only output being that incidental to the removal of flaws from sheets in the course of trimming, cutting, and grading.

TABLE D.—CONSUMPTION AND SOURCES OF MICA SPLITTINGS IN THE UNITED STATES
(Thousands of pounds)

	Indian	Canadian	Madagascan	Domestic	Total[1]
1917	1,580	970	....	134	2,684
1918	1,168	658	....	128	1,954
1919	1,216	874	....	26	2,122
1920	2,154	1,012	....	66	3,234
1921	1,066	216	....	26	1,318
1922	2,282	632	....	22	2,942
1923	[3]	[3]	[3]	[3]	[3]
1924	2,820	590	[2]	[2]	3,410
1925	3,034	786	[2]	[2]	3,820
1926	2,776	347	194	[2]	3,317
1927	1,918	151	184	[2]	2,253
1928	2,508	381	253	[2]	3,142
1929	2,969	507	285	21	3,782
1930	2,451	422	163	[2]	3,036
1931	1,714	163	163	7	2,046
1932	667	74	158	5	904
1933	1,089	84	255	[2]	1,428
1934	1,424	94	245	[2]	1,763
1935	2,151	129	253	[2]	2,533
1936	3,052	103	363	[2]	3,518
1937	3,722	99	527	[2]	4,347
Totals	41,761	8,292	3,043	435	53,553
Per cent	78.0	15.5	5.7	0.8	100.0

[1] Previous to 1923, includes small amounts from countries not listed, chiefly South America; represents only approximate total, consumption, as reports from consumers were not complete.   [2] Small amounts either not reported, or figures not available for publication.
[3] No figures available for 1923.

Stocks.—There are no figures covering stocks in the hands of producers or distributors, and stocks in the hands of consumers are known only for six years, as follows:

	Indian	Canadian	Madagascan	Total
1932	1,360	188	269	1,817
1933	1,179	185	265	1,627
1934	924	200	208	1,332
1935	1,012	139	213	1,364
1936	1,281	52	223	1,556
1937	3,921	77	445	4,443

The 1932 stocks, at the low level of consumption at that time, were equal to 2 years' requirements, but stocks have been decreasing while consumption has been returning to normal from the depression minimum, and the 1936 stocks were equivalent to only 23 weeks' supply at the current rate of consumption, increasing to 53 weeks' supply in 1937.

UTILIZATION OF MICA

The only data which have been located that give information on the distribution of mica to the various industries are estimates of the United States Geological Survey based on the 1918 con-

TABLE VI.—UTILIZATION OF MICA

	Domestic Sheet	Imported Sheet	Total Sheet	Total Splittings	Grand Total
Part A					
Electric insulation	27.4	17.7	45.1	39.7	84.8
Stove fronts	8.9	1.1	10.0	0	10.0
Phonograph disks	0.8	1.3	2.1	0	2.1
Lamp chimneys	0.2	0.9	1.1	0	1.1
Other uses	1.4	0.6	2.0	0	2.0
Totals	38.7	21.6	60.3	39.7	100.0
Part B					
Electric insulation	16.4	14.6	31.0	59.1	90.1
Stove fronts	6.7	0.8	7.5	0	7.5
Phonograph disks	0.4	0.6	1.0	0	1.0
Lamp chimneys	0.1	0.6	0.7	0	0.7
Other uses	0.7	0	0.7	0	0.7
Totals	24.3	16.6	40.9	59.1	100.0
Part C					
Electric insulation	11.0	9.9	20.9	39.7	60.6
Cutting loss	16.5	7.9	24.4	0	24.4
Stove fronts	4.5	0.5	5.0	0	5.0
Cutting loss	4.4	0.5	4.9	0	4.9
Phonograph disks	0.2	0.4	0.6	0	0.6
Cutting loss	0.5	0.9	1.4	0	1.4
Lamp chimneys	0.1	0.4	0.5	0	0.5
Cutting loss	0.1	0.5	0.6	0	0.6
Other uses	0.5	0	0.5	0	0.5
Cutting loss	0.9	0.6	1.5	0	1.5
Total used	16.3	11.2	27.5	39.7	67.2
Cutting loss	22.4	10.4	32.8	0	32.8

Note.—Losses in cutting domestic sheet are almost twice as much as in cutting imported block or sheet, so that the above losses are conservative as applied to current losses in cutting domestic sheet.

sumption, expressed in percentage of the total consumption as shown in Table VI.

In *Part A*, the figures give the percentages of the total uncut sheet mica for each type of use. In the conversion of the uncut into cut sheet, heavy losses are incurred, the final product going into actual use as cut mica being only about one-third of the corresponding weight of uncut sheet for domestic sheet and about one-half for imported sheet (excluding splittings, in which there is practically no loss, as they are used in the irregular shapes, and not cut). The percentage distribution of the finished cut mica is shown in *Part B*. In *Part C*, the finished cut mica is compared with the original uncut weight, in order to put the figures for the product as it actually goes into use in direct comparison with the crude uncut sheet in the form in which it is usually reported in production data, and to emphasize the magnitude of the cutting losses in the various types of use. Omitting splittings, other types of sheet mica, as it goes into use, represent something over half of the original uncut sheet, and much of this cutting waste is used only for the production of ground mica, although doubtless some could be used for punching washers and other small shapes, or for the making of splittings, except that the high cost of the labor involved makes this impracticable.

Since 1918 there have been changes in consumption procedure in many of the smaller uses, particularly reductions in demand through replacement by some other material, such as metal for mica in phonograph disks, with a corresponding increase in the electrical uses. While these changes will not be great, except in a relative degree for the smaller uses, the fact that this distribution is based on a single year's data, compiled during the war period, nearly 20 years ago, makes it advisable to use the figures presented with some caution, as applied to present day conditions.

PRICES

It is extremely difficult to give any adequate idea of the price situation with respect to mica in a brief and concise form, because of the complications resulting from the large number of different sizes and classes, with a wide variation in prices. For example, there are twelve standard sizes of Indian mica, and almost as many different classes, so that to cover the ground completely it would be necessary to list, not one or even several prices for each year, but over one hundred. The domestic situation is not quite so complicated, as fewer of both sizes and classes are involved, but space limitation prevents any other than a brief presentation. The average value of the annual output, so useful in representing annual average prices for metals, is completely useless to indicate even relative variations in prices, since the yield of the different types varies considerably from year to year, even from the same mine, and it is impossible to tell whether a change in the bulk value was due to a change in price or to a difference in quality or sizes included in the total. The problem is still further complicated by the wide fluctuations in the prices from time to time. Top prices that are from four to eight times the low prices for the same grade or class are the rule, rather than the exception; the variations between the best quality of clear mica and the lowest quality of black spotted are of the same order, while those between small sizes and the larger are even greater. A 5 to 10 pound book of 8 by 10 inch mica of good quality may have a value equal to that of a ton of punch mica.

Sheet Mica.—The accompanying graph, Fig. 25, gives a summary of the price situation with respect to domestic mica since 1913, but only in an incomplete and unsatisfactory fashion; these figures, compiled from various sources, give approximate annual average prices for the various sizes up to 1922, and for later years the range of prices during the year. The average prices applied to "rough trimmed sheet mica of good quality"; the range prices cover grades Number 1 and 2 Clear. Lower quality brings a lower price; in general, stained material will command a price in the neighborhood of one-half to two-thirds of the price of clear, while black spotted will stand at one-half to one-third, or less. These curves emphasize strongly the wide range of prices that prevail, the heavy fluctuations, and the general lack of uniformity and organization of the market. Another interesting point shown by the curves is the fact that the condition of the market varies more or less independently for the various sizes, according to the demand at the moment; for example, the range of prices of the smaller sizes is quite close in 1930, and that of the larger sizes is much broader, while, in

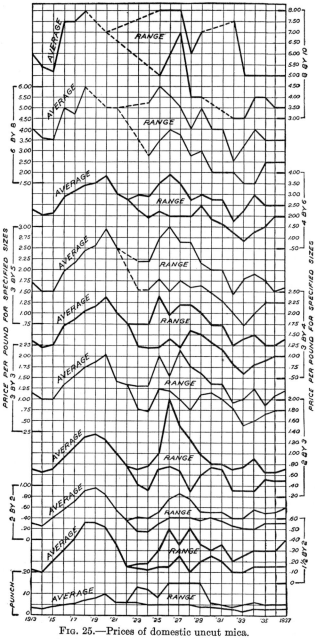

FIG. 25.—Prices of domestic uncut mica.

1926, the range is broad for the small and large sizes, but narrower for the intermediate sizes, and 1927 reverses many of the positions.

It must also be borne in mind that the prices shown are for trimmed, uncut sheet, sorted to produce the sizes specified, and not the cut sheet of these sizes; as has already been pointed out elsewhere, the cutting involves a loss of from one-third to one-half or more of the uncut weight, so that the actual cost of the cut sheet, ready for use, including wastage and labor, will be double or more the price of the uncut sheet.

Splittings.—Splittings have almost disappeared as a domestic product, and for this reason, data on this most strategic form of mica are of even more importance than for other varieties, but, due to the conditions involved, there is comparatively little information on prices. Data are available from which the average price per pound of all splittings consumed may be derived, as well as separate figures from the three chief sources, India, Canada, and Madagascar.

While the bulk of the consumption is of the cheaper grades, sufficient higher priced grades are consumed to distort the average values to a point where they have little real significance, even for relative comparisons. The table below gives for the years 1933–1937 the average New York price, duty paid, for the various grades of Indian splittings, and the average value of the Indian splittings consumed during the year, to show the comparison between the average and the various grades; where two prices are shown, the first is for loose splittings and the second is for book-packed splittings made from a single block, while the other grades are split from irregular shapes. The New York prices in cents per pound for Indian splittings have been as follows:

	1933	1934	1935	1936	1937
No. 4	75–120	75–93	75–93	75–120	....
No. 5	45– 83	45–83	50–80	53– 80	?
No. 5½	35– 75	30–75	30–75	30– 75	....
No. 6					
Firsts	25–60	23–50	23	23–55	34
Seconds	17.5	17.5	17.5	17.5	24
Thirds	13	13	13	13	?
"Cheap"	?	10	10	10	?
Average of consumption	21.4	24.6	22.9	21.3	25.9

TARIFF

The high cost of working the domestic deposits in competition with the cheap labor of the oriental countries that are the chief producers makes tariff protection necessary in order to maintain the industry. The tariff rates of 1909–1913 were all reduced by the 1913 tariff act, but the 1922 and 1930 acts increased many of the rates and added new classifications.

POLITICAL AND COMMERCIAL CONTROL

There is little specific information on political and commercial control in the mica industry. Mica was not included in the subjects studied by The Mineral Inquiry on Nationality of Commercial Control of World Minerals, and there is little said on the matter in Political and Commercial Geology.

TABLE VIII.—TARIFF RATES ON MICA
(In cents per pound or per cent ad valorem)

	1909–1913	1913–1922	1922–1930	1930—
Unmanufactured:				
Waste and scrap....................................	....	....	......	25 %[4]
Untrimmed phlogopite[1]........................	....	....	......	15 %[4]
Rough trimmed only..........................	5c. + 20 %	....	......	....
Other mica valued at				
Not over 15c. per lb...........................	....	4c.	4c.	4c.
Over 15c. per lb...............................	....	25 %	25 %	4c. + 25 %
Manufactured:				
Cut mica.......................................	10c. + 20 %	30 %	30 %	40 %
Punched mica[2] (*Washers*)....................	....	......	40 %	40 %
Films and splittings............................	....	30 %	30 %	....
Not cut or stamped to dimensions				
Not over 0.0012 in. thick....................	....	......	......	25 %
Over 0.0012 in. thick.......................	....	......	......	40 %
Cut or stamped to dimensions...............	....	......	......	45 %
Built-up mica products......................	10c. + 20 %	30 %	40 %	40 %
Mica manufactures[3].........................	10c. + 20 %	30 %	40 %	40 %
Ground or pulverized........................	20 %	15 %	20 %	20 %[4]

Note.—The table headings in roman type cover the entries as they appear in the Tariff Act of 1930; the two headings in italics were entries in former acts that have since been discontinued or modified. [1] From which rectangles not exceeding 1 by 2 inches may be cut. [2] Includes disks, washers, etc. [3] In which mica is the component of chief value. [4] Reduced as follows by new Canadian trade agreement, effective Jan. 1, 1939: waste and scrap 15 per cent; untrimmed 10 per cent; ground 15 per cent.

Including, as it does, the outputs of Canada, India, Rhodesia, and South Africa, as well as a number of the minor producers, British political control covers over 80 per cent of the world sheet mica output since 1913 and an even higher proportion of the present potential producing capacity. French control is limited to Madagascar, and the minor German control in German

East Africa was lost to Great Britain in the war settlements. Other political control rests in the country of origin.

Local commercial control is predominant in British territory, although there is some English capital, as well as some United States ownership in both Canada and India. Spurred by the need for mica to supply the needs of a highly developed electrical industry, Germany had, previous to the World War, obtained such a large measure of control over many Indian mines that the world mica market was at the point of being transferred from London to Hamburg, but this was all changed by the war. There is probably scattered commercial control to a small degree in all producing countries, but not enough to attract general attention.

Ownership of the United States mines is, so far as is known, in the hands of domestic capital, but it is claimed by some in the industry that British control or influence is so prevalent in the firms handling the sale of the domestic production that, so far as the consumer is concerned, there is practically British control of prices.

GENERAL REVIEW OF THE DOMESTIC SITUATION

The strategic situation with respect to mica has no counterpart among other members of the strategic mineral group, and the points of difference are many and varied.

1. Mica is a mineral, used as such, and not for reduction to a metal.

2. Mica is not a single mineral with well defined properties, but a group of minerals, two of which, muscovite and phlogopite, are of chief importance, with some variation in their properties, and with the question still undecided as to whether or not one is better than the other for certain uses.

3. Although extensive tests have demonstrated pretty thoroughly that type for type, some domestic mica is just as good as foreign mica, still there exists in the minds of many consumers a prejudice against domestic and a preference for foreign mica, which only time and experience can erase.

4. Mica must be used as it is found in nature; its properties can not be materially altered or improved by modification of composition, as can those of a metal, by refining. Also the size of mica is fixed by nature, and larger areas than are found in the

natural crystal can be secured only by the sacrifice of some of the original high quality, as the cement used in the making of built-up sheets is not as good as the mica itself. Nevertheless it must be recognized that there are well founded reasons for a preference for foreign mica in many cases, based fundamentally on price and quality. For example, in 1936 New England "clear" No. 5 sheet sold in New York for 90 cents per pound, while Bengal "clear and slightly stained" No. 5 sold at $3.79, duty paid in New York. At first glance this would appear to be a rather heavy differential to overcome, but even so the Bengal was given preference, since about half of the differential was absorbed by the actually greater amount of usable mica in the imported sheet, and the other half by superior quality, even though both were called "clear" mica. Comment has been made elsewhere on the impossibility of establishing uniform standards for quality, and this is responsible for many apparent discrepancies in prices.

5. Mica is produced in a wide variety of qualities and sizes, some of which are in much heavier demand than others. Material suitable for condenser sheets and splittings is the least plentiful in the domestic market, but for different reasons. Condenser sheets are limited by the amount of material mined that has the necessary high quality, while splittings are limited partly by the amount of material available, but still more by the labor costs in their production. Domestic splittings can not be produced by hand labor in competition with cheap Oriental labor, and unless machine splitting is developed to a satisfactory point, an adequate supply of splittings will remain a problem. The bentonite film gives promise of relief for splittings, but not for condenser mica.

As has been seen from Table II, the United States has produced only 26 per cent of its sheet requirements since 1913, and 74 per cent has been supplied by imports. On the surface, it may appear that an import-production ratio of nearly 3:1 is a heavy handicap to overcome, but with a further breakdown of the figures, the situation seems somewhat less formidable. While the domestic production has been only 26 per cent of the required supply, this has practically all been in the cutting sizes, and the cutting sizes imported have been only 16 per cent of the total supply, 57 per cent having been splittings. This means that an increase of 60 per cent in domestic production would have covered the demand for the cutting sizes, but the splittings represent the entire supply.

An increase in domestic production of cutting sizes by 60 per cent above the average level since 1913 is not beyond the realm of possibility; in fact one might almost say that it has been done in the past.   That is, the average output since 1913 has been 1,260,000 pounds, while the average demand has been a trifle over 2,000,000 pounds, a figure that was exceeded by the domestic output in 1923 and again in 1929.   Even if emergency demand should boost requirements somewhat beyond this level, it is still possible that the stimulus of the emergency demand and the higher prices that would prevail might be sufficient, in case of necessity, to enable us to stand on our own feet so far as many of the cutting sizes are concerned; it is chiefly the intermediate sizes of the high quality required for condensers that would still be lacking.

But even granting the possibility of this somewhat optimistic view of the sheet supply, we would still be, as we now are, *entirely* dependent on imported splittings, which comprise over three-quarters of our total imports, and well over one-half of our total consumption.   There seems no possible solution of this difficulty except the satisfactory development of the bentonite film or of machine splitting.   The former would overcome the obstacle, but the latter only partly, as the domestic supply of raw material would be insufficient, even though a satisfactory machine were available.   Many attempts have been made along this line, with gradual improvement in results, but as yet the goal has not been reached.   It is some satisfaction, however, to know that the handicap is one of technical development, rather than of availability of raw material, for there is still truth in the old saw anent the relationship between necessity and invention, and emergency demand has a tendency to bridge speedily many gaps in technical progress that would normally have required years of slow progress.

One of the chief difficulties in determining the extent to which supply can meet the demand is the lack of sufficient data with regard to specific sizes and classes.   At the beginning, we eliminated from the discussion all reference to scrap and ground mica, because supplies of this type of material are plentiful, and output can be expanded readily to meet any anticipated demand. Splittings are likewise eliminated from further consideration, since there is no present possibility of domestic production, though they may be replaced by the bentonite film. This leaves for further consideration the standard sheet sizes, ranging from punch up to 8 by 10-inch sheets. Table E shows the domestic mica output broken down into punch, larger than punch, and total sheet, and compared with the total production, including scrap. While no specific figures have been published, it is believed that the punch mica capacity shown here is able to meet any demand that is likely to be put upon it, and that we may consider punch sizes as not being strategic material. As with scrap mica, such small imports as have been made were mainly due to price competition and commercial conditions rather than to lack of domestic material to meet the demand.

It will be noted that the percentage of sheet in the total output shows a wide variation, from a high of 26.4 per cent in 1918 to a low of 2.04 per cent in 1933, with a marked reduction since 1929, followed by a partial recovery, although the 5.47 per cent attained in 1937 was still well below the 1918–1937 average of 8.45 per cent, and far below the 12.11 per cent average for 1918–1929.

TABLE E.—AVERAGE SIZE DISTRIBUTION OF UNITED STATES MICA PRODUCTION

	Thousands of Pounds			Total Out-put[2]	Percentage of Total in		
	Punch[1]	Larger	Total Sheet		Punch[1]	Larger	Total Sheet
1913	[4]	[4]	1,701	12,344	[4]	[4]	13.77
1914	[4]	[4]	557	8,016	[4]	[4]	6.94
1915	[4]	[4]	554	8,472	[4]	[4]	6.54
1916	[4]	[4]	866	9,732	[4]	[4]	8.90
1917	[4]	[4]	1,276	8,134	[4]	[4]	15.69
1918	1,031[5]	613[5]	1,644	6,228	16.55	9.85	26.40
1919	1,120[5]	426[5]	1,546	8,062	13.89	5.29	19.18
1920	1,154	529	1,683	13,130	8.79	4.03	12.82
1921	676	66	742	5,896	11.46	1.12	12.58
1922	911	167	1,078	14,360	6.34	1.16	7.51
1923	1,794	269	2,063	18,172	9.87	1.48	11.36
1924	1,305	156	1,461	10,878	11.99	1.43	13.42
1925	790	1,004	1,794	21,184	3.73	4.74	8.47
1926	1,843	329	2,172	16,258	11.33	2.02	13.36
1927	1,315	198	1,512	14,072	9.34	1.41	10.74
1928	1,468	213	1,682	17,202	8.53	1.24	9.78
1929	1,752	283	2,035	14,542	12.05	1.95	14.00
1930	1,254	212	1,465	14,930	8.40	1.42	9.82
1931	758	205	963	14,204	5.34	1.44	6.77
1932	258	80	339	14,418	1.79	0.55	2.34
1933	253	111	365	17,866	1.42	0.62	2.04
1934	425	158	584	16,022	2.65	0.99	3.64
1935	670	266	937	25,306[6]	2.65	1.05	3.70
1936	1,018	301	1,319	26,714[6]	3.81	1.13	4.94
1937	1,313	382	1,695	31,014[6]	4.24	1.23	5.47
Average[3]	1,056	299	1,354	16,023	6.59	1.86	8.45

[1] Includes circles. [2] All types of mica, including scrap. [3] Average from 1918–1937. [4] No data published. [5] Estimated. [6] Does not include byproduct scrap mica recovered from operations other than mica mining.

Several factors probably enter into the explanation of these differences. Most of these so-called production figures are really sales, and not true production, except in some of the earlier years, thus involving the unknown question of variations in stocks. Also, in some of the earlier years the amounts reported include some cut mica, while the later years are on a strictly uncut basis, which would reduce the totals of the earlier years by the amount of scrap made in cutting. A factor of considerable importance, particularly in connection with the percentage decrease since 1929, is the rising demand for ground mica, which has probably increased the proportion of scrap recovered from mine waste; also, during recent years there have been large

TABLE F.—AVAILABLE SUPPLY OF MICA LARGER THAN PUNCH SIZE
(Thousands of pounds)

	Production	Imports[1]	Available Supply	Per Cent	
				Domestic	Imported
1918.	613	741[2]	1,354	45.3	54.7
1919.	426	723[2]	1,149	37.1	62.9
1920.	529	1,299	1,828	28.9	71.1
1921.	66	328[2]	394	16.7	82.3
1922.	167	432	599	27.9	72.1
1923.	269	1,124	1,393	19.3	80.7
1924.	156	766	922	16.9	83.1
1925.	1,004	646	1,650	39.2	60.8
1926.	329	870	1,199	27.4	72.6
1927.	198	842	1,040	19.0	81.0
1928.	213	595	808	26.4	73.6
1929.	283	1,402	1,685	16.8	83.2
1930.	212	948	1,160	18.3	81.7
1931.	205	461	666	30.8	69.2
1932.	80	274	354	22.6	78.4
1933.	111	656	767	14.5	85.5
1934.	158	747	905	17.5	82.5
1935.	266	688	954	27.9	72.1
1936.	301	928	1,229	24.5	75.5
1937.	382	1,144	1,526	25.0	75.0
Average.	299	780	1,079	27.7	72.3

[1] Uncut and cut mica.   [2] Partly estimated; probably low, as cut mica is not included.

quantities of scrap mica, suitable only for grinding, recovered as a byproduct from other industries which do not produce sheet mica, but the figures reported as total output cover only the scrap produced in sheet mica operations. It is admitted that the magnitude of these uncertainties materially reduces the possible usefulness of the data in Table E, and may even make it completely unreliable for the purpose of estimating the possible returns of sheet from future total output; but so long as it represents the only basis available for such a classification of sizes, it is given for what it may be worth, with the warning that it should be used with discretion.

With scrap, splittings, and punch mica eliminated, let us now cast a new set-up with respect to the sizes larger than punch. Table F shows the domestic production, imports and available supply of these sizes since 1918, with the percentage distribution. Curiously enough, this indicates that the availability of punch sizes almost exactly balances the lack of splittings, and the deficit supplied by imports is the same as with the total sheet balance already determined, namely, 72.3 per cent as against 74.0 per cent of sheet imported, as shown in Table II. The average requirement of sheet sizes larger than punch has been 1,079,000 pounds, of which 299,000 has been supplied from domestic output, and 780,000 from imports. The maximum output, in 1925, was 1,004,000 pounds, almost equal to the average requirement; the total sheet output was higher in 1923, 1926, and 1929 than in 1925, but, in each of these years, the percentage of punch mica increased much more than did that of the larger sizes, so that the yield of the larger sizes was proportionately low, but, in 1925, the percentage of larger sizes was actually greater than that of punch, a condition not found in any other year. These variations are the result of the pockety character of the mica deposits, and irregularities in working procedure, and emphasize that the figures can not be used indiscriminately.

It is to be regretted that there are no data on which to base a further breakdown of these sizes with respect to imports, but we do find figures on domestic supply during the period 1918–1925, which are shown in Table G, in which are tabulated the percentages of the sheet output and of the total output that fall under each of the standard sizes. Although these data are several years old, they cover a fairly representative period, and are the only basis on which an estimate of the breakdown of total output into sizes can be made. For 1923–1935 this table also shows the sheet output divided into clear and stained grades.

The same comment that was made on the accuracy and usefulness of Table F also applies to Table G, although possibly to a somewhat less degree. While the data are a good presentation of the conditions prevailing during 1918–1925, the changes that have taken place in later years, particularly the reduction in the percentage of sheet in the total output, makes it questionable as to how accurate these figures may be when applied to or combined with those for later years. For this reason, the averages presented should be used with caution, and with the clear under-

TABLE G.—AVERAGE SIZE DISTRIBUTION OF THE UNITED STATES MICA PRODUCTION
(In percentage of sheet output and of total output)

Sizes	Punch	Circle	1½ by 2	2 by 2	2 by 3	3 by 3	3 by 4	3 by 5	4 by 6	6 by 8	Total, %	Clear, %	Stained, %
1918, sheet	62.7		11.6	9.3	8.6	3.0	1.8		3.0		100.0		
Total	16.55		3.06	2.46	2.27	0.79	0.48		0.79		26.40		
1919, sheet	72.4					27.6					100.0		
Total	13.89					5.29					19.18		
1920, sheet	77.2		10.7	5.9	3.6	1.1	0.6		0.9		100.0		
Total	9.89		1.37	0.75	0.46	0.14	0.08		0.11		12.81		
1921, sheet	93.3		1.5	2.6	1.4	0.5	0.3		0.4		100.0		
Total	11.74		0.18	0.33	0.17	0.07	0.04		0.05		12.58		
1922, sheet	85.2		3.8	3.0	3.9	1.3	0.9		1.9		100.0		
Total	6.40		0.29	0.20	0.29	0.10	0.07		0.14		7.51		
1923, sheet	86.4	2.3	3.2	2.5	2.6	1.0	0.7	0.9	0.4		100.0	41.8	58.2
Total	9.82	0.26	0.36	0.28	0.30	0.11	0.08	0.10	0.05		11.36		
1924, sheet	80.4	6.1	4.2	3.4	2.7	1.2	0.7	0.8	0.4	0.1	100.0	44.3	55.7
Total	10.79	0.82	0.56	0.46	0.36	0.16	0.09	0.11	0.05	0.01	13.42		
1925, sheet	77.0	4.6	5.2	5.4	4.0	1.1	1.2		1.5		100.0	47.2	52.8
Total	6.52	0.39	0.44	0.46	0.34	0.09	0.10		0.13		8.47		
Average 1918–25, sheet	75.0	5.0	6.5	5.0	4.4	1.5	1.0	0.9	0.5	0.2	100.0		
Total	9.10	0.61	0.79	0.61	0.52	0.18	0.12	0.11	0.06	0.02	12.12		
1918–35 total	6.88	0.46	0.60	0.46	0.39	0.14	0.09	0.08	0.05	0.01	9.16		

standing that results obtained by their use are only approximations. It must also be remembered that while these data seem
to indicate fair prospects in some lines, that these prospects are
limited by the type of data available to consideration of size
alone, while for condenser mica it is not merely size, but chiefly
quality that places it in the strategic group. The prospective
amount of domestic material of a quality satisfactory for condenser use is comparatively small.

Lack of more certain data on the distribution of sizes from
production, and of any data whatever on imports except the
total, makes it impossible to state with absolute definiteness just
which sizes and classes fall into the strategic group and which
do not, but general information from other sources indicates that
the chief shortages for which imports are required are largely
confined to two classes, condenser sheets and splittings, the first
being a partial dependence, and the latter total. The maintenance of an adequate supply from foreign sources presents no
difficulty under normal conditions, but in an emergency long
distance transportation complicates the problems of supply,
both from the standpoint of the availability of sufficient shipping
facilities to meet the expanded needs of the emergency, and of
the ability to keep trade routes open and free from blockade.
Since the bulk of the supply is from British territory, there will
be no lack of material available for import, except in the unlikely
possibility that Great Britain is on the enemy side in any future
conflict. With the chief sources of supply centering around the
Indian Ocean, it would require a complete blockade of this ocean,
covering traffic both to the east and to the west, to stop imports
at the source; blockading at the destination would necessitate
complete closure of both the Atlantic and Pacific coasts, since,
if only one were closed, imports could be brought in through the
other. With shipping prevented by blockade, the only recourse
would be such stimulation in domestic output as could be made,
supplemented by increased Canadian shipments. Under any
conditions, the Canadian deposits, being those nearest at hand,
would be expected to supply increased amounts; past performance has demonstrated that these deposits are capable of producing at several times their present rate, and, under pressure, they
could supply a considerable proportion of the deficit for splittings
but none of the needs for condenser mica, since the necessary
quality is lacking.

CONCLUSION

The United States is dependent on imports for its entire supply of mica splittings, and for most of the condenser and spark-plug mica. There is a reasonable prospect for self-sufficiency in other types, but these three are strategic to a high degree, with little prospect for any appreciable improvement from domestic sources. While emergency demand may be expected to improve the domestic output somewhat, it is not likely that the increase can keep pace with the demand, and the relative self-sufficiency under emergency may well be less than now.

For splittings there is prospect for relief in two directions: First, the Canadian phlogopite output is capable of considerable expansion under increased price, so that this may be expected to help replace any pronounced shortage from India and Madagascar; and second, there is the possibility of a very extensive substitution of the new bentonite films for built-up mica made from splittings. This substitution has not yet been definitely established as possible, but the prospects are promising. Unfortunately the power loss shown by the bentonite films in their present stage of development is too high for them to be used in condensers, and this fact makes their extensive substitution for splittings a bane as well as a blessing. The output of high quality condenser mica is comparatively small—possibly of the order of 100 tons annually, mostly from India. As has been previously pointed out, the nature of the mica deposits is such that the production of condenser mica can not be made a preferential matter, independent of other output; such recovery as is made must be proportional to the total output. If the demand for other types of mica, and particularly splittings, is materially reduced by the substitution of bentonite, the total output will be seriously affected and the output of condenser mica will automatically decline in proportion, unless other outlets for the product can be developed. The only other alternative to this situation will be an increase in the price of condenser mica to a level that will offset the losses on the other types.

Under these conditions the emergency stocking of a reasonable amount of condenser mica takes on an importance greater than ever before, increasing in the proportion to which the necessity for stocking splittings declines.

CHAPTER XIII

IODINE

There are a number of special features that characterize iodine and differentiate it from other members of the strategic group. In the first place, all others that have been discussed are either metals or mineral combinations of metals, while iodine is an elementary substance, but of a fundamentally non-metallic character. The materials previously discussed are all primarily materials of construction, and as such, they usually go into the making of objects that have repeated or continuous use, and a correspondingly long life of usefulness, although of course a certain small proportion is absorbed in uses where they have a comparatively short life, or may even be used only once; likewise, only a comparatively small proportion of the metals goes into chemical uses. In the case of iodine matters are radically different, for this is used only as a chemical, and as such, all of its uses are ephemeral; iodine can be used only once, and by this use is destroyed or dissipated beyond any possibility of recovery for re-use. There is no pool of iodine "in process of use," which is added to each year by new production and depleted by wear, breakage, or obsolescence, as is the case with the metals. Iodine is either not used or is gone. This year's output must then completely replace that of last year, and not merely supplement it. With iodine, it is a case of *Ave atque vale*.

REQUIREMENTS

The production of iodine has been so irregular from year to year that it is difficult to arrive at a figure for the average requirements for any particular period; annual figures vary from as little as 400 metric tons to as high as 1,600 tons, with a long-time average in the neighborhood of 800 tons over the period 1913–1936; there are clear indications that consumption has increased during this time, but just how much it is difficult to say, although some writers have ventured the opinion that since 1913 the annual consumption has doubled.

USES

The commercial uses of iodine may be subdivided into biological uses, and the purely industrial or technical uses. Small amounts of iodine are used as a chemical reagent in laboratory work, and similar small amounts in various organic compounds and dyes, but the chief demand in the technical field is in the production of the sensitizing solutions used in the manufacture of photographic films, plates, and papers. Although no specific statistics on the various uses have ever been collected, the biological uses probably consume considerably more iodine than do the various technical uses.

Biological Uses.—The lack of a sufficient amount of iodine in the diet has been found to be a cause of goiter, and for a number of years it has been customary to add a small amount of potassium iodide to common salt used for food seasoning, to overcome this difficulty; also, in many districts where there is a known deficiency of iodine in the soils and in the general diet of the people, potassium iodide is added to the water supply in small amounts. While the quantities used in either case are small fractions of one per cent, the bulk of water and salt treated is so great that a considerable amount of iodine is consumed in this way. Within the past few years this same principle has been extended from human foods to animal foods, and now iodine is added to feedstuffs just as it is added to salt and drinking water. Another way in which iodine may be added to the diet is to use small amounts of iodide in fertilizers for soils low in iodine; experience has shown not only that iodine has a definite fertilizer value for certain crops and greatly increases the yield, but that the crop is able to absorb some of the iodine, and thus increase the iodine value of the food thus grown. It is the expansion of these biological uses that has been largely responsible for recent increases in the consumption of iodine, rather than any of the technical uses.

Chemical Uses.—As has already been pointed out, iodine has no uses except of a chemical character, and they might all be discussed under this one heading, but for convenience of discussion, we shall subdivide the chemical uses into commercial uses and medical uses, for it is primarily its medical uses that are responsible for the inclusion of iodine in the strategic list. Iodine goes into use either in compound form, as an iodide of some metal, or in solution in alcohol or a combination of water and potassium iodide; there are practically no uses that call for the pure, solid iodine alone.

Medical Uses.—The chief use of iodine in medicine is externally, as an antiseptic, but there is also some use in internal medicines. Antiseptic use is mainly as a tincture, or solution, of pure iodine either in grain alcohol or in a combination of water and potassium iodide, iodine not being soluble in water alone. Besides this, there are a number of other antiseptic compounds used for dry dressings, of which group the now passé iodoform was once the leading representative, as well as various salves and ointments. Although most of the medical iodine is required in the form of pure iodine or potassium iodide, there is a wide variety of other compounds with minor uses, including iodates and iodides of other metals of the alkali group and, to a lesser extent, of arsenic, iron, manganese, lead, mercury, strontium, and zinc.

The tincture of iodine, or *liquor iodi* as it is now officially designated, whether of the alcoholic or aqueous variety, is cheap, easily prepared, convenient to use, and, above all, is highly effective; this combination of properties makes iodine particularly well adapted as a general antiseptic.

Military Uses.—Aside from the small amounts needed for the various medicinal iodine compounds, the chief military use of iodine is as an antiseptic; the properties listed above make it so well adapted for field use that nothing has yet been found which can fully replace it. It is its value as a field and general antiseptic which is mainly responsible for placing iodine on the strategic list.

Photography has come to be regarded as a necessary adjunct of a military campaign, particularly for aerial work and in the hospital for X-ray work, so that iodine may also be considered as a military essential for these purposes.

SUBSTITUTES

Various other substances have been developed and advocated as an antiseptic for household use and, to some extent, for ordinary medical use. Chief among these are phenol (carbolic acid), alcohol, mercurochrome, and hexylresorcinol, but none of them have the necessary combination of convenience and effectiveness that is found in iodine, so that there is at present no satisfactory substitute for iodine as a field antiseptic, and the same may be said for its use as a general antiseptic as well. Most of the technical uses are of such a character that they too are not susceptible to substitution, and this is, of course, particularly true of the biological uses, although in case of necessity many of these uses could be restricted as not necessary for the general welfare under emergency conditions.

ORES

Strictly speaking, there are no ores of iodine, for although most of the iodine produced is of mineral origin, practically all of it is recovered as a byproduct from operations carried on primarily for the production of some other material than its iodine content. Most of the iodine produced from raw material valued primarily for its iodine content is made from seaweed, and hence is not of mineral origin. A small amount is recovered from mineral waters and volcanic springs, but the chief mineral source is the small iodine content found in the crude sodium nitrate deposits of Chile.

Methods of Recovery.—The oldest method of producing iodine is by burning dried seaweed and recovering the small amount of iodine in the ashes. Although all types of seaweed have the ability to extract small amounts of iodine from the sea water in which they live, the type known as red wracks, of which there are two varieties, carries much more than other types; even so, the iodine content is usually less than 0.3 per cent of the dried weed. Various attempts have been made to devise special machinery for harvesting the seaweed from its growing bed, particularly in the trials made in this country during the World War, but most of the weed gathered in other countries is drift weed, which has been torn loose by storms and cast up on the beach. The dried weed is burned in a shallow trench, producing an ash known as kelp, containing 12 to 30 pounds of iodine per ton; incidentally, by association, the name kelp, formerly applied to the ashes, has come to be used also to designate the type of seaweed gathered for its iodine content. After burning, the ashes are leached with water and the solution, carrying a complex mixture of potassium and sodium salts, and any iodine that was present in the ashes, is then subjected to various purification and separation steps for the recovery of the iodine, and usually also the potash, the processes varying in the different countries.

In order to avoid the cost and trouble of drying and burning the weed, processes have been developed in France and the United States for recovering the iodine directly from the weed, but other complications are involved, the cost of which usually offsets any advantage gained, and the processes are not commercially profitable except when iodine is at a high price level.

Mineral or volcanic spring waters and natural brines containing iodine may be chemically treated for the liberation of the iodine content, which is then recovered in a collecting system. Sea water contains a small percentage of iodine, but the amount is too small for profitable recovery, although for several years a plant has been operating in North Carolina, recovering bromine from sea water, to the extent of several million pounds annually.

The source of about 90 per cent of the world's iodine output, however, is the sodium nitrate deposits of Chile, which average about one pound of iodine per ton, in the form of sodium iodate, although in exceptional cases the content is said to run as high as 1 per cent.

The iodine content of the crude nitrate, which remains in the mother liquor after the crystallization of the nitrate, is liberated by treating the solution with sodium bisulfite or hyposulfite and sulfuric acid, collected in filters, washed, and sublimed in a retort, producing the crude iodine of commerce, with a purity of 99 per cent or better. For extreme high purity, such as is required for medical purposes, a second sublimation is required, but this is usually done by the purchaser of the crude.

Secondary Recovery.—Strictly speaking, there is no secondary recovery of iodine in the usual sense of the term, meaning material recovered for re-use after having been worn out in one form. The nearest approach to this is such recoveries as may be made from plant wastes by manufacturers of iodine products, where the recovered material goes back into plant operations without appearing on the market.

Forms in Which Iodine Appears on the Market.—The primary market deals almost entirely with crude iodine, mostly from Chile, with a purity of 99 per cent or better. In some of the minor producing countries, with different raw materials and different production processes, the product comes to the market in the form of some convenient insoluble iodide, usually copper iodide, which is produced by adding copper sulfate to the solution under treatment.

The secondary market handles iodine in its various commercial forms: (1) crude iodine for technical processes not requiring material of high purity; (2) resublimed iodine of high purity, for medical use, and other types of consumption in which high purity is required; (3) various inorganic salts, mostly iodides or iodates, the iodides of potassium, sodium, and ammonium being the most important; and (4) various organic compounds of iodine, usually for medical use.

RESERVES

Iodine from seaweed is an annual crop, replacing itself by regrowth the following year, and not a wasting asset, depleted by each year's output, as is the case with the mineral sources. Brine and mineral-water sources are plentiful and seem to be good for an indefinite period; the amounts recovered from such sources are small as yet, but may increase if and when the Chilean supply approaches depletion, and prices rise sufficiently to cover production costs, or tariff protection covers the margin.

The reserves of nitrate in Chile are sufficient for a long period of years, particularly with increasing competition from synthetic nitrogen, and the potential iodine supply available from them is sufficient for many generations to come if it could all be saved and eventually utilized. However, under the present system of operation, which wastes all not required for immediate recovery, the Chilean reserves are limited to the life of the nitrate beds. Even so, there is no prospect of a shortage in iodine supply for a long time to come.

Chile.—As has been indicated, about 90 per cent of the world iodine supply comes from Chile, where it is recovered as a by-product in the production of sodium nitrate from the desert deposits in the northern section of the country. The quantity of iodine present in the caliche, or crude nitrate, is far in excess of that required to meet the sales demand, and only a small fraction of it is recovered. During the period 1919–1923 the estimated iodine content of the caliche treated was 102,000 metric tons, and the exports of iodine from Chile in the same years totaled only 6,730 tons, so that, after allowing a generous margin for losses in recovery, the output was well under 10 per cent of that possible if a market could be found for the product. In 1926 one writer estimated the recovery as low as 2 per cent. Since then the production of nitrate has been decreased by about half by competition from synthetic nitrogen compounds, so that, at the present time, the proportion recovered for use is presumably proportionately increased. Since the possible output is so much greater than the demand, the sales are apportioned to producers on a quota basis, in order to prevent demoralization of the market by excessive competition.

This method of procedure, while satisfactory from a purely commercial viewpoint, is much to be regretted from the standpoint of conservation of a valuable mineral resource, the occurrence of which elsewhere in the world is decidedly scanty. It is true that the known reserves of caliche are extensive enough to last for many years, and that the reduced scale of operations resulting from competition from synthetic nitrogen is lengthening the life of the reserves materially; still they are not inexhaustible, and, when they are gone, the large tonnages of iodine that have been wasted in the past are likely to be sadly needed.

United States.—A small amount of iodine was recovered on the Pacific Coast during the war period as a byproduct in the production of potash from kelp, but no figures are available as to the output. Certain oil-well brines in Louisiana and California contain small amounts of iodine, 30 to 70 parts per million, and, beginning in 1928, processes were developed for the treatment of the brines and the recovery of the iodine; these methods were later extended to salt-well brines and sea brines. Since the iodine content is so small, the plants have to work about 25,000 tons of brine to recover a single pound of iodine.

The chief recovery process is based on the absorption of the iodine by activated carbon after liberation by treating the brine with sulfuric acid and sodium nitrate. After absorption the carbon is filtered from the brine, the iodine removed as sodium iodide by leaching, and the carbon is returned to the process. The iodide solution, after concentration and purification, is treated with chlorine and steam, liberating and distilling off the iodine, which is collected in condensers.

Other Countries.—In France, Japan, Norway, and Scotland, iodine is recovered in small amounts from seaweed, the industry in some of these localities dating back 50 years previous to the entry of Chile into the world market in 1867. Russia has some recovery from seaweed, and possibly also from oil-well brines, as some of the Daghestan brines are known to contain iodine; no data are available as to production or processes. In Java, mineral well waters are utilized, and, in Italy, volcanic waters form the basis of operations.

The output in all of these countries is and always has been small, and, except for Java, is mainly for local consumption. With the heavy price reductions that have been made in the past two or three years, it is probable that the industry has suffered heavy declines in most of these countries, particularly those depending on seaweed.

WORLD OUTPUT AND SUPPLY

The character of the entire iodine industry is such that no very definite figures can be obtained on production and supply, since data are lacking from many of the smaller producers, and in some recent years for Chile as well. The average seems to be about 800 metric tons a year, with a minimum of half and a maximum of double that figure. The chief reason for these wide fluctuations is intermittent operation of the recovery plants in Chile; while the amount of iodine present in the crude nitrate, or caliche, is small, it still is several times more than is required to supply the demand, if it were all recovered; this means that recovery plants must either be run continuously for only a partial recovery, or intermittently with full recovery, shutting down the plant when a sufficient stock has been accumulated to cover the sales quota for a reasonable time; since the latter is the more economical method of operation, it is the one followed, with the result that production figures bear no relation to consumption demand.

The same principle is applied to the imports to consuming countries, which are the only other guide to consumption requirements; instead of maintaining continuous small shipments to meet current demands, a stock of considerable size is kept at the chief centers of consumption, which is supplemented by large shipments, sometimes only once or twice a year, as the stock becomes depleted. This being the case, import figures are no better guide to consumption demand than are production figures, except as applied to a long period of years for a general average, and even this is subject to some inaccuracy, due to lack of information as to the amounts of stocks on hand at the beginning and end of the period in question. During the years 1913–1937 the United States imports of iodine averaged 710,000 pounds annually, but in 1924 there were no imports, and in 1916 they rose to 2,033,000 pounds; in three other years they were double the average or higher.

So far as data are available, figures on the world production of iodine are shown in Table I, but unfortunately the data are far from complete, particularly for the minor producing countries. For purposes of comparison, Chilean exports are also included in this table, as they are somewhat more complete than the production figures.

TABLE I.—WORLD PRODUCTION OF IODINE
(Metric tons)

	Chilean Exports	Chile[3]	France	Great Britain	Italy	Japan	Java	Norway	United States	Total[1]
1913	437	434	[2]	[2]	.....	69	[2]	[2]	......	503
1914	489	489	[2]	[2]	.....	[2]	[2]	[2]	......	489
1915	709	709	[2]	[2]	.....	[2]	[2]	[2]	......	709
1916	1,323	1,323	18	36	.....	151	[2]	[2]	......	1,528
1917	760	760	31	45	.....	122	[2]	[2]	......	958
1918	823	908	26	22	.....	119	[2]	[2]	......	1,075
1919	505	505	65	24	.....	83	[2]	[2]	......	677
1920	350	350	45	37	.....	75	[2]	[2]	......	507
1921	534	534	39	32	.....	60	[2]	[2]	......	665
1922	245	207	30	29	.....	55	[2]	4	......	325
1923	471	443	61	36	.....	59	36	4	......	639
1924	591	433	54	47	.....	51	38	4	......	627
1925	867	876	55	25	.....	61	38	5	......	6,060
1926	1,132	841	[2]	[2]	4	63	67	[2]	......	975
1927	871	790	[2]	[2]	4	64	65	[2]	.....	923
1928	788	995	[2]	[2]	.....	53	74	[2]	[2]	1,122
1929	1,314	1,387	[2]	[2]	11	[2]	[2]	[2]	[2]	1,398
1930	307	84	[2]	[2]	19	[2]	136	[2]	[2]	239
1931	133	......	[2]	[2]	26	[2]	127	[2]	[2]	153
1932	280	......	[2]	[2]	30	[2]	137	[2]	79	246
1933	119	196	[2]	[2]	27	[2]	123	[2]	182	528
1934	472	518	[2]	[2]	26	36	114	[2]	142	836
1935	[2]	[2]	[2]	[2]	25	[2]	94	[2]	111	[2]
1936	[2]	[2]	[2]	[2]	29	[2]	109	[2]	102	[2]
1937	[2]	[2]	[2]	[2]	31	[2]	[2]	[2]	136	[2]

[1] Total of known production. [2] Information not available. [3] As officially reported.

UNITED STATES OUTPUT AND SUPPLY

Except for a small and unknown output during the war period, production of iodine in the United States began in 1928, but no production figures were published until 1932. Production reached a maximum of 402,000 pounds in 1933, but active price competition from Chile then reduced prices drastically, and domestic output has since declined considerably, as prices were reduced below the working costs of various plants. Present indications are that production is largely a question of price, and that at a reasonable price level most, if not all, of the domestic demand could be satisfied by domestic production. This, however, is impossible without tariff protection, which has thus far been denied to the industry.

Imports since 1913 have averaged 710,000 pounds annually; supplemented by domestic production during recent years, this gives an average available supply of 776,000 pounds. Assuming for lack of more specific information that the heavy imports of 1933 and 1934 were mainly for the purpose of building up the local stocks to the determined level of 1,000 metric tons (for in the depressed state of industry during these years, these large amounts could scarcely have been required for current demand), and again assuming that later imports were only those required to maintain the stock level, the available supply in 1935 was 622,000 pounds, rising in 1936 to 826,000 pounds. Figures for the domestic production and supply will be found in Table II.

TABLE II.—AVAILABLE SUPPLY OF IODINE IN THE UNITED STATES
(Thousands of pounds)

	Imports	Production	Available Supply
1913	351	....	351
1914	463	....	463
1915	613	....	613
1916	2033	....	2033
1917	610	....	610
1918	407	....	407
1919	1254	....	1254
1920	294	....	294
1921	646	....	646
1922	353	....	353
1923	273	....	273
1924	....	....	....
1925	246	....	246
1926	711	....	711
1927	926	....	926
1928	721	[1]	721
1929	627	[1]	627
1930	494	[1]	494
1931	279	[1]	279
1932	632	174	806
1933	1412	402	1814
1934	1481	284	1765
1935	376	246	622
1936	592	234	826
1937	1967	299	2266

[1] Information not available.

TABLE III.—IMPORTS OF IODINE INTO THE UNITED STATES
(Thousands of pounds or dollars)

	Total Imports[1]	Chilean Crude	Declared Value	Value per Pound	Chilean Price[2]
1913................	351	351	$ 740	$2.11	$2.01
1914................	463	463	....	[3]	2.46
1915................	613	613	1,332	2.17	2.42
1916................	2,033	2,033	5,757	2.83	2.44
1917................	610	602	1,343	2.23	1.92
1918................	407	327	649	1.99	2.64
1919................	1,254	1,248	2,376	1.90	3.04
1920................	294	281	559	1.99	2.76
1921................	646	616	1,353	2.20	2.92
1922................	353	324	943	2.91	3.37
1923................	273	268	877	3.27	3.51
1924................	....	....	...	...	3.36
1925................	246	246	890	3.62	3.67
1926................	711	711	2,272	3.20	3.71
1927................	926	702	2,041	2.91	3.71
1928................	721	721	2,429	3.37	[3]
1929................	627	627	2,249	3.53	[3]
1930................	494	494	1,798	3.64	[3]
1931................	279	278	995	3.58	[3]
1932................	632	628	2,218	3.53	[3]
1933................	1,412	1,401	2,915	2.08	[3]
1934................	1,481	1,479	2,132	1.44	[3]
1935................	376	376	421	1.12	[3]
1936................	592	592	558	0.94	[3]
1937................	1,967	1,967	1,784	0.91	[3]

[1] Imports for consumption; includes both crude and resublimed. [2] Average annual price of Chilean sales. [3] Information not available.

Imports.—Imports of iodine into the United States since 1913 are shown in Table III. During the war period several thousand pounds of resublimed iodine were imported, but since 1921 the total of such imports has been less than 400 pounds, and is negligible, leaving only crude iodine to be considered. The source of the imports was predominantly Chile. During the past few years there have been a few thousand pounds imported from Japan, and occasionally there have been receipts from European countries, usually England or Germany, but these are presumably re-exports of Chilean material.

Imports of iodine compounds are not now recorded, except for potassium iodide since 1930, which has amounted to only a few thousand pounds in the intervening period, and hence is so small that it need not be taken into consideration. During the war period, 1917–1919, imports of potassium iodide exceeded 116,000 pounds, but soon declined to small amounts.

Exports.—Exports of iodine and its compounds are so small that they are not recorded.

Stocks.—Since 1932, the United States sales agency of the Chilean iodine producers has followed the plan of maintaining a minimum stock on hand of 1,000 metric tons; as soon as stocks are depleted to this figure, fresh shipments are imported. Since these shipments are intermittent, only two or three being received in some years, it is not safe to follow the practice used in other cases, and assume an arbitrary average month's shipments to be en route and eventually available in case of emergency; such procedure is perfectly safe with materials that are shipped so regularly and in such quantities that, during any one month, it is a safe assumption that an average month's shipments are en route at the time, but with iodine the shipments are entirely too irregular to be counted on in this fashion. Any shipment en route and received subsequent to the break of an emergency would probably be several times the average month's receipts, based on yearly imports, but there are more than equal odds that an emergency would find no shipments en route, so that in estimating stocks available in case of emergency, this factor is best ignored.

In addition to the stocks maintained by the Chilean sales agency, there is an unknown amount of working stocks in the hands of manufacturers and dealers, and the War Department is authorized to maintain a war-reserve stock of approximately 20,000 pounds, although this is not always fully kept up.

UTILIZATION OF IODINE

No very reliable data are available on the amounts of iodine absorbed by its various uses. In a tariff survey made in 1921, the United States Tariff Commission estimated that 75 per cent of the iodine supply was used in the production of potassium iodide, 7.5 per cent in sodium iodide, 10 per cent in other compounds, and 7.5 per cent as resublimed iodine. Such data as are now available do not seem to check with this estimate, and an attempt has been made to revise the estimate.

The United States Census of Manufactures gives figures on the production of resublimed iodine, potassium iodide, and sodium iodide for alternate years from 1919 to 1933, which show the following totals for the eight years:

Product	Amount	Iodine Content
Resublimed iodine	686,000 lb.	686,000 lb.
Potassium iodide	3,451,000	2,641,000
Sodium iodide	333,000	282,000
Total iodine accounted for		3,609,000 lb.

From these figures the annual average is seen to be 451,000 pounds, distributed as follows:

Resublimed iodine	86,000 lb.
In potassium iodide	330,000
In sodium iodide	35,000

Since the census figures were taken only in alternate years, each was considered to represent its own year and that following, so that the period covered was 1919–1934. Comparing these figures with the iodine supply available during these same years, we find that imports totaled 10,349,000 pounds and production 860,000 pounds, or a total supply of 11,209,000 pounds. In 1932, the iodine sales agency adopted its policy of maintaining stocks at a minimum of 1,000 metric tons, or 2,204,000 pounds; just how much of this stock was accumulated during the years in question is not definitely known, but the large imports of 1933 and 1934, when consumption demand was low, lead one to suspect that the bulk of the stocks came in at this time. Since the imports for 1935 were smaller than usual, it is even possible that stocks at the end of 1934 were somewhat above the minimum, but, since this can not be determined, this possibility can be written off as offsetting any stocks that may have been on hand in 1919.

Assuming, then, the accumulation of the stocks during the period in question, and deducting the 2,204,000 pounds of stocks from the above total, we find an available supply for consumption of 9,005,000 pounds for the 16 years, or an average of 563,000 pounds; this may not be particularly accurate, but it is the best that we can do with the data at hand. This figure compares with the average of 451,000 pounds covered by the census figures in the three specified forms, and leaves 112,000 pounds for uses other than in these forms. This gives us the following approximate distribution of iodine over the entire period:

As resublimed iodine	15 %
As potassium iodide	59 %
As sodium iodide	6 %
In other compounds	20 %

The figure for "other compounds" seems rather high, as may well be the case, considering the method of calculation, as all of the errors involved by the various assumptions made are cumulative in this last figure obtained by difference.

As has already been indicated, from a strategic standpoint the medical uses are the most important, and the extent to which iodine is required for medical purposes is an important part of our problem.   The fact that, except for a small consumption for reagent purposes, practically the entire supply of resublimed iodine is used for antiseptics gives us an angle of attack for our solution of the question.   From the standard formulae of the two tinctures which represent the bulk of this use, and the opinion of medical men as to the approximate proportions in which the two are used, it appears that about 58 per cent of the total iodine content of the tinctures is in the form of resublimed iodine, and 42 per cent is in potassium iodide.   Allowing then for the additional medicinal uses of iodine in other forms, and for the other antiseptic uses, chiefly in organic compounds, the total iodine consumed for medical purposes will approach a figure double that of the supply of resublimed iodine.   If we make no allowance for uses outside of the tinctures, we get a minimum figure of 26 per cent of the total supply required; if we go to the other extreme, and assume that the total requirement is double the amount of resublimed, we have a maximum of 30 per cent; taking an intermediate point, we may then assume that of the total available supply of iodine, about 28 per cent is required for medical purposes.   Again, this assumption may not be any too accurate, but at least it is a first approximation of a figure that, so far as is known, has never before been attempted.

Similar approximations for the biological uses would be useful, but for the time being, there are no data on which to base even an approximation.   Additions of iodine are being made, usually as potassium iodide, to feeds for cattle, horses, sheep, hogs, foxes, dogs, rabbits, and poultry.   The amounts added are small, usually not more than one or two ounces of iodide per ton of feed, but the use of such additions has spread to such a point that it is reported that sales of potassium iodide for this purpose amount to about 250,000 pounds per year, equivalent to 190,000 pounds of iodine, most of which is in addition to the average consumption already estimated.

PRICES

There are shown in Table III the average annual prices as reported by the Chilean producers' association from 1913 to 1927, since when these figures are not available.   For the remaining years, the best guide as to price is the average declared value of the imports. The declared value of imports is supposed to be the fair selling price of the product in the country of origin, but this valuation is often understated in the import declaration; this is seen to have been the case with iodine valuations up to 1925, when the declared valuation checks quite closely with the Chilean sales price, and it is believed that the import valuations since then are fairly representative of the true price of the product.

For many years some 70 to 90 per cent of the world's iodine supply was produced by a closely controlled group of Chilean producers, and under an international cartel agreement, with prices under monopoly control stabilized at a level of about $4 per pound in New York, although various estimates have shown that the crude material could be laid down in New York at a small fraction of this price, production costs at some plants having been as low as 25 cents per pound.

This situation was maintained until domestic producers entered the market with amounts covering a large proportion of the demand, when the Chilean producers withdrew from the cartel and entered the market independently on a competitive basis. Successive reductions in price, beginning late in 1932 and still under way, have cut the price until it is now less than one-quarter of its former level.

Chilean iodine and domestic iodine are both byproducts of another recovery process, but since the concentration of the Chilean raw material is about 1 pound per ton, while that of the domestic is only 1 pound in 25,000 tons, the Chilean production costs are far below domestic costs, and it is possible for the Chilean producers to undersell the domestic producers, while still retaining a fair profit, and thus completely prevent domestic production, unless the government comes to the aid of the domestic producer with tariff protection sufficient to offset the difference in cost. Until recently prices have not been so low as to prohibit domestic production entirely, though it has been materially reduced from the high level of 1933; but, with a price of 81 cents per pound for Chilean material, set in October, 1936, it would seem that the profit of the domestic producers must be approaching the vanishing point, if indeed that point has not already been passed.

The low prices of the past four years have also seriously affected production in other countries, particularly those dependent on seaweed as a source, as their working costs are far higher than those of the domestic producers.

Table A shows how the domestic industry has been forced to reduce prices of its product, in competition with the imported Chilean iodine.

TABLE A.—PRODUCTION, IMPORTS, AND VALUE OF IODINE IN THE UNITED STATES

	Production (Pounds)	Total Value	Value per Pound	Chilean Imports (Pounds)	Total Value	Value per Pound
1931				278,000	$995,000	$3.58
1932	174,000	$396,000	$2.28	628,000	2,218,000	3.53
1933	402,000	669,000	1.67	1,401,000	2,915,000	2.08
1934	284,000	343,000	1.20	1,479,000	2,132,000	1.44
1935	246,000	249,000	1.01	376,000	421,000	1.12
1936	234,000	213,000	0.91	592,000	558,000	0.94
1937	299,000	242,000	0.81	1,967,000	1,784,000	0.91

TARIFF

Crude iodine has been on the free list in all of the tariff acts of the past 50 years, but except for those of 1894 and 1913, resublimed iodine has been dutiable. The present rate, Act of 1930, is 10 cents per pound, as compared with 20 cents under the Act of 1922; this, however, is largely nominal, for imports of resublimed iodine are negligible in amount. Potassium iodide carries a duty of 25 cents per pound under the Act of 1930; compounds not specifically provided for take a rate of 25 per cent ad valorem in both the present act and its predecessor.

POLITICAL AND COMMERCIAL CONTROL

Since Chile is the only country having had an exportable surplus of iodine of any magnitude; it is the only one in which the factors of political and commercial control have been of any importance. In general, iodine being a byproduct of the nitrate industry, the conditions for iodine are much the same as for nitrate. Commercial control through capital investment was predominantly American, though including some British, French, German, and Spanish capital; in 1930 the nitrate industry was reorganized as a state monopoly, one-half owned by the government and one-half by the former owners. Due to various conflicting factors, including the growing output of synthetic nitrogen compounds, the breakdown of the international nitrogen cartel and the subsequent drop in nitrate prices, the generally depressed conditions of business and agriculture, and internal political and financial difficulties in Chile, this scheme failed, and in January, 1932, the government ordered the dissolution of the monopoly and the return of the industry to private ownership. Early in 1934 a second reorganization was made, and a monopoly was established for the sale of nitrates and iodine.

So far as iodine is concerned, sales have been under a monopoly control of one kind or another for the past 50 years, and it is only since the beginning of domestic production that Chilean iodine has come into the market on a competitive basis. Attempts are now under way to develop the Japanese industry on an export basis.

GENERAL REVIEW OF THE DOMESTIC SITUATION

Since the domestic production of iodine was established, and has been demonstrated to be capable of producing a large proportion, if not all, of the domestic requirements if the price level is right, the strategic position has been materially changed. Another move in the right direction is the maintenance of stocks at 1,000 metric tons by the Chilean sales agency. This stock is in itself greater than the War Department's estimate of the total needs for army, navy, and civilian needs for a two-year emergency program, without taking into account the possibilities for continued importation or of domestic production, which is one of the greatest uncertainties in the problem, due to the harmful effects that present low prices may have on the ability to maintain domestic output and keep the plants in operating condition. Even should the domestic industry pass out of existence for the time being under the pressure of price competition, it has been definitely established that, in case of need, iodine can be produced at home, and either new plants or expansion of existing capacity can be built and placed in operation in a comparatively short time, should the need arise. On the other hand, in case an unforeseen shortage should arise, and the sea lanes to Chile were still open, a single cargo boat could bring in an ample supply for all needs, should conditions with respect to labor and materials make it inadvisable to embark on a program of new plant construction to bridge the shortage.

The recent entry of the Chilean producers into the market on a competitive basis, with sharp reductions in prices, has been accom-

panied by an organized research and educational program that
may well expand the uses and demand for iodine by quite measur-
able proportions, and so change to a marked degree the picture of
apparent available emergency supplies.   It was this possibility
that was the chief reason for retaining iodine on the strategic
list for the time being, instead of removing it to the critical list
as was eventually done in January, 1939.

CONCLUSION

Between the development of the domestic producing industry
and the maintenance of minimum stocks of 1,000 metric tons by
the Chilean sales agency, there is no apparent danger of a domestic
shortage of iodine under emergency conditions, and in January
1939, iodine was transferred from the strategic to the critical list;
this is justified by the need for an occasional survey of the
industry in order to keep posted on any important changes that
may take place that would change the present status of affairs,
particularly any marked increase in consumption that would
shorten the life of the stocks on hand, or any reduction in domestic capacity that would result in decreased supply.   The latter
possibility should be definitely guarded against by the establishment of a moderate duty on crude iodine, and by proportionate
changes in the present duty on other iodine products, sufficient
to cover the difference between Chilean and domestic production
costs to a point that would keep at least part of our plant capacity
in operation.

From a national defense standpoint it is not necessary that the
duty should be sufficiently great to make the country independent of outside sources, but only enough to insure prices that will
keep a good working nucleus in operation, around which necessary expansions in output might be built in case of emergency
demand.   This can be accomplished at only a moderate increase
over present prices, and the increased cost would be well invested
as an insurance premium against future shortage.   Should the
present plant capacity be allowed to become idle, obsolescent,
and dismantled, and the experienced technical direction scattered,
the expenditure of time, money, and effort necessary to rehabili-
tate the industry will be much greater than that needed merely to
expand the present capacity.   There is not sufficient information
at hand to permit an estimate as to the amount of tariff protec-

tion that would be necessary in order to permit the domestic industry to continue on a satisfactory basis, but, even if it should be necessary to double the present price and bring things back to the status of 1933, when the domestic production was at its maximum, the price would still be less than half that charged by the Chilean producers before domestic production made prices strictly competitive.

Every other strategic commodity of which the United States has an appreciable output is given the benefit of tariff protection, even though in some cases it has been shown not to be of real value to the industry, and there is no good reason why the iodine industry should not have the same degree of protection that the others enjoy. The industry was refused protection in 1934, and since then has suffered serious reductions in output, with good prospects of complete annihilation unless this decision is reconsidered soon. The relation of the industry to the national defense should be a valid reason for granting protection, even if other reasons are not considered sufficient.

CHAPTER XIV

NITROGEN

In many ways the history of the nitrogen situation is one of the most interesting in the entire group of strategic materials, largely because of the close concentration of practically the entire world supply of mineral nitrates in a series of deposits in Chile, and of the ensuing efforts to offset the resulting dependence of the entire world on this single remote source of supply. The fundamental feature of a strategic material is that its centers of production fail to coincide with the centers of consumption, with the secondary complication of an undue concentration of the raw material in a limited number of localities. In no case are these conditions more fully met than with mineral nitrates.

The basic consumers of nitrogen are agriculture and the various branches of the chemical industry, and the development of the consuming industries has been largely determined by the development, first, of the Chilean nitrate deposits and, later, of other sources of nitrogen from coal, and, finally, from the air.

The Chilean deposits were known as early as 1809, and the first commercial development was in 1825. The raw material was so plentiful, and so much higher in nitrate content than the many scattered low grade deposits that had previously supplied the demand, that Chile soon took precedence over all other countries as a source of nitrates, with the result that the estimated output to date is in excess of 85,000,000 metric tons of nitrate, from some 700,000,000 tons of raw material, locally known as caliche. For more than half a century the Chilean deposits reigned supreme as a source of chemical nitrogen. Then distillation of coal, first in gas retorts and later in byproduct coke ovens, began to supply increasing amounts of nitrogen in the form of ammonium sulfate. At the same time, small amounts were obtained from various organic sources, such as leather and hoof scraps, the distillation of bones, slaughter house wastes, and bird guano, but the total from these sources was comparatively small, and is disregarded in the present discussion, which is confined to nitrogen from mineral sources, commonly termed chemical nitrogen.

By 1900 it is estimated that of the total world output of chemical nitrogen, Chilean nitrates furnished two-thirds and coal byproducts one-third. Shortly after this we find the development of fixation processes for taking nitrogen from the air; the first recorded production by the cyanamid process was in 1906, and by the arc processes in 1907. A few years later these were supplemented by the more important processes for the direct synthesis of ammonia from nitrogen and hydrogen. The growth of these competing sources has been so great that, during 1932–1935, the proportion of the total supplied by Chilean nitrate had dropped to 6.6 per cent, while coal byproducts had increased to 18.5 per cent, cyanamid to 10.6 per cent, and synthetic processes to 64.3 per cent. In other words, mineral nitrogen then supplied only one-quarter of the total, where 30 years ago it furnished the entire output, and the various methods of utilizing the nitrogen of the air are now responsible for three-quarters of the output and are still increasing, not because the Chilean supplies are not sufficient to meet the demand, but because of the desire to eliminate dependence on a remote source of supply.

It is true that the figures for mineral nitrogen, as shown in Table I, are abnormally low during the past few years, due to the heavy reduction in Chilean output during the period of the depression, while at the same time the reduction in synthetic production was comparatively small (86 per cent drop between 1929 and 1932 for Chilean nitrate, against only 13 per cent for synthetic nitrogen), but an even more important feature is the fact that each year has seen material additions to synthetic plant capacity, replacing a corresponding amount of future possible demand for Chilean nitrate. As a result of the operation of this new synthetic plant capacity, synthetic nitrogen in 1935 reached a level well above the former 1929 record high, while the Chilean nitrate output stood at only 37 per cent of the 1929 high. Even in 1929, due to the continued additions to synthetic plant capacity, mineral nitrogen had declined to 44 per cent of the total, and, even if in 1935 it had succeeded in climbing back to this former level, it would merely have been holding its own, while at the same time synthetic nitrogen was building up a 35 per cent increase, so that by 1935 mineral nitrogen would still have dwindled from 44 per cent to 37 per cent of the total.

REQUIREMENTS

The world requirements for chemical nitrogen have been growing rapidly. The pre-war level in 1913 was 772,000 metric tons, as compared with 300,000 tons in 1900, and war demand increased this to 1,052,000 tons. The post-war minimum was 725,000 tons, or only slightly lower than the pre-war level, with a recovery that brought the 1924 output considerably above the 1918 war maximum and swept on to a record of 2,181,000 tons in 1929. The depression minimum in 1931 was 1,602,000 tons, only 27 per cent less than the 1929 high, which had again been exceeded by 1935 with an all-time record of 2,222,000 tons, increasing to 2,788,000 tons in 1937. The trend of production and the proportions of the total obtained from the various sources are shown in Table I, and in the accompanying graph, Fig. 26.

USES

The various uses of nitrogen in industry account for about 27 per cent of the total consumption during recent years, and this in a much wider variety of forms than is the case with fertilizer uses.

The largest single use in this field is in the form of explosives, which account for 33 per cent of the industrial and 9 per cent of the total consumption since 1924; of the total explosives nitrogen, 33 per cent was derived from ammonium nitrate, 44 per cent from sodium nitrate, and 23 per cent from other sources.

Much of the nitrogen used in explosives goes into the production process in the form of nitric acid, but in addition to this, other chemical uses of nitric acid constitute the second largest consumption in industrial uses, requiring about 21 per cent of the industrial and 6 per cent of the total consumption.

About 18 per cent of the industrial consumption is used in a variety of chemicals—ammonium salts, nitrates, cyanides, et cetera; this chemical group also includes a considerable but declining demand in the manufacture of soda ash by the ammonia process. Refrigeration uses 12 per cent of the industrial consumption, and other miscellaneous uses 15 per cent. The corresponding percentages of the total consumption are 5 per cent for chemicals, 3 per cent for refrigeration, and 4 per cent for miscellaneous.

Based on the nitrogen content of the total imports of sodium nitrate, which serves as the main source of nitric acid in its various forms and uses, either free or combined, we find in fertilizers 87 per cent of the imports consumed as sodium nitrate and 5 per cent in other nitrate compounds; in explosives, 12 per cent as sodium nitrate and 5 per cent as ammonium nitrate; adding to these 18 per cent in nitric acid and 2 per cent in chemical nitrates, we have a total of 129 per cent, indicating that nearly one-quarter of the total nitrate nitrogen consumed came from synthetic processes.

This brief summary gives only the types of uses for the more important types of compounds; the various individual compounds and the specific uses for which they are employed are so varied and so numerous that merely to list all of them would require more space than is available.

Agricultural Uses.—By far the outstanding use for chemical nitrogen is in agriculture in the compounding of fertilizers. The chief forms in which nitrogen is used in fertilizers are ammonium sulfate, sodium nitrate, calcium cyanamid, a mixture of ammonium sulfate and nitrate, calcium nitrate, potassium nitrate, ammonium phosphate, urea, and a mixture of urea and calcium nitrate. It is estimated that about 73 per cent of the domestic nitrogen consumption since 1924 has been in fertilizers. The data on production, imports and consumption shown later in Tables II and VI indicate that of the total nitrogen imported as sodium nitrate during the period 1924–1935, about 87 per cent was utilized in fertilizers; during the same period the amount of nitrogen consumed in fertilizers in the form of ammonium sulfate was more than double the domestic production from mineral sources plus imports, indicating the use of a large amount of material of synthetic origin. Formerly sodium nitrate was the favorite source of fertilizer nitrogen, but since 1927 the use of ammonium sulfate has been predominant, exceeding that of sodium nitrate by 30 per cent.

Military Uses.—There are no specific military uses of nitrogen that are primarily different from the ordinary uses listed above, but the demand in practically all of these lines would be largely increased by war demand. Indirectly, nitrogen is important as a determining factor in the food supply, and, even more important from a military standpoint is the fact that it is the basis of every type of military explosive; it is in these two types of use that we are primarily concerned with nitrogen as a strategic material.

SUBSTITUTES

There is practically no opportunity for substitution for nitrogen itself, for lack of other compounds that will do the work that those of nitrogen will do, but as between the different forms in which the nitrogen may be used, there is a limited amount of choice; for example, it is possible to substitute sodium nitrate for ammonium nitrate in amatol (an explosive mixture of trinitro-toluol and ammonium nitrate) although the product will be less efficient. In general, however, the possibilities for substitution are so limited as to be of little importance.

ORES

Generally speaking, the chemical nitrogen of commerce is derived, either directly or indirectly, from one of three basic sources: mineral nitrates, fossil organic matter, or the air.

Natural mineral nitrates are limited to a very few metals, of which sodium nitrate is the only one of broad commercial importance, with potassium nitrate a very poor second. Other nitrate minerals, including the nitrates of calcium, barium, magnesium, and copper, are of mineralogical interest only.

All living matter, both animal and vegetable, contains combined nitrogen. The fossil organic matter which we mine and use as coal contains 1–2 per cent of nitrogen, part of which is driven off as ammonia when the coal is heated; the coking of coal in the byproduct coking oven or in the gas retort makes possible the recovery of this ammonia in the form of ammonium sulfate, and as byproduct coking gradually replaced the former beehive ovens, a source of chemical nitrogen was developed which has supplied from 20 to 40 per cent of the demand.

Since the time of the first thunder storm on earth, lightning discharges in the atmosphere have been the cause of the formation of small amounts of oxides of nitrogen in the air, which eventually reached the soil dissolved in rain. Although it has been estimated that each year lightning causes the fixation of about 100,000,000 tons of atmospheric nitrogen, fifty times the largest amount ever produced by the efforts of man, four-fifths of this is lost in the sea, and much of the remainder on land that is nonproductive, so that the agricultural effect is small; in fact, this apparently enormous amount figures out to an average of less than 2 pounds per acre, although in some areas the actual figure is considerably larger, depending on weather conditions, with a maximum of 9 pounds per acre. However, it was not until the ingenuity of man devised methods by which the fixation of atmospheric nitrogen could be caused to proceed at will, rather than at the whims of nature, that the unlimited supply of nitrogen in the atmosphere became a material factor in the world nitrogen problem. This has been accomplished within the past 30 years, and has been developed on such a rapidly increasing scale that now three-quarters of the commercial nitrogen supply is taken from the air.

Each of these three sources involves problems so different from the others that they must be discussed separately.

Mineral Nitrates.—As has been indicated above, sodium nitrate is the only nitrogen mineral of importance, and although numerous minor deposits are known, widely scattered over the earth, the only ones of commercial value are those scattered over the desert regions of northern Chile in an area some 400 miles long, and from 5 to 40 miles wide. The entire region is without vegetation or fuel, and is devoid of rainfall or local water supply, except for one small river. Despite these handicaps, an industry was built up which, at its peak, absorbed the efforts and furnished the livelihood of as much as 10 per cent of the total population of Chile.

The deposits of ore, or caliche, are highly irregular in all of their physical aspects; in thickness they range from a few inches up to 14 feet; some are directly on the surface and others have an over-burden, usually of 1–4 feet, but in some cases as high as 25 feet; the sodium nitrate content may run as high as 40 per cent, or as low as 10 per cent or less, the material mined usually falling within the limits of 14–25 per cent. The sodium nitrate content is accompanied by 2–3 per cent of potassium nitrate, considerable amounts of common salt, and smaller quantities of the sulfates of sodium, calcium, and magnesium, with fractional amounts of borates and iodates. These soluble salts are accompanied by varying amounts of insoluble matter, usually 40–50 per cent, but sometimes less.

Treatment.—After mining by open-cut methods, the caliche is transported to the treatment plant, where the nitrate is recovered by leaching with water, decantation, and crystallization, with side processes for the recovery of potassium nitrate and iodine. The Shanks process for the treatment of caliche, with minor modifications, was practically the only method used from its introduction about 1884 until 1923, when the Guggenheim process was started. About two-thirds of the present production capacity is Shanks process and one-third Guggenheim process.

The Shanks process was never highly efficient; a minimum nitrate content of 12–14 per cent was required in the caliche; the average recovery was about 65–70 per cent in the caliche treated; fuel and labor costs were high, the former averaging 50 per cent and the latter 40–45 per cent of the total cost. By using improved methods of leaching and crystallization, and waste heat recovery to replace direct heating, the Guggenheim process has reduced fuel costs by about three-quarters, while at the same time mechanical handling has made a similar cut in labor costs. The recovery was increased to 85–90 per cent, and the minimum nitrate content of the caliche treated was reduced to 8–9 per cent, which is equivalent to more than doubling the nitrate recovered from a given area.

Byproduct Nitrogen.—The recovery of nitrogen in the coking of coal is purely a byproduct development, and although the nitrogen obtained is of mineral origin, the coal from which it comes can hardly be classed as an ore of nitrogen, since it is not mined primarily for its nitrogen content.

The recovery process is fairly simple; part of the nitrogen of the coal is distilled off in the coking operation as ammonia, which is separated from the other gases by washing, distillation of the wash liquor, and absorption of the liberated ammonia in dilute sulfuric acid, from which the solid ammonium sulfate is crystallized. In some plants the ammonia liquor may be sold as such, and in others, usually in Europe, hydrochloric acid is used in the absorption, to produce ammonium chloride. The average yield of ammonium sulfate is about 1 per cent of the weight of the coal coked, part of the nitrogen content remaining in the coke, and part in the tar and gases.

Atmospheric Nitrogen.—For the conversion of atmospheric nitrogen into a commercial compound it must be combined with some other element or compound; due to the inert chemical character of nitrogen, this is accomplished only with difficulty, but after long research three basic methods have been developed.

1. When nitrogen is passed over calcium carbide, CaC_2, at a temperature of about 1,000° Centigrade, calcium cyanamid, $CaCN_2$, is formed, which may be used directly as a fertilizer, may be treated with steam to form ammonia gas, or may be converted by other methods into other cyanide compounds.

2. By a carefully controlled high-tension discharge of electricity, part of the nitrogen and oxygen of the air may be combined to form nitrous oxide, NO, which on cooling oxidizes to the dioxide, NO_2, which may be absorbed in water to form nitric acid, HNO_3.

3. The most important process, and the latest to be developed, utilizes catalytic action at high temperature and pressure to promote the combination of a mixture of nitrogen and hydrogen to form ammonia gas, NH_3, which may be used as such, converted to any desired ammonia salt, or by another catalytic process, in the presence of air to supply the oxygen, may be oxidized to nitric acid.

Secondary Recovery.—The character of the uses of nitrogen is such that there is no possibility of secondary recovery, beyond such small saving as can be made in various factory operations.

Forms in Which Nitrogen Appears on the Market.—There are of course an enormous number of different compounds of nitrogen on the market, but here we are concerned only with the primary forms produced in the processes mentioned above. The secondary forms which are so abundantly utilized in industry are practically all derived from the primary forms herein considered. They need not therefore be given separate consideration.

Chilean nitrate comes on the market in one of three forms; the commonest is a salt of 95–96 per cent purity, although some is produced as high as 98 per cent, and, in addition, some plants make a special so-called potash nitrate, carrying 30–40 per cent of potash, but, since the potassium nitrate content of the caliche is small, the amounts of this third grade are not important.

Byproduct nitrogen from the coking of coal is mostly marketed as ammonium sulfate, with some 15–20 per cent of the output sold as ammonia liquor. However, if conditions demanded it, almost any other ammonia compound desired might be produced, although the additional complications in the process would increase the cost.

Cyanamid nitrogen, as has been indicated, may be sold as cyanamid, or after conversion into ammonia or cyanides.

The product of the electric discharge, or arc processes, may be marketed as nitric acid, calcium nitrate, or sodium nitrite.

The primary product of all of the various catalytic processes is ammonia gas, which may be marketed as such, or after conversion into some other ammonia compound, or nitric acid.

ORE RESERVES

The situation with regard to reserves of course varies widely with the different sources of nitrogen, but in all cases the reserves are so large that there is no prospect of shortage of supply. For the fixation processes, which draw their supply of nitrogen from the air, the supply is of course unlimited in any locality where installation may be desirable. The reserves of mineral nitrogen are definitely limited by the amounts of coal or caliche available, but in both cases the life of the known reserves is measured in generations, rather than years, and the additional probable reserves are of equal magnitude. Another mineral source which has as yet not been drawn on, but which in the future may supply appreciable amounts of byproduct nitrogen, is found in the large deposits of oil shale; these shales have not yet been commercially exploited in the United States, and only to a minor extent in other countries, but they form a considerable reserve of byproduct nitrogen, as well as of petroleum, for they carry a nitrogen content similar to that of coal, which may be recovered as a byproduct during distillation.

The known coal reserves of the United States are sufficient to maintain the present rate of consumption for more than 3,000 years, so there is no prospect of shortage in that direction for a long time to come. Furthermore, although byproduct nitrogen is now furnishing about one-third of our total domestic consumption, this one-third is recovered only from coal going to byproduct coke ovens and gas plants, which constitutes only about one-seventh of the total coal consumption, and present methods recover only about 20–25 per cent of the nitrogen content of the coal. This one-third of the total nitrogen consumption then represents only 3–4 per cent of the total nitrogen content of the entire coal consumption of the country, so that comparatively small improvements in the nitrogen recovery, or still smaller extensions in application of byproduct recovery to the various uses of coal could supply amounts of byproduct nitrogen far in excess of the total domestic requirements. Unfortunately, at the present time there are no immediate prospects for much improvement along either of these lines.

In the field of natural nitrates, the reserves are also large enough to obviate any possibility of shortage of supply for several generations to come, while, at the same time, the rapid expansion of synthetic processes is reducing the demand made on the Chilean deposits. In 1923 an official government report was made on the results obtained in an examination of an area of 5,811 square kilometers out of some 200,000 square kilometers known to be nitrate bearing. This area, which had produced about two-thirds of the total output made up to that time, was reported to have originally contained 290,000,000 metric tons of nitrate, of which 45,000,000 tons had been recovered. Since the Shanks process, the only one then in use, recovers only about two-thirds of the nitrate in the caliche, we may then assume that this production used 67,000,000 tons of the original content, leaving 227,000,000 tons for future recovery in this area alone, with presumably an even greater amount in the much larger area not yet examined. In view of the improvements in recovery made by the Guggenheim process, increasing the yield and reducing the grade workable, and of the later reductions in output caused by competition from synthetic nitrogen, this known reserve will now last much longer than the 100 years assigned to it at the time, and the probable reserves may be pretty safely assumed to be considerably greater than known reserves.

WORLD OUTPUT AND SUPPLY

The world supply of mineral nitrogen, originally from Chile nitrate, and later supplemented by byproduct nitrogen from coal, first came into competition with the atmospheric fixation processes in 1906. Due to the extensive research involved, early progress in fixation was slow, and in 1913 only 8 per cent of the world supply came from this source against 55 per cent from Chile nitrate and 37 per cent from coal. During the war period, development was speeded up, particularly in Germany and the United States, and by 1918 fixation processes furnished 23 per cent of the supply, against 42 per cent from nitrate and 35 per cent from coal. After the postwar depression, expansion of the fixation processes was still more rapid; plant capacity has continued to expand, even in the face of the industrial depression following 1929, and finally reached a point where three-quarters of the total output was from fixation processes. By 1934 the plant capacity of all processes had reached a total of 4,612,000 metric tons, or more than double the maximum demand that has ever been placed on the industry; of this total capacity, 63.6 per cent was in synthetic processes and 10.6 per cent in cyanamid processes, or a total of 74.2 per cent in fixation processes, against 12.2 per cent in byproduct processes and 13.6 per cent still being obtained from Chile nitrate. This heavy overdevelopment of production capacity, which has now reached a point at which the fixation capacity of the world is sufficient to supply the entire demand without calling on the mineral sources at all, is partly due to ordinary industrial competition for a growing market, but is also in large measure attributable to a desire in various countries to be relieved of their dependence on a remote source of supply under control of a monopoly, and to establish a production capacity sufficient to meet possible future demands, both ordinary and emergency.

Data of the production from the different sources and processes, in terms of nitrogen content, both in tonnage and percentage, are in Table I*a*, as well as total installed plant capacity; these data are carried back to 1900, to antedate the beginning of the fixation processes, and thus show their full effect on the industry. Figure 26 also shows this same data in graphical form. In Table I*b* the annual production is shown for the various important producing countries; unfortunately data are lacking for this table between 1914 and 1923, except for Chile, United States, and the total, and lack of space prevents the division of the country totals to show the amounts contributed by the various processes, beyond the fact that the entire Chilean output is from natural nitrates, while that of all other countries is divided between byproduct nitrogen and that fixed from air.

Natural Nitrates.—Sufficient has already been said in preceding paragraphs in regard to the unique position of Chile as a producer

of natural nitrates that nothing more need be added in the way
of general discussion. Since, however, this output represents
that of the entire world, it may be well to include some data
of the industry beyond that given in the world output data in
Tables I*a* and I*b*; therefore the more pertinent features of the
Chilean industry are shown in Table B, insofar as information
is available.

Production of natural nitrates in countries other than Chile
is so small as to be entirely negligible from a world standpoint,

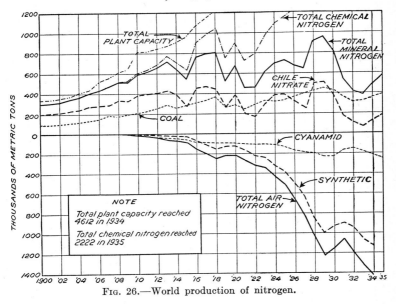

Fig. 26.—World production of nitrogen.

and even largely so from a local standpoint. There is a small
output of potassium nitrate in India, which in recent years has
ranged from 4,000 to 10,000 tons, although in 1918 it was as
high as 25,000 tons. The only other productions reported are
insignificant amounts of nitrate-bearing shales in Egypt, China
and Spain, which are used locally as a fertilizer.

In the United States there is no production of natural nitrates,
and no prospect of the possibility of such production, since all
known deposits are of far too low a grade. During the World
War numerous occurrences in various states were investigated,
and sporadic attention has been given to the subject in more
recent years. All told, several hundred small deposits have been
examined in 23 states, but in no case was material found of suffi-

TABLE Ia.—WORLD NITROGEN OUTPUT AND CAPACITY¹
(Thousands of metric tons)

Year	Chilean Nitrate	Coal	Total Mineral	Cyanamid	Synthetic	Total Air	Total Chemical Nitrogen²	Estimated Plant Capacity	Percentage of Total from						Per Cent of Plant Capacity in Use
									Chilean Nitrate	Coal	Mineral Sources	Cyanamid	Synthetic	Air	
1900	200	100	300				300	344	67	33	100				87
1901	213	100	313				313	349	68	32	100				89
1902	214	105	319				319	359	67	33	100				89
1903	230	113	343				343	374	67	33	100				92
1904	241	124	365				365	414	66	34	100				88
1905	271	134	405				405	439	67	33	100				92
1906	282	149	431	0.1		0.1	431	524	65+	35-	99.98	0.02		0.02	82
1907	286	187	473	.3	0.2	0.5	473	559	60+	40-	99.9	0.06	0.04	0.1	85
1908	306	179	485	.5	1	1.5	487	609	63-	37+	99.7	0.1	0.2	0.3	80
1909	327	190	517	2	2	4	520	649	63	36+	99.3	0.4	0.3	0.7	80
1910	381	206	586	4	5	9	595	814	64	35	98.5	0.7	0.8	1.5	73
1911	390	224	614	11	7	18	632	818	62	35	97	2	1	3	77
1912	400	252	652	26	9	35	687	848	58	37	95	4	1	5	81
1913	428	284	712	38	22	60	772	874	55	37	92	5	3	8	88
1914	381	257	638	41	27	68	706	908	54	36	90	6	4	10	78
1915	271	273	544	50	35	85	630	967	43	43	86	8	6	14	65
1916	451	306	757	80	70	150	907	1,114	50	34	84	9-	8-	16	81
1917	464	332	796	86	112	198	994	1,218	47	33	80	9	11	20	82
1918	442	365	807	89	156	245	1,052	1,367	42	35	77	8	15	23	77
1919	264	261	525	91	134	225	750	1,422	35	35	70	12	18	30	53
1920	390	289	679	94	129	223	902	1,407	43	32	75	10+	14+	25	64
1921	203	250	453	103	169	272	725	1,398	28	35-	63	14	23	37	52
1922	166	294	460	105	226	331	791	1,382	21	37	58	13	29	42	57
1923	294	323	617	102	246	348	965	1,468	31-	34-	64	11	25	36	66
1924	374	320	694	109	323	432	1,126	1,556	33	28	61	10	29	39	72
1925	393	334	727	132	383	515	1,252	1,724	31	37	68	11	31	42	73
1926	314	361	675	165	501	666	1,341	1,874	23	27	50	12	38	50	72
1927	251	399	650	189	638	827	1,477	2,171	17	27	44	13	43	56	68
1928	493	423	916	195	857	1,052	1,968	2,501	25	22	47	10	43	53	79
1929	503	451	954	227	1,000	1,227	2,181	2,973	23	21	44	10	46	56	73

TABLE Ia.—WORLD NITROGEN OUTPUT AND CAPACITY¹ (Continued)

	Chilean Nitrate	Coal	Total Mineral	Cyanamid	Synthetic	Total Air	Total Chemical Nitrogen²	Estimated Plant Capacity	Percentage of Total from						Per Cent of Plant Capacity in Use
									Chilean Nitrate	Coal	Mineral Sources	Cyanamid	Synthetic	Air	
1930	381	432	813	232	924	1,156	1,979	3,553	19	22	41	12	47	59	55
1931	175	360	535	168	899	1,067	1,602	4,037	11	23	34	10	56	66	40
1932	109	314	423	151	1,042	1,193	1,616	4,343	7	19	26	9	65	74	37
1933	69	324	393	180	1,146	1,326	1,719	4,496	4	19	23	10	67	77	38
1934	131	360	491	213	1,222	1,435	1,926	4,612	7	19	26	11	63	74	42
1935	185	394	579	251	1,400	1,651	2,230	4,700?	8+	17+	26	11	63	74	47
1936	199	452	651	280	1,614	1,894	2,545	·..·5,500?		18			63	74	?
1937	215	471	686	298	1,804	2,102	2,788		8	17	25	11	65—	75	51

¹ Most of the detailed international data in this and the following tables are adapted from the recent Report No. 114 (Second Series), issued by the U. S. Tariff Commission, with occasional inserts from other sources; those interested in the subject will find in this report a wealth of additional information which lack of space prohibits including here. ² For some reason not explained, the world total nitrogen output as given in this table differs considerably from the figures included in the table of production by countries (Table Ib), covering the years 1913 and 1924–1934.

TABLE Ib.—WORLD PRODUCTION OF CHEMICAL NITROGEN
(Thousands of metric tons)

	Chile	Germany	United States	Great Britain	Japan	France	Norway	Italy	Belgium	Netherlands	Poland	Canada	Others[1]	Total
1913	433	120	35	91	4	17	20	5	10	2	3	12	12	764
1914	348	a	a	a	a	a	a	a	a	a	a	a	a	706
1915	249	a	a	a	a	a	a	a	a	a	a	a	a	630
1916	322	a	54	a	a	a	a	a	a	a	a	a	a	907
1917	335	a	a	a	a	a	a	a	a	a	a	a	a	994
1918	405	a	a	a	a	a	a	a	a	a	a	a	a	1,052
1919	239	a	79	a	a	a	a	a	a	a	a	a	a	750
1920	359	a	93	a	a	a	a	a	a	a	a	a	a	902
1921	186	a	67	a	a	a	a	a	a	a	a	a	a	725
1922	152	a	89	a	a	a	a	a	a	a	a	a	a	791
1923	269	a	132	a	a	a	a	a	a	a	a	a	a	965
1924	375	427	118	98	34	31	23	15	13	7	14	16	27	1,198
1925	394	508	137	94	38	39	29	14	13	7	21	19	34	1,347
1926	315	613	151	71	44	50	33	23	17	9	28	25	42	1,421
1927	252	709	161	103	49	59	34	31	23	9	33	24	50	1,537
1928	495	842	200	134	69	71	46	44	28	10	43	33	58	2,073
1929	504	807	289	198	83	93	68	51	40	12	49	57	64	2,315
1930	382	614	254	168	140	117	80	62	39	31	45	39	59	2,030
1931	175	543	198	137	154	105	66	54	54	79	34	17	52	1,668
1932	109	415	163	162	173	136	62	57	80	94	28	21	66	1,566
1933	69	390	210	145	185	157	54	73	78	76	29	34	93	1,593
1934	129	420	233	128	189	171	60	84	100	57	32	37	143	1,783
Totals[3]	3,199	6,288	2,114	1,438	1,158	1,029	555	508	485	391	356	322	688	18,531
Percentage[4]	17.2	33.9	11.4	7.9	6.2	5.6	3.0	2.8	2.6	2.1	1.9	1.7	3.7	100.0

[1] Includes Russia, Czecho-Slovakia, Yugoslavia, Sweden, Spain, Switzerland, South Africa, Hungary, Australia, India, Austria, and Rumania.
[2] Not available. [3] 1924–1934 only.

TABLE A.—WORLD CAPACITY FOR PRODUCTION OF CHEMICAL NITROGEN[1]
(Thousands of metric tons)

	Synthetic		Cyanamid		Byproduct		Mineral Nitrates		Country Total	
	Capacity	Per Cent of World Total	Capacity	Per Cent of World Total	Capacity	Per Cent of World Total	Capacity	Per Cent of World Total	Capacity	Per Cent of World Total
Germany	1,030	35.2	180	36.7	124	22.1			1,334	29.0
Chile							626	100	626	13.6
United States	310	10.6			181	32.2			491	10.6
Great Britain	245	8.3	40	8.2	110	19.5			354	7.7
France	249	8.5	63	12.9	45	8.1			334	7.2
Japan	198	6.8	6	1.2	10	1.7			271	5.9
Belgium	186	6.3	4	0.8	25	4.4			217	4.7
Russia	165	5.6	20	4.1	15	2.7			184	4.0
Italy	112	3.8			5	1.0			138	3.0
Netherlands	111	3.8	15	3.1	10	1.8			121	2.6
Norway	105	3.6	71	14.5	[3]				120	2.6
Canada	32	1.1	38	7.7	10	1.8			113	2.5
Poland	64	2.2	52	10.6	6	1.1			108	2.3
Other Countries[2]	125	4.2			21	3.7			199	4.3
World Total	2,932		489		562		626		4,610	
Per Cent of Total	63.6		10.6		12.2		13.6			

[1] As of January 1, 1934. [2] Includes, in order of magnitude, Yugoslavia, Czecho-Slovakia, Manchuria, Switzerland, Sweden, Spain, South Africa, Hungary, Rumania, India, Austria, Australia, and Denmark. [3] Less than 500 tons.

cient richness even to approach the possibility of commercial operation.

Byproduct Nitrogen.—Although natural nitrates are, practically speaking, limited to a single locality, the recovery of byproduct nitrogen from coal treated in byproduct coke ovens or in gas retorts is possible wherever these operations are carried on with any magnitude. Since by far the largest consumer of coke is the iron blast furnace, it follows that the leading iron

TABLE B.—THE NITRATE INDUSTRY IN CHILE
(Thousands of metric tons)

	Caliche Treated	Oficinas Working	Nitrate Produced	Total Exports	Exports to U. S.[1]	Per cent to U. S.	Stocks at Year End		
							World	Chile	United States
1913	23,466	127	2,772	2,738	616	23	1,747	480	71
1914	21,452	137	2,463	1,847	610	33	[3]	1,071	114
1915	17,888	116	1,755	2,023	883	44	[3]	777	222
1916	24,658	123	2,913	2,981	1,245	42	[3]	695	150
1917	24,315	129	3,001	2,776	1,579	57	[3]	883	284
1918	23,540	125	2,859	2,919	1,690	58	[3]	812	[3]
1919	13,512	125	1,703	804	610	76	2,152	[3]	[3]
1920	20,184[2]	97	2,523	2,746	813	30	[3]	1,305	[3]
1921	10,455	101	1,310	1,193	242	20	2,676	1,491	[3]
1922	8,136	53	1,071	1,252	744	59	1,958	1,232	[3]
1923	15,158	82	1,903	2,243	930	41	1,634	931	[3]
1924	[3]	94	2,403	2,333	960	41	1,721	884	92
1925	[3]	96	2,524	2,519	1,193	47	1,735	881	128
1926	[3]	93	2,016	1,614	816	51	1,834	1,279	202
1927	[3]	49	1,614	2,375	748	32	1,528	523	190
1928	[3]	65	3,163	2,133	1,014	48	2,133	884	265
1929	[3]	69	3,238	2,842	975	34	2,622	1,178	300
1930	[3]	71	2,496	1,785	531	30	2,939	1,780	400
1931	[3]	33	1,128	1,454	514	35	2,737	1,450	445
1932	[3]	10	708	235	26	11	1,992	1,313	425
1933	[3]	10	439	693	148	21	[3]	1,059	[3]
1934	[3]	14	824	1,257	329	26	1,204	[3]	[3]
1935[2]	[3]	21	1,176	1,309	397	30	[3]	[3]	[3]
1936[2]	[3]	22	1,262	1,427	480	34	[3]	[3]	[3]
1937[2]	[3]	[3]	1,380	1,500	639	43	[3]	[3]	[3]

[1] Deliveries in the United States in 1913–1923; official Chilean exports in 1924–1934; United States imports, 1936–1937. [2] Estimated. [3] Not available.

producing countries are also the largest producers of byproduct nitrogen; Germany, United States, and Great Britain account for 75 per cent of the production, while France and Belgium supply about half of the remainder. The proportion of the world nitrogen output supplied from coal has been as high as 40 per cent, but the expansion of the fixation processes since the war period has reduced this proportion by half, though the actual tonnages now being produced are more than double those when the higher percentage prevailed. Lack of space prevents the presentation of data on the production in various countries, but the approximate distribution of the output by processes may be estimated from the figures in Table A, showing the plant capacity installed in the leading producing countries.

Air Nitrogen.—As with byproduct nitrogen, lack of space precludes the presentation of detailed data on country outputs, but Table A shows the extent of plant capacity installed for the various processes in all of the important countries. These figures emphasize strongly the rapid growth of the fixed nitrogen industry, particularly the synthetic processes, which account for 63.6 per cent of the 1934 plant capacity, against 10.6 per cent for cyanamid, 12.2 per cent for byproduct nitrogen, and 13.6 per cent for natural nitrates. Of the synthetic group, all but about 9,000 tons, or 0.2 per cent, is in ammonia plants of one type or another, the smaller figure representing the few scattered arc-process plants, most of which are in Norway.

By far the most outstanding feature of the whole nitrogen situation is the fact that at the present time the combined capacity of the nitrogen plants drawing their nitrogen supply from the air now totals about three-quarters of the entire world capacity for all types of nitrogen recovery; furthermore, since the total capacity now available is more than twice as great as any demand that has thus far been placed upon it, this means that air nitrogen alone could supply present needs, with a better than 50 per cent margin left over for increased emergency demand, without drawing on the mineral sources at all, if this turned out to be desirable or necessary. Even under these conditions, byproduct nitrogen has continued to expand, because of its low cost of recovery, and, while nitrate production has been severely handicapped by the competition of cheap ammonia, there is little possibility that it can be completely crowded out of the market by this competition.

UNITED STATES OUTPUT AND SUPPLY

The production of mineral nitrogen in the United States is limited to that recovered as a byproduct from gas and coke plants. Synthetic production was attempted in 1919, but did not actually get into successful operation until 1921, and grew slowly for the first decade. Declines during the depression years affected mineral sources more than synthetic, and, since 1932, the synthetic output has exceeded that from mineral sources. Another interesting side light is the effect of the depression on the distribution of byproduct nitrogen between gas and coke plants; since gas is largely used for domestic purposes, while coke goes mainly into industrial use, the depression decline in nitrogen recovered from coke plants was much greater than that from gas plants, with the result that the proportion recovered by gas plants about doubled during the worst years of the depression, but is now receding to more normal figures as the industrial demand for coke increases.

The mineral nitrogen production of the United States, being entirely a byproduct, is limited in amount, not by the demand for nitrogen, but by the demand for coke and gas, and is only a fraction of the total requirement. Hence, in the earlier years, when this constituted the entire output of the country, only 20–25 per cent of the requirements could be obtained from domestic sources. During the 'twenties the domestic production showed considerable increase, with the percentage of the supply from domestic sources just about doubled, until the expanding capacity of the synthetic plants reached a point where it more than offset the increases from byproduct sources. Synthetic production has so far outstripped the byproduct output that it is now larger by 50 per cent; in 1935, byproduct nitrogen made up only 30 per cent of the available supply, against 45 per cent for synthetic nitrogen.

The proportion of the world output consumed in the United States has also undergone a considerable change. Increasing from 20 per cent in 1913 to 37 per cent in 1918, there was a decline to the pre-war level during the post-war depression, following which it recovered to 26 per cent in 1923, but has since been gradually declining; even in 1929, when the domestic supply reached its peak tonnage, the percentage had dropped to 20 per cent, due to the rapid expansion of synthetic production throughout the world, and especially in Europe, and this trend is still continuing.

Details of domestic production, imports, exports, and available supply are shown in Table II.

Imports.—Between increases in domestic production from both byproduct and synthetic sources, and in the face of a consumption that has nearly trebled in amount since 1913, total imports have declined by more than one-half, from 76 per cent of the supply in 1913 to 37 per cent in 1935. Most of this decline has been

TABLE II.—AVAILABLE SUPPLY OF CHEMICAL NITROGEN IN THE UNITED STATES
(Thousands of metric tons of nitrogen content)

Year	Domestic Production from					Imports in						Available Supply	Percentage of Supply in				Per Cent of World Output Used in U. S.
	Coke Plants	Gas Plants	Total By-product	Synthetic Processes	Total Output	Sodium Nitrate	Ammonium Sulfate[1]	Other Fertilizers	Industrial Chemicals	Total Imports	Exports		By-product	Synthetic	Imports	Exports	
1913	28	7	36	.....	36	93	11	8[2]	[3]	115[5]	[3]	151	24	.....	76	[3]	20
1914	27	9	36	.....	36	88	15	9[2]	[3]	116[5]	[3]	152	24	.....	76	[3]	22
1915	32	9[2]	41	.....	41	122	7	7[2]	[3]	140[5]	[3]	181	23	.....	77	[3]	29
1916	44	10	54	.....	54	193	3	11[2]	[3]	210[5]	[3]	264	20	.....	80	[3]	29
1917	52	8	61	.....	61	245	2	10[2]	[3]	260[5]	[3]	321	19	.....	81	[3]	32
1918	65	5	70	.....	70	303	1	10[2]	[3]	317[5]	[3]	387	19	.....	81	[3]	37
1919	70	9	79	0.3	79	65	[4]	15[2]	[3]	82[5]	11	150	53	4	54	7	20
1920	88	5	93	0.3	93	210	[4]	25[2]	[3]	238[5]	19	313	30	4	76	6	35
1921	61	5	67	0.2	67	59	1	4[2]	[3]	64[5]	22	110	61	4	59	20	15
1922	84	5	89	0.6	89	86	1	10[2]	[3]	100[5]	31	158	56	4	63	20	20
1923	108	5	113[2]	5	118	141	1	18[2]	[3]	163[5]	32	249	45	2	66	13	26
1924	99	9	108	10	118	156	1	19	7	183	32	269	40	4	66	12	26
1925	116	9	125	12	137	176	5	24	8	214	33	318	39	6	67	10	24
1926	125	10	135	16	151	145	6	23	8	183	44	289	46	7	63	15	20
1927	128	11	139	22	161	119	16	29	8	171	33	300	47	7	57	11	20
1928	141	13	154	46	199	164	30	37	9	240	26	413	37	11	58	6	20
1929	150	16	166	123	289	148	8	41	9	214	38	465	36	26	46	8	20
1930	133	14	147	107	254	92	9	47	6	155	25	383	38	28	40	6	19
1931	95	14	110	88	198	90	25	23	5	142	31	309	35	29	46	10	19
1932	58	12	69	94	164	8	64	20	4	96	32	227	31	41	42	14	15
1933	71	14	85	125	209	20	73	24	5	123	21	310	27	40	40	7	19
1934	81	16	97	136	233	48	39	32	4	123	34	322	30	42	38	10	18
1935	93	12	105	160	265	64	25	36	5	129	43	351	30	45	37	12	16
Totals	1,952	227	2,179	945	3,124	2,835	343	482	118[5]	3,778	507	6,392	34	15	59	8	22
Per Cent	30.5	3.6	34.1	14.8	48.9	44.4	5.4	7.2	1.8	59.1	8.0						

[1] Includes mixed ammonium sulfate and nitrate. [2] Estimated from incomplete data. [3] Data not available. [4] Less than 500 tons. [5] Includes an estimate of imports during 1913–1923.

in the imports of sodium nitrate, which have dropped off heavily since 1925, as synthetic production increased.   On the other hand, imports of other forms of nitrogen have increased somewhat, particularly ammonium sulfate.   Imports of industrial nitrogen have never been large, and have declined slightly.

Exports.—The amounts of nitrogen exported from the United States have never been of any great size, as is to be expected in view of the status of the domestic output.   They reached 20 per cent of the available supply in the disturbed period of the postwar depression, when consumption was abnormally low, but, since then, have averaged only about one-half of this amount. The exports have been divided in the ratio of about 5 per cent industrial forms and 95 per cent fertilizer nitrogen, of which well over one-half was ammonium sulfate.

In addition to the domestic exports, the available supply should be still further decreased by the re-exports of foreign nitrogen, but these amounts are so small that they would make scarcely any appreciable difference, and, as the figures are scattered and incomplete, no attempt has been made to collect them. In most years it is probable that the amounts involved would be less than those discarded from the figures given in the table in rounding the actual amounts to even thousands of tons.

Consumption.—In general, figures on available supply approximate consumption only when taken over a long period of years, or when allowance is made for the annual fluctuations in stocks. Details of actual consumption of nitrogen for its more important forms and uses, during the years 1914 and 1924–1935, are shown later in Table VI, in the discussion of utilization.

Stocks.—Partial data on stocks of sodium nitrate will be found in Table B.   Nothing is available on stocks of other forms of nitrogen.

UTILIZATION OF NITROGEN

The details of the utilization of nitrogen in its more important forms and uses in the United States, for the years 1914 and 1924–1935, are shown in Table VI.   Fertilizer uses took 72.7 per cent of the total, and industrial uses 27.3 per cent.   Of the former, 27.8 per cent was as sodium nitrate, 31.0 per cent as ammonium sulfate, and 5.6 per cent as cyanamid; of the industrial uses, nitric acid (aside from that used in explosives) took 5.8 per cent,

TABLE VI.—UTILIZATION OF NITROGEN IN THE UNITED STATES
(Thousands of metric tons of nitrogen content)

Year	Fertilizer Uses					Industrial Uses						Total Consumption
	Sodium Nitrate	Ammonium Sulfate	Calcium Cyanimid	Other Forms	Total Fertilizer	Nitric Acid[2]	Explosives	Chemical Salts	Refrigeration	Miscellaneous	Total Industrial	
1914	54	32	6	......	91	16	32	21	4	......	72	164
1924	103	59	15	1	178	13	34	19	9	14	89	267
1925	113	73	20	2	208	14	35	19	10	14	92	301
1926	91	73	20	8	191	15	38	19	11	14	96	287
1927	77	88	18	19	202	16	35	17	11	15	94	296
1928	113	118	23	32	289	20	34	18	13	15	101	389
1929	123	114	27	32	296	26	36	20	14	16	112	409
1930	96	117	23	47	282	23	32	15	13	14	96	379
1931	81	95	9	32	217	21	24	12	11	11	78	295
1932	39	109	11	19	178	18	17	12	10	9	66	245
1933	62	118	11	23	214	17	18	14	9	10	68	282
1934	77	118	16	41	252	19	23	14	8	12	75	327
1935	94	111	23	63	290	22	22	16	7	14	82	371
Total[1]	1,069	1,193	216	319	2,797	224	348	195	126	158	1,049	3,848
Percentage[1]	27.8	31.0	5.6	8.3	72.7	5.8	9.0	5.1	3.3	4.1	27.3	100.0

[1] Not including 1914. [2] Not including nitric acid used in explosives manufacture.

explosives 9.0 per cent, various chemical salts 5.1 per cent, and refrigeration 3.3 per cent.

Under normal conditions the largest industrial use of nitrogen is in explosives, although the amount is not as large as might be expected; however, war demand will make a heavy increase in this rather modest demand, for it will then be augmented not only by the direct munitions requirements, but also by heavy increases in many of the normal lines of consumption, especially mining.

PRICES

In discussion of prices, the details of all of the wide variety of forms in which nitrogen is used will be avoided, and attention

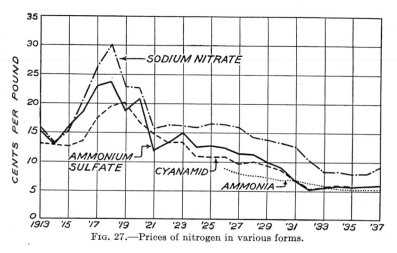

Fig. 27.—Prices of nitrogen in various forms.

will be centered on the four primary forms—sodium nitrate, ammonium sulfate, cyanamid, and anhydrous ammonia. In order to put these prices on a strictly comparable basis, they are given in Fig. 27, not in cents per pound of the commodity itself, but per pound of nitrogen contained in it. In this way the differences in cost of nitrogen from the different sources can be seen at a glance.

It was early recognized that Chile had a world monopoly on nitrate production, with comparatively little competition from other nitrogen compounds, and prices were accordingly held at a level well above that required by the cost of production. The prices of all of the other forms of nitrogen were based on the price fixed by the Chilean monopoly for sodium nitrate. It was not until the nitrogen from other sources took a definite lead in production that this was changed.

In the early years, when the production of byproduct nitrogen was comparatively small, its price ranged slightly higher than that of nitrate nitrogen, but from 1905 to 1915 both averaged about the same price; since 1915 ammonium sulfate has been definitely lower in price, and since 1921 the output of byproduct nitrogen has been well in advance of that of nitrate nitrogen. For 10 years previous to the beginning of the World War the price of both nitrate and byproduct nitrogen had averaged about 15 cents per pound. War demand doubled the price of nitrate nitrogen, but byproduct nitrogen increased somewhat less. After the close of the war, nitrate nitrogen dropped back to about its pre-war level, but there still remained a differential of 3–4 cents per pound in favor of byproduct nitrogen.

In 1921 air nitrogen exceeded in output both nitrate and byproduct nitrogen, and by 1928 the predominance of air nitrogen was so heavy that the former price for nitrate nitrogen could no longer be maintained in the face of the lower production cost of ammonia. A gradual lowering of the prices of all forms of nitrogen began, which lasted until 1933, since when prices have been fairly well stabilized at about 6 cents per pound for the nitrogen content of ammonium sulfate, anhydrous ammonia and cyanamid, but nitrate nitrogen still maintains a slightly higher level, at about 8 cents per pound.

Anhydrous ammonia from the synthetic process has become the foremost nitrogen compound, and its price now rules the market for other forms, rather than following them, as was formerly the case. The prices of all other forms of nitrogen have closely followed the downward trend established by ammonia as the synthetic process gained in importance and magnitude. Ammonia prices previous to 1926 were for cylinder shipments, and were so much greater than the later tank-car prices for bulk shipments that there is no basis for comparison. Cyanamid nitrogen has at most times held a level closely comparable with that of ammonium sulfate, but the differential of 2–3 cents per pound formerly ruling in favor of cyanamid has gradually disappeared.

TARIFF

From August, 1862, to December, 1870, there was a duty of 1 per cent per pound on sodium nitrate imported into the United States, but since then it has entered duty free. The other basic compound of mineral origin, ammonium sulfate, is now on the free list, but during 1922–1930 it carried a duty of $5.60 per long ton. Nitrogen fixed by synthetic processes has also been

TABLE VIII.—TARIFF RATES ON NITROGEN COMPOUNDS
(In cents per pound, or per cent ad valorem)

	1909–1913	1913–1922	1922–1930	1930—
Industrial Chemicals				
Acids—nitric	....	Free	Free	Free
Ammonium compounds				
Anhydrous ammonia	....	2½c.	2½c.	2½c.
Carbonate[1]	1½c.	¾c.	1½c.	2c.
Chloride	¾c.	¾c.	1¼c.	1¼c.
Gas liquor	....	10%	20%	....
Nitrate	....	Free	1c.	1c.
Perchlorate	....	Free	1½c.	1½c.
Phosphate[2]	25%	1c.	1½c.	1½c.
Cyanide salts, n.s.p.f.[3]	....	....	Free	Free
Lead nitrate	....	1¼c.	3c.	3c.
Picric acid	....	7c. + 60%	7c. + 60%	7c. + 60%
Potassium compounds				
Cyanide	12½%	Free	Free	Free
Ferricyanide	8c.	2c.	7c.	7c.
Ferrocyanide	4c.	1¼c.	4c.	4c.
Nitrate, refined	½c.	$7/ton	½c.	1c.
Sodium compounds				
Cyanide	Free	Free	Free	Free
Ferrocyanide	2c.	¾c.	2c.	2c.
Nitrite	2c.	½c.	3c.	4½c.
Fertilizers				
Ammonium compounds				
Sulfate	....	Free	$5.60/ton	Free
Sulfate-nitrate	....	....	Free	Free
Phosphate[4]	....	....	1½c.	Free
Calcium cyanamid	Free	Free	Free	Free
Calcium nitrate	Free	Free	Free	Free
Potassium nitrate, crude	Free	Free	Free	Free
Sodium nitrate	Free	Free	Free	Free
Urea[5]	....	25%	35%	Free
Fertilizer mixtures	....	Free	Free	Free
Fertilizer materials, n.e.s.[6]	Free	Free	Free	Free

NOTE.—Leaders indicate that the product is not listed in the tariff act in question, though it may be included elsewhere under a blanket coverage.

[1] Includes bicarbonate after 1922. [2] For industrial use only. [3] n.s.p.f., not specially provided for. [4] For fertilizer use only. [5] Included mixtures of urea and calcium nitrate after 1930. [6] n.e.s., not elsewhere specified.

on the free list in calcium cyanamid, but in anhydrous ammonia has carried a duty of 2½ cents per pound since 1913. The accompanying table shows the tariff rates on all of the more important nitrogen compounds, but does not include some of the minor items, of which only small amounts are imported, particularly if the commodity is not imported primarily for its nitrogen content, even though it is listed in the tariff schedule; also, many minor items are included only in a blanket coverage under such headings as "Other compounds not elsewhere specified."

In reviewing Table VIII it is particularly interesting to note in the succeeding tariff acts the trend which has finally placed all fertilizer materials on the free list, while rates on most of the industrial compounds are increasing. This has a special political significance, and is a manifestation of the same political expediency which later led to the formation of the Tennessee Valley Authority, with a blanket warrant to improve and cheapen fertilizers in any way that its judgment dictated.

POLITICAL AND COMMERCIAL CONTROL

More different phases and variants of political and commercial control have been utilized in connection with the nitrogen industry than in any other strategic mineral. The ordinary lines of both political and commercial control, such as have been discussed in connection with other commodities, operated in the usual fashion, but proved insufficient to cover the ground, and in addition to these we have two additional factors entering into the situation:

First, practically complete monopolistic control of production and prices of sodium nitrate, so long as this was the primary source of world nitrogen;

And later, when synthetic nitrogen took precedence in production and in the market, a system of international cartel control of prices, and production and export quotas.

As we look back over the developments of the past 30 years, we can see that the second of these was the direct and almost inevitable outgrowth of the conditions which led to and developed from the first. The major factors involved are chiefly concerned with sodium nitrate and synthetic ammonia; the outputs of the arc processes and the cyanamid process are too small in proportion to have had very much effect, but such as it was fell on the side of the synthetic production; the byproduct nitrogen output is much larger, but it is so widely distributed that only nationality of capital ownership and the ordinary features of political control are concerned.

Early in the history of the nitrate industry the advantages of monopoly control of the industry were realized, and the producers formed an association for the control of production and prices, which has continued to operate in one form or another, although the advent of large quantities of cheaper synthetic nitrogen eventually nullified the price control. So long as Chile was the leading nitrogen producer, the entire world was dependent on this remote source for the bulk of its nitrogen supply, at whatever price the monopoly dictated, but the condition was one of long standing and had come to be more or less generally accepted as a necessary evil.   Little was done to remedy the situation beyond fostering such other supplementary sources as were available, until the advent of the World War emphasized in a most uncomfortable fashion the handicap of the remoteness and inaccessibility of the Chilean supply.

It is true that the European Allies and the United States were able, with some difficulty, and at a heavy increase in price, to maintain their necessary shipments of nitrate from Chile, through the naval control of England over sea traffic, and at the same time to blockade German ports and prevent her importation of nitrates; but, while this fact made shipments possible, it did not in any way simplify the problems involved in long distance shipping of large tonnages with insufficient shipping facilities. While the German blockade was an important advantage to the Allies from a military standpoint and became for the time being a commercial advantage for the Chilean government and the producers, it turned out to be the factor that eventually led to the overthrow of Chilean supremacy in the nitrogen industry. Up to this time the various fixation processes were in hardly more than an experimental stage of development, but the inability to import nitrate made it necessary for Germany to turn to the fixation processes for their required nitrogen supply, with the result that under the pressure of this imperative demand, the synthetic industry was put on its feet in a fraction of the time that probably otherwise would have been required.

At the same time, such a furor was raised in the United States over possible shortage of supply that construction was started on two government owned plants, one cyanamid and one synthetic; while the construction of these plants had not yet been completed at the time of the Armistice and they contributed nothing to the war supply of nitrogen, they did give a considerable impetus to the development of the fixation industry in this country, in spite of the fact that neither was ever operated commercially and the synthetic plant was a failure.

Following the war there was a veritable epidemic of agitation for national self-sufficiency in various countries whose sources of supply of imported materials had been disturbed by the war, and in this race nitrogen has led the field. Plant capacity has been multiplied to such an extent that, as already mentioned, the synthetic plants alone can now supply more nitrogen than has ever before been required, without reference to the nitrate and byproduct capacity. This has not seriously affected the byproduct side of the industry, which by its nature of byproduct recovery can be operated on a very small margin, but it has decimated the ranks of the Chilean producers.

The existence of a total production capacity about twice the size of the demand necessitated a new form of control in the industry, to prevent cut-throat competition, flooding the market, and the inevitable resulting fall of prices below the cost of production. As a result, there was organized in 1929 an International Nitrogen Cartel, for the purpose of establishing price control and production and export quotas in the industry. As has been the case with all such cartel arrangements, there has been much jockeying for advantage in quotas, and more or less difficulty in coming to a final agreement, but the cartel has been renewed from year to year, with various readjustments, and still remains in operation, although there have been some lapses through failure to reach a new agreement before the expiration of the old one.

As a result of the hardships imposed on the Chilean producers by their loss of supremacy in the market, and the consequent shrinkage in sales, which was later intensified by the world-wide economic depression, heroic measures had to be taken to keep the industry on its feet. The first effort to cope with the situation was the abandonment in 1927 by the Chilean Nitrate Producers' Association of their former uniform price policy, in order to meet the declining prices of synthetic nitrogen. The next stage in the development was the entry of the Chilean producers into the nitrogen cartel in 1930. However, cartel membership did not materially improve the situation, and 1931 brought an entire reorganization which was in effect a nationalization of the industry, since the Chilean government participated in the holding company to the extent of 50 per cent of its stock, the other 50 per cent being distributed among the former owners of the plants taken over.

Although this optimistic effort was organized for a period of 60 years, it was involved in political and financial difficulties from the beginning, which prevented it from ever functioning to any practical extent, and early in 1933 it was dissolved and the plants were turned back to their former owners; the two largest producers retained a separate identity, but thirty-four smaller plants were grouped together in a third organization, so that at the present time there are in effect only three producers. All three of these work under a sales corporation, organized in 1934, which fixes the production quotas of the plants, and has a monopoly on the sale and export of the products.

There is little specific information as to commercial control through capital ownership. It is understood that recent ownership is largely foreign, with United States capital the leading factor, but including also British, French, and Spanish capital; no information is available either on the actual proportions in which these are represented or on the amount of local Chilean capital involved.

At the beginning of the World War, about one-third of the Chilean production capacity was owned by German capital, and this fact led to one of the most interesting examples of the possibility of the manipulation of political control to secure a military advantage. The German-owned plants could not export their product to Germany, and of course they refused to sell to the Allies or to the United States, which was actively engaged in furnishing munitions to the Allies. Hence, by the time the United States entered the war there was a large accumulation of German-owned nitrate in Chile. At the same time, Chilean currency was constantly depreciating for lack of gold to support it, since the main Chilean gold reserves had been deposited in German banks, which refused to release it. When this condition became known to the United States military authorities, arrangements were made with Chile for governmental seizure of the German nitrates, in reprisal for the refusal to release Chilean gold; the nitrates were then sold by the Chilean government to the United States for gold to support their declining currency.

GENERAL REVIEW OF THE DOMESTIC SITUATION

Before discussing the general status of the nitrogen industry in the United States, each of the four basic types of production will first be considered briefly, as a foundation for the broader problem.

1. The United States has no domestic production of natural nitrates, and no prospect of ever being able to develop one from the small, scattered, low grade deposits that are known to exist.

2. The main source of byproduct nitrogen is the byproduct coke oven, the production from retort gas plants being comparatively small. The first byproduct coke ovens were built in the United States in 1893, and, 20 years later, at the outbreak of the World War, domestic byproduct nitrogen was supplying 24 per cent of the consumption. Still more rapid growth followed, and by 1923 the production was larger than the total pre-war domestic consumption, and the peak output in 1929 was still larger by nearly one-third. The main chance for increased production of byproduct nitrogen centers in possible expansion of the demand for byproduct coke.

3. There is as yet no cyanamid nitrogen production in the United States. As a war measure, a cyanamid plant with a rated capacity of about 36,000 metric tons of fixed nitrogen annually was built at Muscle Shoals, Alabama, but construction was not completed until after the Armistice, and the plant was never operated, except for a two-weeks' trial run early in 1919. The act creating the Tennessee Valley Authority in 1933 authorized this agency to utilize the Muscle Shoals plant in its program of improving and cheapening fertilizers in any way that its judgment dictated; and, since by this time the plant has largely become obsolete for the purpose for which it was built, it is understood that it has been partially dismantled in order to use some of the equipment for other purposes. Although there is no cyanamid plant in operation within the United States, the largest plant of this kind in the world, rated at about 71,000 metric tons of fixed nitrogen annually, is situated immediately adjacent to the United States border, at Niagara Falls, Canada, and a large proportion of its output is exported to the United States.

4. One of the earliest attempts to utilize the nitrogen of the air by direct synthesis was started at Niagara Falls, New York, in 1902, using the Bradley and Lovejoy process, an arc process for the oxidation of nitrogen. This attempt was not successful, nor were several other experimental efforts, including the plant for the direct synthesis of ammonia, built by the Government at the same time as the Muscle Shoals cyanamid plant. The first successful synthetic ammonia plant in the country was built in 1921, and this was followed by several others. One of these was closed down in 1929; a second was remodeled for the production of another product, but may be considered a potential producer should demand justify the shift back to the original operation.

All told, the present synthetic ammonia capacity is equivalent to about 310,000 metric tons of nitrogen, 88 per cent of which is in two plants, one of 100,000 short tons capacity near Charleston, West Virginia, and the other of twice this size at Hopewell, West Virginia, with seven smaller plants.

Potential Production Capacity.—Byproduct coke ovens in use or under construction at the end of 1936 were reported to have an annual capacity for treating 91,900,000 short tons of coal, operating at full capacity. At an average recovery of 22 pounds of ammonium sulfate per ton of coal treated, this is equivalent to a possible recovery of 917,000 metric tons of ammonium sulfate, or 189,000 tons of nitrogen. This figure includes the ammonia recovered from gas plants using byproduct coke ovens for city gas production, but does not include that from other gas plants; corresponding figures for these plants are not available, but it is estimated that the total byproduct nitrogen capacity from all sources would be in the neighborhood of 200,000 metric tons.

With 200,000 tons of capacity in byproduct nitrogen, and 310,000 tons in synthetic nitrogen, we then have a present total potential capacity of 510,000 tons, which is 75 per cent greater than the largest production on record, and 25 per cent greater than the largest consumption figure on record, both of which records were made in 1929. Expansion to meet possible emergency demand in excess of this capacity would mainly center in the enlargement of present synthetic capacity; it is reported that the Charleston plant could be almost doubled in capacity at short notice, and that the Hopewell plant has 90,000 short tons of additional capacity in stand-by condition. Including such minor increases as might be obtained from increased coke-plant construction in the meantime and possible further replacement of beehive coke with byproduct, and calling on the present unused capacity and the quick additions that may be made on emergency demand, there could be made available nearly 700,000 tons of nitrogen annually.

These figures show a considerable surplus when balanced against estimated requirements, even when the ordinary civilian uses are augmented by emergency demand and increased by an estimated munitions requirement of 100,000 tons annually. But, should a shortage occur through any unforeseen development, it may be partly offset by retaining some 30,000 tons a year of former exports and, if necessary, by restriction of agricultural use, since there is a sufficient amount of nitrogen stored in most soils to permit of considerable reduction in current fertilizer consumption for one, or even two years, without serious effect on the food supply, though of course continued deprivation of the soil of the usual nitrogen additions would result in heavy decreases in yield.

CONCLUSION

All told, probably greater progress has been made toward self-sufficiency in nitrogen supply than is the case with any other strategic mineral product; during the World War a deficiency of 80 per cent in the consumption requirements had to be supplied by imports, but since then byproduct recovery has expanded and a whole new synthetic industry has come into existence, with the result that current imports have already declined by more than half, and could be reduced still further if conditions demanded it.   The United States is no longer dependent on Chilean nitrate for its nitrogen supply, and in fact could dispense with it entirely if necessary.   Nitrate imports still continue, though in greatly lessened amounts, and probably would persist in the event of war, if the sea lanes remained open, and might even increase during the early months of the emergency, while domestic production was being expanded.   However, in case imports are blocked, there is no present reason to anticipate any serious shortage, beyond a possible temporary one in the early months.   Such a shortage as might possibly develop is likely to be more in the capacity for the conversion of ammonia to nitric acid, rather than in the primary nitrogen fixation capacity; this is the chief factor that might make increased nitrate imports desirable, at least for a time.

Although nitrogen remained on the official strategic or critical lists of the War Department until recently, it was no longer there from the standpoint of possible shortage of supply of raw material, but solely because of the plant equipment problem, particularly in the conversion of ammonia to nitric acid.   In 1936 nitrogen was removed from the strategic list, and nitric acid and ammonia were placed on the critical list; in January 1939 these two items were transferred to the newly organized essential list (see Chapter I, p. 6).

CHAPTER XV

DOMESTIC SELF-SUFFICIENCY

In the preceding chapters the various members of the strategic minerals group have each been discussed in some detail, and the present chapter will be devoted to a summary of all members of the group from one specific angle—namely, the degree of domestic self-sufficiency, or the percentage of the annual consumption that is supplied by the domestic production, as in this way one can best secure a general picture of the status of the group as a whole, and the relative importance of the various members. To accomplish this most readily, the domestic production, consumption, and percentage of self-sufficiency of each of the twelve members of the group have been compiled in tabular form and shown in a graph for the full 25-year period since 1913. In the case of aluminum, the figures are shown both for the metal and the ore, and in addition the combined self-sufficiency ratio is calculated, to show the total aluminum available, whether the exports and imports involved in determining the consumption were in the form of bauxite or metal. Each of these graphs and tables is then followed by a brief discussion of the salient features pertaining to the material in question.

The consumption figures are based on production plus imports, less exports, but at best complete coverage can not be secured, for exports and imports in manufactured form under the main headings are usually reported only by value and not by weight, and many manufactured items under other headings include parts made of metals covered by the list. In addition, it is also impossible in most cases to take into account variations in stocks, since these are not recorded. For these reasons, the figures labeled consumption, as a matter of convenience and brevity, really represent not true consumption, but rather the supply available for consumption.

To assist still further in securing this general picture, the self-sufficiency ratios of the different members of the strategic list are tabulated below for various important times in the 25-year period—in 1913, at the peak year of war production, at the peak year of the pre-depression and post-depression eras, and finally the average for the entire period.

SELF-SUFFICIENCY RATIOS FOR THE STRATEGIC MINERALS

		Pre-war, 1913	War Peak	Pre-de-pression Peak	Post-de-pression Peak	Period Average
I.	Tin	0.1	0.1	0.1	0.2	0.1
	Nickel	3	1	4	0.2	1
II.	Chromium	0.5	45	0.3	0.4	4
	Manganese	1	36	12	4	8
III.	Antimony	22	14	19	9	17
	Mica	43	37	31	16	26
	Bauxite	91	105	67	64	75
	Aluminum	66	121	91	89	75
	Combined	60	125	55	46	66
IV.	Tungsten	42	70	40	37	36
	Mercury	95	118	122	47	63
V.	Platinum	1	15	5	11	6
	Iodine				13	19[1]
	Nitrogen	24	18	66	84	51

[1] Average since 1932, when production was first reported.

From inspection of the self-sufficiency ratios, the strategic list can readily be divided into the five indicated groups, differentiated as follows:

I. Those for which the self-sufficiency ratio is practically zero, with no prospect for improvement; this group includes Tin and Nickel.

II. Those for which the self-sufficiency ratio is normally very low, but which are subject to a marked improvement under emergency demand; this group includes Chromium and Manganese.

III. Those with a moderate degree of self-sufficiency under ordinary conditions, but with little prospect for marked improvement under emergency demand; this group includes Antimony, Mica, and Bauxite and Aluminum.

IV. Those with a moderate degree of self-sufficiency under ordinary conditions, and a possibility for material improvement under emergency demand; this group includes Tungsten, and Mercury.

V. Those having been removed from the official list after developing a safe margin of reserve supply or a high degree of self-sufficiency; this group includes Platinum, Iodine, and Nitrogen.

From the standpoint of accessibility of material for use, the importance of the various items decreases as one proceeds down the list as arranged above, but this can not be said to represent the full strategic importance of the materials in question; for this the relative accessibility of the various sources of supply must also be taken into consideration, with respect to possible interruption of supply from the more remote sources, and also another factor which is of even greater importance—the specific use for which each product is required. Each is important in its own field, but the relative importance varies with the type of use, and no hard and fast values can be assigned arbitrarily to any of them. For this reason, no fixed order of importance can be made, except under some specific set of conditions, and then only with full knowledge of the sacrifices that must be made if a shortage of one material results from efforts to secure more of something else.

In order to economize on space in the setting of the tables, the headings of the columns are abbreviated as follows:

For production   *Prod.*
For consumption   *Cons.*
For self-sufficiency   *Suff.*

For convenience in locating desired material, the various commodities are arranged in alphabetical order, rather than in the groups as listed on the preceding page.

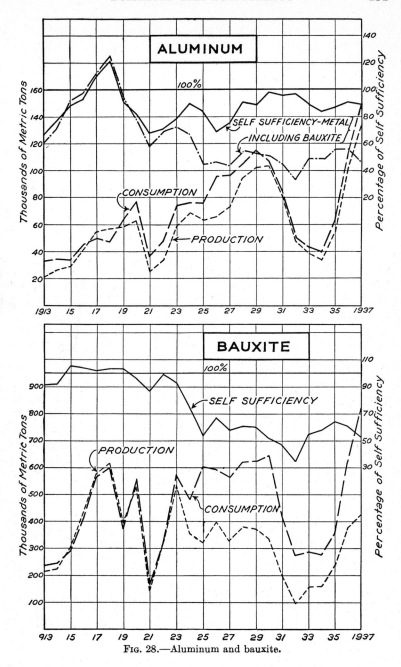

FIG. 28.—Aluminum and bauxite.

ALUMINUM AND BAUXITE
(In thousands of metric tons)

	Aluminum			Bauxite			Total Suff.
Year	Prod.	Cons.	Suff.	Prod.	Cons.	Suff.	
1913	21	32	66	213	235	91	60
1914	26.3	34.3	77	223	243	92	71
1915	28.9	32.9	88	302	289	105	92
1916	42.0	45.0	93	432	414	104	97
1917	55.0	50.0	110	578	564	102	112
1918	57.0	46.9	121	615	599	103	125
1919	58.1	63.8	91	383	371	103	94
1920	62.6	76.5	82	530	551	96	79
1921	24.5	36.3	68	142	164	87	59
1922	33.6	47.7	71	315	319	99	70
1923	58.5	74.0	79	531	572	93	73
1924	68.3	76.2	90	353	480	74	67
1925	63.5	76.0	84	322	601	54	45
1926	65.8	95.5	69	399	596	67	46
1927	72.6	96.6	75	326	564	58	44
1928	95.3	105.0	91	381	622	61	55
1929	102.1	115.3	89	373	624	60	53
1930	103.9	106.4	98	336	646	52	51
1931	80.5	84.2	96	199	420	47	45
1932	47.6	49.0	97	98	278	35	34
1933	38.6	43.5	89	157	287	55	49
1934	33.6	39.9	84	160	277	58	49
1935	54.1	62.0	87	238	357	64	56
1936	102.0	112.2	91	378	620	61	56
1937	133.0	150.2	89	427	818	52	46
Total	1,528.4	1,751.4	87	10,549	14,004	75	66

Bauxite is the only item in the strategic list which, within the 25-year period under discussion, has shown a consistent growth in production sufficient to develop an excess supply over a period of several years in succession, as happened during the war period, but the drain on the ore reserves was too great to maintain this rate of production, and as soon as war demand ceased, production began to drop, and continued to decline to below the pre-war level. Although the production tonnage has increased with increasing demand for the metal, it has failed to keep pace with consumption, and the self-sufficiency ratios have shown a consistent and almost continuous decline. The self-sufficiency averages for the successive 5-year periods were 100 per cent, 99 per cent, 69 per cent, 54 per cent, and 58 per cent; post-depression recovery was responsible for the increase in the last period, but this failed to keep up in 1937, when the percentage dropped to 52 per cent, the lowest figure in the entire 25 years, except for the nadir of the depression.

It is primarily the shortage of ore supply, and not lack of reduction capacity, that is responsible for the addition of aluminum to the strategic list. Since 1913 the metal output has more than quadrupled in amount, but only by constantly drawing more and more heavily on foreign sources for the necessary bauxite supply. Imports of metal have remained at a comparatively low level, and although the post-war depression cut the metal self-sufficiency temporarily below its normal level, outside of this period the self-sufficiency level has for the most part been maintained between 80 and 90 per cent, with the years of the depression showing figures near 100 per cent.

The table shows the self-sufficiency figures not only for metal and ore separately, but also for the two combined, giving the percentage of domestic production in the entire consumption, regardless of whether the imported material was brought into the country in the form of metal or of bauxite. This total self-sufficiency rose from 60 per cent in 1913 to a maximum of 125 per cent in 1918 and then dropped with the declining bauxite output; since 1925 it has ranged mostly from 45 per cent to 55 per cent.

Attention should be called to one source of inaccuracy in these figures other than those mentioned in the preceding general discussion. Due to the fact that in the domestic export statistics bauxite and purified alumina are reported together, the exports as reported are lower than if they were converted to the bauxite equivalent. Since the separate figures are not reported, the true bauxite exports can not be determined, and since in some years the alumina was a material proportion of the total, the consumption figures obtained after deduction of the exports are somewhat too high, and the corresponding self-sufficiency figures are too low.

The chief source of foreign imports is British Guiana and Surinam, with New Orleans and Mobile as the receiving ports, so that most of the voyage may be made in the Caribbean Sea and the Gulf of Mexico, both of which are more favorable to the protection of shipping than would be the case in the open ocean, with correspondingly less liability of shipments being interrupted in the event of war, and hence greater security in the maintenance of the necessary flow of imports to supplement the failing domestic supply.

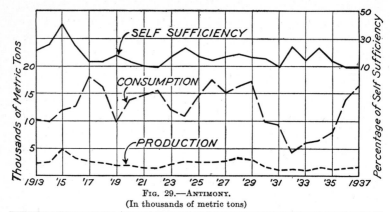

FIG. 29.—ANTIMONY.
(In thousands of metric tons)

Year	Prod.	Cons.	Suff.	Year	Prod.	Cons.	Suff.
1913	2.3	10.5	22	1926	2.4	17.6	14
1914	2.5	9.8	26	1927	2.5	15.0	17
1915	4.9	12.0	41	1928	3.1	16.4	19
1916	3.2	12.7	25	1929	2.8	17.1	16
1917	2.5	18.1	14	1930	1.5	10.0	15
1918	2.3	16.3	14	1931	0.9	9.2	9
1919	1.8	9.9	18	1932	1.0	4.1	24
1920	1.8	13.9	13	1933	0.8	5.7	14
1921	1.4	14.6	10	1934	1.5	6.3	24
1922	1.3	15.5	9	1935	1.0	7.5	13
1923	2.0	12.0	17	1936	1.3	13.5	10
1924	2.5	10.7	23	1937	1.5	16.2	9
1925	2.4	14.4	17	Total	51.2	309.0	17

There is no way of securing accurate data on domestic antimony production; the official statistics report the antimony content of the ore output, and also the antimony content of antimonial lead produced, but neither of these covers the exact production; probably most of the ore goes to the lead smelters, but these also use lead ores containing antimony, some of which may have been of foreign origin. The best approximation that can be reached is to use the antimony content of the hard lead production; while this probably contains some antimony of foreign origin, this is offset by domestic ores which do not reach the lead smelter, but are used in some other way. However, when the self-sufficiency is as low as 10–20 per cent, such small errors as there may be in the domestic output figures largely disappear, and have little real importance.

The United States has no established metal production from domestic ores, other than in hard lead, and never has had, except for a small temporary one during the war period, although since 1931 there has been in operation a domestic smelting plant using imported ores, chiefly from Mexico and South America, which has been supplying from one-quarter to one-third of the current demand, and has not yet been operated at its full capacity. This has correspondingly increased the ore imports and reduced the metal imports; while the country is still just as dependent as ever on foreign sources, the strategic position is materially improved by the existence of a domestic smelting plant, since this increases the stocks of both ore and metal in the country, as well as improving the situation in other ways, but the location of the plant, on the Texas border, is not all that could be desired from a defense standpoint, although it is the logical one from an economic standpoint, since the bulk of the ore supply is drawn from Mexico. The plant would be particularly difficult to protect in an emergency involving Mexico as an unfriendly nation, which is not at all impossible. The establishment of domestic smelting has not had any appreciable effect on the domestic production of antimony ore, and thus far there seems to be but little chance for much improvement in this direction.

An important feature of the domestic market is the extent to which the demand for antimony oxide has expanded during the past few years, most of it being produced domestically, but from imported ores; at the same time there has been a marked reduction in the demand for metal, so that while the total consumption in all forms remains about the same, the distribution between oxide and metal has been radically altered.

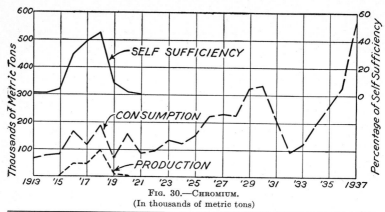

Fig. 30.—Chromium.
(In thousands of metric tons)

Year	Prod.	Cons.	Suff.	Year	Prod.	Cons.	Suff.
1913..............	0.3	66.4	1	1926..............	0.1	220.0	......
1914..............	0.6	76.3	1	1927..............	0.2	226.6	......
1915..............	3.3	82.3	4	1928..............	0.7	222.3	......
1916..............	47.8	165.8	29	1929..............	0.3	324.8	......
1917..............	44.4	117.6	38	1930..............	0.1	332.4	......
1918..............	83.7	185.5	45	1931..............	0.3	216.6	......
1919..............	5.2	68.8	8	1932..............	0.2	91.1	......
1920..............	2.5	158.3	2	1933..............	0.8	119.6	1
1921..............	0.3	84.3	......	1934..............	0.4	196.0	......
1922..............	0.4	92.8	......	1935..............	0.5	263.9	......
1923..............	0.2	134.8	......	1936..............	0.3	330.1	......
1924..............	0.3	121.5	......	1937..............	2.4	565.8	......
1925..............	0.1	153.6	......	Total..............	195.4	4,707.2	4

The figures listed above are those for the only commercial ore of chromium, chromite; imports and exports of metal and alloys are so small that they can be ignored. Domestic production has been of significant proportions only during the war period, and since 1920 there has been only one year in which the self-sufficiency exceeded 0.5 per cent. Although self-sufficiency was built up during the war period to a maximum of 45 per cent of the then comparatively small consumption, production practically stopped with the cessation of war demand and war prices, and has since been so low that the average for the entire period has been only 4 per cent. During the past 10 years the metal uses, as distinguished from the refractory and chemical uses, have increased heavily, and it is largely to this that the marked expansion in consumption has been due. In fact, so many new applications have been developed for chromium in various alloys, particularly the stainless steels and the nickel-chromium type of high-temperature alloy, that consumption has been expanded to such a point that all former bases of comparison and of calculation of possible requirements have become obsolete, as probable requirements have been more than doubled over those of the war period. Current statistics show that the production of stainless steels in 1937 approximated 140,000 tons, about five times the output for 1932, and while the exact chromium content is not reported, but it is estimated that the consumption of chromite for this purpose alone was probably about 75,000 tons—and that for a use which a few years ago was non-existent.

The 1937 consumption of 566,000 tons was apparently heavily inflated by surplus purchases for stocks, in view of the rapidly expanding demand, rising prices, and the uncertainty of world political conditions, but it is impossible to say just what proportion of the total went into stocks and what into actual production.

In view of the increasing demand, particular care must be taken in making estimates for probable future consumption; emergency stocks calculated on the basis of current consumption a few years ago would be entirely inadequate to supply present rates of consumption, let alone possible increases due to emergency demand.

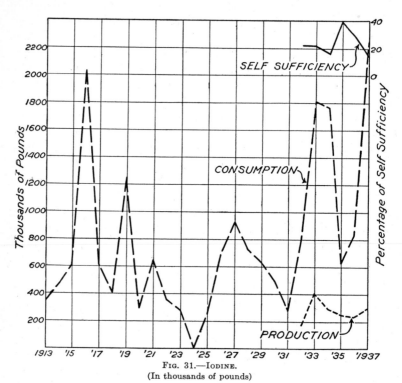

FIG. 31.—IODINE.
(In thousands of pounds)

Year	Prod.	Cons.	Suff.	Year	Prod.	Cons.	Suff.
1913	......	351	......	1926	......	711	......
1914	......	463	......	1927	......	926	......
1915	......	613	......	1928	......	721	......
1916	......	2,033	......	1929	......	627	......
1917	......	610	......	1930	......	494	......
1918	......	407	......	1931	......	279	......
1919	......	1,254	......	1932	174	806	22
1920	......	294	......	1933	402	1,814	22
1921	......	646	......	1934	284	1,765	16
1922	......	353	......	1935	246	622	40
1934	......	273	......	1936	234	826	28
1924	......	......	......	1937	299	2,266	13
1925	......	246	......				

The only measure of domestic iodine consumption is the quantity imported or produced, and since the imports are highly irregular from year to year, they can only show an average consumption over a long period of years. The annual fluctuations in imports have no real connection with corresponding changes in consumption, due to the fact that the importers maintain large stocks, which are replenished periodically when they go below a set minimum (now understood to be 1,000 tons); frequently only one or two large shipments are received in a year, and occasionally a whole year has passed without new shipments. Domestic production did not begin until recently, and has been restricted by heavy competition from imported material, with no protective tariff to support it. Even though the domestic output has not been permitted to reach large proportions, it has been sufficient to reduce the price of the imported product from $4–$5 per pound to less than $1, and it has been established that the domestic resources are sufficient to be capable of supplying most, if not all the demand in case imports were cut off, although this would of course involve a material increase in price above the present level. This fact, supplemented by the large stocks maintained by the importers, led to the recent transfer of iodine from the official list of strategic mineral supplies to the critical list. However, there is practically no hope that the domestic iodine industry will ever become self-supporting, unless it is protected by a tariff.

The use of iodine in stock and poultry feeds is causing a marked increase in iodine consumption, and if this keeps on at the present rate the stocks maintained by the importers will no longer be sufficient to maintain consumption for a reasonable period. This will necessitate periodical increases in the stocks proportionate to the increased demand if the present emergency status of iodine is to remain unimpaired with respect to current consumption. On the other hand, the new uses, while highly desirable as to the results obtained, are not strictly essential from an emergency standpoint, and if conditions required, these uses could be temporarily restricted or abandoned if it became necessary to prolong the life of the stocks in an emergency.

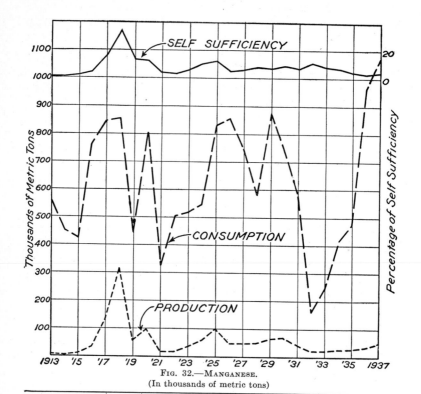

Fig. 32.—Manganese.

(In thousands of metric tons)

Year	Prod.	Cons.	Suff.	Year	Prod.	Cons.	Suff.
1913.............	4.1	561	1	1926.............	47.0	857	5
1914.............	2.7	451	1	1927.............	45.5	747	6
1915.............	9.8	426	2	1928.............	47.6	581	8
1916.............	32.0	764	4	1929.............	61.3	877	7
1917.............	131.5	847	16	1930.............	68.1	744	9
1918.............	310.8	857	36	1931.............	39.9	588	7
1919.............	55.8	449	13	1932.............	18.1	160	11
1920.............	95.9	805	12	1933.............	19.5	246	8
1921.............	13.7	326	4	1934.............	26.9	415	7
1922.............	13.6	503	3	1935.............	26.9	475	4
1923.............	32.0	520	6	1936.............	32.6	963	3
1924.............	57.4	547	10	1937.............	40.9	1,066	4
1925.............	99.9	833	12	Total.............	1,233.5	15,508	8

The domestic manganese production has never been of any importance until shortage of outside supplies forced the expansion of the home output during the war period. It having been demonstrated that appreciable amounts could be obtained, a serious attempt was made after the war to establish the domestic industry on a permanent basis, but competition from the established foreign sources, and later from additional new deposits, has prevented any extensive domestic production. The figures listed above are based entirely on ore, and consumption is adjusted to include the approximate ore equivalent of metal and alloys imported or exported.

The heavy expansion of apparent consumption in 1936 and 1937 was somewhat higher than actual current consumption, as considerable amounts of ore were added to stocks, in order that consumers might be assured of future supplies.

Although the self-sufficiency ratio during the past 10 years has been quite low, it would be possible in an emergency to increase production considerably, just as was done during the World War, although possibly not to the same extent, unless research work now under way succeeds in making low grade ores available for the production of high grade metal and alloys. Should this be accomplished, the large domestic low grade deposits can supply any demand that may be put on them.

Pending the successful utilization of low grade ores, dependence for domestic supplies is limited by the size and grade of the reserves to an amount that is patently inadequate. On the other hand, in order to meet possible emergency shortage, the stocks of ore in the hands of consumers and in bonded warehouses have been increased heavily in the past two years, and now represent a supply sufficient for about two years at current rates of consumption, or a year and a half at probably emergency demand. Under these conditions, the emergency status of manganese has not been fully met, but it is in a fairly adequate position so long as the stocks are maintained at their present level.

FIG. 33.—MERCURY.
(In thousands of pounds)

Year	Prod.	Cons.	Suff.	Year	Prod.	Cons.	Suff.
1913.............	1,516	1,601	95	1926.............	573	2,512	22
1914.............	1,241	1,749	71	1927.............	846	2,362	36
1915.............	1,577	1,746	90	1928.............	1,358	2,465	55
1916.............	2,245	2,003	112	1929.............	1,800	2,934	61
1917.............	2,712	2,295	118	1930.............	1,638	1,821	90
1918.............	2,466	2,738	90	1931.............	1,897	1,560	122
1919.............	1,606	1,721	93	1932.............	959	1,238	77
1920.............	1,004	1,951	51	1933.............	735	2,279	32
1921.............	475	1,240	38	1934.............	1,174	1,949	60
1922.............	478	1,725	28	1935.............	1,321	1,915	69
1923.............	595	1,926	37	1936.............	1,259	2,614	48
1924.............	756	1,728	44	1937.............	1,255	2,658	47
1925.............	688	2,237	31	Total.............	32,174	50,967	63

In the strategic list mercury stands alone as the one member of the group of which the United States was once the world's leading producer, with two-thirds of the total output; but the fabulously rich ores of the California mines decreased in metal content as they were worked deeper and deeper, and the output gradually declined to such a point that the country has not been consistently self-supporting for nearly 50 years, and it has only been under abnormal conditions that a surplus supply has been produced by the domestic mines. War demand brought a surplus supply in 1916 and 1917, and the disturbed conditions of 1931 again made exports possible, but except for these three years, dependence on outside sources of supply has been so pronounced that in ten of the last 25 years the self-sufficiency ratio has been below 50 per cent, in seven years it has been below 40 per cent, and in two years it has gone below 30 per cent. During most of the other years the self-sufficiency has ranged from 50 per cent to 90 per cent, with an average of 63 per cent for the 25-year period.

It is significant to note that each successive peak of production is on a lower level than the preceding one, that of 1918 having reached 2,712,000 pounds, while that of 1929 stopped at 1,800,000 pounds, and that of 1935 reached only 1,331,000 pounds, and the decreasing tenor of the ore in the lower levels of the mines may be expected to result in still smaller future outputs. While there is still a possibility that future emergency demand may be largely supplied from domestic sources, this can be accomplished only at a considerable increase in price.

The future trend of the mercury industry of the world, and to some extent of the United States, will be determined shortly in the international settlements that will follow the close of the Spanish Civil War. The greater portion of the world's production capacity is now controlled by two Fascist countries whose general interests are closely allied, but whose specific interests in the mercury industry are so sharply opposed as to form a possible stumbling block in the future relations of the two countries.

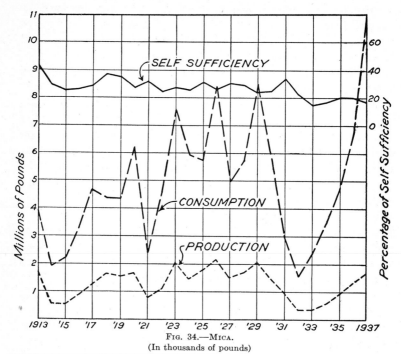

FIG. 34.—MICA.
(In thousands of pounds)

Year	Prod.	Cons.	Suff.	Year	Prod.	Cons.	Suff.
1913	1,701	3,951	43	1926	2,172	8,350	26
1914	557	1,917	29	1927	1,512	4,971	30
1915	554	2,194	25	1928	1,682	5,787	29
1916	866	3,277	26	1929	2,035	8,508	24
1917	1,277	4,637	28	1930	1,465	5,747	25
1918	1,644	4,394	37	1931	962	2,931	33
1919	1,546	4,376	35	1932	339	1,572	22
1920	1,683	6,183	27	1933	365	2,382	15
1921	742	2,392	31	1934	584	3,486	17
1922	1,078	4,528	24	1935	937	4,707	20
1923	2,063	7,526	27	1936	1,319	6,756	20
1924	1,461	5,921	25	1937	1,695	10,845	16
1925	1,794	5,745	31	Total	32,033	123,080	26

The domestic self-sufficiency level for mica has never been very high, the pre-war figure of 43 per cent not having been exceeded since that time, but the industry has been characterized by a rather narrow range of fluctuations in the sufficiency, most years falling between 24 per cent and 37 per cent. Supply has followed demand so closely that until 1932 the self-sufficiency ratio did not go outside these limits. The depression years were marked by unusually low outputs, and subsequent recovery has been slow. This is largely traceable to increased demand for mica splittings for use in built-up shapes, rather than for the better and larger grades of sheet mica. Since the domestic industry can not hope to compete with low-wage Oriental labor in the preparation of splittings until a satisfactory mechanical splitting process is developed, imports must supply practically the entire demand for splittings, which now make up 75–80 per cent of the imports. The domestic sheet output is almost entirely in the sizes larger than splittings, and because of the high labor cost involved, such domestic material as would be suitable for splittings must be sold as scrap or ground mica. Separation of the consumption figures into splittings and larger sizes would give a domestic self-sufficiency ratio better than 50 per cent for recent years, instead of 15–20 per cent, but the figure for splittings would be practically zero. The only readily accessible foreign supplies are found in Canada, but even if the available Canadian supplies are combined with the domestic supply, the total would still be too small to cope with emergency demand without marked expansion.

The future status of mica as a strategic material will undergo a marked change in the near future if present attempts to develop insulating films from bentonite prove as successful as the early tests seem to indicate. If this material can be developed into a satisfactory substitute for splittings and condenser mica, little concern need be felt for the future, and a good substitute for either of the two will go a long way toward solving the problem of self-sufficiency for a most essential material that has heretofore baffled all attempts at satisfactory substitution.

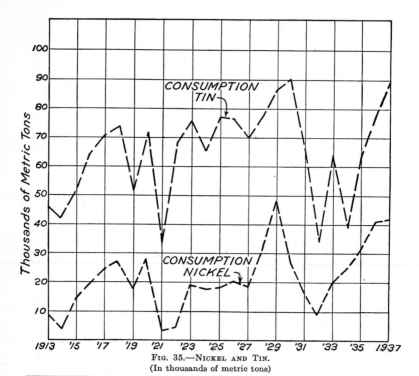

FIG. 35.—NICKEL AND TIN.
(In thousands of metric tons)

Year	Nickel		Tin, Cons.	Year	Nickel		Tin, Cons.
	Prod.	Cons.			Prod.	Cons.	
1913	0.2	8.5	46.5	1926	0.2	20.1	76.7
1914	0.4	3.8	42.5	1927	0.7	18.7	70.1
1915	0.7	14.4	52.4	1928	0.4	30.3	77.7
1916	0.7	19.3	64.2	1929	0.3	47.9	86.6
1917	0.3	24.5	70.8	1930	0.3	26.4	90.2
1918	0.4	27.0	73.6	1931	0.3	14.8	65.4
1919	0.4	17.6	51.4	1932	0.2	8.8	34.2
1920	0.3	23.9	72.0	1933	0.1	20.3	63.7
1921	0.1	2.7	33.5	1934	0.1	23.4	39.3
1922	0.2	4.0	68.3	1935	0.1	31.2	63.2
1923	0.1	18.9	75.8	1936	0.1	41.3	77.0
1924	0.2	17.6	65.6	1937	0.2	42.1	89.4
1925	0.2	18.0	77.1				

With no domestic nickel production outside of the small byproduct recovery from copper refining, the self-sufficiency ratio for the metal has averaged only a little over 1 per cent, and except for 1927, when the recovery reached the unusual amount of 700 tons, has not appreciably exceeded the average except in years of abnormally low consumption.　For all practical purposes the United States can be considered entirely dependent on outside sources for its nickel supply, and with domestic resources limited to scattered low grade deposits, there is little prospect for improving the situation even under extreme emergency conditions, but the seriousness of the situation is much reduced by the close proximity of the Canadian deposits, which are controlled by United States capital.　American access to these deposits would be extremely difficult to prevent.

Tin, like nickel, may also be said to be practically non-existent so far as domestic resources are concerned, and furthermore, this statement may be extended to cover the entire continent of North America.　The recoverable tin content of ores mined in the United States since 1913 has been only a little over 1,000 tons, or about 0.05 per cent of the consumption during the same period, and about 98 per cent of this total was produced in Alaska, so far removed from the centers of consumption that most of it was shipped to the Orient for smelting.　To make the situation still worse, the nearest source of supply is Bolivia, and these ores are much poorer in quality than those from the Orient, and more costly to smelt and refine.

With nickel the urgency of the situation is still further alleviated by the large stocks of metal maintained in the United States by the Canadian producers and the domestic consumers.　No data are available on the size of these stocks, but it is known that while they are not sufficient to cover the two or three year period which is now the usual basis for estimating emergency stocks, they are sufficient, when measured alongside the accessibility of the Canadian supplies, to cover the bulk of any demand that it likely to be put upon them.　On the other hand, tin stocks are comparatively small, and only an active program of emergency stocking can be depended on to fill the gap that is likely to develop between supply and emergency demand.

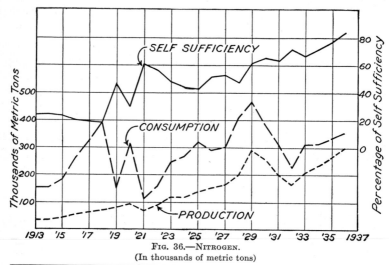

FIG. 36.—NITROGEN.
(In thousands of metric tons)

Year.	Prod.	Cons.	Suff.	Year.	Prod.	Cons.	Suff.
1913.............	35.6	151	24	1925.............	137.1	318.4	43
1914.............	35.7	152	24	1926.............	151.0	289.5	52
1915.............	41.0	181	23	1927.............	161.2	300.2	53
1916.............	53.9	264	20	1928.............	199.4	413.2	48
1917.............	60.7	321	19	1929.............	289.3	465.8	62
1918.............	69.9	388	18	1930.............	253.6	383.7	66
1919.............	79.2	150	47	1931.............	198.4	310.0	64
1920.............	93.2	313	30	1932.............	163.1	227.5	72
1921.............	66.9	110	61	1933.............	209.3	311.3	67
1922.............	89.4	158	56	1934.............	232.9	312.7	75
1923.............	117.9	249	48	1935.............	263.3	337.5	78
1924.............	117.6	268.4	44	1936.............	301.0	357.7	84

Although in the earlier years the United States was largely dependent on Chile for combined nitrogen, except for such nitrogen compounds as could be recovered from the byproducts of coke and gas plants, since the close of the war period the development of synthetic processes for the production on various compounds from the nitrogen of the air has progressed rapidly, and there is now sufficient synthetic capacity available to supply not only the normal demand, but also a reasonably large emergency demand. As a result, nitrogen as such has recently been removed from the official strategic list, but for commercial reasons imports from Chile and other sources still persist, but in decreasingly small proportions. Domestic self-sufficiency reached 84 per cent in 1936, with 1937 figures not yet available. Imports of nitrogen compounds in 1937 increased nearly 20 per cent over 1936, most of the increase being in Chilean nitrate, so that unless domestic production increased by more than this amount, the self-sufficiency ratio for the year decreased.

Domestic nitrogen consumption is still far below the 1929 level, and is not recovering as rapidly as might be expected; unless the present rate of recovery improves, the former high point will not be reached again before 1941, while most other industries had regained the 1929 level by 1936 or 1937, and some as early as 1935. It is not anticipated, however, that in the course of further recovery the domestic industry will fall appreciably below its present level of self-sufficiency. With favorable conditions its present ratio of self-sufficiency may even be somewhat improved.

From a strategic standpoint the primary nitrogen compounds are no longer a matter for material concern, but the capacity to convert the primary products of the various synthetic processes into the desired end products still requires some attention. The gradual decline in the urgency of the situation has been marked by the transfer of nitrogen from the strategic to the critical list in 1936, and finally to the new essential list in January 1939.

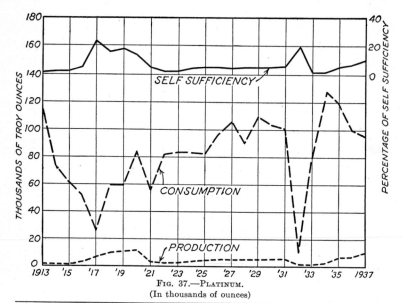

Fig. 37.—Platinum.
(In thousands of ounces)

Year	Prod.	Cons.	Suff.	Year	Prod.	Cons.	Suff.
1913	1.0	118	1	1926	4.9	97.6	5
1914	1.5	72	2	1927	4.4	106.6	4
1915	1.2	60	2	1928	4.6	94.3	5
1916	2.8	50.9	5	1929	5.6	110.6	5
1917	6.3	26.8	23	1930	5.3	104.0	5
1918	9.7	59.1	16	1931	5.6	90.0	6
1919	10.5	59.2	18	1932	1.9	10.0	19
1920	11.5	85.1	14	1933	1.3	84.6	2
1921	2.9	56.5	5	1934	3.0	129.7	2
1922	2.0	91.4	2	1935	6.6	119.2	6
1923	2.1	83.9	2	1936	7.4	99.5	7
1924	3.5	83.9	4	1937	9.3	86.6	11
1925	4.3	82.7	5	Total	119.2	2062.2	6

In platinum we find the apparently anomalous situation that the metal has only recently been removed from the official strategic list, in spite of the fact that the average self-sufficiency ratio since 1913 is only 6 per cent, and the present ratio is only slightly higher, and still much less than during the war period, when the metal was considered highly strategic. The explanation of this lies partly in the substitutes that have been developed for many of its uses, partly in increased accumulated stocks of metal in use since the war period, particularly in nonessential lines that could be diverted in time of emergency, and partly in the emergency stocks that have been held by the War Department since the war period. As a result of this combination of conditions, it seems likely that in spite of low domestic production, no severe shortage of supply would be encountered under an emergency, particularly since conditions would have to be pushed to the extreme to prevent at least partial access to Colombian sources, while the Canadian supplies are even more accessible to the United States.

Canada is at present the world's largest producer of platinum, and except under the unlikely contingency of the United States being opposed to Britain in any future difficulty, arrangements could doubtless be made to divert to the United States any required amount of the residues from the Canadian nickel refinery, although at present these go to England for refining. In addition, the domestic production is increasing, through new deposits in Alaska, and as in the war period, byproduct recoveries from domestic copper and gold refining would immediately increase when emergency demand increases the outputs of these metals. While this applies to emergency conditions, in normal times platinum continues to be required from outside sources in large quantities, though the increasing Alaskan output promises to reduce the necessity for imports by a substantial amount, preliminary estimates on 1938 production from this source being in excess of 28,000 ounces of crude.

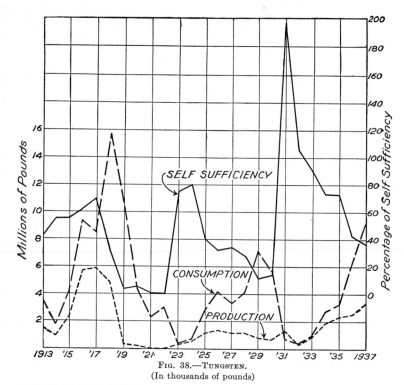

FIG. 38.—TUNGSTEN.
(In thousands of pounds)

Year	Prod.	Cons.	Suff.	Year	Prod.	Cons.	Suff.
1913	1,463	3,511	42	1926	1,315	4,175	32
1914	942	1,716	55	1927	1,108	3,290	34
1915	2,220	4,068	55	1928	1,150	4,106	28
1916	5,640	9,328	62	1929	790	7,154	11
1917	5,848	8,411	70	1930	668	4,642	14
1918	4,818	15,734	31	1931	1,336	679	197
1919	311	10,660	3	1932	377	370	102
1920	206	4,402	5	1933	852	962	89
1921	......	2,257	0	1934	1,950	2,701	72
1922	......	2,907	0	1935	2,281	3,187	72
1923	229	304	75	1936	2,489	5,956	42
1924	538	677	80	1937	3,335	9,031	37
1925	1,133	2,817	40	Total	40,999	113,045	36

Tungsten production in the United States is a high cost operation as compared with that of the rest of the world, particularly the Orient, which supplies the bulk of the output, and can be carried on only under high tariff protection, which was established in 1922, after the domestic industry had been completely idle for two years. Even so, production has been highly erratic, fluctuating with variations in world price and with changes in domestic demand. While 70 per cent of the 8,411,000 pounds consumed in 1918 was domestic production, this proportion dropped to 32 per cent of 4,175,000 pounds in 1926, and to 11 per cent of 7,154,000 pounds in 1929; on the other hand, in 1931, imports dropped heavily and domestic tungsten was exported in considerable amounts, and again to a lesser extent in 1932. The combined effect of the recovery from the depression and the stimulation to the industry from the re-armament programs in various countries has resulted in a steady increase in both production and consumption, to the highest levels since the war period, but since demand has led supply, the self-sufficiency ratio has been steadily decreasing since 1931.

All told, tungsten has shown wider variations in the self-sufficiency ratios than any other member of the strategic group, from zero in 1921 and 1922 to 197 per cent in 1931, with a subsequent decline. These figures are, however, only approximate, as data on both imports and exports are incomplete, and some items have had to be omitted, and others estimated from partial data.

It has only recently been reported that increased ore reserves have been developed which will increase possible domestic production to a point approximately equal to peace time requirements, but the full effect of this on the strategic status of the metal can not be measured until after a year or two of operation under the new conditions. It would seem, though, that if the claims for increased reserves are substantiated by increased output, a material reduction might be made in stockpile requirements, dropping them to a point sufficient to cover the time required to expand production to the estimated level of emergency demand.

CHAPTER XVI

STRATEGIC MINERAL SUPPLIES IN FOREIGN COUNTRIES

With the fever for re-armament that has taken possession of so much of the world during the past few years, strategic mineral supplies have attracted more attention than at any other time since the World War. In the development of a well balanced munitions program, adequate supplies of all of the important mineral commodities are a prerequisite, and if these supplies are not available from domestic sources, they must be secured elsewhere; this requires a greater consumption of time and energy than if the materials were directly at hand, and hence it naturally follows that the munitions program is automatically slowed down, or is kept up only by a correspondingly greater expenditure of effort. All of this leads to the logical conclusion that that country is best prepared to develop its maximum war effort which has to waste the least amount of its energy on maintaining the supply of deficient materials.

COMPARATIVE STATUS OF MINERALS

In order to evaluate the comparative status of the various countries with regard to strategic mineral supplies, Fig. 39 has been prepared, including data on the United States and the six leading foreign countries for 25 mineral commodities that are important in the development of a war program; several less important minerals of a more purely industrial character have been disregarded. The list includes 13 metallic and 12 non-metallic minerals. In many cases it will be found that while a country does not have an adequate production capacity for certain metallic ores, it may have a smelting capacity greater than the ore production capacity, the remaining ore requirements being supplied by imports. This is an important differentiation, and for all of the metallic minerals both mine production and smelter production capacity are indicated.

454

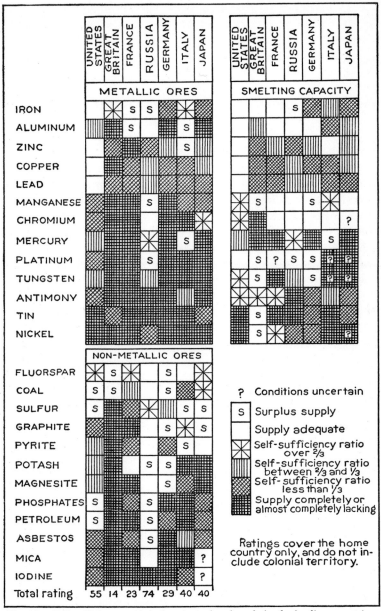

Fig. 39.—Self-sufficiency ratings for strategic minerals in the leading countries.

The markings of the chart show the approximate degree of self-sufficiency, or ratio of production to consumption, for the various countries and minerals during the past few years. In most cases the results are fairly definite, but due to occasional rapid changes from year to year no attempt has been made to classify the results more closely than into rough groupings of surplus, adequate and deficient, scaling partial deficiency into thirds. In a few cases information is lacking, and the status can not be definitely determined. In arranging the chart, the minerals in the metallic and non-metallic groups have been named approximately in the order of increasing total deficiency for all countries combined; while this order is only approximate, it still gives a rough relative measure of the strategic importance of the various minerals. It will be noted that the major metals, iron, aluminum, zinc, copper and lead, head the list as those most plentiful, while the less common metals follow; of the more common metals, tin and nickel are the only ones that have widespread strategic importance, both of these being available only in comparatively small amounts in all of the seven countries. Of the non-metallics, the most important are the fuels, coal and petroleum; the former is comparatively plentiful, but the latter falls far down the list, and is plentiful only in the United States and Russia. In general, the non-metallics have a much higher degree of self-sufficiency than the metallics.

COMPARATIVE STATUS OF COUNTRIES

Interesting though the comparison of the relative status of the various minerals may be, a far more important factor is the comparison of the different countries with each other, especially at the present time, for it gives some insight into the question as to the amount of effort that will be required for any given country to develop and maintain a munitions program. The attention of the reader is therefore directed to a comparative study of the vertical columns of the chart, rather than the horizontal ones. At a glance it is readily seen that no country has an adequate supply of all of the minerals listed, and on the other hand, none is deficient in all of them, but that the general degree of self-sufficiency varies between rather wide limits. Inspection of the chart shows that Russia is more or less deficient in 10 of the listed minerals (not including the metals), while the United States has a deficiency in 17, Italy 19, Germany and Japan each 20, France 22, and Great Britain 23. We can not say, however, that because country A has a list of 10 strategic minerals, while country B has a list of 20, that A is necessarily better equipped than B. The number alone, nor even the amounts or cost involved, form no definite criterion, since the degree of deficiency, the effort required to meet it, the essentiality of the uses, and many other factors come into play, most of which are intangible and can be assigned no specific value.

It would be not only quite interesting but also extremely valuable if there were some way in which the amounts of the various deficient minerals could be weighted and combined to make a total deficiency factor, but unfortunately this is not possible. It would be a comparatively simple matter to total the amounts of all of the deficiencies, but when done, the result would have no real meaning without some way of weighting each separate commodity according to its relative value in the program as a whole; but each one has so many different uses, of such a wide variety or degree of essentiality, that such a scheme is impossible to accomplish. From a strategic standpoint, the lack of a ton of manganese ore is just about as important as the lack of 80 tons of steel, since the manganese is required for the production of the steel in its finished form; or, having both the manganese and the steel, all finished and made up into projectiles, of what use are these if there is still lacking the thimblefull of mercury needed to supply the primers that are required to make the projectiles function?

While it is impossible to arrive at any single factor that definitely measures the total deficiency of a country, this does not mean that it is not worth while to go as far as we can toward evaluating the comparative status of the various leading countries with regard to strategic mineral supplies. In the first place, it will be noticed that aside from Russia, the United States has the smallest deficiency list. While Russia shows a status that superficially stands higher, there is really little basis for a direct comparison of Russia with any of the other countries in the list, and least of all with the United States. The extent of the deficiency is measured largely by the extent of the country's industrial development, and while Russia has made extensive improvements in an industrial way during the past few years, there is still a wide gap between the industrial status of Russia and the other countries. Furthermore, the information available on Russian production and consumption is far less complete than for any of the others, and the data presented are subject to a wider margin of error. On the other hand, Russia is so great in area, and has so many undeveloped or partially developed resources, that the latent possibilities are greater than for any other country.

Although Germany and Japan each show a list of 20 deficiencies, and Italy 19, the degree of deficiency varies with each, being on the whole greatest with Germany, and less with Italy and Japan, although with the latter there is again some degree of uncertainty, due to the fact that since the outbreak of the Sino-Japanese war many of the Japanese statistics have been suppressed, and the estimates made may not represent the true status of the country.

SELF-SUFFICIENCY FACTORS

France comes next in the list, slightly lower than Germany, while Great Britain falls lowest, largely because of the limited variety of minerals found within the comparatively small area of the country.

Although it has already been stated that no specific deficiency factor can be derived that will express the exact status of a country, the general set-up of the chart lends itself readily to a very rough approximation of such a factor. In the first place, we have established four degrees of self-sufficiency, to which we may arbitrarily assign the weightings 4, 3, 2, and 1, for the successive decreasing steps of adequate, over $\frac{2}{3}$, between $\frac{2}{3}$ and $\frac{1}{3}$, and less than $\frac{1}{3}$; in the second place, we have listed 25 minerals. Combining these two, we would have for complete self-sufficiency of all 25 minerals a factor of 100, which would be reduced correspondingly for lesser degrees of self-sufficiency for individual minerals, as indicated above. Applying these arbitrary figures to the ratings shown in the chart, we arrive at a self-sufficiency rating of 76 for Russia, 55 for the United States, 40 for Japan and Italy, 29 for Germany, 23 for France, and 14 for the Great Britain. It is frankly admitted that these figures are only rough approximations, and lack all of the refinement of a mathematical weighting of the individual minerals. Crude as they may be, the comparative figures here presented may prove to be of some value as a first approximation of a comparative deficiency rating.

While, as has been said above, it is impossible to assign an exact mathematical value to the many intangible parts that would have to be included in a true weighted factor, we can make a rough approximation of the weighting, which will convert the first approximation derived above into a second approximation, which will more nearly represent the true comparative status of the countries. In a recent lecture at Princeton University

TABLE A.—WEIGHTED SELF-SUFFICIENCY FACTORS

	Relative Weight	United States	Great Britain	France	Russia	Germany	Italy	Japan
Aluminum..	6	3	....	6	6	....	6	....
Antimony...	2	0.5	....	....	....	....	1	....
Chromium..	4	1	....	....	4	....	....	3
Copper.....	8	8	....	2	4	2	2	4
Iron........	12	12	9	12	12	3	9	3
Lead.......	6	6	1.5	1.5	32	1.5	1.5	1.5
Manganese..	6	1.5	....	....	6	....	1.5	1.5
Mercury....	3	1.5	....	....	2	....	3	....
Nickel......	4	....	....	....	1	....	....	....
Platinum...	1	0.2	....	....	1	....	....	....
Tin........	4	....	1	....	....	....	....	1
Tungsten...	3	1.5	....	....	1.5	....	....	....
Zinc........	6	6	1.5	....	1.5	3	6.0	3
Asbestos....	0.4	0.1	....	0.1	0.4	....	0.1	0.1
Coal........	16	16	16	8	16	16	4	12
Fluorspar...	0.6	0.5	0.6	0.5	0.6	0.6	0.6	0.5
Graphite....	0.4	0.1	....	....	0.4	0.4	0.3	0.4
Iodine......	0.4	0.1	....	....	....	....	0.1	0.4
Magnesite..	0.6	0.3	....	....	0.6	0.6	0.1	....
Mica.......	0.6	0.2	....	....	0.6	....	....	0.6
Petroleum..	10	10	....	....	10	2.5	....	2.5
Phosphates..	2	2	....	0.5	2	....	....	0.5
Potash.....	2	1	....	2	2	2	....	....
Pyrite......	1	0.5	....	0.3	1	0.3	1	1
Sulfur......	1	1	....	0.2	0.7	0.5	1	1
Total.....	100	73.0	29.6	33.1	76.3	32.4	37.2	36.0

on "Mineral Resources and International Strife" Prof. Edward Sampson made a comparative study of relative production ability of the various countries of the world, in which he weighted the output of the different minerals according to their relative commercial importance. Similar ratings for the 25 minerals in our list have been estimated by raising or lowering the previous arbitrary 4 per cent assigned to each, according to their relative importance in the maintenance of a war effort, varying between a high of 16 per cent for coal, and a minimum of 0.4 per cent for iodine and graphite. It is to be understood that the relative ratings assigned to the different minerals are merely the writer's estimate of their comparative importance; they vary somewhat from the corresponding values used by Sampson, and since they can be arrived at only as a matter of personal opinion, the figures would vary more or less with each individual who made a similar estimate; eventually, it is hoped that additional estimates of this kind may be obtained from a number of different authorities, so that the values may be averaged to give a result that represents the combined judgement of a number of individuals, rather than the isolated opinion of a single person.   For the time being, however, Table A, on page 459, indicates the comparative self-sufficiency factors for the different countries, derived as outlined above, from the assigned relative weightings for each mineral, and the self-sufficiency ratios for these minerals in the different countries, as indicated in Fig. 39.

Following is a comparison of the factors derived from the various sources:

	Weighted Production Factor[1]	Unweighted Self-sufficiency Factor	Weighted Self-sufficiency Factor
United States	29	55	73
Great Britain	4.5	14	30
France	4.7	23	33
Russia	9.2	74	76
Germany	8.2	29	32
Italy	1.5	40	37
Japan	2.9	40	36

[1] Weighted production factor for 1936, as calculated by Sampson, in percentage of total world production.

As would be expected, the weighted values show considerable variation from the unweighted ones, and even though the weight assigned may vary somewhat from the proper values, the weighted results are most certainly a closer representation of the real situation than the unweighted ones.   It is interesting to note that the values of the weighted self-sufficiency factor fall definitely into two groups: a high group, including the United States and Russia, and a low group, including all the other countries. In comparing these figures one with another one must not lose sight of the fact that the production factor is the measure of a country's ability to produce, in comparison with that of the rest of the world, while the self-sufficiency factor is the measure of its ability to produce, in comparison with its own ability to consume.   This will explain some of the apparent discrepancies in the table. The Russian self-sufficiency factor is high because, although the production factor is relatively low, the consumption demand is also low, leaving only a small gap between production and consumption. Germany's production factor, which is only slightly less than that of Russia, has to meet a very much higher consumption demand, with the result that the self-sufficiency factor drops to the lowest in the list. The self-sufficiency factors of Italy and Japan, and of Great Britain and France, are about on a par with that of Germany, although the production factor of the latter two are much higher than the former, indicating a proportionately higher consumption demand, intermediate between that of Italy and Japan on the one hand and of Germany on the other. The position of the United States ranks highest of all, for with a production factor almost equal to the other six combined (29 against 31), the heavy consumption demand is met to a sufficient degree to maintain a self-sufficiency factor of 73.

CONSUMPTION FACTORS

Since the production factor is a direct measure of production, while the self-sufficiency factor is a measure of the ability of production to keep pace with consumption, dividing the first factor by the second will give us a third, or consumption factor, which will be an approximate measure of the total consumption demand in the various countries for the entire group of minerals, weighted according to their relative importance.

CONSUMPTION FACTORS FOR MINERALS

United States	40	
Great Britain	15	⎫
France	14	⎬ 41
Russia	12	⎭
Germany	25	⎫
Italy	4	⎬ 37
Japan	8	⎭

While these are purely arbitrary factors, which have no meaning except in comparison with each other, they provide a very convenient scale for comparing the consumption demand of the various countries for mineral raw materials. Considered singly, they indicate the United States far in the lead, followed by Germany at a level one-third lower. Great Britain, France and Russia all fall, in the order named, at about the same level, with each about one-third of the United States rate. Japan and Italy come at the bottom of the list, with comparatively low values, both together being on a par with Russia. Arranged in groups, we find the countries listed falling into three groups of equal size: the United States with its factor of 40; Great Britain, France and Russia with a total of 41; and Germany, Italy and Japan, with a total of 37. The combination of Britain and France against Germany and Italy are well balanced, each with a total of 29, while the addition of Russia to the former, and of Japan to the latter leaves the Axis powers with a deficiency of 4 points, or about 10 per cent of the total, as represented by these arbitrary factors.

It is hoped that the comparative figures presented in these charts and tables may prove to be of some value as an indication of the relative ability of the various countries to meet the demand for strategic minerals. In making use of these data it must be remembered that since this is the first time that such relative evaluations have been attempted, too much can not be expected in the way of accuracy. However, the results as presented are a rough approximation and may serve as a basis for further study and refinement.

RELATIVE PRODUCTION ABILITY

At various times other charts and tables have been prepared, showing some feature of the relative status of the more important countries, the latest of which is that which appeared recently in a publication of the U. S. Bureau of Mines entitled "An Analysis of the Strategic Minerals Problem of the United States," by J. W. Finch and J. W. Furness. Although this publication has appeared only within the past few weeks, the chart has apparently been carried over unrevised from an earlier use, since it still lists Germany deficient in magnesite and graphite, of which there are adequate supplies since the incorporation into the Reich of Austria and Czecho-Slovakia; other entries also indicate that the chart has not been brought down to date. This chart has therefore been used as a pattern for Fig. 40, which presents much the same data as to surplus, adequate, and deficient supplies as was shown in Fig. 39, but in a form such that it is possible to supplement the previous data with additional

METALLIC ORES	UNITED STATES				GREAT BRITAIN				FRANCE				RUSSIA				GERMANY				ITALY				JAPAN			
	A	B	C	D	A	B	C	D	A	B	C	D	A	B	C	D	A	B	C	D	A	B	C	D	A	B	C	D
IRON		•			○		•		◉					•					•			◉			◉			
ALUMINUM	○	•			○					•	•			•				•	•						○			•
ZINC	○	•			○		•				•				•			•				•			◉			
COPPER	○	•			○						•			•					•				•		◉			
LEAD	◉				○		•		○		•				•				•				•		◉			
MANGANESE		◉			○						•				•	•			•				•		◉			
CHROMIUM		◉			○						•	○			•	•			•					•	◉			
MERCURY		•					•				•			•				•	•			•						•
PLATINUM		◉			○						•				•	•			•		○		•					•
TUNGSTEN		•			○						•				•			•					•					•
ANTIMONY			•		○		•		○		•				•					•			•					•
TIN			•		○		•				•				•				•				•			•		
NICKEL	○		•		○		•				•				•				•				•		○			•
NON-METALS																												
FLUORSPAR		•			◉						•				•		•				○	•					•	
COAL	•				◉						•				•		•						•		○		•	
SULFUR	•						•				•			•			•					•					•	
GRAPHITE		◉			○						•	○			•		•						•		◉			
PYRITE		◉			○						•			•					•			•				◉		
POTASH		•			○					•	•			•				•					•					•
MAGNESITE		•			○						•			•				•				•						•
PHOSPHATES	•				○						•	○		•					•				•		◉			
PETROLEUM	◉				○						•			•	•		•						•		◉			
ASBESTOS	○	•			○						•			•	•				•			•					•	
MICA		◉			○						•	○			•			•					•		○	•		
IODINE	○	•			○						•				•					•			•				•	

● Indicates the status of the mineral within the political boundaries of the home country

○ Indicates the status of the mineral as altered by sources under political or commercial control

◉ Indicates an improved condition within the limits of the designation; e.g., an increase in the surplus, an improvement in an inadequate supply, or a change from a supply whose adequacy is questionable to one fully adequate, yet with no material surplus for export

A = Surplus supply   B = Adequate supply   C = Inadequate supply   D = No appreciable supply

FIG. 40.—Indicated production ability of the principal consuming countries for strategic minerals.

symbols to indicate those cases in which the purely domestic production of the country may be extended by output from outside the boundaries of the home country, from sources under its political or commercial control; that is, this second symbol includes production in colonial territory, and in foreign countries where the ownership of the deposit is vested in domestic capital, the presumption being that the home country has first call on production under its political or commercial control. While normally this is true, the conditions prevailing in time of war may make this impossible to realize, however desirable it may be in principle. First, shortage of transportation facilities may make it difficult or impossible to ship ores from a remote colony to the home country; second, even though the necessary shipping facilities may be available, shipments will be subject to war hazards and blockade by the enemy; and finally, sources commercially controlled in enemy territory will not be available, since the local political control will take precedence over foreign commercial control, and will prevent shipment to an enemy country. Hence, in visualizing the possible sources of supply outside the home country, caution must be exercised not to place undue emphasis on the ability of political and commercial control to supplement the normal domestic output, since full access to these remote supplies is questionable. One is fully justified, however, in surveying the possibilities that arise from political and commercial control of such sources of supply, providing the situation is carefully weighed, without undue optimism.

POLITICAL AND COMMERCIAL CONTROL

A survey of this second chart shows that on this basis the conditions indicated in the first chart may in some cases be radically changed. The situation with respect to Germany remains unchanged, for she has no colonies, and comparatively little commercial control in foreign mining areas, and the status of Italy also remains about the same. Japan has some outside areas on which to draw, but on the whole the possible difference is comparatively small; only with coal would there be any material improvement. The combined Axis powers then can expect little in the way of help of this character, though the trade agreements which Germany has been making with adjacent countries will be of some assistance.

France has colonial sources of chromite, lead, graphite and phosphates which, if available, will be sufficient to offset shortage of these commodities.   The lead and phosphates lie just across the Mediterranean in northern Africa, but even so their access is questionable, while the graphite comes from Madagascar and the chromite from New Caledonia.   All possibilities considered, it would appear that France could expect little material help from colonial sources, because of inaccessibility of location.

It is chiefly with British supplies that colonial sources may be expected to alter the domestic status; in this case, colonies are numerous and widely scattered, and while many are remote, the country has the advantage of a powerful navy to protect its sea routes.   British colonial mineral resources are so extensive and so varied that on an Empire basis the domestic deficiencies would be decimated both in number and amount, with mercury, antimony, potash, petroleum and sulfur the only ones of importance that would remain, and with most of these, especially petroleum, commercial control might further improve the situation.

SIGNIFICANCE OF COMMERCIAL DATA

The commercial statistics of a country may have a pronounced military significance, when interpreted in the proper fashion. For this purpose, the data most useful are those on consumption or supply available for consumption, such as has been built up for the United States in the previous chapters of this book. Since detailed data of this type have not yet been developed for other countries, import statistics will be utilized to illustrate the character of the inferences that may be derived from such material.   In the accompanying Tables B, C, and D, are presented the recent figures for some of the more important minerals imported into Germany, Italy and Japan, the three countries in which military activities have been most pronounced during the past few years.   For convenience these data have been compiled from the statistical reports of the Imperial Institute (London) for the years 1929 to 1937, with the addition of such 1937 estimates for Japan as are available from other sources.   Since limitations of space preclude a detailed exposition, each table has been limited to eight of the more important strategic minerals of the country in question.

In all three tables one may readily trace the effect of the country's military activities, although in some cases these are obscured

TABLE B.—IMPORTS OF STRATEGIC MINERALS INTO GERMANY
(Thousands of long tons)

	Iron Ore	Iron and Steel	Bauxite	Manga-nese Ore	Nickel		Petro-leum	Pyrite
					Ore	Metal		
1929........	16,685	660	381	384	13.6	4.7	1,643	1,152
1930........	13,670	430	296	330	11.6	2.9	2,725	944
1931........	6,959	308	208	160	19.3	2.8	2,374	695
1932........	3,397	247	198	105	17.4	2.4	2,020	641
1933........	4,499	528	235	130	34.0	4.6	2,127	836
1934........	8,134	714	321	221	37.0	5.4	2,450	972
1935........	13,839	458	498	388	28.6	6.1	2,976	1,002
1936........	18,178	510	966	226	17.4	3.5	3,374	1,026
1937........	20,295	792	1,292	545	19.7	3.6	3,372	1,441
1938........	21,581	1,675	1,165	419	33.7	4.1	3,900	1,398

TABLE C.—IMPORTS OF STRATEGIC MINERALS INTO ITALY
(Thousands of long tons)

	Iron Ore	Iron and Steel	Copper	Lead		Phos-phates	Petro-leum	Coal
				Ore	Metal			
1929........	209	1,195	59	3.5	24.3	848	1,261	14,308
1930........	232	1,018	54	10.0	17.7	940	1,478	12,640
1931........	160	702	56	12.4	15.4	513	1,472	10,912
1932........	91	537	55	15.2	8.8	447	1,477	8,633
1933........	235	704	62	17.5	8.6	719	1,687	9,405
1934........	290	817	65	36.8	6.0	737	1,808	12,527
1935........	184	1,119	92	19.9	29.8	667	2,054	14,333
1936........	39	448	85	21.3	8.7	758	1,794	9,638
1937........	180	599	79	13.2	10.9	954	2,538	12,701
1938........	379	1,063	79	13.5	9.0	862	2,579	12,850

TABLE D.—IMPORTS OF STRATEGIC MINERALS INTO JAPAN
(Thousands of long tons)

	Iron Ore	Iron and Steel	Copper	Lead	Zinc		Petro-leum	Coal
					Ore	Metal		
1929........	1,914	1,172	4.9	60	28.0	29.8	2,121	3,203
1930........	1,942	893	1.2	55	18.7	24.9	2,193	2,650
1931........	1,525	589	0.2	53	24.5	22.5	2,333	2,650
1932........	1,459	1,005	0.3	55	35.0	23.5	2,340	2,673
1933........	1,500	1,738	13.1	66	37.2	29.8	2,487	3,441
1934........	2,098	2,090	46.2	93	12.9	29.8	3,025	3,997
1935........	3,350	2,846	64.2	89	40.6	37.2	3,675	3,985
1936........	3,720	2,644	47.0	94	47.3	45.8	4,073	4,134
1937........	5,500	2,750	95	111	28	41	4,650	4,356

by the simultaneous recovery from the world-wide industrial depression. The preparation by Italy for the Ethiopian campaign and for the recent activities are clearly reflected in her imports of strategic minerals, and the same is true for recent developments in Germany and Japan. To bring this out even more clearly, in Table E these data have been converted into index figures, by dividing the total imports listed for each year by the total for 1929. While this method of handling is crude, with no relative weighting of the various items, it shows some interesting results. It emphasizes quite pointedly the German activities of the last three years; it shows clearly the Italian preparations for the Ethiopian campaign in 1935, and a recent activity that has risen almost to the 1935 level; and most of all it points out the Japanese preparations for operations in China, extending back to 1933.

TABLE E.—INDEX OF IMPORT ACTIVITY IN STRATEGIC MINERALS

	Germany	Italy	Japan
1929	100	100	100
1930	88	92	91
1931	51	77	84
1932	32	63	89
1933	40	72	109
1934	61	91	136
1935	92	103	165
1936	116	71	176
1937	133	95	204
1938	144	100	?

That the significance of data of this kind is fully realized in official circles is evidenced by the fact that publication of Italian trade statistics was suspended during the Ethiopian campaign, and that Japanese statistics have been withheld since July 1937.

STOCK ACCUMULATIONS

Closer examination of individual items will frequently yield interesting and valuable results. For example, take the data on German manganese, presented in Table F.

If we assume that the rate of importation during 1922–1926 was approximately that required by the normal consumption per ton of steel, this would mean that for the 223,154,000 tons of steel covered by the table, some 2,860,000 tons of manganese ore would have been required, while the supply available was 4,011,-000 tons; in other words, imports have been such as to provide a surplus supply of about 1,151,000 tons.

Trade statistics also show that about 1922 France began to import manganese ore in greater amounts than her steel output

would require, though it was not until 1924 that the surplus
became large enough to be of importance. Detailed data are
not available, from which one might arrive at an approximate
estimate of the stocks that have been accumulated, but they are
apparently considerably greater than the German stocks. Some
idea of the scale to which imports were inflated may be had from
the fact that since 1922 French imports of manganese ore have
been almost as great as those of the United States, although the
steel output which they cover has been only about one-quarter
that of the United States. There are similar indications of
accumulations in Belgium; Russia apparently has built up greater
stocks than any other country, in spite of the fact that ore
resources are plentiful; and the stocks situation in the United
States has already been discussed in the chapter on *Manganese*.

TABLE F.—MANGANESE SUPPLY IN GERMANY

	Steel Output (Metric Tons)	Manganese Ore Available (Metric Tons)	Manganese Ore per Ton of Steel (Kilograms)
1922–26	52,397,000	670,000	12.8
1927	16,311,000	366,000	22.4
1928	14,517,000	258,000	17.8
1929	16,246,000	357,000	22.0
1930	11,539,000	339,000	29.4
1931	8,292,000	135,000	16.3
1932	5,746,000	70,000	12.2
1933	7,586,000	97,000	12.8
1934	11,886,000	188,000	15.8
1935	16,419,000	373,000	22.7
1936	19,158,000	202,000	10.5
1937	19,816,000	530,000	26.7
1938	23,242,000	426,000	18.3

During the period 1911–1923 the world steel output was
880,100,000 long tons, and of manganese ore 21,400,000 tons,
or 54.5 pounds of ore for each ton of steel. During 1924–1937
the corresponding figures were 1,301,000 tons of steel and
43,300,000 tons of manganese ore, or 74.3 pounds per ton of
steel, an increase of 19.8 pounds, most of which has been going
into stocks. If these figures are to be relied on, this would
account for a total stock accumulation of 11,680,000 tons of
manganese ore, an amount which seems almost incredible, and
yet, when we analyze the situation in the various countries we
find that this is not greatly in excess of the amounts that can be
more or less roughly accounted for, either as mine stocks in the
hands of producers, or as surplus accumulations in the hands of
consumers.

CONCLUSION

The preceding paragraphs present only a few of the pertinent uses which may be made of international statistics of production, trade and consumption. Those of an inquisitive turn of mind may find plenty of other examples, though unfortunately they are likely to find the data available lacking in many respects. However, a little ingenuity and extra work will often serve to correct these difficulties. For example, Japan is at present withholding the publication of trade statistics, but one who wishes to know the imports of any commodity can turn to the export statistics of the producing countries and find a close approximation of the desired figure by totaling the amounts exported to Japan; in like manner, an approximation of Japanese exports can be secured by totaling the imports received from Japan by the leading consuming countries. These and many other subterfuges must be utilized if one is to secure the results desired, and even then necessary items may still be found lacking. The use of international statistics is gradually expanding, however, and the field of strategic mineral supplies is one of the most fruitful ones open to those who desire to keep posted on the current military aspirations of any country. While data of this kind will not tell you specifically how many airplanes Russia or Germany has built during the year, it will give you a large amount of highly useful information on the basic raw materials for this and other industries.

CHAPTER XVII

COMMERCIAL INTERESTS VERSUS POLITICAL INTERESTS

In the preceding chapter emphasis has been placed on the amounts of strategic minerals that have been imported by Germany, Italy and Japan, as a part of their programs of expansion. In the development of these programs, which have been partly individual and partly joint activities, these three countries have acted in variance with the established interests of many other countries, especially those of Great Britain, France, Russia, and the United States. Each of the latter have at numerous times within the past five years had occasion to enter diplomatic protests against each of the former, as a result of the development of the programs. The popular designation of these two groups as the "Have" and the "Have Not" nations emphasizes the purely materialistic aspects of the conflict, while the more dignified diplomatic designation as Democratic Powers and Dictatorships hinges more on the ideological features at issue. Since we are here primarily concerned with materialistic phases of the problem, presumably we should adhere to the former designation, especially since this will in advance prevent anyone from raising the issue as to just how many of the so-called Democratic Powers still remain true democracies.

For the moment we are not concerned with either the theories or practice of governmental procedure, or with any of the ideological features involved in it, but only with the extent to which the "Have Not" nations have endeavored to remedy their shortages of mineral raw materials, and their manner in going about it. This can be accomplished in only two ways: first, by acquiring additional territory which includes the desired materials; or second, by securing the necessary materials by purchase or barter. There are some features of these methods of procedure that warrant brief mention, even though space is lacking for a detailed presentation of all phases of the problem.

470

While the existence of mineral raw materials in the areas that have been the object of aggression has not been the sole basis for the aggression, but has in most cases been supplemented by other reasons more or less pertinent, there still remains a striking degree of coincidence in the extent to which it has developed that the countries which have been found to be so sadly in need of "protection" and "cooperation" also have within their boundaries more or less extensive deposits of minerals of which the aggressor has only a scanty supply.

It is definitely established that the "Have Not's" are attempting to build themselves up to a position of greater self-sufficiency with respect to mineral raw materials.   It is also definitely established that the "Have Not" nations have, in the furtherance of their aims, transgressed on the established interests of the "Have" nations.   It is assumed that these premises require no argument.   The condition of the world during the latter months of 1938 and the early months of 1939 is a tacit admission that the "Have Not's" have succeeded in attaining a position such that they can, if they wish, attempt to secure by force of arms what they have not yet been able to secure by negotiation and "appeasement."   This is what Italy did in Ethiopia in 1935, and more recently in Albania; it is what Japan has been doing in Manchuria and China since 1932; and it is what the rest of the world fears that Germany and Italy may decide to do in the near future.   Lacking domestic supplies of certain fundamental raw materials, none of the "Have Not's" could have attained their present position without access to supplies from other sources.   This brings us to the very pertinent question: *Whence have come the strategic mineral supplies that have made possible the present situation?*

Naturally, the "Have Not's" must supply their needs from the "Have's."   The extent to which this has been carried out may be illustrated by some of the trade statistics, selecting only a few from the many that might be used.   Since 1935 more than a third of the iron ore imported by Germany has been from France and Algeria; of the manganese ore imported in the same period, 44 per cent came from South Africa, 16 per cent from India, and 24 per cent from Russia; of the copper imports, 15 per cent came from the United States, 17 per cent from Belgian Congo, and 31 per cent from British territory; of the chromite imports, 35 per cent came from South Africa, and smaller amounts from Rhodesia and New Caledonia; of the lead imports, 16 per cent came from British territory and 12 per cent from Belgium, while considerable proportions of the lead ore imports also came from British territory.

In Italy, the bulk of the iron ore imports has been obtained from the French and British colonies in Africa, and coal imports from Great Britain have been of the order of 2,000,000 tons a year. Manganese ore has come largely from India and Russia, and phosphates from Tunis and Morocco.

In Japan, pig iron imports have been largely from India, lead and zinc from Canada and India, and copper from the United States.

All told, a surprisingly large percentage of the strategic mineral imports of Germany, Italy and Japan have been obtained from Great Britain and France, or their colonies, with a smaller amount from Russia. The United States has also entered the picture in a large way. Since 1935 the United States has supplied 15 per cent of the German copper imports, 30 per cent of the Italian, and practically all of the Japanese. Since 1933 the United States has shipped to Japan nearly 9,000,000 tons of iron and steel and 100,000,000 barrels of petroleum products. At the same time that our Government was entering protests against the Japanese invasions of Manchuria and China, these acts of aggression were being made possible by our own exports to Japan of iron and steel and copper and oil.

This brings us face to face with the age-old conflict between commercial interests and political interests, and the question as to which shall take precedence. Commercial interests with products to sell naturally wish to expand their markets, and in this they are encouraged to develop export sales. As a result of this attitude, the past few years has seen the development of the "Have Not" nations from a position of almost complete military ineffectiveness to one where they now threaten the peace of the world, and this has been accomplished not with their own resources, but largely with imports received from the very nations whose peace is now threatened. There is no way in which a result of this kind could have been prevented, except by concerted action, and this there has been no effective means of accomplishing. As has been so frequently pointed out in earlier chapters, in the discussion of various commodities, there is no distinct border line that can be drawn between development for military aggression and development for peaceful industry. This being the case, there was no point at which it could be definitely said that the imports in question were for use in aggression; hence there was no point at which a halt could be called, and even though such a point had been clearly marked, no action would have been effective that did not include all countries shipping to the supposed aggressor.

In the organization of the League of Nations it had been planned that the sanctions provisions should supply the remedy for such a situation, since these provided means by which the aggressor could be deprived of strategic supplies from without. Had these provisions been placed firmly in operation at the beginning of the Japanese invasion of Manchuria, later developments would most certainly have taken a radically different course. Unfortunately, there were political reasons on the part of Britain and France that made it seem inexpedient to put sanctions into operation against Japan. Although it was not realized at the time, this proved to be the first step in the complete breakdown of the sanctions provisions. When Italy started the Ethiopian campaign, sanctions were advocated as a remedy, this time with the support of Britain and France, but with the Japanese case as a precedent, some nations refused to participate in the application of sanctions against Italy, and as a result the sanctions had little ultimate effect beyond rousing the ire of Italy against those countries which did apply them. Still later, with Spain, sanctions were not even attempted, but an even more ineffectual program of nonintervention was inaugurated, which eventually turned out to be a farce. These three successive steps in the disintegration of the plans for collective action against aggressors left the "Have Not's" free to proceed at will with the strengthening of their armory with weapons destined in case of need to be turned against those who had supplied them.

It is not within the scope of this volume to enter into a lengthy discussion of problems of this character, but they are so closely related, in fact so intimately interwoven with the prime object of this discussion that it is impossible to pass them by without touching on some of these crucial points that must be cleared up if the world is to remain at peace in the years to come.

INDEX

A

Algeria, antimony, 250, 251
Alumina (*see* Aluminum)
Aluminum, 200
  Austria, 213, 215
  beneficiation, 205
  British Guiana, 208, 212, 215
  Canada, 213, 216
  commercial control, 231
  consumption, 225
  Czecho-Slovakia, 208
  domestic situation, 235
  exports, 224
  forms on market, 207
  France, 208, 212, 213, 216
  French Morocco, 208
  Germany, 213, 217
  Gold Coast, 208
  Great Britain, 213, 217
  Greece, 209, 212, 217
  Hungary, 209, 212, 217
  imports, 224
  India, 209
  Italy, 209, 212, 213, 218
  metallurgy, 206
  Netherlands East Indies, 212, 218
  Norway, 213, 218
  Nyasaland, 209
  ore reserves, 208
  ores, 205
  political control, 231
  prices, 227
  requirements, 200
  Rumania, 209
  Russia, 209, 212, 213, 219
  secondary recovery, 207
  self-sufficiency, 431
  smelting, 225
  stocks, 225
  substitutes, 204

Aluminum, Surinam, 209, 212, 219
  Switzerland, 213, 219
  tariff, 231
  United States, 209, 212, 213, 219
    output and supply, 221, 223
  uses, 201
  utilization, 226
  world output and supply, 210, 213
  Yugoslavia, 210, 220
Antimony, 238
  Algeria, 250, 251
  Australia, 251, 252
  beneficiation, 243
  Bolivia, 251, 252
  China, 251, 253, 259, 260
  commercial control, 269
  consumption, 260
  Czecho-Slovakia, 251, 254
  domestic situation, 270
  exports, 260
  forms on market, 246
  France, 251, 254
  imports, 256
  Italy, 251, 254
  metallurgy, 244
  Mexico, 251, 255, 259, 260
  ore reserves, 246
  ores, 242
  political control, 269
  prices, 264
  requirements, 239
  secondary recovery, 245
  self-sufficiency, 434
  smelting, 261
  stocks, 261
  substitutes, 241
  tariff, 268
  United States, 251, 255
    output and supply, 256
  uses, 239

Antimony, utilization, 262
  world output and supply, 247
Argentina, mica, 349, 351
  tungsten, 140, 141, 142, 150
Australia, antimony, 251, 252
  tin, 174, 175, 176, 186, 188
    smelting, 182
  tungsten, 140, 141, 142, 150
Austria, aluminum, 213, 215
  mercury, 286

B

Bauxite (*see also* Aluminum)
  prices, 227, 230
  self-sufficiency, 431
  utilization, 226
Belgian Congo, tin, 174
  smelting, 175, 183, 188
Belgium, tin smelting, 175, 182, 188
Beneficiation, aluminum, 205
  antimony, 243
  bauxite, 205
  chromium, 105
  manganese, 35
  mercury, 281
  mica, 344
  platinum, 314
  tin, 167
  tungsten, 136
Bibliography, 11
Bolivia, antimony, 251, 252, 259, 260
  tin, 174, 175, 176, 186, 188
  tungsten, 140, 141, 143, 150
Brazil, chromium, 121
  manganese, 43, 44, 45, 50, 51
British Guiana, aluminum, 215
  bauxite, 208, 212, 215
Burma, nickel, 84
  tin, 174, 178, 188
  tungsten, 140, 141, 145
  (*See also* India)

C

Canada, aluminum, 213, 216
  chromium, 112, 121

Canada, mica, 349, 351, 359
  nickel, 81, 83, 85
  platinum, 319, 320
Chile, iodine, 382, 385
  nitrogen, 408, 410, 412
China, antimony, 251, 253, 259, 260
  mercury, 286, 287
  tin, 174, 175, 177, 186, 188
    smelting, 182
  tungsten, 140, 141, 143, 150
Chromium, 97
  beneficiation, 105
  Canada, 112, 121
  commercial control, 125
  Cuba, 110, 111, 113, 121, 122
  domestic situation, 126
  forms on market, 108
  Greece, 110, 111, 113, 121, 122
  imports, 120
  India, 110, 111, 113, 121, 122
  Japan, 110, 111, 114
  metallurgy, 107
  New Caledonia, 110, 111, 114, 121, 122
  ore reserves, 108
  ores, 104
  political control, 125
  prices, 122
  requirements, 98
  Russia, 110, 111, 116, 121, 122
  secondary recovery, 107
  self-sufficiency, 436
  South Africa, 110, 111, 114, 121, 122
  Southern Rhodesia, 110, 111, 115, 121, 122
  substitutes, 104
  tariff, 124
  Turkey, 110, 111, 115, 121, 122
  United States, 110, 111, 117
    output and supply, 118
  uses, 98
  world output and supply, 109
  Yugoslavia, 117
Colombia, platinum, 320, 321, 327
Commercial vs. political interests, 470
Conservation of supplies, 20, 24

Consumption, aluminum, 223, 225
  antimony, 260
  bauxite, 222
  chromium, 119
  iodine, 386
  manganese, 51
  mercury, 293
  mica, 360
  nickel, 87
  nitrogen, 416
  platinum, 329
  tin, 189
  tungsten, 150
Consumption factors, 461
  France, 461
  Germany, 461
  Great Britain, 461
  Italy, 461
  Japan, 461
  Russia, 461
  United States, 461
Control (*see* Political control)
Control measures, 27
Critical list, 6, 8
Critical minerals, 1, 6, 8
Cuba, chromium, 110, 111, 113, 121, 122
  manganese, 43, 44, 45, 50, 51
Czecho-Slovakia, aluminum, 208
  antimony, 250, 254
  manganese, 43, 45, 46
  mercury, 286, 287

D

Domestic self-sufficiency, 428
  aluminum, 431
  antimony, 434
  bauxite, 431
  chromium, 436
  iodine, 438
  manganese, 440
  mercury, 442
  mica, 444
  nickel, 446
  nitrogen, 448
  platinum, 450
  tin, 446
  tungsten, 452

Domestic situation, aluminum, 235
  antimony, 270
  chromium, 126
  iodine, 393
  manganese, 64
  mercury, 299
  mica, 368
  nickel, 95
  nitrogen, 424
  platinum, 335
  tin, 198
  tungsten, 159
Dutch Guiana (*see* Surinam)

E

Egypt, manganese, 43, 45, 46
Emergency stocks, 22
England (*see* Great Britain)
Essential list, 6
Exports, aluminum, 224
  antimony, 260
  bauxite, 224
  iodine, 387
  manganese, 51
  mercury, 292
  mica, 360
  nickel, 89
  nitrogen, 416
  platinum, 329
  tin, 188
  tungsten, 150

F

Forms on market, aluminum, 207
  antimony, 246
  chromium, 108
  iodine, 381
  manganese, 38
  mercury, 282
  mica, 347
  nickel, 79
  nitrogen, 403
  platinum, 315
  tin, 170
  tungsten, 138

France, aluminum, 213, 216
  antimony, 251, 254, 260
  bauxite, 208, 212, 216
  consumption factor, 461
  production ability, 463
  self-sufficiency factor, 455, 459, 460
  strategic mineral supplies, 455, 459, 460
  tin, consumption, 189
French Morocco, bauxite, 208

G

Germany, aluminum, 213, 217
  consumption factor, 461
  manganese supply, 467
  mercury, 287
  nickel, 84
  production ability, 463
  self-sufficiency factor, 455, 459, 460
  strategic mineral supplies, 455, 459, 460
  strategic minerals, imports, 466, 471
    index, 467
  tin, consumption, 189
    smelting, 175, 182, 186
Gold Coast, bauxite, 208
  manganese, 43, 45, 46, 50, 51
Grading and classifying mica, 346
Great Britain, aluminum, 213, 217
  consumption factor, 461
  production ability, 463
  self-sufficiency factor, 455, 459, 460
  strategic mineral supplies, 455, 459, 460
  tin, 174, 178
    consumption, 189
    smelting, 175, 182, 186, 188
  tungsten, 145
Greece, aluminum, 217
  bauxite, 209, 212, 217
  chromium, 110, 111, 113, 121, 122
  nickel, 81, 83
Guatemala, chromium, 121

H

Hungary, aluminum, 217
  bauxite, 209, 212, 217

I

Illustrations, list of, xvii
Imports, aluminum, 224
  antimony, 256
  bauxite, 224
  chromium, 120
  iodine, 387
  manganese, 49
  mercury, 290
  mica, 360
  nickel, 88
  nitrogen, 414
  platinum, 325
  strategic minerals, Germany, 466
    Italy, 466
    Japan, 466
  tin, 185, 186, 188
  tungsten, 148
India, bauxite, 209
  chromite, 110, 111, 113, 121, 122
  manganese, 43, 45, 46, 50, 51
  mica, 349, 352, 359
  nickel, 81, 83
  tin, 174, 178, 188
    (*See also* Burma)
Indo-China, tungsten, 140, 141, 145
Iodine, 377
  Chile, 382, 385
  commercial control, 392
  domestic situation, 393
  exports, 387
  forms on market, 381
  imports, 387
  methods of recovery, 380
  ore reserves, 382
  ores, 380
  political control, 392
  prices, 390
  requirements, 377
  secondary recovery, 381
  self-sufficiency, 438

Iodine, stocks, 387
  substitutes, 379
  tariff, 392
  United States, 383, 385, 386
    output and supply, 385
  uses, 378
  utilization, 388
  world output and supply, 384
Italy, aluminum, 212, 218
  antimony, 251, 254
  bauxite, 209, 213, 218
  consumption factor, 461
  mercury, 286, 287, 292
  production ability, 463
  self-sufficiency factor, 455, 459, 460
  strategic minerals, imports, 455, 459, 460, 466, 472
    index, 467
  tin, consumption, 189

J

Japan, chromite, 110, 111, 114
  consumption factor, 461
  production ability, 463
  self-sufficiency factor, 455, 459, 460
  strategic minerals, imports, 455, 459, 460, 466, 472
    index, 467
  tin, consumption, 189
  tungsten, 140, 141, 145, 151

L

List of illustrations, xvii
List of tables, xv
Lists, critical, 6, 8
  essential, 6, 8
  official, 7, 8
  strategic, 2, 8
  unofficial, 7, 8

M

Madagascar, mica, 349, 354, 359
Malaya, tin, 174, 175, 178, 186, 188
  smelting, 181
  tungsten, 140, 141, 146, 150

Manganese, 31
  beneficiation, 35
  Brazil, 43, 44, 45, 50, 51
  commercial control, 63
  consumption, 51
  Cuba, 43, 44, 45, 50, 51
  Czecho-Slovakia, 43, 45, 46
  domestic situation, 64
  Egypt, 43, 45, 46
  exports, 51
  forms on market, 38
  Gold Coast, 43, 45, 46, 50, 51
  imports, 49
  India, 43, 45, 46, 50, 51
  metallurgy, 37
  ore reserves, 38
  ores, 34
  political control, 63
  prices, 58
  requirements, 32
  Russia, 43, 45, 46, 50, 51
  secondary recovery, 38
  self-sufficiency, 440
  South Africa, 43, 45, 47
  stocks, 51
  substitutes, 34
  supply, Germany, 467
  tariff, 60
  United States, 43, 45, 47
    output and supply, 48
  uses, 31
  utilization, 54
  world output and supply, 41
Mercury, 274
  Austria, 286
  beneficiation, 281
  China, 286, 287
  commercial control, 298
  consumption, 293
  Czecho-Slovakia, 286, 287
  domestic situation, 299
  exports, 292
  forms on market, 282
  Germany, 287
  imports, 290
  Italy, 286, 287, 292
  metallurgy, 282
  Mexico, 286, 287, 292

Mercury, ore reserves, 283
  ores, 280
  political control, 298
  prices, 294
  requirements, 275
  Russia, 286, 287
  secondary recovery, 282
  self-sufficiency, 442
  Spain, 286, 288, 292
  stocks, 293
  substitutes, 279
  tariff, 298
  United States, 286, 288
    output and supply, 289
  uses, 276
  utilization, 293
  world output and supply, 284
Metallurgy, aluminum, 206
  antimony, 244
  chromium, 107
  manganese, 37
  mercury, 282
  nickel, 77
  platinum, 314
  tin, 167
  tungsten, 136
Methods of recovery, iodine, 380
Mexico, antimony, 251, 255, 259, 260
  mercury, 286, 287, 292
  tungsten, 150
Mica, 339
  Argentina, 349, 351
  Canada, 349, 351, 359
  classifying, 346
  commercial control, 367
  consumption, 360
  domestic situation, 368
  exports, 360
  forms on market, 347
  grading and classifying, 346
  imports, 360
  India, 349, 352, 359
  Madagascar, 349, 354, 359
  ore reserves, 347
  ores, 344
  political control, 367
  preparation, 344

Mica, prices, 363
  requirements, 341
  Rhodesia, 355
  Russia, 355
  secondary recovery, 347
  self-sufficiency, 444
  South Africa, 355
  stocks, 361
  substitutes, 343
  tariff, 367
  United States, 349, 356
    output and supply, 357
  uses, 342
  utilization, 362
  world output and supply, 348
Minerals, critical, 1, 6, 8
  essential, 7, 8
  strategic, 1, 2, 8, 455, 459, 460, 463

N

Netherlands, tin smelting, 175, 182, 186, 188
Netherlands East Indies, aluminum, 218
  bauxite, 212, 218
  tin, 174, 175, 179, 186, 188
    smelting, 182
New Caledonia, chromium, 110, 111, 114, 121, 122
  nickel, 81, 84, 85
Nickel, 70
  Burma, 84
  Canada, 81, 83, 85
  commercial control, 93
  domestic situation, 95
  exports, 89
  forms on market, 79
  Germany, 84
  imports, 88
  metallurgy, 77
  New Caledonia, 81, 84, 85
  Norway, 81, 83, 86
  ore reserves, 79
  ores, 76
  political control, 93
  prices, 89
  requirements, 71

Nickel, secondary recovery, 78
  self-sufficiency, 446
  substitutes, 75
  United States, 81, 83, 86
    output and supply, 87
  uses, 71
  utilization, 90
  world output and supply, 80
Nigeria, tin, 174, 177
Nitrogen, 396
  commercial control, 421
  consumption, 416
  domestic situation, 424
  exports, 416
  forms on market, 403
  imports, 414
  ore reserves, 404
  ores, 400
  political control, 421
  prices, 418
  requirements, 398
  secondary recovery, 403
  self-sufficiency, 448
  substitutes, 400
  stocks, 416
  tariff, 420
  treatment, 402
  United States output and supply,
    413
  uses, 398
  utilization, 416
  world output and supply, 404
Norway, aluminum, 213, 218
  nickel, 81, 83, 86
Nyasaland, bauxite, 209

O

Official lists, 7
Ore dressing (*see* Beneficiation)
Ore reserves, aluminum, 208
  antimony, 246
  chromium, 108
  iodine, 382
  manganese, 38
  mercury, 283
  mica, 347
  nickel, 79

Ore reserves, nitrogen, 404
  platinum, 316
  tin, 170
  tungsten, 138
Ores, aluminum, 205
  antimony, 242
  chromium, 104
  iodine, 380
  manganese, 34
  mercury, 280
  mica, 344
  nickel, 76
  nitrogen, 400
  platinum, 312
  tin, 166
  tungsten, 134

P

Peru, tungsten, 150
Philippines, chromium, 121, 122
Platinum, 305
  beneficiation, 314
  Canada, 319, 320
  Colombia, 320, 321, 327
  commercial control, 335
  consumption, 329
  domestic situation, 335
  exports, 329
  forms on market, 315
  imports, 325
  metallurgy, 314
  ore reserves, 316
  ores, 312
  political control, 335
  prices, 331
  requirements, 306
  Russia, 320, 322, 327
  secondary recovery, 315
  self-sufficiency, 450
  South Africa, 320, 322
  stocks, 329
  substitutes, 310
  tariff, 334
  United States, 320, 323
    output and supply, 324
  uses, 306
  utilization, 329
  world output and supply, 316

Political control, 27, 464
  aluminum, 321
  antimony, 269
  chromium, 125
  iodine, 392
  manganese, 63
  mercury, 298
  mica, 367
  nickel, 93
  nitrogen, 421
  platinum, 335
  tin, 195
  tungsten, 157
Political vs. commercial interests,
  470
Portugal, tungsten, 140, 141, 146
Prices, aluminum, 227
  antimony, 264
  bauxite, 227, 230
  chromium, 122
  iodine, 390
  manganese, 58
  mercury, 294
  mica, 363
  nickel, 89
  nitrogen, 418
  platinum, 331
  tin, 192
  tungsten, 157

Q

Quicksilver (*see* Mercury)

R

Relative production ability, 462,
  463
  France, 462, 463
  Germany, 462, 463
  Great Britain, 462, 463
  Italy, 462, 463
  Japan, 462, 463
  Russia, 462, 463
  United States, 462, 463
Requirements, aluminum, 200
  antimony, 239
  chromium, 98
  iodine, 377
  manganese, 31

Requirements, mercury, 275
  mica, 341
  nickel, 71
  nitrogen, 398
  platinum, 306
  tin, 163
  tungsten, 130
Reserves in use, 21
Reserves, ore (*see* Ore reserves)
Rhodesia, mica, 355
Rumania, bauxite, 209
Russia, aluminum, 213, 219
  bauxite, 209, 212, 219
  chromium, 110, 111, 116, 121, 122
  consumption factor, 461
  manganese, 43, 45, 46, 50, 51
  mercury, 286, 287
  mica, 355
  platinum, 320, 322, 327
  production ability, 463
  self-sufficiency factor, 455, 459,
    460
  strategic mineral supplies, 455,
    459, 460, 463
  tin, consumption, 189

S

Scrap recovery (*see* Secondary recovery)
Secondary recovery, 21
  aluminum, 207
  antimony, 245
  chromium, 107
  iodine, 381
  manganese, 38
  mercury, 282
  mica, 347
  nickel, 78
  nitrogen, 403
  platinum, 315
  tin, 169
  tungsten, 137
Self-sufficiency, aluminum, 431
  antimony, 434
  bauxite, 431
  chromium, 436
  iodine, 438
  manganese, 440

Self-sufficiency, mercury, 442
  mica, 444
  nickel, 446
  nitrogen, 448
  platinum, 450
  tin, 446
  tungsten, 452
Self-sufficiency factors, 455, 458
  France, 455, 459, 460, 463
  Germany, 455, 459, 460, 463
  Great Britain, 455, 459, 460, 463
  Italy, 455, 459, 460, 463
  Japan, 455, 459, 460, 463
  Russia, 455, 459, 460, 463
  United States, 455, 459, 460, 463
Shortages, 16
Siam, tin, 180
  tungsten, 146
Significance of commercial data, 465
Smelting, aluminum, 225
  antimony, 261
  tin, 180
South Africa, chromium, 110, 111,
    114, 121, 122
  manganese, 43, 45, 47
  mica, 355
  platinum, 320, 322
Southern Rhodesia, chromium, 110,
    111, 115, 121, 122
  mica, 355
Spain, mercury, 286, 288, 292
  tungsten, 146
Stock accumulations, 467
Stocks, aluminum, 225
  antimony, 261
  emergency, 22
  iodine, 387
  manganese, 51
    Germany, 467
  mercury, 293
  mica, 361
  nitrogen, 416
  platinum, 329
  tin, 191
  tungsten, 151
Strategic list, 2
Strategic minerals, 1, 2, 8, 455, 459,
    460, 463

Strategic minerals, aluminum, 200
  antimony, 238
  bibliography, 11
  classification, 29
  chromium, 97
  domestic self-sufficiency, 428
  foreign self-sufficiency, 455, 459,
    460, 463
  general survey, 15
  imports, Germany, 466
    index, 467
    Italy, 466
    Japan, 466
  iodine, 377
  manganese, 31
  mercury, 274
  mica, 339
  nickel, 70
  nitrogen, 396
  platinum, 305
  self-sufficiency, 428, 455
  supplies, foreign countries, 454
    France, 455, 459, 460, 463
    Germany, 455, 459, 460, 463
    Great Britain, 455, 459, 460,
      463
    Italy, 455, 459, 460, 463
    Japan, 455, 459, 460, 463
    Russia, 455, 459, 460, 463
    United States, 455, 459, 460, 463
  tin, 162
  tungsten, 130
Strategy, use of, 27
Substitutes, 24, 30
  aluminum, 204
  antimony, 241
  chromium, 104
  iodine, 379
  manganese, 34
  mercury, 279
  mica, 343
  nickel, 75
  nitrogen, 400
  platinum, 310
  tin, 165
  tungsten, 134
Supply, development of, 19
  maintenance of, 19

Surinam, aluminum, 219
  bauxite, 209, 212, 219
Switzerland, aluminum, 213, 219

T

Tariff, aluminum, 231
  antimony, 268
  bauxite, 231
  chromium, 124
  iodine, 392
  manganese, 60
  mercury, 298
  mica, 367
  nickel, 93
  nitrogen, 420
  platinum, 334
  tin, 194
  tungsten, 155
Tin, 162
  Australia, 174, 175, 176, 186, 188
  beneficiation, 167
  Bolivia, 174, 175, 176, 186, 188
  Burma, 174, 178, 188
  China, 174, 175, 177, 186, 188
  commercial control, 195
  consumption, 189
  domestic situation, 198
  exports, 188
  forms on market, 170
  Great Britain, 174, 175, 178, 182,
    186, 188
  Malaya, 174, 175, 178, 181, 186,
    188
  metallurgy, 167
  Netherlands East Indies, 174,
    175, 179, 186, 188
  Nigeria, 174, 177
  ore reserves, 170
  ores, 166
  political control, 195
  prices, 192
  requirements, 163
  secondary recovery, 169
  self-sufficiency, 446
  Siam, 180
  smelting, 180
    Australia, 182
    Belgian Congo, 183

Tin, smelting, China, 182
    Germany, 182
    Great Britain, 182
    Malaya, 181
    Netherlands, 182
    Netherlands East Indies, 182
    United States, 174, 183
  stocks, 191
  substitutes, 165
  tariff, 194
  United States, 183
    output and supply, 183
  uses, 164
  utilization, 191
  world output and supply, 171
Tonkin (see Indo-China)
Treatment, nitrogen, 402
Tungsten, 130
  Argentina, 140, 141, 142, 150
  Australia, 140, 141, 142, 150
  beneficiation, 136
  Bolivia, 143, 150
  Burma, 140, 141, 145
  China, 140, 141, 143, 150
  commercial control, 157
  consumption, 150
  domestic situation, 159
  exports, 150
  forms on market, 138
  Great Britain, 145
  imports, 148
  Indo-China, 140, 141, 145
  Japan, 140, 141, 145, 151
  Malaya, 140, 141, 146, 150
  metallurgy, 136
  ore reserves, 138
  ores, 134
  political control, 157
  Portugal, 140, 141, 146
  prices, 151
  requirements, 130
  secondary recovery, 137
  self-sufficiency, 452
  Siam, 146
  Spain, 146
  stocks, 151
  substitutes, 134
  tariff, 155

Tungsten, United States, 140, 141, 146
  output and supply, 147
  uses, 131
  world output and supply, 139
Turkey, chromium, 110, 111, 115, 121, 122

U

Union of Socialist Soviet Republics (*see* Russia)
Union of South Africa (*see* South Africa)
United Kingdom (*see* Great Britain)
United States, aluminum, 213, 219
  antimony, 251, 255
  bauxite, 209, 212, 219
  chromium, 110, 111, 117
  consumption factor, 461
  iodine, 383, 385, 386
  manganese, 43, 45, 47
  mercury, 286, 288
  mica, 349, 356
  mica, 349, 356
  nickel, 81, 83, 86
  platinum, 320, 323
  production ability, 463
  self-sufficiency factor, 455, 459, 460
  strategic mineral supplies, 455, 459, 460, 463
  tin, 183
    smelting, 174, 183
  tungsten, 140, 141, 146
United States output and supply, aluminum, 221, 223
  antimony, 256
  bauxite, 222
  chromium, 118
  iodine, 385
  manganese, 48
  mercury, 289
  mica, 357
  nickel, 87
  nitrogen, 413
  platinum, 324
  tin, 183
  tungsten, 147

Uses, of aluminum, 201
  antimony, 239
  chromium, 98
  iodine, 378
  manganese, 31
  mercury, 276
  mica, 342
  nickel, 71
  nitrogen, 398
  platinum, 306
  tin, 164
  tungsten, 131
  (*See also* Utilization)
U. S. S. R. (*see* Russia)
Utilization, of aluminum, 226
  antimony, 262
  bauxite, 226
  iodine, 388
  manganese, 54
  mercury, 293
  mica, 362
  nickel, 90
  nitrogen, 416
  platinum, 329
  tin, 191
  (*See also* Uses)

W

World output and supply, aluminum, 210, 213
  antimony, 247
  bauxite, 212
  chromium, 109
  iodine, 384
  manganese, 41
  mercury, 284
  mica, 348
  nickel, 80
  nitrogen, 405
  platinum, 316
  tin, 171
  tungsten, 139

Y

Yugoslavia, aluminum, 220
  bauxite, 210, 212, 220
  chromite, 110, 111, 117